anthropology

Second Custom Edition for the University of Montana

CAROL R. EMBER

MELVIN EMBER

PETER N. PEREGRINE

Taken from:

Anthropology, Thirteenth Edition
by Carol R. Ember, Melvin Ember, and Peter N. Peregrine

Learning Solutions

New York   Boston   San Francisco
London   Toronto   Sydney   Tokyo   Singapore   Madrid
Mexico City   Munich   Paris   Cape Town   Hong Kong   Montreal

Cover Art: Courtesy of Blend Images, PhotoDisc/Getty Images, S. Olsen/K. Mizra, Japan, Norway, Morocco, and Nigeria

Taken from:

Anthropology, Thirteenth Edition
by Carol R. Ember, Melvin Ember, and Peter N. Peregrine
Copyright © 2011, 2007, 2005, 2002, 1999 by Pearson Education, Inc.
Published by Prentice Hall
Upper Saddle River, New Jersey 07458

This special edition published in cooperation with Pearson Learning Solutions.

All trademarks, service marks, registered trademarks, and registered service marks are the property of their respective owners and are used herein for identification purposes only.

Pearson Learning Solutions, 501 Boylston Street, Suite 900, Boston, MA 02116
A Pearson Education Company
www.pearsoned.com

Printed in the United States of America

2 3 4 5 6 7 8 9 10 V051 14 13 12 11 10

000200010270568293

MP

ISBN 10: 0-558-65922-5
ISBN 13: 978-0-558-65922-56

dedication

For Mel–

Always the optimist, who believed that there were laws governing human behavior that could be found if you thought hard enough, worked hard enough, and tested ideas against the anthropological record.

1933–2009

brief contents

contents

boxes

new perspectives on gender

preface

This thirteenth edition of *Anthropology* represents the most significant revision of the text since the tenth edition. In the tenth edition, we put more emphasis to biological anthropology and the holistic four-field approach that we consider central to the discipline of anthropology. In the eleventh and twelfth editions, we expanded our vision of holistic anthropology with increased coverage of applied anthropology (called by some the fifth field of anthropology).

In this, the thirteenth edition, we emphasize the importance of applied or practicing anthropology even more by including one applied box feature in every chapter and incorporating more applied work into the text itself. In addition, we have integrated the discussion of the four-fields further by thoroughly revising the way we present anthropological method and theory. Instead of having separate chapters on methods in cultural anthropology and in physical anthropology and archaeology, we now have a single chapter that presents anthropological research within the framework of the scientific process. Similarly, instead of separate discussions of theoretical approaches in cultural anthropology and other subfields, we now have a single chapter representing the important theoretical perspectives used by anthropologists as a whole. We have placed these two new chapters near the front of the book to emphasize the importance of method and theory in understanding the discipline of anthropology.

To highlight culture change and the impact of globalization, we now have a chapter called "Culture and Culture Change." We have also moved specific examples of culture change into their respective subject chapters.

This edition is slightly shorter than recent editions, with 28 chapters rather than 31. We have combined some chapters and integrated material on applied anthropology into others. For example, what was a separate chapter on medical anthropology is now part of a larger chapter on applied anthropology, and information on medical anthropology is found in relevant places elsewhere in the text.

We have always tried to go beyond descriptions to explain not only *what* humans are and were like, but also *why* they got to be that way, in all their variety. This edition is no different. An important part of updating the text is finding new explanations, and we try to communicate the necessity to evaluate these new explanations logically as well as on the basis of the available evidence. Throughout the book, we try to communicate that no idea, including ideas put forward in textbooks, should be accepted even tentatively without supporting tests that could have gone the other way.

ORGANIZATION OF THE TEXT

Part I: Introduction

We see anthropology as a unified discipline that combines the insights of ethnographers, linguists, archaeologists, and physical anthropologists to create a holistic understanding of humans. In this section, we introduce the discipline of anthropology, outline its history and its major theoretical perspectives, and give an overview of the methods employed by anthropologists.

Chapter 1: What Is Anthropology? Chapter 1 introduces the student to anthropology. We discuss what we think is distinctive about anthropology in general, and about each of its subfields in particular. We outline how each of the subfields is related to other disciplines such as biology, psychology, and sociology. We direct attention to the increasing importance of applied anthropology and the importance of understanding others in today's more globalized world. There are three boxes on individual anthropologists—an archaeologist, an ethnographer, and an applied anthropologist—and their work.

Chapter 2: History of Anthropological Theory This new chapter combines sections from several chapters in earlier editions to provide an introduction to major theoretical approaches used by anthropologists in the past and present. The chapter begins with a discussion of the evolution of evolutionary thinking—an approach that, at least in its later manifestations, underlies a considerable amount of the anthropological research we present in the text. We describe a number of older evolutionary and nonevolutionary approaches specific to anthropology. We then outline current theoretical approaches and explain how they influence anthropological research today. We explain how older approaches are not necessarily discarded. Some older approaches, particularly with regard to evolution, have withstood the test of time. The first box uses a research question about the Abelam of New Guinea to illustrate how different theoretical approaches suggest different types of answers. The second, a new applied box, describes the relationship between theory and practice to illustrate how anthropologists employ theory to solve research problems.

Chapter 3: Research Methods in Anthropology In this new chapter, we begin by discussing what it means to explain and what kinds of evidence are needed to evaluate an explanation. We then describe the major types of study in anthropology—ethnography, within-culture comparisons, regional comparisons, worldwide cross-cultural comparisons, and historical research. We follow this with a brief introduction to the unique methods that archaeologists and biological anthropologists use, and end with a discussion of ethics in anthropological research. The first box explores changes in gender roles during the Shell Mound Archaic period in the southeastern United States. The new applied box describes work that forensic anthropologists conducted to identify the remains of Philip II of Macedon.

Part II: Human Evolution

This section of the book focuses on the evolution of humans from early mammals to the present. We emphasize evolution as both a foundational and potentially unifying perspective within anthropology. We also emphasize the fact that humans continue to adapt to their environments both physically and culturally. Thus, anthropology must combine biological understanding and cultural understanding if we wish to develop an accurate understanding of humans.

Chapter 4: Genetics and Evolution This chapter discusses evolutionary theory as it applies to all forms of life, including humans. Following an extensive review of genetics and the processes of evolution, including natural selection and what it means, we discuss how natural selection may operate on behavioral traits and how cultural evolution differs from biological evolution. We provide a thorough discussion of creationism and intelligent design. A key task in this revision was balancing the explosion of new information on human genetics and the need to provide an overview for students. The first box, a new applied box, features the emerging issue of who owns DNA samples. The second box feature examines evidence suggesting that evolution proceeds abruptly rather than slowly and steadily.

Chapter 5: Human Variation and Adaptation We have moved this chapter forward in the book in response to reviewers' comments. We bring the discussion of human genetics and evolution into the present, dealing with physical variation in living human populations and how physical anthropologists study and explain such variation. We examine how both the physical environment and the cultural environment play important roles in human physical variation. In a section on "race" and racism, we discuss why many anthropologists think the concept of "race" as applied to humans is not scientifically useful. We discuss the myths of racism and how "race" is largely a social category in humans. A new applied anthropology box explores the use of "race" in physical anthropology, and another box examines physical differences between native and immigrant populations.

Chapter 6: The Living Primates This chapter describes the living nonhuman primates and their variable adaptations as background for understanding the evolution of primates in general and humans in particular. After describing the various kinds of primates, we discuss the distinctive features of humans in comparison with the other primates. The chapter ends with a discussion of some possible explanations of how the primates differ—in body and brain size, size of social group, and female sexuality. The applied anthropology box feature deals with how and why many primates are endangered and how they might be protected. Another box feature describes a primatologist and some of her work.

Chapter 7: Primate Evolution: From Early Primates To Hominoids This chapter begins with the emergence of the early primates and ends with what we know or suspect about the Miocene apes, one of whom (known or unknown) was ancestral to bipedal hominids. We link major trends in primate evolution to broader environmental changes that may have caused natural selection to favor new traits. In this revision, we have added material on genetic evidence of primate origins and evolution. To highlight how theory is generated and revised, the first box deals with how a paleoanthropologist has reexamined his own theory of primate origins. A box on current research describes a giant ape that lived at the same time as the first humans, and why that ape may have become extinct. A new applied anthropology box discusses the importance of studying the diversity of primates, both ancient and modern, for understanding our planet's biodiversity.

Chapter 8: The First Hominids This chapter discusses the evolution of bipedal locomotion—the most distinctive feature of the group that includes our genus and those of our direct ancestors, the australopithecines. We discuss the various types of australopithecines and how they might have evolved. This chapter has been extensively revised to include discussions of new species and theories of hominid evolution. It also contains an expanded discussion of gracile australopithecines. There are two boxes. The new applied anthropology box describes anthropometry—the method used to measure humans, both ancient and modern—and how it is used in research and industry. The second box discusses new australopithecine finds and how they appear to fit into our current understanding of human evolution.

Part III: Cultural Evolution

Humans are unique in our ability to use culture to adapt to new or changing environments, both physical and cultural. In this section, we discuss evidence for when and how culture developed, and what may have fostered more complex cultural developments over time. We examine the emergence of agriculture, settled communities, and complex political and economic systems in the framework of cultural adaptation.

Chapter 9: The Origins of Culture and the Emergence of *Homo* This chapter examines the first clear evidences of cultural behavior—stone tools—and other clues suggesting that early hominids had begun to develop culture around 2.5 million years ago. In this edition, we have expanded our discussion about what culture is and how it may have evolved. We also discuss the hominids—the first members of our genus, *Homo*—who are most likely responsible for the early signs of cultural behavior, and *Homo erectus,* the first hominid to leave Africa and the first to demonstrate complex cultural behavior. The new applied anthropology box explains how archaeologists and paleoanthropologists use stone tools to help identify sites needing protection through historic preservation laws. The second box discusses research on when hominids first migrated out of Africa.

Chapter 10: The Emergence of *Homo sapiens* This chapter examines the transition between *Homo erectus* and *Homo sapiens* and the emergence of modern-looking humans. We give special consideration to the Neandertals and the question of their relationship to modern humans. In this edition, we report on the new evidence from ancient Neandertal DNA, which shows Neandertals to be a distinct species from modern humans, but with fascinating and familiar features, like red hair. While keeping a balance between the various models of modern human origins, we also provide new evidence from genetics and fossils that seems to demonstrate the "Out of Africa" model or an extension of it is the best model for modern human origins. The applied anthropology box describes how forensic anthropologists reconstruct the faces of early humans. The second box examines patterns of growth and development among Neandertals as a way of evaluating how long their period of infancy was.

Chapter 11: The Upper Paleolithic World This chapter considers the cultures of modern humans in the period before agriculture developed—roughly 40,000 years to 10,000 years ago. We examine their tools, their economies, and their art—the first art made by humans. For this edition, we have expanded our discussion of genetic and linguistic evidence for the timing and process of human colonization of North and South America. The first box considers how women are depicted in Upper Paleolithic art. A new applied anthropology box discusses the evidence that the first colonists of the Americas may have died out, and may be only distantly related to modern Native Americans.

Chapter 12: Origins of Food Production and Settled Life This chapter deals with the emergence of broad-spectrum collecting and settled life, and then the domestication of plants and animals, in various parts of the world. Our discussion focuses mainly on the possible causes and consequences of these developments in Mesoamerica and the Near East, the areas best known for these developments, but we also consider Southeast Asia, Africa, North and South America, and Europe. The new applied anthropology box describes the work of

archaeologists who are re-creating ancient agricultural systems in the Andes and elsewhere to help local populations produce more food. The box on current research describes how researchers are finding out about ancient diets from chemical analysis of bones and teeth.

Chapter 13: Origins of Cities and States This chapter deals with the rise of civilizations in various parts of the world and the theories that have been offered to explain the development of state-type political systems. Our focus is on the evolution of cities and states in Mesoamerica and the Near East, the areas archaeologists know best, but we also discuss the rise of cities and states in South America, South Asia, China, and Africa. We discuss how states affect people living in them and their environments. We conclude with a discussion of the decline and collapse of states. This chapter features several boxes. A new applied anthropology box describes how archaeological data are being used to create models of long-term environmental change, focused on the impact of cities and states on their local environments. A box on new perspectives on gender discusses the links between imperialism, colonialism, and the state.

Part IV: Cultural Variation

In most of the chapters that follow, we try to convey the range of cultural variation with ethnographic examples from all over the world. Wherever we can, we discuss possible explanations of why societies may be similar or different in regard to some aspect of culture. If anthropologists have no explanation as yet for the variation, we say so. But if we have some idea of the conditions that may be related to a particular kind of variation, even if we do not know yet why they are related, we discuss that too. If we are to train students to go beyond what we know now, we have to tell them what we do not know, as well as what we think we know.

Chapter 14: Culture and Culture Change This extensively revised chapter emphasizes that culture is always changing. Our previous edition discussed culture change, ethnogenesis, and globalization near the end of the book. We have brought this material forward and integrated it into the present chapter. Particular aspects of culture change—economic, political, religious, and so on—are now included in their respective chapters. This chapter introduces the concept of culture and now includes a discussion of some of the controversies surrounding the concept. Rather than simply defining culture, we try to convey a feeling for what culture is. Throughout the chapter, we discuss individual variation and how such variation may be the beginning of new cultural patterns. We also discuss attitudes that hinder the study of culture, cultural relativism and the issue of human rights, patterning of culture, culture and adaptation, and mechanisms of culture change, before getting to the emergence of new cultures and the impact of globalization. The first box, on culture change and persistence in China, discusses what has changed because of government intervention and what has nevertheless persisted. The second box discusses an applied anthropologist's view of why Bedouin are reluctant to settle down. The third box discusses the increasing cultural diversity within countries of the world as a result of immigration and migration.

Chapter 15: Communication and Language We begin by discussing communication in humans and other animals. We have expanded our discussion of nonverbal human communication to include kinesics and paralanguage. We describe the debate about the degree of difference between human and nonhuman primate language abilities. We discuss the origins of language and how creoles and children's language acquisition may help us understand the origins. We have expanded our section on creoles to discuss pidgin languages as well. We describe the fundamentals of descriptive linguistics and the processes of linguistic divergence. After discussing the interrelationships between language and other aspects of culture, we discuss the ethnography of speaking and the differences in speech by status, gender, and ethnicity. We discuss interethnic or intercultural communication, indicating how linguists can play a role in helping people improve their cross-cultural communication. At the end of the chapter, we discuss writing and literacy. The first box, an applied box, discusses language extinction and what some anthropologists are doing about it. The second box, discusses why some immigrant groups retain their "mother tongues" longer than others. And to stimulate thinking about the possible impact of language on thought, we ask in the last box whether the English language promotes sexist thinking.

Chapter 16: Getting Food Chapter 16 discusses how societies vary in getting their food, how they have changed over time, and how the variation seems to affect other kinds of cultural variation—including variation in economic systems, social stratification, and political life. We include a discussion of "market foragers" to emphasize that most people in a modern market economy are not in fact producers of food. We have expanded our discussion of complex foragers for this edition. Although it is commonly thought that industrialization is mainly to blame for negative developments in the environment, the first box explores where particular foods came from and how different foods and cuisines spread around the world as people migrated. Our second box deals with the negative effects in preindustrial times of irrigation, animal grazing, and overhunting.

Chapter 17: Economic Systems In this extensively revised chapter, we emphasize recent change by incorporating material that used to be in a separate chapter on culture change. We now discuss commercialization by way of migratory labor and remittances, nonagricultural commercial production, supplementary cash crops, and commercial and industrial agriculture. Chapter 17 begins with a discussion of how societies vary in the ways they allocate resources (what is "property" and what ownership may mean), convert or transform resources through

labor into usable goods, and distribute and perhaps exchange goods and services. We have added new research on the effects of money on sharing and a discussion of informal banking systems (*hawala* brokers). The first extensively updated box addresses the controversy over whether communal ownership leads to economic disaster. The second box discusses the impact of working abroad and sending money home. The third updated applied box illustrates the impact of the world system on local economies, with special reference to the deforestation of the Amazon.

Chapter 18: Social Stratification: Class, Ethnicity, and Racism This chapter explores the variation in degree of social stratification and how the various forms of social inequality may develop. We discuss how egalitarian societies work hard to prevent dominance, and the controversy about whether pastoral societies with individual ownership of animals are egalitarian. We then discuss the recognition of social class and how people in the United States generally deny the existence of class. We have expanded our section on caste, adding a discussion of occupational caste in Africa. The discussion of Rwanda is extensively revised to convey the sometimes complex relationship between class, caste, and ethnicity. We end with an extensive discussion of "race," racism, and ethnicity and how they often relate to the inequitable distribution of resources. We have added a new discussion of the very different concepts of "race" in Latin America. The updated first box discusses social stratification on the global level—how the gap between rich and poor countries has been widening, and what may account for that trend. The second box discusses possible reasons for disparities in death by disease between African Americans and European Americans.

Chapter 19: Culture and the Individual Anthropology, with its focus on culture, may seem to ignore the individual. In this extensively revised chapter (formerly "Psychology and Culture"), we discuss how understanding individuals and psychological processes is vital to anthropological understanding, including understanding culture change. We open with a discussion of some of the universals of psychological development, emphasizing the need for psychological research to incorporate research on humans the world over. In a new section on the anthropology of childhood, we discuss the importance of the long period in which the young are dependent on parents for learning as well as nonparental figures, and how important it is to look at children, too often ignored, as agents. We identify some larger processes that may influence personality, such as the native theories ("ethnotheories"), adaptation, as well as possible genetic or physiological influences. We then turn to understanding more specific variation in childrearing, including a new section on parent-child play. After discussing some differences in perception, cognition, and behaviors in adults, we turn to how understanding psychological processes may help us understand cultural variation. The chapter closes with a new section on the individual as an agent of culture change. The applied anthropology box refers to a comparison of preschools in Japan, China, and the United States, discussing how schools may consciously and unconsciously teach values. The second box discusses the idea that women may have a different sense of themselves than men have, and therefore a different sense of morality.

Chapter 20: Sex, Gender, and Culture

In the first part of Chapter 20, we open with a section on culturally varying gender concepts, including cultures that have more than two genders. We also add a discussion of transgender. We discuss how and why sex and gender differences vary cross-culturally. In addition to discussing the gender division of labor in primary and secondary subsistence, we have added additional material on women hunters and discuss what impact it has on theories about the gender division of labor. In the second part of the chapter, we discuss variation in sexual attitudes and practices. Following revised sections on marital sex and extramarital sex, there is an expanded discussion of homosexuality, including female-female relationships. In the first box, we examine cross-cultural research about why some societies allow women to participate in combat. A second box discusses research on why women's political participation may be increasing in some Coast Salish communities of western Washington State and British Columbia, now that they have elected councils. The last is a new applied anthropology box that examines the impact of economic development on women's status.

Chapter 21: Marriage and the Family

We have revised our section on the universality of marriage with a new discussion of the Na exception in China. After discussing various theories about why marriage might be universal, we move on to discuss variation in how one marries, restrictions on marriage, whom one should marry, and how many one should marry. We close with a discussion of variation in family form. We introduce recent research on the Hadza that supports one of the theories about marriage. We then discuss the phenomenon of couples choosing to live together, and we have updated our discussion of polygyny and polyandry. We have added a new section on adoption. To better prepare students for understanding kinship charts in the chapter that follows, we have introduced a new diagram explaining different types of family structures. The first box discusses arranged marriage and how it has changed among South Asian immigrants in England and the United States. To introduce topics regarding the husband-wife relationship that are only beginning to be investigated, the second box discusses variation in love, intimacy, and sexual jealousy. The third updated box discusses why one-parent families are on the increase in countries like ours. The fourth box, a new applied box, discusses extended families and social security.

Chapter 22: Marital Residence and Kinship

This chapter has been rearranged so that explanations of all types of residence can be found together. We hope the discussion of kinship now flows more smoothly. In addition to explaining the variation that exists in marital residence,

kinship structure, and kinship terminology, this chapter emphasizes how understanding residence is important for understanding social life. We have revised our artwork on kinship terminology in a way we hope will make that subject easier to understand. The first box discusses the possible relationship between neolocality and adolescent rebellion. The second box discusses the role that Chinese lineages play in supporting migration and making a living in the diaspora. The third box is on how variation in residence and kinship affects the lives of women. The new applied box discusses how cross-cultural research on the floor area of residences in matrilocal versus patrilocal societies can be used to help archaeologists make inferences about the past.

Chapter 23: Associations and Interest Groups

We discuss the importance of associations in many parts of the world, distinguishing them on whether they are nonvoluntary (common in more egalitarian societies) or voluntary, increasingly important in the modern world. Associations also vary in the degree to which they are based on universally ascribed characteristics (like age and sex), variably ascribed characteristics (like ethnicity), or achieved characteristics. The first box, which is a new applied box, looks at the importance of NGOs in bringing about change at the local and international levels. The second updated box addresses the question of whether separate women's associations increase women's status and power. The third box discusses why street gangs develop and why they often become violent. The last box discusses the role of ethnic associations in Chinatowns in North America.

Chapter 24: Political Life: Social Order and Disorder

We look at how societies have varied in their levels of political organization, the various ways people become leaders, the degree to which they participate in the political process, and the peaceful and violent methods of resolving conflict. We have added new material on different types of states, ranging from the more autocratic to the less autocratic that rely more on collective action and where leaders avoid personal aggrandizement. We have also expanded our discussion of peaceful societies. We discuss how colonialization has transformed legal systems and ways of making decisions, and we have expanded our discussion of states as empires. The first box discusses the role of migrants in the growth of cities. The second box, an applied box, deals with the cross-national and cross-cultural relationship between economic development and democracy. The third box deals with how new local courts among the Abelam of New Guinea are allowing women to address sexual grievances.

Chapter 25: Religion and Magic

Consistent with increasing the visibility of culture change, we have added a major section on religious change at the end of this chapter. After discussing why religion may be culturally universal, we discuss variation in religious belief and practice with extensive examples. We have expanded our sections on life after death, divination, and our discussion of why women may predominate in possession trances before moving onto religious change. In this new section we discuss the possible causes of religious conversion, revitalization movements, and fundamentalist movements. The new applied box raises the question of whether and to what degree religion promotes moral behavior, cooperation, and harmony. The second discusses the role of colonialism in religious change. The last box discusses the emergence of new religions and points out that nearly all the major churches or religions in the world began as minority sects or cults.

Chapter 26: The Arts After discussing how art might be defined and the appearance of the earliest art, we discuss variation in the visual arts, music, and folklore, and review how some of those variations might be explained. In regard to how the arts change over time, we discuss the myth that the art of "simpler" peoples is timeless, and how arts have changed as a result of European contact. We address the role of ethnocentrism in studies of art with a section on how Western museums and art critics look at the visual art of less complex cultures. In the section on body adornment, we discuss how permanent or nonpermanent body markings may relate to variation in political systems. The first box, on applied anthropology, explores ancient and more recent rock art and the methods that can be used to help preserve it. The second box, dealing with universal symbolism in art, reviews recent research on the emotions displayed in masks. The last box, discusses the global spread of popular music.

Part V: Using Anthropology

Anthropology is not a discipline that focuses on pure research; rather, most anthropologists believe their work is truly valuable only if it can be used to improve the lives of others. In this section, we examine how anthropological knowledge is used in a variety of settings and toward a variety of ends.

Chapter 27: Applied, Practicing, and Medical Anthropology This chapter now integrates medical anthropology and, in the course of doing so, is extensively revised. The field of applied or practicing anthropology is very diverse. In this chapter, we first focus on general issues: ethics, evaluating the effects of planned change, and the difficulties of implementing change. In the course of this discussion, we cover a variety of projects, mostly development projects. We then turn to several other kinds of application: *cultural resource management*, the "social impact" studies required in connection with many government or private programs, and *forensic anthropology*—the use of physical anthropology to help identify human remains and assist in solving crimes. The forensic section is considerably revised to deal with identification difficulties associated with age, sex, and "race." The previous box on reforestation in Haiti is now incorporated into the text. The chapter concludes with an extensive discussion of the application of anthropological knowledge to the study of health and illness. The three applied boxes discuss how

anthropologists have been able to help in business, evaluating why an applied medical project didn't work, and the last explores eating disorders, biology, and the cultural construction of beauty.

Chapter 28: Global Problems In this chapter, we discuss the relationship between basic and applied research, and how research may suggest possible solutions to various global social problems, including natural disasters and famines, homelessness, crime, family violence, war, and terrorism. The section on family violence has been updated with new research on corporal punishment and the effects of television on children. This chapter has four boxes. One updated box is on global warming and our dependence on oil. The second is a new applied box about the problem of corporal punishment of children and what might be done about it to discourage it. The third is on ethnic conflicts and whether or not they are inevitable. The last box describes how the problem of refugees has become a global problem.

FEATURES NEW TO THIS EDITION

Applied Anthropology Boxes in Each Chapter. Anthropology is not a discipline focused on pure research. Most anthropologists want their work to be actively used to help others. And in our increasingly interconnected world, it would seem that anthropological knowledge would become increasingly valuable for understanding others. For these reasons, we decided to emphasize applied anthropology in this revision of our text. Adding an applied anthropology box to each chapter, we hope, will provide students a better understanding of the vast range of issues to which anthropological knowledge can be usefully applied.

Features Retained in This Edition

Current Research and Issues Boxes. These boxes deal with current research, topics students may have heard about in the news, and research controversies in anthropology. Examples include variation in love, intimacy, and sexual jealousy in the husband-wife relationship; whether inequality between countries is increasing; whether ethnic conflicts are ancient hatreds; and human rights versus cultural relativity.

Migrants and Immigrants Boxes. These boxes deal with humans on the move, and how migration and immigration have impacted recent and contemporary social life. Examples include why some immigrant groups retained their "mother tongues" longer than others, the spread of foods in recent times, arranging marriages in the diaspora, and the problem of refugees.

New Perspectives on Gender Boxes. These boxes involve issues pertaining to sex and gender, both in anthropology and everyday life. Examples are sexism in language, separate women's associations and women's status and power, and morality in women versus men.

Dorling Kindersley Maps To emphasize important themes, we have adapted maps originally produced by Dorling Kindersley—a leading publisher of educational maps.

Map Table of Contents:

Student-Friendly Pedagogy

Readability. We derive a lot of pleasure from trying to describe research findings, especially complicated ones, in ways that introductory students can understand. Thus, we try to minimize technical jargon, using only those terms students must know to appreciate the achievements of anthropology and to take advanced courses. We think readability is important, not only because it may enhance the reader's understanding of what we write, but also because it should make learning about anthropology more enjoyable! When new terms are introduced, which of course must happen sometimes, they are set off in boldface type and defined in the text (and in the glossary at the end of the book).

Glossary. At the end of each chapter, we list the new terms that have been introduced; these terms were identified by boldface type and are defined in the text. We deliberately do not repeat the definitions at the end of the chapter to allow students to ask themselves if they know the terms. However, we do provide page numbers to find the definitions, and we also provide all the definitions again in the Glossary at the end of the book.

Summaries. In addition to the outline provided at the beginning of each chapter, each chapter has a detailed summary at the end that will help students review the major concepts and findings discussed.

Critical Questions. We provide three or four questions at the end of each chapter that will stimulate thinking about the implications of the chapter. The questions do not ask for repetition of what is in the text. We want students to imagine, to go beyond what we know or think we know.

End of Book Notes. Because we believe in the importance of documentation, we think it essential to tell our readers, both professionals and students, what our conclusions are based on. Usually the basis is published research. The abbreviated notes in this edition provide information to find the complete citation in the bibliography at the end of the book.

SUPPLEMENTS

This textbook is part of a complete teaching and learning package that has been carefully created to enhance the topics discussed in the text.

MyAnthroLab is an interactive and instructive multimedia site designed to help students and instructors save time and improve results. It offers access to a wealth of resources geared to meet the individual teaching and learning needs of every instructor and student. Combining an ebook, video, audio, multimedia simulations, research support, and assessment, MyAnthroLab engages students and gives them the tools they need to enhance their performance in the course. Please see your Pearson sales representative for more information about **MyAnthroLab** or visit the website at www.myanthrolab.com.

Instructor's Resource Manual with Tests: (0-205-73884-2) For each chapter in the text, this valuable resource provides a detailed outline, list of objectives, discussion questions, and classroom activities. In addition, test questions in multiple-choice and short-answer formats are available for each chapter; the answers to all questions are page-referenced to the text. For easy access, this manual is available within the instructor section of MyAnthroLab for *Anthropology,* Thirteenth Edition, or at www.pearsonhighered.com/irc.

MyTest: (0-205-73890-7) This computerized software allows instructors to create their own personalized exams, to edit any or all of the existing test questions and to add new questions. Other special features of this program include random generation of test questions, creation of alternate versions of the same test, scrambling question sequence, and test preview before printing. For easy access, this software is available within the instructor section of MyAnthroLab for *Anthropology,* Thirteenth Edition, or at www.pearsonhighered.com/irc.

PowerPoint™ Presentation Slides: (0-205-73886-9) These PowerPoint slides combine text and graphics for each chapter to help instructors convey anthropological principles in a clear and engaging way. In addition, Classroom Response System (CRS) In-Class Questions allow instant, class-wide responses to chapter-specific questions during a lecture to gauge student comprehension. For easy access, they are available within the instructor section of MyAnthroLab for *Anthropology,* Thirteenth Edition, or at www.pearsonhighered.com/irc.

Strategies in Teaching Anthropology, Sixth Edition (0-205-71123-5) Unique in focus and content, this book focuses on the "how" of teaching anthropology across all four fields and provides a wide array of associated learning outcomes and student activities. It is a valuable single-source compendium of strategies and teaching "tricks of the trade" from a group of seasoned teaching anthropologists, working in a variety of teaching settings, who share their pedagogical techniques, knowledge, and observations.

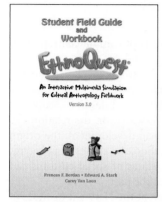

EthnoQuest®: (0-13-185013-X) This interactive multimedia simulation includes a series of 10 ethnographic encounters with the culture of a fictional Mexican village set in a computer-based learning environment. It provides students with a realistic problem-solving experience and is designed to help students experience the fieldwork of a cultural anthropologist. Please see your Pearson sales representative for more information about **EthnoQuest®.**

The Dorling Kindersley/Prentice Hall Atlas of Anthropology Beautifully illustrated by Dorling Kindersley, with narrative by leading archaeological author Brian M. Fagan, this striking atlas features 30 full-color maps, timelines, and illustrations to offer a highly visual but explanatory geographical overview of topics from all four fields of anthropology. Please contact your Prentice Hall representative for ordering information.

ACKNOWLEDGMENTS

We thank the people at Prentice Hall for all their help, and particularly Nancy Roberts, Publisher for Anthropology; Marianne Peters-Riordan and Jill Traut for seeing the manuscript through the production process; and Beth Brenzel for photo research.

We want to thank the following for reviewing our chapters and making suggestions about them:

Alice Baldwin-Jones, *City College of New York*
Richard E. Blanton, *Purdue University*
James L. Boone, *University of New Mexico*
Beau Bowers, *Central Piedmont Community College*
Gregory Campbell, *University of Montana*
Garrett Cook, *Baylor University*
Daniel R. Maher, *University of Arkansas-Fort Smith*
Sheperd Jenks, *Albuquerque TVI Community College*
Max E. White, *Piedmont College*
Jean M. Wynn, *Manchester Community College*

Thank you all, named and unnamed, who gave us advice.

Carol R. Ember, Melvin Ember,
and Peter N. Peregrine

about the authors

Carol R. Ember started at Antioch College as a chemistry major. She began taking social science courses because some were required, but she soon found herself intrigued. There were lots of questions without answers, and she became excited about the possibility of a research career in social science. She spent a year in graduate school at Cornell studying sociology before continuing on to Harvard, where she studied anthropology, primarily with John and Beatrice Whiting.

For her PhD dissertation, she worked among the Luo of Kenya. While there, she noticed that many boys were assigned "girls' work," such as babysitting and household chores, because their mothers (who did most of the agriculture) did not have enough girls to help out. She decided to study the possible effects of task assignment on the social behavior of boys. Using systematic behavior observations, she compared girls, boys who did a great deal of girls' work, and boys who did little such work. She found that boys assigned girls' work were intermediate in many social behaviors, compared with the other boys and girls. Later, she did cross-cultural research on variation in marriage, family, descent groups, and war and peace, mainly in collaboration with Melvin Ember, whom she married in 1970. All of these cross-cultural studies tested theories on data for worldwide samples of societies.

From 1970 to 1996, she taught at Hunter College of the City University of New York. She has served as president of the Society of Cross-Cultural Research and was one of the directors of the Summer Institutes in Comparative Anthropological Research, which were funded by the National Science Foundation. She is president-elect of the Society for Anthropological Sciences. Since 1996, she has served as executive director of the Human Relations Area Files, Inc., a nonprofit research agency at Yale University. She is currently acting president of that organization.

After graduating from Columbia College, Melvin Ember went to Yale University for his PhD. His mentor at Yale was George Peter Murdock, an anthropologist who was instrumental in promoting cross-cultural research and building a full-text database on the cultures of the world to facilitate cross-cultural hypothesis testing. This database came to be known as the Human Relations Area Files (HRAF) because it was originally sponsored by the Institute of Human Relations at Yale. Growing in annual installments and now distributed in electronic format, the HRAF database currently covers more than 385 cultures, past and present, all over the world.

Melvin Ember did fieldwork for his dissertation in American Samoa, where he conducted a comparison of three villages to study the effects of commercialization on political life. In addition, he did research on descent groups and how they changed with the increase of buying and selling. His cross-cultural studies focused originally on variation in marital residence and descent groups. He has also done cross-cultural research on the relationship between economic and political development, the origin and extension of the incest taboo, the causes of polygyny, and how archaeological correlates of social customs can help us draw inferences about the past.

After four years of research at the National Institute of Mental Health, he taught at Antioch College and then Hunter College of the City University of New York. He has served as president of the Society for Cross-Cultural Research. From 1987 until his death in September, 2009, he was president of the Human Relations Area Files, Inc., a nonprofit research agency at Yale University.

Peter N. Peregrine came to anthropology after completing an undergraduate degree in English. He found anthropology's social scientific approach to understanding humans more appealing than the humanistic approach he had learned as an English major. He undertook an ethnohistorical study of the relationship between Jesuit missionaries and Native American peoples for his master's degree and realized that he needed to study archaeology to understand the cultural interactions experienced by Native Americans prior to contact with the Jesuits.

While working on his PhD at Purdue University, Peter Peregrine did research on the prehistoric Mississippian cultures of the eastern United States. He found that interactions between groups were common and had been shaping Native American cultures for centuries. Native Americans approached contact with the Jesuits simply as another in a long string of intercultural exchanges. He also found that relatively little research had been done on Native American interactions and decided that comparative research was a good place to begin examining the topic. In 1990, he participated in the Summer Institute in Comparative Anthropological Research, where he met Carol R. Ember and Melvin Ember.

Peter Peregrine taught at Juniata College and is currently professor and chair of the anthropology department at Lawrence University in Appleton, Wisconsin. He serves as research associate for the eHRAF Collection of Archaeology and is president of the Society for Anthropological Sciences. He continues to do archaeological research, and to teach anthropology and archaeology to undergraduate students.

Carol R. Ember,
Melvin Ember,
Peter N. Peregrine

anthropology

What Is Anthropology?

nthropology, by definition, is a discipline of infinite curiosity about human beings. The term comes from the Greek *anthropos* for "man, human" and *logos* for "study." Anthropologists seek answers to an enormous variety of questions about humans. They are interested in both universals and differences in human populations. They want to discover when, where, and why humans appeared on the earth, how and why they have changed since then, and how and why modern human populations vary in their biological and cultural features. Anthropology has a practical side too. Applied and practicing anthropologists put anthropological methods, information, and results to use, in efforts to solve practical problems.

Defining anthropology as the study of human beings is not complete, however, for such a definition would appear to incorporate a whole catalog of disciplines: sociology, psychology, political science, economics, history, human biology, and perhaps even the humanistic disciplines of philosophy and literature. Needless to say, practitioners of the many other disciplines concerned with humans would not be happy to be regarded as being in subbranches of anthropology. After all, most of those disciplines have existed longer than anthropology, and each is somewhat distinctive. There must, then, be something unique about anthropology—a reason for its having developed as a separate discipline and for its having retained a separate identity over the last 100 years.

● ○ ●

THE SCOPE OF ANTHROPOLOGY

Anthropologists are generally thought of as individuals who travel to little-known corners of the world to study exotic peoples or who dig deep into the earth to uncover the fossil remains or the tools and pots of people who lived long ago. These views, though clearly stereotyped, do indicate how anthropology differs from other disciplines concerned with humans. Anthropology is broader in scope, both geographically and historically. Anthropology is concerned explicitly and directly with all varieties of people throughout the world, not just those close at hand or within a limited area. Anthropologists are also interested in people of all periods. Beginning with the immediate ancestors of humans, who lived a few million years ago, anthropology traces the development of humans until the present. Every part of the world that has ever contained a human population is of interest to anthropologists.

Anthropologists have not always been as global and comprehensive in their concerns as they are today. Traditionally, they concentrated on non-Western cultures and left the study of Western civilization and similarly complex societies, with their recorded histories, to other disciplines. In recent years, however, this division of labor among the disciplines has begun to disappear. Now anthropologists work in their own and other complex societies.

What induces anthropologists to choose so broad a subject for study? In part, they are motivated by the belief that any suggested generalization about human beings, any possible explanation of some characteristic of human culture or biology, should be shown to apply to many times and places of human existence. If a generalization or explanation does not prove to apply widely, anthropologists are entitled or even obliged to be skeptical about it.

3

The skeptical attitude, in the absence of persuasive evidence, is our best protection against accepting invalid ideas about humans.

For example, when American educators discovered in the 1960s that African American schoolchildren rarely drank milk, they assumed that lack of money or education was the cause. But evidence from anthropology suggested a different explanation. Anthropologists had known for years that people do not drink fresh milk in many parts of the world where milking animals are kept; rather, they sour it before they drink it, or they make it into cheese. Why they do so is now clear. Many people lack the enzyme lactase that is necessary for breaking down lactose, the sugar in milk. When such people drink regular milk, it actually interferes with digestion. Not only is the lactose in milk not digested, but other nutrients are less likely to be digested as well; in many cases, drinking milk will cause cramps, stomach gas, diarrhea, and nausea. Studies indicate that milk intolerance is found in many parts of the world.[1] The condition is common in adulthood among Asians, southern Europeans, Arabs and Jews, West Africans, Inuit (Eskimos), and North and South American native peoples, as well as African Americans. Because anthropologists are acquainted with human life in an enormous variety of geographic and historical settings, they are often able to correct mistaken beliefs about different groups of people.

THE HOLISTIC APPROACH

In addition to the worldwide as well as historical scope of anthropology, another distinguishing feature of the discipline is its **holistic,** or multifaceted, approach to the study of human beings. Anthropologists study not only all varieties of people but many aspects of human experience as well. For example, when describing a group of people, an anthropologist might discuss the history of the area in which the people live, the physical environment, the organization of family life, the general features of their language, the group's settlement patterns, political and economic systems, religion, and styles of art and dress. The goal is not just to understand these aspects separately, but to understand the connections between different aspects of physical and social life. Throughout this book, we will see that patterns of traits regularly co-occur. We not only want to identify those patterns or regularities; we want to explain them.

In the past, individual anthropologists tried to cover as many subjects as possible. Today, as in many other disciplines, so much information has been accumulated that anthropologists tend to specialize in one topic or area. Thus, one anthropologist may investigate the physical characteristics of some of our prehistoric ancestors. Another may study the biological effect of the environment on a human population over time. Still another will concentrate on many customs of a particular group of people. Despite this specialization, however, the discipline of anthropology retains its holistic orientation in that its many different specialties, taken together, describe many aspects of human existence, both past and present.

THE ANTHROPOLOGICAL CURIOSITY

Thus far, we have described anthropology as being broader in scope, both historically and geographically, and more holistic in approach than other disciplines concerned with human beings. But this statement again implies that anthropology is the all-inclusive human science. How, then, is anthropology really different from the other disciplines? We suggest that anthropology's distinctiveness lies principally in the kind of curiosity it arouses.

In studying a human population, anthropologists tend to focus on *typical* characteristics (traits, customs) of that population: People in many societies depend on agriculture. Why? And where and when did people first start to farm? Why do some populations have lighter skin than others? Why do some languages contain more terms for color than others? Why do some societies have more political participation than others? Individuals may provide information to anthropologists, but the anthropological curiosity mostly focuses on the typical characteristics of human groups and how to understand and explain them. For example, whereas economists take a monetary system for granted and study how it operates, anthropologists would ask how frequently monetary systems are found, why they vary, and why only some societies during the last few thousand years used money. This is not to imply that anthropologists are not interested in variation within human groups. In understanding a political system, anthropologists might want to know why certain people tend to be leaders, or why rural communities operate differently than urban ones. Or, variation in a physical trait might be related to susceptibility to a particular disease. Rather, a focus on typical characteristics of human groups—how and why populations and their characteristics have varied around the globe and throughout the ages—is what mainly distinguishes anthropology from other disciplines.

FIELDS OF ANTHROPOLOGY

Different anthropologists concentrate on different characteristics of societies. Some are concerned primarily with *biological* or *physical characteristics* of human populations; others are interested principally in what we call *cultural characteristics.* Hence, there are two broad classifications of subject matter in anthropology: **biological (physical) anthropology** and **cultural anthropology.** Biological anthropology is one major field of anthropology. Cultural anthropology is divided into three major subfields—archaeology, linguistics, and ethnology. Ethnology, the study of recent cultures, is now usually referred to by the parent name, cultural anthropology (see Figure 1–1). Crosscutting these four fields is a fifth, **applied** or **practicing anthropology.**

Biological Anthropology

Biological (physical) anthropology seeks to answer two distinct sets of questions. The first set includes questions

FIGURE 1–1 The Subdivisions of Anthropology
The four major subdisciplines of anthropology (in bold letters) may be classified according to subject matter (biological or cultural) and according to the period with which each is concerned (distant past versus recent past and present). There are applications of anthropology in all four subdisciplines.

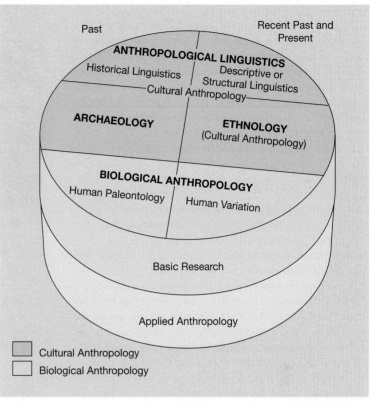

about the emergence of humans and their later evolution (this focus is called **human paleontology** or **paleoanthropology**). The second set includes questions about how and why contemporary human populations vary biologically (this focus is called **human variation**).

To reconstruct human evolution, human paleontologists search for and study the buried, hardened remains or impressions—known as **fossils**—of humans, prehumans, and related animals. Paleontologists working in East Africa, for instance, have excavated the fossil remains of humanlike beings that lived more than 4 million years ago. These findings have suggested the approximate dates when our ancestors began to develop two-legged walking, very flexible hands, and a larger brain.

In attempting to clarify evolutionary relationships, human paleontologists may use not only the fossil record but also geological information on the succession of climates, environments, and plant and animal populations. Moreover, when reconstructing the past of humans, paleontologists are also interested in the behavior and evolution of our closest relatives among the mammals—the prosimians, monkeys, and apes, which, like ourselves, are members of the order of **Primates.** Anthropologists, psychologists, and biologists who specialize in the study of primates are called **primatologists.** The various species of primates are observed in the wild and in the laboratory. One especially popular subject of study is the chimpanzee, which bears a close resemblance to humans in behavior and physical appearance, has a similar blood chemistry, and is susceptible to many of the same diseases. It now appears that chimpanzees share 99 percent of their genes with humans.[2]

Birute Galdikas works with two orangutans in Borneo.

From primate studies, biological anthropologists try to discover characteristics that are distinctly human, as opposed to those that might be part of the primate heritage. With this information, they may be able to infer what our prehistoric ancestors were like. The inferences from primate studies are checked against the fossil record. The evidence from the earth, collected in bits and pieces, is correlated with scientific observations of our closest living relatives. In short, biological anthropologists piece together bits of information obtained from different sources. They construct theories that explain the changes observed in the fossil record and then attempt to evaluate their theories by checking one kind of evidence against another. Human paleontology thus overlaps disciplines such as geology, general vertebrate (and particularly primate) paleontology, comparative anatomy, and the study of comparative primate behavior.

The second major focus of biological anthropology, the study of human variation, investigates how and why contemporary human populations differ in biological or physical characteristics. All living people belong to one species, **Homo sapiens,** for all can successfully interbreed. Yet, much varies among human populations. Investigators of human variation ask such questions as: Why are some peoples taller than others? How have human populations adapted physically to their environmental conditions? Are some peoples, such as Inuit (Eskimos), better equipped than other peoples to endure cold? Does darker skin pigmentation offer special protection against the tropical sun?

To understand better the biological variations observable among contemporary human populations, biological anthropologists use the principles, concepts, and techniques of at least three other disciplines: human genetics (the study of human traits that are inherited), population biology (the study of environmental effects on, and interaction with, population characteristics), and epidemiology (the study of how and why diseases affect different populations in different ways). Research on human variation, therefore, overlaps research in other fields. Biological anthropologists, however, are concerned most with human populations and how they vary biologically.

Cultural Anthropology

Cultural anthropology is concerned with how and why cultures vary or are similar in the past and present. But what is culture? The concept of culture is so central to anthropology, we will devote a whole chapter to the concept and how culture changes. Briefly, the term *culture* refers to the customary ways that a particular population or society thinks and behaves. The culture of a social group includes many things—from the language that people speak, the way children are brought up, the roles assigned to males and females, religious beliefs and practices, and preferences in music. Anthropologists are interested in all of these and other learned behaviors and ideas that have come to be widely shared or customary in the group. The three main branches of cultural anthropology are **archaeology** (the study of past cultures, primarily through their material remains), **anthropological linguistics** (the anthropological study of languages), and **ethnology** (the study of existing and recent cultures), now usually referred to by the parent name, *cultural anthropology.*

Archaeology Archaeologists seek not only to reconstruct the daily life and customs of peoples who lived in the past but also to trace cultural changes and to offer possible explanations for those changes. This concern is similar to that of historians, but archaeologists reach much farther back in time. Historians deal only with societies that left written records and are therefore limited to the last 5,000 years of human history. Human societies, however, have existed for more than a million years, and only a small proportion in the last 5,000 years had writing. For all those past societies lacking a written record, archaeologists serve as historians. Lacking written records for study, archaeologists must try to reconstruct history from the remains of human cultures. Some of these remains are as grand as the Mayan temples discovered at Chichén Itzá in Yucatán, Mexico. More often, they are as ordinary as bits of broken pottery, stone tools, and garbage heaps.

Most archaeologists deal with **prehistory,** the time before written records. But a specialty within archaeology, called **historical archaeology,** studies the remains of recent peoples who left written records. This specialty, as its name implies, employs the methods of both archaeologists and historians to study recent societies for which there is both archaeological and historical information.

In trying to understand how and why ways of life have changed through time in different parts of the world, archaeologists collect materials from sites of human

In urban areas before new construction begins, archaeologists may be called upon to excavate and record information on historical sites, as here in New York City.

occupation. Usually, these sites must be unearthed. On the basis of materials they have excavated and otherwise collected, they then ask various questions: Where, when, and why did the distinctive human characteristic of toolmaking first emerge? Where, when, and why did agriculture first develop? Where, when, and why did people first begin to live in cities?

To collect the data they need to suggest answers to these and other questions, archaeologists use techniques and findings borrowed from other disciplines, as well as what they can infer from anthropological studies of recent and contemporary cultures. For example, to guess where to dig for evidence of early toolmaking, archaeologists rely on geology to tell them where sites of early human occupation are likely to be found, because of erosion and uplifting, near the surface of the earth. To infer when agriculture first developed, archaeologists date the relevant excavated materials by a process originally developed by chemical scientists. To try to understand why cities first emerged, archaeologists may use information from historians, geographers, and others about how recent and contemporary cities are related economically and politically to their hinterlands. If we can discover what recent and contemporary cities have in common, we can speculate on why cities developed originally. Thus, archaeologists use information from the present and recent past in trying to understand the distant past.

Anthropological Linguistics Anthropological linguistics is another branch of cultural anthropology. Linguistics, or the study of languages, is a somewhat older discipline than anthropology, but the early linguists concentrated on the study of languages that had been written for a long time—languages such as English that had been written for nearly a thousand years. Anthropological linguists began to do fieldwork in places where the language was not yet written. This meant that anthropologists could not consult a dictionary or grammar to help them learn the language. Instead, they first had to construct a dictionary and grammar. Then they could study the structure and history of the language.

new perspectives on gender

Researcher at Work: Elizabeth M. Brumfiel

Now a professor of anthropology at Northwestern University, Elizabeth M. Brumfiel became interested in the origins of social inequality when she was an undergraduate. Archaeologists had known for some time that substantial wealth differences between families developed only recently (archaeologically speaking), that is, only after about 6,000 years ago. The archaeological indicators of inequality are fairly clear—elaborate burials with valuable goods for some families and large differences in houses and possessions. However, why the transformation occurred was not so clear. When she was in graduate school at the University of Michigan, Brumfiel says, she didn't accept the then-current explanation that inequality provided benefits to the society (e.g., the standard of living of most people improved as the leaders got richer). Consequently, for her PhD research in central Mexico, she began to test the "benefit" explanation in an area that had been independent politically at first and then became part of the Aztec Empire. She studied the surface material remains in the area and historical documents written by Europeans and Aztec nobility. Her findings contradicted the benefit explanation of social inequality; she found little improvement in the standard of living of the local people after the Aztec Empire had absorbed them.

Another important part of her research agenda was understanding the lives of women. How were they affected by the expansion of the Aztec Empire? Did their work change? How were women portrayed in art? In the Aztec capital of

Dona Maria (right) interpreting during the meeting of Cortez and Montezuma II in 1519. Women like Dona Maria apparently held high status in Aztec culture.

Tenochtitlán, images of militarism and masculinity became increasingly important with the growth of the empire, and sculptures showed women in positions of work (e.g., kneeling). However, the images of women in the area of Brumfiel's fieldwork did not change. For example, most of the sculptures after the Aztecs had taken over still showed women standing, not kneeling.

Like many anthropologists, Brumfiel asked herself how she could contribute to the community in which she did her fieldwork. She decided to design an exhibit to display the successes of the people who had lived in the area for 1,200 years. The exhibit tells the people of Xaltocan what she found out from her studies.

As she continues to explore issues about the origins of inequality and the position of women, Brumfiel is quite comfortable with knowing that someone will think that she has "gotten it wrong, and will set out on a lifetime of archaeological research to find her own answers."

Source: Brumfiel 2009.

Like biological anthropologists, linguists study changes that have taken place over time, as well as contemporary variation. Some anthropological linguists are concerned with the emergence of language and also with the divergence of languages over thousands of years. The study of how languages change over time and how they may be related is known as **historical linguistics.** Anthropological linguists are also interested in how contemporary languages differ, especially in their construction. This focus of linguistics is generally called **descriptive** or **structural linguistics.** The study of how language is used in social contexts is called **sociolinguistics.**

In contrast with human paleontologists and archaeologists, who have physical remains to help them reconstruct change over time, historical linguists deal only with languages—and usually unwritten ones at that. (Remember

current research and issues

Researcher at Work: Terence E. Hays

Books and articles often report research in a straightforward manner: here's the problem, here's the answer—that kind of thing. However, many researchers know from experience that knowledge does not always come in a straightforward manner. A professor at Rhode Island College, Terence E. Hays has reflected on the twists and turns in his fieldwork among the Ndumba in the Eastern Highlands province of Papua New Guinea. He first started studying whether different types of people (e.g., women and men) had different types of plant knowledge and whether they classified plants differently. (The interest in plant and animal classification, *ethnobiology*, is closely connected with linguistic research.) In the course of his first fieldwork, in 1972, he witnessed an initiation ceremony for 10- to 12-year-old males—a dramatic and traumatic rite of passage ceremony that included the physical trauma of nosebleeding as well as the social traumas of "attacks" by women and seclusion in the forest. The ceremony was full of symbolism of why the sexes needed to avoid each other. Although he collected stories and myths about plants for his research on ethnobiology, he kept uncovering themes in the stories about the danger of men associating with women.

Hays's curiosity was aroused about these ceremonies and myths. How

Terence Hays during fieldwork in New Guinea.

important are myths in perpetuating cultural themes? Do other societies that have separate men's houses have similar myths? He realized when he returned home from the field that many societies have similar stories. Are these stories generally linked to initiation rites and to physical segregation of the sexes? Answering these questions required comparison, so he embarked on collecting myths and folktales from colleagues who worked in other New Guinea Highland societies. In the course of collecting these comparative materials, he realized he didn't have all

the ethnographic information he needed, so he went back to the field to get it. As Hays remarked, "As an ethnographer I was continually faced with the question, How do you know it's true? But even when I could reach a (hard-won) conviction that something was true for the Ndumba, the second question awaited: How do you know it's generally true, which you can't know without comparison?"

Source: Hays 2009.

that writing is only about 5,000 years old, and most languages since then have not been written.) Because unwritten languages must be heard to be studied, they do not leave any trace once speakers have died. Linguists interested in reconstructing the history of unwritten languages must begin in the present, with comparisons of contemporary languages. On the basis of these comparisons, they draw inferences about the kinds of change in language that may have occurred in the past and that may account for similarities and differences observed in the present. Historical linguists typically ask such questions as these: Did two or more contemporary languages diverge from a common ancestral language? If they are related, how far back in time did they begin to differ?

Unlike historical linguists, the descriptive (or structural) linguists are typically concerned with discovering and recording the principles that determine how sounds and words are put together in speech. For example, a structural description of a particular language might tell us that the sounds *t* and *k* are interchangeable in a word without causing a difference in meaning. In American Samoa, one could say *Tutuila* or *Kukuila* as the name of the largest island, and everyone, except perhaps newly arrived anthropologists who know little about the Samoan language yet, would understand that the same island was being mentioned.

Sociolinguists are interested in the social aspects of language, including what people speak about and how they interact conversationally, their attitudes toward speakers of other dialects or languages, and how people speak differently in different social contexts. In English, for example, we do not address everyone we meet in the same way. "Hi, Sandy" may be the customary way a person greets a friend. But we would probably feel uncomfortable addressing a doctor by a first name; instead, we would probably say, "Good morning, Dr. Brown." Such variations in language use, which are determined by the social status of the people being addressed, are significant for sociolinguists.

Ethnology (Cultural Anthropology)   Ethnologists, or cultural anthropologists, try to understand how and why peoples today and in the recent past differ or are similar in their customary ways of thinking and acting. Also, how and why do cultures develop and change? How does one aspect of culture affect others? Cultural anthropologists ask questions such as: Why is the custom of marriage nearly universal in all cultures? What explains why families live with or near their kin in some societies, but not in other societies? What changes result from the introduction of money to a previously noncommercial economy? When family members move far away to work, what are the impacts on social relationships? What happens when a society is severely stressed because of natural disasters or violent conflicts? The aim of ethnologists is largely the same as that of archaeologists. However, ethnologists generally use data collected through observation and interviews of living peoples. Archaeologists, on the other hand, must work with fragmentary remains of past cultures, on the basis of which they can only make inferences about the customs of prehistoric peoples.

One type of ethnologist, **ethnographers,** usually spend a year or so living with, talking to, and observing the people whose customs they are studying. This fieldwork provides the data for a detailed description (an **ethnography**) of customary behavior and thought. Ethnographers vary in the degree to which they strive for completeness in their coverage of cultural and social life. Earlier ethnographers tended to strive for holistic coverage; more recent ethnographers have tended to specialize or focus on narrower realms such as ritual healing or curing, interaction with the environment, effects of modernization or globalization, or gender issues. Ethnographies often go beyond description; they may address current anthropological issues or try to explain some aspect of culture.

Many cultures have undergone extensive change in the recent past so trying to understand what life was like in earlier times is important. Ethnographers can ask older people what life was like when they were young, and information about the past may be contained in historical documents usually not written by anthropologists. An **ethnohistorian** studies how the ways of life of a particular group of people have changed over time. Ethnohistorians investigate written documents such as missionary accounts, reports by traders and explorers, and government records, to try to establish the cultural changes that have occurred. Unlike ethnographers, who rely mostly on their own observations and interviewing, ethnohistorians rely on the reports of others. Often, they must attempt to piece together and make sense of widely scattered, and even apparently contradictory, information. Thus, the ethnohistorian's research is very much like that of a historian, except that ethnohistorians are usually concerned with the history of a people who did not themselves leave written records. Ethnohistorians try to reconstruct the recent history of a people and may also suggest why certain changes in their way of life took place.

Ethnographic and ethnohistorical research is very time-consuming, and it is a rare for one person to study more than a few cultures. The **cross-cultural researcher** (who may be a cultural anthropologist or some other kind of social scientist,) is interested in discovering general patterns about cultural traits—what is universal, what is variable, why traits vary, and what the consequences of the variability might be. Why, for example, is there more gender inequality in some societies than in others? Is family violence related to aggression in other areas of life? What are the effects of living in a very unpredictable environment? In testing possible answers to such questions, cross-cultural researchers use data from samples of cultures (usually described initially by ethnographers) to try to arrive at explanations or relationships that hold across cultures. Archaeologists may find the results of cross-cultural research useful for making inferences about the past, particularly if they can discover material indicators of cultural variation.

Because ethnologists may be interested in many aspects of customary behavior and thought—from economic behavior to political behavior to styles of art, music, and religion—ethnology overlaps with disciplines that concentrate on some particular aspect of human existence, such as sociology, psychology, economics, political science, art, music, and comparative religion. But the distinctive feature of cultural anthropology is its interest in how all these aspects of human existence vary from society to society, in all historical periods, and in all parts of the world.

Applied Anthropology

All knowledge may turn out to be useful. In the physical and biological sciences, it is well understood that technological breakthroughs like DNA splicing, spacecraft docking in outer space, and the development of miniscule computer chips could not have taken place without an enormous amount of basic research to uncover the laws of nature in the physical and biological worlds. If we did not understand fundamental principles, the technological achievements we are so proud of would not be possible. Researchers are often simply driven by curiosity, with no thought to where the research might lead, which is why such research is sometimes called *basic research*. The same is true of the social sciences. If a researcher finds out that societies with combative sports tend to have more wars, it may lead to other inquiries about the relationships between one kind of aggression and another. The knowledge acquired may ultimately lead to discovering ways to correct social problems, such as family violence and war.

applied anthropology

Getting Development Programs to Notice Women's Contributions to Agriculture

When Anita Spring first did fieldwork in Zambia in the 1970s, she was not particularly interested in agriculture. Rather, medical anthropology was her interest. Her work focused on customary healing practices, particularly involving women and children. She was surprised at the end of the year when a delegation of women came to tell her that she didn't understand what it meant to be a woman. "To be a woman is to be a farmer," they said. She admits that it took her a while to pay attention to women as farmers, but then she began to participate in efforts to provide technical assistance to them. Like many others interested in women in development, Spring realized that all too often development agents downplay women's contributions to agriculture.

How does one bring about change in male-centered attitudes and practices? One way is to document how much women actually

contribute to agriculture. Beginning with the influential writing of Ester Boserup in *Woman's Role in Economic Development* (1970), scholars began to report that in Africa south of the Sahara, in the Caribbean, and in parts of Southeast Asia, women were the principal farmers or agricultural laborers. Moreover, as agriculture became more complex, it required more work time in the fields, so the women's contribution to agriculture increased. In addition, men increasingly went away to work, so women had to do much of what used to be men's work on the farms.

In the 1980s, Spring designed and directed the Women in Agricultural Development Project in Malawi, funded by the Office of Women in the U.S. Agency for International Development. Rather than focusing just on women, the project aimed to collect data on both female and male

agriculturalists and how development agents treated them. The project did more than collect information; mini-projects were set up and evaluated so that successful training techniques could be passed on to development agents in other regions. Spring points out that the success of the program was due not just to the design of the project. Much of the success depended on the interest and willingness of Malawi itself to change. It didn't hurt that the United Nations and other donor organizations increasingly focused attention on women. It takes the efforts of many to bring about change. Increasingly, applied anthropologists like Anita Spring are involved in these efforts from beginning to end, from the design stage to implementation and evaluation.

Source: Spring 1995; 2000b.

Whereas basic research may ultimately help to solve practical problems, applied research is more explicit in its practical goals. Today, more than half of all professional anthropologists are applied, or practicing, anthropologists.[3] Applied or practicing anthropology is explicit in its concern with making anthropological knowledge useful.[4] Applied anthropologists may be trained in any or all of the subfields of anthropology. In contrast to basic researchers, who are almost always employed in colleges, universities, and museums, applied anthropologists are commonly employed in settings outside traditional academia, including government agencies, international development agencies, private consulting firms, businesses, public health organizations, medical schools, law offices, community development agencies, and charitable foundations.

Biological anthropologists may be called upon to give forensic evidence in court, or they may work in public health, or design clothes and equipment to fit human anatomy. Archaeologists may be involved in preserving and exhibiting artifacts for museums and in doing contract work to find and preserve cultural sites that might be damaged by construction or excavation. Linguists may work in bilingual educational training programs or may work on ways to improve communication. Ethnologists

may work in a wide variety of applied projects ranging from community development, urban planning, health care, and agricultural improvement to personnel and organizational management and assessment of the impact of change programs on people's lives.[5] We discuss applied anthropology in boxes in almost all chapters and more fully in the last part of this book "Using Anthropology."

SPECIALIZATION

As disciplines grow, they tend to develop more and more specialties. This trend is probably inevitable because, as knowledge accumulates and methods become more advanced, there is a limit to what any one person can reasonably keep track of. So, in addition to the general divisions we have outlined already, particular anthropologists tend to identify themselves with a variety of specializations. Anthropologists commonly have a geographic specialty, which may be as broad as Old World or New World or as narrow as the southwestern United States. Those who study the past (archaeologists or human paleontologists) may also specialize in different time periods. Ethnologists often specialize in more specific subject

Forensic anthropology is one kind of applied anthropology. Kathy Reichs is a forensic anthropologist working in a medical examiner's office.

matters in addition to one or two cultural areas. Just as most of the chapters in this book refer to broad subject specialties, so do some ethnologists identify themselves as *economic anthropologists, political anthropologists,* or *psychological anthropologists.* Others may identify themselves by theoretical orientations, such as *cultural ecologists,* who are concerned with the relationship between culture and the physical and social environments. These specialties are not mutually exclusive, however. A cultural ecologist, for example, might be interested in the effects of the environment on economic behavior, political behavior, or how people bring up their children.

Does specialization isolate an anthropologist from other kinds of research? Not necessarily. Some specialties have to draw on information from several fields, inside and outside anthropology. For example, *medical anthropologists* study the cultural and biological contexts of human health and illness. Thus, they need to understand the economy, diet, and patterns of social interaction, as well as attitudes and beliefs regarding illness and health. In addition, they may need to draw on research in human genetics, public health, and medicine.

THE RELEVANCE OF ANTHROPOLOGY

Anthropology is a comparatively young discipline. Anthropologists only began to go to live with people in faraway places in the late 1800s. Compared to our knowledge of the physical laws of nature, we know much less about people, about how and why they behave as they do. That anthropology and other sciences dealing with humans began to develop only relatively recently is not in itself a sufficient reason for our knowing less than in the physical sciences. Why, in our quest for knowledge of all kinds, did we wait so long to study ourselves? Leslie White suggests that those phenomena most remote from us and least significant as determinants of human behavior were the first to be studied. The reason, he surmises, is that humans like to think of themselves as citadels of free will, subject to no

laws of nature. Hence, there is no need to see ourselves as objects to be explained.[6]

The idea that it is impossible to account for human behavior scientifically, either because our actions and beliefs are too individualistic and complex or because human beings are understandable only in otherworldly terms, is a self-fulfilling notion. We cannot discover principles explaining human behavior if we neither believe such principles exist nor bother to look for them. The result is assured from the beginning. People who do not believe in principles of human behavior will be reinforced by their finding none. If we are to increase our understanding of human beings, we first have to believe it is possible to do so.

If we aim to understand humans, it is essential that we study humans in all times and places. We must study ancient humans and modern humans. We must study their cultures and their biology. How else can we understand what is true of humans generally or how they are capable of varying? If we study just our own society, we may come up only with explanations that are culture-bound, not general or applicable to most or all humans. Anthropology is useful, then, to the degree that it contributes to our understanding of human beings everywhere.

In addition, anthropology is relevant because it helps us avoid misunderstandings between peoples. If we can understand why other groups are different from ourselves, we might have less reason to condemn them for behavior that appears strange to us. We may then come to realize that many differences between peoples are products of physical and cultural adaptations to different environments. For example, someone who first finds out about the !Kung as they lived in the Kalahari Desert of southern Africa in the 1950s might assume that the !Kung were "backward." (The exclamation point in the name *!Kung* signifies one of the clicking sounds made with the tongue by speakers of the !Kung language.) The !Kung wore little clothing, had few possessions, lived in meager shelters, and enjoyed none of our technological niceties like radio and computers. But let us reflect on how a typical North American community might react if it awoke to find itself in an environment similar to that in which the !Kung lived. The people would find that the arid land makes both agriculture and animal husbandry impossible, and they might have to think about adopting a nomadic existence. They might then discard many of their material possessions so that they could travel easily, to take advantage of changing water and food supplies. Because of the extreme heat and the lack of extra water for laundry, they might find it more practical to be almost naked than to wear clothes. They would undoubtedly find it impossible to build elaborate homes. For social security, they might start to share the food brought into the group. Thus, if they survived at all, they might end up looking and acting far more like the !Kung looked than like typical North Americans.

Physical differences, too, may be seen as results of adaptations to the environment. For example, in our society, we admire people who are tall and slim. If these same

A large number of emigrants from the former Soviet Union, particularly from Black Sea cities and towns such as Odessa, live in the Brighton Beach neighborhood of Brooklyn. Migrant and immigrant communities, such as "Little Odessa," are an increasing focus of anthropological study.

individuals were forced to live above the Arctic Circle, however, they might wish they could trade their tall, slim bodies for short, compact ones, because stocky physiques conserve body heat more effectively and may therefore be more adaptive in cold climates.

Exposure to anthropology might help to alleviate some of the misunderstandings that arise between people of different cultural groups from subtle causes operating below the level of consciousness. For example, different cultures have different conceptions of the gestures and interpersonal distances that are appropriate under various circumstances. Arabs consider it proper to stand close enough to other people to smell them.[7] On the basis of the popularity of deodorants in our culture, we can deduce that Americans prefer to keep the olfactory dimension out of interpersonal relations. We may feel that a person who comes too close is being too intimate. We should remember, however, that this person may only be acting according to a culturally conditioned conception of what is proper in a given situation. If our intolerance for others results in part from a lack of understanding of why peoples vary, then the knowledge that anthropologists accumulate may help lessen that intolerance.

As the world becomes increasingly interconnected or globalized, the importance of understanding and trying to respect cultural and physical differences becomes more and more important. Minor misunderstandings can escalate quickly into more serious problems. Even when powerful countries think they are being helpful, they may convey that other countries are inferior. They may also unknowingly promote behaviors that are not in the best interest of the people they are trying to help. At the extreme, misunderstandings can lead to violent confrontations. In today's world, going to war with modern weapons of mass destruction can kill more people than ever before.

Is understanding and respecting cultural and biological differences enough? Although education is undoubtedly useful, many anthropologists think that more explicit attention has to be paid toward solving real world problems

at both the global and local levels. At the global level, we have to deal with many types of violent conflict, the degradation of the environment, the growing inequality between rich and poor countries, and major threats to health. At the local level, we have to grapple with whether particular development plans are advantageous and how to improve nutrition and health of particular societies. One solution does not necessarily fit all—what's good for some may not be good for others in different circumstances. To find out if some change will be advantageous requires careful study. Many ethical issues arise. Is it ethical to try to interfere with other people's lives? Is it ethical not to, if they are suffering or ask for help?

Knowledge of our past may bring both a feeling of humility and a sense of accomplishment. If we are to attempt to deal with the problems of our world, we must be aware of our vulnerability so that we do not think that problems will solve themselves. But we also have to think enough of our accomplishments to believe that we can find solutions to problems. Much of the trouble we get into may be a result of feelings of self-importance and invulnerability—in short, our lack of humility. Knowing something about our evolutionary past may help us to understand and accept our place in the biological world. Just as for any other form of life, there is no guarantee that any particular human population, or even the entire human species, will perpetuate itself indefinitely. The earth changes, the environment changes, and humanity itself changes. What survives and flourishes in the present might not do so in the future.

Yet, our vulnerability should not make us feel powerless. We have many reasons to feel confident about the future. Consider what we have accomplished so far. By means of tools and weapons fashioned from sticks and stones, we were able to hunt animals larger and more powerful than ourselves. We discovered how to make fire, and we learned to use it to keep ourselves warm and to cook our food. As we domesticated plants and animals, we gained greater control over our food supply and were able to establish more permanent settlements. We mined and smelted ores to fashion more durable tools. We built cities and irrigation systems, monuments and ships. We made it possible to travel from one continent to another in a single day. We conquered some illnesses and prolonged human life.

In short, human beings and their cultures have changed considerably over the course of history. Human populations have often been able to adapt to changing circumstances. Let us hope that humans continue to adapt to the challenges of the present and future.

SUMMARY ● ○ ○

1. Anthropology is literally the study of human beings. It differs from other disciplines concerned with people in that it is broader in scope. It is concerned with humans in all places of the world (not simply those places close to us), and it traces human evolution and cultural development from millions of years ago to the present day.

2. Another distinguishing feature of anthropology is its holistic approach to the study of human beings. Anthropologists study not only all varieties of people but also all aspects of those peoples' experiences and how different aspects of life relate to each other.

3. Anthropologists are commonly concerned with identifying and explaining typical characteristics (traits and customs) of particular human populations.

4. Biological or physical anthropology is one of the major fields of the discipline. Biological anthropology studies the emergence of humans and their later physical evolution (the focus called human paleontology). It also studies how and why contemporary human populations vary biologically (the focus called human variation).

5. Another broad area of concern to anthropology is cultural anthropology. Its three subfields—archaeology, anthropological linguistics, and ethnology (now usually referred to by the parent name, *cultural anthropology*)—all deal with aspects of human culture, that is, with the customary ways of thinking and behaving of particular societies.

6. Archaeologists seek not only to reconstruct the daily life and customs of prehistoric peoples but also to trace cultural changes and offer possible explanations for those changes. Therefore, archaeologists try to reconstruct history from the remains of human cultures.

7. Anthropological linguists are concerned with the emergence of language and with the divergence of languages over time (a subject known as historical linguistics). They also study how contemporary languages differ, both in construction (descriptive or structural linguistics) and in actual speech (sociolinguistics).

8. Ethnologists (now often called simply cultural anthropologists) seek to understand how and why peoples of today and the recent past differ or are similar in their customary ways of thinking and acting. One type of ethnologist, the ethnographer, usually spends a year or so living with and talking to a particular population and observing their customs. Later, ethnographers may prepare a detailed description (an ethnography) of many or some aspects of cultural and social life. Another type of ethnologist, the ethnohistorian, investigates written documents to determine how the ways of life of a particular group of people have changed over time. A third type of ethnologist, the cross-cultural researcher, studies data collected by ethnographers and ethnohistorians for a sample of cultures and attempts to discover which explanations of particular customs may be generally applicable.

9. In all four major subdisciplines of anthropology are applied anthropologists, people who apply anthropological knowledge to achieve more practical goals, usually in the service of an agency outside the traditional academic setting.

10. Anthropology may help people to be more tolerant. Anthropological studies can show us why other people are the way they are, both culturally and physically. Customs or actions that appear improper or offensive to us may be other peoples' adaptations to particular environmental and social conditions.

11. Anthropology is also valuable in that knowledge of our past may bring us both a feeling of humility and a sense of accomplishment. Like any other form of life, we have no guarantee that any particular human population will perpetuate itself indefinitely. Yet, knowledge of our achievements in the past may give us confidence in our ability to solve the problems of the future.

GLOSSARY TERMS ○ ● ○

anthropological linguistics **6**	ethnohistorian **9**
anthropology **2**	ethnology **6**
applied (practicing) anthropology **4**	fossils **5**
archaeology **6**	historical archaeology **6**
biological (physical) anthropology **4**	historical linguistics **7**
cross-cultural researcher **9**	holistic **4**
cultural anthropology **4**	*Homo sapiens* **5**
descriptive (structural) linguistics **7**	human paleontology **5**
ethnographer **9**	human variation **5**
ethnography **9**	paleoanthropology **5**
	prehistory **6**
	Primates **5**
	primatologists **5**
	sociolinguistics **7**

CRITICAL QUESTIONS ○ ○ ●

1. Why study anthropology? What are its goals, and how is it useful?

2. How does anthropology differ from other fields of study you've encountered that deal with humans? (Compare with psychology, sociology, political science, history, or biology, among others.)

3. What do you think about the suggestion that anthropology is the fundamental discipline studying humans?

PEARSON
myanthrolab

Read the chapter by Terence E. Hays, "From Ethnographer to Comparativist and Back Again," on MyAnthroLab, and answer the following questions:

1. Many researchers find that their interests change when they go to the field. What did Hays start out studying? What did he get more interested in?

2. Explain why Hays thinks that you need both ethnography and comparison.

History of Anthropological Theory

istorians of anthropology often trace the birth of the discipline to the 16th-century encounters between Europeans and native peoples in Africa and the Americas. For Europeans, these peoples and their practices often seemed bizarre or irrational, yet to live and work with them, it was important to understand their cultures. This need for cross-cultural understanding was one of the roots of anthropology. The other was the emerging focus on evolution. The recognition that species were not stable but changed over time emerged in parallel with the idea that societies changed over time. Together, these ideas launched the notion that other cultures could be changed, that they could and should be "civilized." The movement by Europeans to "civilize" others between the 16th and 19th centuries destroyed some of the world's cultural diversity, but the field of anthropology emerged out of those efforts. As we shall see, we have knowledge of those cultures that were changed or destroyed by the "civilizing" efforts of European explorers and colonists largely because of the efforts of early anthropologists.

While anthropology may have been born out of its largely colonialist background, anthropologists are now overwhelmingly inclined to support the value of other ways of life and try to support the needs of peoples formerly colonized or dominated by powerful nation-states.

As we review the history of anthropological ideas, keep in mind that, although many of the early points of view were later rejected and replaced, not all ideas suffer the same fate. Evolutionary theory, for example, has been modified substantially over the years, but much of the theory of natural selection put forward by Darwin in the mid-1800s has been supported by empirical evidence and has withstood the test of time. Also keep in mind that some of the ideas we discuss are more properly *theoretical orientations* rather than theories. A **theoretical orientation** is a general idea about how phenomena are to be explained; *theories*, as we discuss more fully in the next chapter, are more specific explanations that can be tested with empirical evidence. ● ○ ●

THE EVOLUTION OF EVOLUTION

Older Western ideas about nature's creatures were very different from Charles Darwin's theory of *evolution,* which suggested that different species developed, one from another, over long periods of time. In the 5th millennium B.C., the Greek philosophers Plato and Aristotle believed that animals and plants form a single, graded continuum going from more perfection to less perfection. Humans, of course, were at the top of this scale. Later Greek philosophers added the idea that the creator gave life or "radiance" first to humans, but some of that essence was lost at each subsequent creation.[1] Macrobius, summarizing the thinking of Plotinus, used an image that was to persist for centuries, the image of what

came to be called the "chain of being": "The attentive observer will discover a connection of parts, from the Supreme God down to the last dregs of things, mutually linked together and without a break. And this is Homer's golden chain, which God, he says, bade hand down from heaven to earth."[2]

Belief in the chain of being was accompanied by the conviction that an animal or plant species could not become extinct. In fact, all things were linked to one another in a chain, and all links were necessary. Moreover, the notion of extinction threatened people's trust in God; it was unthinkable that a whole group of God's creations could simply disappear.

The idea of the chain of being persisted through the years, but philosophers, scientists, poets, and theologians did not discuss it extensively until the 18th century. Those discussions prepared the way for evolutionary theory. Ironically, although the chain of being did not allow for evolution, its idea that nature had an order of things encouraged studies of natural history and comparative anatomical studies, which stimulated the development of the idea of evolution. People were also now motivated to look for previously unknown creatures. Moreover, humans were not shocked when naturalists suggested that humans were close to apes. This notion was perfectly consistent with the idea of a chain of being; apes were simply thought to have been created with less perfection.

Early in the 18th century, an influential scientist, Carolus Linnaeus (1707–1778), classified plants and animals in a *systema naturae,* which placed humans in the same order (Primates) as apes and monkeys. Linnaeus did not suggest an evolutionary relationship between humans and apes; he mostly accepted the notion that all species were created by God and fixed in their form. Not surprisingly, then, Linnaeus is often viewed as an anti-evolutionist. But Linnaeus's hierarchical classification scheme, in descending order from kingdom to class, order, **genus** (a group of related species), and species, provided a framework for the idea that humans, apes, and monkeys had a common ancestor.

Others did not believe that species were fixed in their form. According to Jean-Baptiste Lamarck (1744–1829), acquired characteristics could be inherited and therefore species could evolve; individuals who in their lifetime developed characteristics helpful to survival would pass those characteristics on to future generations, thereby changing the physical makeup of the species. For example, Lamarck explained the long neck of the giraffe as the result of successive generations of giraffes stretching their necks to reach the high leaves of trees. The stretched muscles and bones of the necks were somehow transmitted to the offspring of the neck-stretching giraffes, and eventually all giraffes came to have long necks. But because Lamarck and later biologists failed to produce evidence to support the hypothesis that acquired characteristics can be inherited, this explanation of evolution is now generally dismissed.[3]

By the 19th century, some thinkers were beginning to accept evolution whereas others were trying to refute it. For example, Georges Cuvier (1769–1832) was a leading opponent of evolution. Cuvier's theory of catastrophism proposed that a quick series of catastrophes accounted for changes in

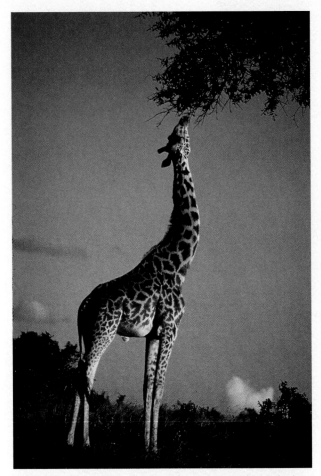

The giraffe's long neck is adaptive for eating tree leaves high off the ground. When food is scarce, longer-necked giraffes would get more food and reproduce more successfully than shorter-necked giraffes; in this environment, natural selection would favor giraffes with longer necks.

the earth and the fossil record. Cataclysms and upheavals such as Noah's flood had killed off previous sets of living creatures, which each time were replaced by new creations.

Major changes in geological thinking occurred in the 19th century. Earlier, geologist James Hutton (1726–1797) had questioned catastrophism, but his work was largely ignored. In contrast, Sir Charles Lyell's (1797–1875) volumes of the *Principles of Geology* (1830–1833), which built on Hutton's earlier work, received immediate acclaim. Their concept of *uniformitarianism* suggested that the earth is constantly being shaped and reshaped by natural forces that have operated over a vast stretch of time. Lyell also discussed the formation of geological strata and paleontology. He used fossilized fauna to define different geological epochs. Lyell's works were read avidly by Charles Darwin before and during Darwin's now-famous voyage on the *Beagle.* The two corresponded and subsequently became friends.

After studying changes in plants, fossil animals, and varieties of domestic and wild pigeons, Charles Darwin (1809–1882) rejected the notion that each species was created at one time in a fixed form. The results of his investigations pointed clearly, he thought, to the evolution of species through the mechanism of natural selection. While Darwin was completing his book on the subject, naturalist

Alfred Russel Wallace (1823–1913) sent him a manuscript that came to conclusions about the evolution of species that matched Darwin's own.[4] In 1858, the two men presented the astonishing theory of natural selection to their colleagues at a meeting of the Linnaean Society of London.[5]

In 1859, when Darwin published *The Origin of Species by Means of Natural Selection*,[6] he wrote, "I am fully convinced that species are not immutable; but that those belonging to what are called the same genera are lineal descendants of some other and generally extinct species, in the same manner as the acknowledged varieties of any one species."[7] His conclusions outraged those who believed in the biblical account of creation, and the result was bitter controversy that continues to this day.[8]

Although Darwin's idea of evolution by natural selection was strongly challenged when first published (particularly, as illustrated here, the idea that humans and primates shared a common ancestor), it has withstood rigorous testing and is the foundation of many anthropological theories.

Until 1871, when his *The Descent of Man* was published, Darwin avoided stating categorically that humans were descended from nonhuman forms, but the implications of his theory were clear. People immediately began to take sides. In June 1860, at the annual meeting of the British Association for the Advancement of Science, Bishop Wilberforce saw an opportunity to attack the Darwinists. Concluding his speech, he faced Thomas Huxley, one of the Darwinists' chief advocates, and inquired, "Was it through his grandfather or his grandmother that he claimed descent from a monkey?" Huxley responded,

> If . . . the question is put to me would I rather have a miserable ape for a grandfather than a man highly endowed by nature and possessing great means and influence and yet who employs those faculties and that influence for the mere purpose of introducing ridicule into a grave scientific discussion—I unhesitatingly affirm my preference for the ape.[9]

Although Huxley's retort to Bishop Wilberforce displays both humor and quick wit, it does not answer the bishop's question very well. A better answer, and one we pursue in the chapter on genetics and evolution, is that Darwinists would claim that we descended from monkeys neither through our grandmother or our grandfather, but that both we and monkeys are descended from a common ancestor who lived long ago. Darwinists would further argue that natural selection was the process through which the physical and genetic form of that common ancestor diverged to become both monkey and human.

EARLY ANTHROPOLOGICAL THEORY

In anthropology, as in any discipline, there is a continual ebb and flow of ideas. One theoretical orientation will arise and may grow in popularity until another is proposed in opposition to it. Often, one orientation will capitalize on those aspects of a problem that a previous orientation ignored or played down. In our survey of many of the orientations that have developed since the emergence of anthropology as a professional discipline, we follow an approximate historical sequence. As we discuss each school of thought, we will indicate what kinds of information or phenomena it emphasizes (if it does) as explanatory factors. Some of these orientations have passed into history by now; others continue to attract adherents.

Early Evolutionism

In the early years of anthropology, Darwinism had a strong impact on theory. The prevailing view was that culture generally develops (or evolves) in a uniform and progressive manner, just as Darwin argued species did. It was thought that most societies pass through the same series of stages, to arrive ultimately at a common end. The sources of culture change were generally assumed to be embedded within the culture from the beginning, and therefore the ultimate course of development was thought to be internally determined. Two 19th-century anthropologists whose writings exemplified the theory that culture generally evolves uniformly and progressively were Edward B. Tylor (1832–1917) and Lewis Henry Morgan (1818–1881).

Tylor maintained that culture evolved from the simple to the complex and that all societies passed through three basic stages of development: from savagery through barbarism to civilization.[10] "Progress" was therefore possible for all. To account for cultural variation, Tylor and other early evolutionists postulated that different contemporary societies were at different stages of evolution. According to this view, the "simpler" peoples of the day had not yet reached "higher" stages. Tylor believed there was a kind of psychic unity among all peoples that explained parallel evolutionary sequences in different cultural traditions. In other words, because of the basic similarities common to all peoples, different societies often find the same solutions to the same problems independently. But Tylor also noted that cultural traits may spread from one society to another by simple *diffusion*—the borrowing by one culture of a trait belonging to another as the result of contact between the two.

Another 19th-century proponent of uniform and progressive cultural evolution was Lewis Henry Morgan. A lawyer in upstate New York, Morgan became interested in the local Iroquois Indians and defended their reservation in a land-grant case. In gratitude, the Iroquois "adopted" Morgan.

In his best-known work, *Ancient Society,* Morgan postulated several sequences in the evolution of human culture. For example, he speculated that the family evolved through six stages. Human society began as a "horde living in promiscuity," with no sexual prohibitions and no real family structure. Next was a stage in which a group of brothers was married to a group of sisters and brother-sister matings were permitted. In the third stage, group marriage was practiced, but brothers and sisters were not allowed to mate. The fourth stage was characterized by a loosely paired male and female who still lived with other people. Then came the husband-dominant family, in which the husband could have more than one wife simultaneously. Finally, the stage of civilization was distinguished by the monogamous family, with just one wife and one husband who were relatively equal in status.[11] However, Morgan's postulated sequence for the evolution of the family is not supported by the enormous amount of ethnographic data that has been collected since his time. For example, no recent society generally practices group marriage or allows brother-sister mating. (In the chapter on marriage and the family, we discuss how recent cultures have varied in regard to marriage customs.)

The evolutionism of Tylor, Morgan, and others of the 19th century is largely rejected today. For one thing, their theories cannot satisfactorily account for cultural variation. The "psychic unity of mankind" or "germs of thought" that were postulated to account for parallel evolution cannot also account for cultural differences. Another weakness in the early evolutionist theories is that they cannot explain why some societies have regressed or even become extinct. Finally, although other societies may have progressed to "civilization," some of them have not passed through all the stages. Thus, early evolutionist theory cannot explain the details of cultural evolution and variation as anthropology now knows them.

"Race" Theory

Evolutionism also influenced another branch of anthropological theory, one that posited that the reason human cultures differed in their behaviors was because they represented separate subspecies of humans, or "races." This idea was also influenced by the fact that, by the 19th century at least, it became clear that few cultures were being "civilized" in the way Europeans expected. Rather than attribute this to the strength of cultural tradition, some attributed it to the innate capabilities of the people—in other words, to their "race." Members of "uncivilized

The 19th-century belief that progress was a universal in social change had a profound impact on early anthropological theorists such as Edward B. Tylor and Lewis Henry Morgan.

THE PROGRESS OF THE CENTURY.

races" were, by their very nature, incapable of being "civilized." Such ideas were widely held and supported during the late 19th and early 20th centuries and, as we shall see, American anthropology played a large role in showing that "race" theory was unsupported in a variety of contexts. Unfortunately, "race" theory persists in some disciplines.

The roots of "race" theory are fairly easy to trace.[12] As discussed earlier, the classification of plants and animals into distinct biological groups began with the work of Linneaus. In his *systema natura*, humans are classified into four distinct "races" (American, European, Asiatic, and African), each defined not only by physical characteristics but also by emotional and behavioral ones. Similarly, Johann Blumenbach (1752–1840), a founder of the field of biological anthropology, divided humans into five "races" (Caucasian, Mongolian, Malayan, Ethiopian, and American). Interestingly, each of his races relates to peoples of recently colonized areas, and Blumenbach makes clear that the purpose of his division of humanity is to help classify the variety of humans that European colonists were encountering at the time.

Samuel Morton (1799–1851), a Philadelphia physician, was the first to explicitly link "race" with behavior and intelligence. Morton collected and measured the skulls of Native Americans, and, in *Crania Americana* (1839), concluded that not only were Native Americans a separate "race," but their behavioral differences from European Americans were rooted in the physical structures of their brains. Expanding his study, he examined skulls of ancient Egyptians, and, in *Crania Aegyptiaca* (1844), concluded that "race" differences were ancient and unchanging.

The presumed fixity of these "race" differences was essential, not only to justify the exploitive relationships of colonialism and slavery, but also to fight against Darwin's idea of evolution. If God created the world in a fixed and stable form, then "races" should be fixed as well. Thus, not surprisingly, one of the 19th century's strongest critics of evolution, Harvard naturalist Louis Agassiz (1807–1873), was also one of the century's most outspoken supporters of "race" theory. Between 1863 and 1865, Agassiz measured thousands of Civil War soldiers, and used the data he collected to argue that significant and stable differences existed between people of African versus European descent. He implied that these differences illustrated God's creation of human "races."

By the turn of the 20th century, "race" theory was being used in attempts to shape the structure of society. Eminent British scientist Francis Galton (1822–1911) promoted a social and political movement aimed at manipulating "races" by selectively breeding humans with desirable characteristics and preventing those with undesirable ones from having offspring. **Eugenics**, as this movement was called, was widely accepted in Europe, and had strong supporters in the United States, support that continues to this day. For example, in *The Bell Curve* (1994), Richard Herrnstein and Charles Murray assert that there are "race" differences in IQ (and, consequently, success in life), and suggest that social policies should discourage "races" deemed to have low IQs from having many children.

The scholarly use of "race" theory declined precipitously following World War II, when the Nazi genocide against "races" that they viewed as inferior exposed the idea's dangerous potential. At the same time, advances in biological anthropology began to demonstrate that "race" itself was an analytical concept with very little utility. By the 1970s, biologists were able to show that purely genetic races of humans are not clearly identifiable, and therefore

Race theory was used to justify the exploitive relationships of slavery and colonialism. In this 19th-century advertisement, a slave gathers cocoa beans to be made into chocolate for European consumption.

not applicable to humans.[13] Still, "race" theory has not disappeared completely.[14]

Diffusionism

In the late 19th and early 20th centuries, although the cultural evolutionism of Tylor and Morgan was still popular and "race" theory was at its height, diffusionism began to take hold among anthropologists in several parts of the world. The two main schools with a diffusionist viewpoint were the British and the German-Austrian.

The main spokesmen for the British school of diffusionism were G. Elliott Smith, William J. Perry, and W. H. R. Rivers. Smith and Perry stated that most aspects of higher civilization were developed in Egypt (which was relatively advanced because of its early development of agriculture) and were then diffused throughout the world as other peoples came into contact with the Egyptians.[15] People, they believed, are inherently uninventive and invariably prefer to borrow the inventions of another culture rather than develop ideas for themselves. This viewpoint was never widely accepted, and it has now been abandoned completely.

Inspired by Friedrich Ratzel, Fritz Graebner and Father Wilhelm Schmidt led the early 20th-century German-Austrian diffusionist school. This school also held that people borrow from others because they are basically uninventive. In contrast to Smith and Perry of the British school, who assumed that all cultural traits originated in one place (Egypt) and filtered out to cultures throughout the world, the German-Austrian school suggested the existence and diffusion of several different cultural complexes (*Kulturkreise*, plural in German).[16] Like the British diffusionists, however, the *Kulturkreis* (singular) school provided little documentation for the historical relationships it assumed.

A separate American diffusionist school of thought, led by Clark Wissler and Alfred Kroeber, also arose in the first few decades of the 20th century, but it was more modest in its claims. The American diffusionists attributed the characteristic features of a culture area to a geographical *culture center*, where the traits were first developed and from which they then diffused outward. This theory led Wissler to formulate his age-area principle: If a given trait diffuses outward from a single culture center, it follows that the most widely distributed traits found to exist around such a center must be the oldest traits.[17]

Although most anthropologists today acknowledge the spread of traits by diffusion, few try to account for most aspects of cultural development and variation in terms of diffusion. For one thing, the diffusionists dealt only in a very superficial way with the question of how cultural traits are transferred from one society to another. The failing was a serious one, because one of the things we want to explain is why a culture accepts, rejects, or modifies a trait that one of its neighbors has. Also, even if it could be demonstrated how and why a trait diffused outward from a cultural center, we would still be no closer to an explanation of how or why the trait developed within that center in the first place.

LATER ANTHROPOLOGICAL THEORY

The beginning of the 20th century brought the end of evolutionism's reign in cultural anthropology. Its leading opponent was Franz Boas (1858–1942), whose main disagreement with the evolutionists involved their assumption that universal laws governed all human culture. Boas pointed out that these 19th-century individuals lacked sufficient data (as did Boas himself) to formulate many useful generalizations. Boas also strongly opposed "race" theory, and made significant contributions to the study of human variation that demonstrated how supposedly "racial," and supposedly biological, characteristics actually varied depending on where a person grew up. Boas almost single-handedly brought about the decline of "race" theory in America, as well as trained the first generation of American anthropologists, including (among others) Alfred Kroeber, Robert Lowie, Edward Sapir, Melville Herskovits, and Margaret Mead.[18]

Historical Particularism

Boas stressed the apparently enormous complexity of cultural variation, and perhaps because of this complexity he believed it was premature to formulate universal laws. He felt that single cultural traits had to be studied in the context of the society in which they appeared. In 1896, Boas published an article entitled "The Limitation of the Comparative Method of Anthropology,"[19] which dealt with his objections to the evolutionist approach. In it, he stated that anthropologists should spend less time developing theories based on insufficient data. Rather, they should devote their energies to collecting as much data as possible, as quickly as possible, before cultures disappeared (as so many already had, after contact with foreign societies). He asserted that valid interpretations could be made and theories proposed only after this body of data was gathered.

Boas expected that, if a tremendous quantity of data was collected, the laws governing cultural variation would emerge from the mass of information by themselves. According to the method he advocated, the essence of science is to mistrust all expectations and to rely only on facts. But, the "facts" that are recorded, even by the most diligent observer, will necessarily reflect what that individual considers important. Collecting done without some preliminary theorizing, without ideas about what to expect, is meaningless, for the facts that are most important may be ignored whereas irrelevant ones may be recorded. Although it was appropriate for Boas to criticize previous "armchair theorizing," his concern with innumerable local details did not encourage a belief that it might be possible to explain the major variations in culture that anthropologists observe.

Psychological Approaches

In the 1920s, some American anthropologists began to study the relationship between culture and personality.

Although there are varying opinions about how the culture-and-personality school got started, the writings of Sigmund Freud and other psychoanalysts were undoubtedly influential. Edward Sapir, one of Boas's earliest students, reviewed psychoanalytical books and seems to have influenced two other students of Boas—Ruth Benedict and Margaret Mead—who became early proponents of a psychological orientation.[20]

In seminars at Columbia University in the 1930s and 1940s, Ralph Linton, an anthropologist, and Abram Kardiner, a psychoanalyst, developed important ideas for culture-and-personality studies. Kardiner suggested that there is a *basic personality* in every culture that is produced by *primary institutions* (such as type of household, subsistence, and childrearing practices). In other words, just as children's later personalities may be shaped by their earlier experiences, the personalities of adults in a society should be shaped by common cultural experiences. In turn, the *basic personality* gives rise to other institutions (such as art, folklore, and religion), called *secondary institutions*, which are viewed as projections from basic personality. John Whiting and Irvin Child independently put forward a similar and somewhat more elaborated theoretical framework somewhat later.[21] If similar primary institutions exist, it follows that similar personality outcomes and similar secondary institutions should be predicted. Indeed, as we will see in the chapter on culture and the individual, many subsequent cross-cultural studies have supported these connections.

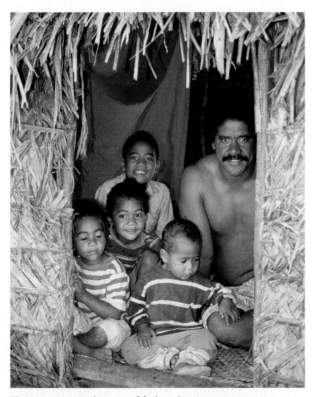

The presence or absence of fathers has important consequences for psychological development, and some societies have much more father presence than others. This Tongan father in the South Pacific is shown with his family.

As time went on, the focus of the psychological approach broadened and diversified. There was more interest in diversity of personality within societies and in universals across human societies. Through this focus on universals, human development from infancy through adolescence, as well as thought processes and emotional responses, was examined to understand human nature. The interest in cultural differences did not disappear but focused more on particular societies—particularly their ethnopsychologies (native psychological concepts and theories), or concepts of the self and emotion.[22]

To generalize about the psychological approach to cultural anthropology, then, we may say that it explicitly employs psychological concepts and methods to help understand cultural differences and similarities.[23] In the chapter on culture and the individual, we discuss psychological approaches in more detail.

Functionalism

In Europe, the reaction against evolution was not as dramatic as in the United States, but a clear division between the diffusionists and those who came to be known as *functionalists* emerged by the 1930s. **Functionalism** in social science looks for the part (function) that some aspect of culture or social life plays in maintaining a cultural system. Two quite different schools of functionalism arose in conjunction with two British anthropologists—Bronislaw Malinowski (1884–1942) and Arthur Reginald Radcliffe-Brown (1881–1955).

Malinowski's version of functionalism assumes that all cultural traits serve the needs of *individuals* in a society; that is, they satisfy some *basic* or *derived need* of the members of the group. Basic needs include nutrition, reproduction, bodily comfort, safety, relaxation, movement, and growth. Some aspects of the culture satisfy these basic needs and give rise to derived needs that must also be satisfied. For example, culture traits that satisfy the basic need for food give rise to the secondary, or derived, need for cooperation in food collection or production. Societies will in turn develop forms of political organization and social control that guarantee the required cooperation. How did Malinowski explain such things as religion and magic? He suggested that, because humans always live with a certain amount of uncertainty and anxiety, they need stability and continuity. Religion and magic are functional in that they serve those needs.[24]

Unlike Malinowski, Radcliffe-Brown felt that the various aspects of social behavior *maintain* a *society's social structure* rather than satisfying individual needs. By social structure, he meant the total network of existing social relationships in a society.[25] The phrase *structural-functionalism* is often used to describe Radcliffe-Brown's approach. To explain how different societies deal with the tensions that are likely to develop among people related through marriage, Radcliffe-Brown suggested that societies do one of two things: They may develop strict rules forbidding the people involved ever to interact face-to-face (as do the Navajos, for example, in requiring a man to avoid his mother-in-law). They may also allow mutual disrespect and teasing between the in-laws. Radcliffe-Brown suggested that avoidance is likely to occur between in-laws of different generations, whereas disrespectful teasing is likely between in-laws of the same generation.[26] Both avoidance and teasing, he suggested, are ways to avoid real conflict and help maintain the social structure. (American mother-in-law jokes may also help relieve tension.)

The major objection to Malinowski's functionalism is that it cannot readily account for cultural variation. Most of the needs he identified, such as the need for food, are universal: All societies must deal with them if they are to survive. Thus, although the functionalist approach may tell us why all societies engage in food-getting, it cannot tell why different societies have different food-getting practices. In other words, functionalism does not explain why certain specific cultural patterns arise to fulfill a need that might be fulfilled just as easily by any of a number of alternative possibilities.

A major problem of the structural-functionalist approach is that it is difficult to determine whether a particular custom is in fact functional in the sense of contributing to the maintenance of the social system. In biology, the contribution an organ makes to the health or life of an animal can be assessed by removing it. But we cannot subtract a cultural trait from a society to see if the trait really does contribute to the maintenance of that group. It is conceivable that certain customs within a society may be neutral or even detrimental to its maintenance. Moreover, we cannot assume that all of a society's customs are functional merely because the society is functioning at the moment. Even if we are able to assess whether a particular custom is functional, this theoretical orientation fails to deal with the question of why a particular society chooses to meet its structural needs in a particular way. A given problem does not necessarily have only one solution. We must still explain why one of several possible solutions is chosen.

Neoevolution

The evolutionary approach to cultural variation did not die with the 19th century. Beginning in the 1940s, Leslie A. White (1900–1975) attacked the Boasian emphasis on historical particularism and championed the evolutionist orientation.

Though quickly labeled a neoevolutionist, White rejected the term, insisting that his approach did not depart significantly from the theories adopted in the 19th century. What White did add to the classical evolutionist approach was a conception of culture as an energy-capturing system. According to his "basic law" of cultural evolution, "other factors remaining constant, *culture evolves as the amount of energy harnessed per capita per year is increased or as the efficiency of the instrumental means of putting the energy to work is increased.*"[27] In other words, a more advanced technology gives humans control over more energy (human, animal, solar, and so on), and cultures expand and change as a result.

White's orientation has been criticized for the same reasons that the ideas of Tylor and Morgan were. In describing what has happened in the evolution of human culture, he assumed that cultural evolution is determined strictly by conditions (preeminently technological ones) inside the culture. That is, he explicitly denied the possibility of environmental, historical, or psychological influences on cultural evolution. The main problem with such an orientation is that it cannot explain why some cultures evolve whereas others either do not evolve or become extinct. White's theory of energy capture sidesteps the question of why only some cultures are able to increase their energy capture.

Julian H. Steward (1902–1972), another later evolutionist, divided evolutionary thought into three schools: unilinear, universal, and multilinear.[28] Steward believed that Morgan and Tylor's theories exemplified the unilinear approach to cultural evolution, the classical 19th-century orientation that attempted to place particular cultures on the rungs of a sort of evolutionary ladder. Universal evolutionists such as Leslie White, on the other hand, were concerned with culture in the broad sense, rather than with individual cultures. Steward classified himself as a multilinear evolutionist: one who deals with the evolution of particular cultures and only with demonstrated sequences of parallel culture change in different areas.

Steward was concerned with explaining specific cultural differences and similarities. Consequently, he was critical of White's vague generalities and his disregard of environmental influences. White, on the other hand, asserted that Steward fell into the historical-particularist trap of paying too much attention to particular cases.

Marshall Sahlins (born 1930) and Elman Service (1915–1996), who were students and colleagues of both White and Steward, combined the views of those two individuals by recognizing two kinds of evolution—specific and general.[29] **Specific evolution** refers to the particular sequence of change and adaptation of a particular society in a given environment. **General evolution** refers to a general progress of human society, in which higher forms (having higher-energy capture) arise from and surpass lower forms. Thus, specific evolution is similar to Steward's multilinear evolution, and general evolution resembles White's universal evolution. Although this synthesis does serve to integrate the two points of view, it does not give us a way of explaining why general evolutionary progress has occurred. But, unlike the early evolutionists, some of the later evolutionists did suggest a mechanism to account for the evolution of particular cultures—namely, adaptation to particular environments.

Structuralism

Claude Lévi-Strauss (1908–2009) was the leading proponent of an approach to cultural analysis called **structuralism.** Lévi-Strauss's structuralism differs from that of Radcliffe-Brown. Whereas Radcliffe-Brown concentrated on how the elements of a society function as a system, Lévi-Strauss concentrates more on the origins of the systems themselves. He sees culture, as expressed in art, ritual, and the patterns of daily life, as a surface representation of the underlying structure of the human mind. Consider, for example, how he tries to account for what anthropologists call a *moiety system*. Such a system is said to exist if a society is divided into two large intermarrying kin groups (each called a *moiety*, probably derived from the French word *moitié*, meaning "half"). Lévi-Strauss says that moiety systems reflect the human mind's predisposition to think and behave in terms of *binary oppositions* (contrasts between one thing and another).[30] Clearly, a moiety system involves a binary opposition: You are born into one of two groups and you marry someone in the other. The problem with Lévi-Strauss's explanation of moieties is that he is postulating a constant—the human mind's supposed dualism—to account for a cultural feature that is not universal. Moiety systems are found in only a relatively small number of societies, so how could something that is universal explain something else that is not?

Lévi-Strauss's interpretations of cultural phenomena (which tend to be far more involved and difficult to follow than the example just described) have concentrated on the presumed cognitive processes of people, the ways in which people supposedly perceive and classify things in the world around them. In studies such as *The Savage Mind* and *The Raw and the Cooked*, he suggested that even technologically simple groups often construct elaborate systems of classification of plants and animals, not only for practical purposes but also out of a need for such intellectual activity.[31]

Structuralism has influenced thinking not only in France; Britain too has been receptive. But the British structuralists, such as Edmund Leach, Rodney Needham, and Mary Douglas, do not follow Lévi-Strauss in looking for panhuman or universal principles in the human mind. Rather, they concentrate on applying structural analysis to particular societies and particular social institutions.[32] For example, Mary Douglas discusses an argument that took place in her home over whether soup is an "appropriate" supper. She suggests that meals (in her household and in culturally similar households) have certain structural principles. They have contrasts—hot and cold, bland and spiced, liquid and semiliquid—and various textures. They must incorporate cereals, vegetables, and animal protein. Douglas concludes that, if the food served does not follow these principles, it cannot be considered a meal.[33]

Some structuralist writings have been criticized for their concentration on abstruse, theoretical analysis at the expense of observation and evidence. For example, it is not always clear how Lévi-Strauss derived a particular structuralist interpretation, and in the absence of any systematically collected supporting evidence, readers must decide whether the interpretation seems plausible. Thus, Lévi-Strauss's studies have come to be regarded by many as vague and untestable, as self-contained intellectual constructs with little explanatory value. Moreover, even if some universal patterns underlie cultural phenomena, universals or constants cannot explain cultural differences.

Ethnoscience and Cognitive Anthropology

Lévi-Strauss's structuralist approach involves intuitively grasping the rules of thought that may underlie a given culture. An ethnographic approach known as **ethnoscience** attempts to derive these rules from a logical analysis of ethnographic data that are kept as free as possible from contamination by the observer's own cultural biases. Rather than collecting data according to a predetermined set of anthropological categories (referred to as an *etic* view), ethnoscientists seek to understand a people's world from their point of view (an *emic* view). Studying their language using systematic elicitation techniques, ethnoscientists try to formulate the rules that underlie the cultural domains. The rules are believed to be comparable to the grammatical rules that generate the correct use of the language. Research commonly focuses on kinship terms, plant and animal taxonomies, and disease classification. Ethnoscience was an early kind of *cognitive anthropology*.[34] Later researchers developed techniques to test whether the rules presumably uncovered were being followed by other members of the society and how much "cultural consensus" there was on these rules. (As we will see later, techniques for evaluating cultural consensus also provide ways of choosing the best people to interview, who are likely to be most knowledgeable about the culture.) Cognitive anthropologists also branched out to studying decision making, cultural goals and motivations, and discourse analysis.[35]

Many ethnoscientists think that, if we can discover the rules that generate cultural behavior, we can explain much of what people do and why they do it. Probably individuals do generally act according to the conscious and unconscious rules they have internalized. But we still need to understand why a particular society has developed the particular cultural rules it has. Just as a grammar does not explain how a language came to be what it is, an ethnoscientific discovery of a culture's rules does not explain why those rules developed.

Cultural Ecology

Some anthropologists are concerned mostly with the influence of environment on culture. Julian Steward was one of the first to advocate the study of **cultural ecology**—the analysis of the relationship between a culture and its environment. Steward felt that the explanation for some aspects of cultural variation could be found in the adaptation of societies to their particular environments. But rather than merely hypothesize that the environment did or did not determine cultural variation, Steward wished to resolve the question *empirically*—that is, he wanted to carry out investigations to evaluate his viewpoint.[36]

Steward felt, however, that cultural ecology must be separated from *biological ecology*, the study of the relationships between organisms and their environment. Later cultural ecologists, such as Andrew Vayda and Roy Rappaport, wished to incorporate principles of biological ecology into the study of cultural ecology to make a

Sometimes you can have too many pigs. A pig feast solves this problem and maintains or creates close ties between groups. Here we see preparations for a pig feast on the island of Tanna in the New Hebrides.

single science of ecology.[37] In their view, cultural traits, just like biological traits, can be considered adaptive or maladaptive. Cultural ecologists assume that cultural adaptation involves the mechanism of *natural selection*—the more frequent survival and reproduction of the better adapted. Environment, including the physical and social environments, affects the development of culture traits in that "individuals or populations behaving in certain different ways have different degrees of success in survival and reproduction and, consequently, in the transmission of their ways of behaving from generation to generation."[38]

Consider how culture and environment may interact among the Tsembaga, who live in the interior of New Guinea.[39] The Tsembaga live mainly on the root crops and greens they grow in home gardens; they also raise pigs. The pigs are seldom eaten; instead, they keep residential areas clean by consuming garbage, and they help prepare the soil for planting by rooting in it. Small numbers of pigs are easy to keep and require little care; they run free all day, returning at night to eat whatever substandard tubers are found in the course of their owners' harvesting of their daily rations. But problems arise when the pig herd grows large. Often there are not enough substandard tubers, and then the pigs must be fed human rations. Also, a large herd is likely to intrude upon garden crops. If one person's pig invades a neighbor's garden, the garden owner often retaliates by killing the offending pig. In turn, the dead animal's owner may kill the garden owner, the garden owner's wife, or one of his pigs. As the number of such feuds

increases, people begin to put as much distance as possible between their pigs and other people's gardens.

Rappaport suggests that, to cope with the problem of pig overpopulation, the Tsembaga developed an elaborate cycle of rituals involving the slaughter of large numbers of surplus pigs. The cultural practice of ritual pig feasts can be viewed as a possible adaptation to environmental factors that produce a surplus pig population. But it is hard to know if the ritual pig feasts are more adaptive than other possible solutions to the problem of pig overpopulation. For example, it might be more adaptive to slaughter and eat pigs regularly so that pig herds never get too large. Without being able to contrast the effects of alternative solutions, a cultural ecologist studying a single society may find it difficult to obtain evidence that a custom already in place is more adaptive than other possible solutions to the problem.

More recent ecological anthropologists have criticized the earlier ecologists for having an overly narrow view of a bounded culture in an isolated environment and have considered the environment in a broader context—moving well beyond the local ecosystem to national and even international levels.[40] As we will discuss shortly, hardly any people on earth are unaffected by larger political, social, and environmental forces.

Political Economy

Like cultural ecology, the school of thought known as **political economy** assumes that external forces explain the way a society changes and adapts. But it is not the natural environment, or the social environment in general, that is central to the approach of political economy. What is central is the social and political impact of those powerful state societies (principally Spain, Portugal, Britain, and France) that transformed the world by colonialism and imperialism after the mid-1400s, and fostered the development of a worldwide economy or world system.[41] Scholars now realize that imperialism is at least 5,000 years old; most, if not all, of the first civilizations were imperialistic. Imperialistic expansion of the first state societies was linked to expanding commercialization, the growth of buying and selling.[42] Today, of course, the entire world is linked commercially. Not surprisingly, the political economy orientation grew in importance as the global reach of capitalism accelerated.

Some of the earliest figures associated with the political economy approach in anthropology were trained at Columbia University when Julian Steward was a professor there. For those students, Steward's cultural ecology was insufficiently attentive to recent world history. For example, Eric Wolf and Sidney Mintz argued that the communities they studied in Puerto Rico developed as they did because of colonialism and the establishment of plantations to supply sugar and coffee to Europe and North America.[43] And Eleanor Leacock, who studied the Montagnais-Naskapi Indians of Labrador, suggested that their system of family hunting territories was not an old characteristic, present before European contact, but developed instead out of the Indians' early involvement in the European-introduced fur trade.[44]

Central to the later and continuing intellectual development of political economy in anthropology are the writings, published in the 1960s and 1970s, of two political sociologists, André Gunder Frank and Immanuel Wallerstein. Frank suggested that the development of a region (Europe, for example) depended on the suppression of development or underdevelopment of other regions (for example, the New World, Africa). He argued that, if we want to understand why a country remains underdeveloped, we must understand how developed nations exploit it.[45] Frank is concerned with what happened in the underdeveloped world. Wallerstein is more concerned with how capitalism developed in the privileged countries and how the expansionist requirements of the capitalist countries led to the emergence of the world system.[46]

The political economy or world-system view has inspired many anthropologists to study history more explicitly and to explore the impact of external political and economic processes on local events and cultures in the underdeveloped world. In the past, when anthropologists first started doing fieldwork in the far corners of the world, they could imagine that the cultures they were studying or reconstructing could be investigated as if those cultures were more or less isolated from external influences and forces. In the modern world, such isolation hardly exists. The political economy approach has reminded us that the world, every part of it, is interconnected, for better or worse.

RECENT DEVELOPMENTS IN ANTHROPOLOGICAL THEORY

In recent years, anthropology has seen a range of new approaches incorporated into anthropological theory. Many of these approaches have been adopted from other disciplines, such as evolutionary biology and literary criticism. They are providing anthropology with an increasing breadth of thought from which to address the many questions of interest to anthropologists today.

Evolutionary Ecology Approaches

The various approaches discussed here share the idea that natural selection can operate on the behavioral or social characteristics of populations, not just on their physical traits. If so, some of the human behavior we observe, including those behaviors that vary by society, might be explained by evolutionary principles. Two important works by biologists introduced these ideas to anthropology: Edward O. Wilson's book *Sociobiology: The New Synthesis* and Richard D. Alexander's article "The Search for a General Theory of Behavior."[47] **Sociobiology** was the term for this evolutionary approach. More recently, scholars have introduced varying theoretical modifications. The main theoretical perspectives are **behavioral ecology**, **evolutionary psychology,** and **dual-inheritance theory.**[48]

Before looking at how these orientations differ from each other, let us first see how evolutionary ecological theories, particularly behavioral ecology and evolutionary psychology, differ from cultural ecology. Although both orientations assume the importance of natural selection in cultural evolution, they differ in important ways. Cultural ecology focuses mostly on what biologists would call **group selection:** Cultural ecologists talk mostly about how a certain behavioral or social characteristic may be adaptive for a group or society in a given environment. (A newly emergent behavioral or social trait that is adaptive is likely to be passed on to future generations by cultural transmission.) In contrast, evolutionary ecology focuses more on what biologists call **individual selection:** Evolutionary ecologists talk mostly about how a certain characteristic may be adaptive for an individual in a given environment.[49] *Adaptive* means the ability of individuals to get their genes into future generations. This viewpoint implies that behavior is transmitted in some way (by genes or learning) to people who share your genes (usually offspring).[50] If a certain behavior is adaptive for individuals in a particular environment (or a particular historical context in which these individuals are able to reproduce more than others), it should become more widespread in future generations as the individuals with those traits increase in number. Whereas a cultural ecologist such as Rappaport might consider how ritual pig feasts were adaptive for the Tsembaga as a whole, evolutionary ecologists would insist that to speak of adaptation it must be shown how the pig feasts benefited individuals and their closest kin.

Behavioral ecology typically tries to understand the relationship of human behavior to the environment.[51] In addition to the principle of individual selection, behavioral ecologists point to the importance of analyzing economic tradeoffs because individuals have limited time and resources. As we will see later in the economics chapter, the theory of *optimal foraging* is used to explain the decision-making behavior of recent hunter-gatherers. Evolutionary psychology, on the other hand, is more interested in universal human psychology. It is argued that human psychology was primarily adapted to the environment that characterized most of human history—our hunting-gathering way of life.[52] Dual-inheritance theory, in contrast to the other evolutionary perspectives, gives much more importance to culture as part of the evolutionary process. Dual inheritance refers to both genes and culture playing different but nonetheless important and interactive roles in transmitting traits to future generations.[53]

The behavioral ecological approaches have led to an active program of research in anthropology. However, these approaches have aroused considerable controversy, particularly from those cultural anthropologists who do not believe that biological considerations have much to do with understanding culture.

Feminist Approaches

Women have played an important role in the history of anthropology. Margaret Mead, Ruth Benedict, and Mary Douglas are just a few of the women who have made lasting contributions to the discipline. Yet the study of women and women's roles in other cultures was relatively rare, and, by the 1960s, women anthropologists began asking why women were not a more important focus of research. It was not accidental that this movement coincided with the "women's movement" in the United States. One group of scholars argued that women were in subservient positions in all cultures, and hence were largely "invisible" to anthropologists studying those cultures. Another group argued that, although women historically held positions of power and authority in many cultures, the impact of colonization and capitalism had moved them into subservient positions. In either case, it became clear to these scholars that a focused effort on studying the roles of women was necessary, and feminist anthropology was born.

Feminist anthropology is a highly diverse area of research. Feminist anthropologists share an interest in the role of women in culture, but vary widely in how they approach this common interest. Some feminist anthropologists take an overtly political stance, seeing their task as identifying ways in which women are exploited and working to overcome them. Others simply try to understand women's lives and how they differ from those of men. Despite the diversity, feminist anthropology shares a critical assessment of traditional scholarship and understanding the importance of power.[54] In these ways, feminist anthropology shares a good deal with the political economy perspective as well as postmodernism, which we discuss shortly. In some cases, entirely new understandings of other cultures have come from feminist scholarship. For example, Annette Weiner studied the same culture that Malinowski had, in the Trobriand Islands, and found that Malinowski had overlooked an entire women-run economic system.[55] Similarly, Sally Slocum pointed out that, although hunting was a focus for paleoanthropologists interested in human origins, the gathering of wild foods, typically a female activity, was hardly discussed at all, even though gathered foods are more important than hunted foods in the diets of some recent foragers. Slocum's work forced paleoanthropologists to consider the role of gathered foods and, consequently, of women, in human evolution.[56]

One of the most important effects feminist research has had on anthropology is the recognition that perceptions of other cultures are shaped by the observer's culture and how the observer behaves in the field. Male researchers may not be able to ask about or observe some women's roles, just as women may not be able to ask about or observe some men's roles. More broadly, feminist scholarship suggested that the scientific approach was only one way of studying other cultures, and that different ways of studying other cultures might lead to different understandings. From this insight grew two powerful theoretical agendas that continue to affect anthropology today.

One agenda stemming from feminist scholarship is that science is inherently male in its orientation and that its impact on the world has been to further the subjugation of women. But female scientists would strongly disagree: Science is neither male nor female. A second agenda, less radical than the first, is to experiment with alternative ways of studying and describing other

Women have recently become a more important focus of research in anthropology. A Trobriand Island woman in Papua New Guinea stacks yams during the yam harvest festival.

applied anthropology

The Relationship Between Theory and Practice

Applied anthropology in the United States goes back to the late 1800s, when the government focused on "applied ethnology" to help with the administration of programs dealing with Native Americans, but it was only during and after the Great Depression and World War II that applied anthropological work increased significantly. Applied work during this earlier time usually involved research and consultation, with no active role in bringing about change. However, by the 1950s and afterward, applied anthropologists began to be more involved in directed social change.

Applied anthropology came to maturity at the same time that anthropology was re-discovering the importance of theory. As the influence of Boas and historical particularism waned, American anthropologists began to explore new areas of theory, and began to collaborate with ecologists, economists, and others to develop the variety of theoretical perspectives that populate the discipline today. In putting anthropology to use, applied anthropologists draw upon theoretical orientations and specific theories within those orientations. To illustrate this, we will draw upon examples from nutritional anthropology, a field that involves anthropologists from all the major subdisciplines.

Applied nutritional anthropologists are actively engaged in matters of public health, such as how infants are fed and grow, gender inequality in access to food, dietary insufficiencies, and serious malnutrition and starvation. Three of the most important theoretical perspectives involve ecology, evolutionary adaptation, and political economy. The ecological perspective not only emphasizes the effects of the physical and social environment on what people grow, the technology they use, and their patterns of consumption, but also considers the effects of these patterns on the environment. Adaptation can involve genetic changes, such as the ability of some populations to digest raw milk, or cultural adaptations such as developing processing techniques to make certain plants edible (i.e., bitter manioc that contains toxic amounts of cyanide prior to processing). The political economy perspective points to inequalities in nutrition due to class and status differences within societies and the increasing disparity between the developed and undeveloped societies around the world. In working on change programs to improve nutrition, applied anthropologists have to be pragmatic—to try to find theories that may help understand and therefore help solve some problem. They often work with practitioners from different fields and are not likely to be dogmatic about which theoretical orientation to draw upon.

Applied anthropologists do not see themselves as simply borrowing theory; they see their work as central to the task of theory building. For one thing, the work of applied anthropologists provides a "natural laboratory" for evaluating theory, where hypotheses can be tested empirically. Further, in applying new aspects of or challenges to the theory, ones not encountered in more academic or pure research settings, are often brought to light. Finally, because theory is closely linked to methods (as the information that a theory identifies as being important will shape the way researchers collect information), applied anthropologists are often at the forefront of methodological innovation.

Sources: Eddy and Partridge 1987; C. Hill 2000; Himmelgreen and Crooks 2005; Pelto et al. 2000; Van Willigen 2002, 25–30.

cultures, ways that give more voice to the people being studied and that allow for the feelings, opinions, and insights of the observer to be openly expressed in anthropological writing. Many of these feminist anthropologists have used personal narratives, storytelling, and even poetry as ways to express their understanding of the cultures they have studied.[57]

Interpretive Approaches

The "literary turn" in anthropology, in which anthropologists began to experiment with fiction, personal insights, and even poetry as forms of ethnography, did not come solely out of feminist anthropology. Since the 1960s, writers in the field of literary criticism have influenced the development of a variety of "interpretive" approaches in cultural anthropology, particularly with respect to ethnography.[58] Clifford Geertz (1926–2006) popularized the idea that a culture is like a literary text that can be analyzed for meaning, as the ethnographer interprets it. According to Geertz, ethnographers choose to interpret the meaning of things in their field cultures that are of interest to themselves. Then they try to convey their interpretations of cultural meaning to people of their own culture. Thus, according to Geertz, ethnographers are a kind of selective intercultural translator.[59]

For many interpretive anthropologists, the goal of anthropology is to understand what it means to be a person living in a particular culture, rather than to explain why cultures vary. The task of understanding meaning, these scholars claim, cannot be achieved scientifically, but can only be approached through forms of literary analysis. Among the most important of these is **hermeneutics**—the study of meaning. Using hermeneutics, anthropologists might examine a particular behavior, closely examining the interactions of people, the language they use, and the symbols they employ (both physical and linguistic) to derive what that behavior means to the people engaged in it. One of the most famous examples is Geertz's analysis of cockfighting on the Indonesian island of Bali, which he suggests reflects, and thus allows us to comprehend, the Balinese worldview.[60]

A key facet of interpretive analyses is that they are openly subjective and personal. Geertz's interpretation of the Balinese cockfight is neither right nor wrong—it is simply his. Another anthropologist viewing the same phenomenon might come to a completely different interpretation. Interpretive anthropologists accept this as part of the nature of being human. They suggest that no human sees the world in quite the same way, so that no interpretation of human behavior can or should be the same. Anthropology, then, becomes a reflection of the anthropologist as much as it is a description of other peoples. For many anthropologists, this self-centered approach makes interpretive anthropology very unappealing; for others, it is the only truthful way to work.

Some anthropologists think that interpretation is the only achievable goal in cultural anthropology because they do not believe it is possible to describe or measure cultural phenomena (and other things involving humans) in objective or unbiased ways. Scientific anthropologists do not agree. To be sure, interpretive ethnographies might provide insights. But we do not have to believe what an interpretation suggests, no matter how eloquently it is stated. (We are rarely given objective evidence to support the interpretation.) Scientific researchers have developed many techniques for minimizing bias and increasing the objectivity of measurement. Thus, interpretative anthropologists who deny the possibility of scientific understanding of human behavior and thinking may not know how much has been achieved so far by scientific studies of cultural phenomena, which we try to convey in the chapters that follow.

As Dan Sperber has suggested, the task of interpretation in cultural anthropology is clearly different from the task of explanation.[61] The goal of interpretation is to convey intuitive understanding of human experiences in a *particular* culture (intuitive in the sense of not requiring conscious reasoning or systematic methods of inquiry). Thus, interpretative ethnographers are like novelists (or literary critics). In contrast, the goal of explanation is to provide causal and general understanding of cultural phenomena (causal in the sense of mechanisms that account for why something comes to be shared in a population, and general in the sense of applying to a number of similar cases).

Does the goal (interpretation vs. explanation) preclude or invalidate the other? We don't think so. We share Sperber's view that interpretation and explanation are not

opposed goals: They are just different kinds of understanding. Indeed, an intuitive interpretation described in causal and general terms might turn out, when scientifically tested, to be a powerful explanation.

Postmodernist Approaches

Postmodernism in its broadest sense rejects "modernism." There are many postmodern movements—in the arts, in literature, in philosophy, in history, and in anthropology, among others. In anthropology, *post-structuralism* is a closely related term. It is difficult to summarize what postmodernism is in anthropology because postmodernism itself rejects authoritative definitions and any one narrative of events.[62] Not only is all knowledge subjective in the postmodern view, it is also actively shaped by the political powers-that-be. One of the most influential postmodern theorists is the French philosopher Michel Foucault (1926–1984). Foucault argued that those in political power were able to shape the way accepted truths were defined. In the modern age, truth is defined through science, and science, in turn, is controlled by Western political and intellectual elites.[63] Science, then, is not only a way of understanding the world, it is a way of controlling and dominating it. Many of the others who had an influence on post-structuralism or postmodernism also were important French intellectuals—for example, Pierre Bourdieu, Roland Barthes, Jacques Lacan, and Jacques Derrida. Whereas structuralism was implicitly comparative—looking for similarities in underlying structure—post-structuralism emphasizes extreme relativity, not only between, but also within cultures.

Postmodernism questions the whole enterprise of ethnography. Ethnography is viewed as being "constructed," almost as a work of fiction.[64] For anthropologists who accept the postmodern view of science, anthropology is just another tool used by dominant powers to control others. By studying others "objectively," we dehumanize the people being studied. Turning people into objects for study allows them to become objects that can be molded and used by the political powers-that-be. Postmodern anthropologists have not given up writing about other cultures, but have experimented with different styles of ethnography, such as having a variety of different people speak for themselves.[65]

Not surprisingly, the postmodern movement in anthropology, which effectively questioned all the descriptive work from the past and present, as well as all the attempts to test and evaluate theory, created an enormous schism in anthropology, one that is still present today. How can anthropology continue to exist if its efforts contribute to the domination and control of others? Postmodern scholars answer that anthropology must transform itself into a purely activist discipline that seeks to express the voices of the dominated rather than to study or interpret them. Anthropology should be a conduit for the disenfranchised and subjugated to be heard. Even so, does that preclude anthropology from being scientific?

current research and issues

Evaluating Alternative Theories

In working among the Abelam of New Guinea, Richard Scaglion was puzzled why they invest so much energy in growing giant ceremonial yams, sometimes more than 10 feet long. As well, why do they abstain from sex for six months while they grow them? Of course, to try to understand, we need to know much more about the Abelam way of life. Scaglion had read about them, lived among them, and talked to them, but, as many ethnographers have discovered, answers to *why* questions don't just leap out at you. Answers, at least tentative ones, often come from theoretical orientations that suggest how or where to look for answers. Scaglion considers several possibilities. As Donald Tuzin had suggested for a nearby group, the Plains Arapesh, yams may be symbols of, or stand for, shared cultural understandings. (Looking for the meanings of symbols is a kind of interpretative

approach to ethnographic data.) The Abelam think of yams as having souls that appreciate tranquillity. Yams also have family lines; at marriage, the joining of family lines is symbolized by planting different yam lines in the same garden. During the yam-growing cycle (remember that yams appreciate tranquillity), lethal warfare and conflict become channeled mostly into competitive but nonlethal yam-growing contests. So yam growing may be functional in the sense that it helps to foster harmony.

Then again, ceremonial yam growing may have adaptive ecological consequences. Just as the Tsembaga pig feasts seemed to keep human population in line with resources, Scaglion thinks that ceremonial yam growing did too. Growing pig populations damage gardens and create conflicts, but pigs are also given away during competitive yam ceremonies, so the pig population declines. Wild

animals that are hunted also have a chance to replenish themselves because hunting is frowned upon during the yam-growing cycle.

As Scaglion's discussion illustrates, theoretical orientations help researchers derive explanations. They do not have to be "rival" explanations, in the sense that one has to be right and others wrong; more than one theory may help explain some phenomenon. But we can't assume that a theory is correct and helps us to understand just because it sounds good. The important point is that we need something more to evaluate theory. As we discuss in the next chapter, we have to find ways to test a theory against evidence. Until we do that, we really don't know how many, or if indeed any, of the theories available are helpful.

Source: Scaglion 2009a.

The Pragmatic Approach

Many, perhaps most, anthropologists do not have a particular theoretical orientation that drives their research agenda. In the interest of being honest about our own orientations, we consider ourselves to be in this category. We do believe that anthropology can strive for humanistic understanding and be scientific at the same time. The important priority for us is the research question. Whatever the research question you ask, it is important to see what others have said about that question. The various theories may come from different orientations, but the important thing is not where ideas come from, but where they lead you and what you can predict. Similarly, for us, there is also no one correct method of conducting research. Different strategies have advantages and disadvantages, and progress is most likely by examining theoretical ideas from different vantage points. To be sure, it is not likely that any one researcher will be completely open to all points of view. It is all the more important then for different researchers with different perspectives to tackle the same research questions.

To a great extent, the scientific study of human behavior depends upon the belief that it is possible to find

answers to puzzling questions about humans. If you do not believe that there are answers, you will not waste your time looking. Our belief that the scientific study of humans and their cultures is possible is bolstered by the many patterns we have already discovered. Although postmodern, interpretive, and some feminist approaches have challenged the very foundations of anthropology, anthropology as a discipline continues to thrive. In part, this is because anthropologists have learned important lessons from the work of feminist, interpretive, and postmodern scholars. No anthropologist working today could ignore women's roles, for example. It is no longer possible to ignore half of humanity. Understanding meaning, along with explaining variation, is now a parallel goal of anthropology. Anthropologists realize that their knowledge of others is possibly subjective and imperfect, but that doesn't mean it is impossible to study humans and their cultures scientifically.

The Future

It is difficult to predict what anthropological theory will be like in the future. Some ideas are likely to be discarded or ignored, and others revised. Scholarly disciplines and theories are very much the products of their times, and understanding how and why ideas have changed is part of what we need to understand. But some theoretical approaches and theories lead to greater understanding because they are more predictive of the world around us. In the next chapter, we examine the logic of explanation and evidence and how theory can be tested by anthropological research.

SUMMARY ● ○ ○

1. Which aspects of life anthropologists concentrate on usually reflects their theoretical orientation, subject interest, or preferred method of research.

2. A theoretical orientation is usually a general attitude about how cultural phenomena are to be explained.

3. Ideas about evolution took a long time to take hold because they contradicted the biblical view of events; species were viewed as fixed in their form by the creator. But in the 18th and early 19th centuries, increasing evidence suggested that evolution was a viable theory. In geology, the concept of uniformitarianism suggested that the earth is constantly subject to shaping and reshaping by natural forces working over vast stretches of time. A number of thinkers during this period began to discuss evolution and how it might occur.

4. The prevailing theoretical orientation in anthropology during the 19th century was based on a belief that culture generally evolves in a uniform and progressive manner; that is, most societies were believed to pass through the same series of stages, to arrive ultimately at a common end. Two proponents of this early theory of cultural evolution were Edward B. Tylor and Lewis Henry Morgan.

5. The diffusionist approach, popular in the late 19th and early 20th centuries, was developed by two main schools—the British and the German-Austrian. In general, diffusionists believed that most aspects of high civilization had emerged in culture centers from which they then diffused outward.

6. During the early 20th century, the leading opponent of evolutionism was Franz Boas, whose historical particularism rejected the way in which early evolutionists had assumed that universal laws governed all human culture. Boas stressed the importance of collecting as much anthropological data as possible, from which the laws governing cultural variation would supposedly emerge by themselves.

7. The psychological orientation in anthropology, which began in the 1920s, seeks to understand how psychological factors and processes may help us explain cultural practices.

8. Functionalism in social science looks for the part (function) that some aspect of culture or social life plays in maintaining a cultural system. There are two quite different schools of functionalism. Malinowski's version of functionalism assumes that all cultural traits serve the needs of *individuals* in a society. Radcliffe-Brown's felt that the various aspects of social behavior maintain a *society's social structure* rather than satisfying individual needs.

9. In the 1940s, Leslie A. White revived the evolutionary approach to cultural development. White believed that technological development, or the amount of energy harnessed per capita, was the main driving force creating cultural evolution. Anthropologists such as Julian H. Steward, Marshall Sahlins, and Elman Service have also presented evolutionary viewpoints.

10. Claude Lévi-Strauss was the leading proponent of structuralism. Lévi-Strauss saw culture, as it was expressed in art, ritual, and the patterns of daily life, as a surface representation of the underlying patterns of the human mind.

11. Whereas Lévi-Strauss's structuralist approach involves intuitively grasping the rules of thought that may underlie a given culture, an ethnographic approach known as ethnoscience attempts to derive these rules from a logical analysis of data—particularly the words people use to describe their activities. In this way, ethnoscientists try to formulate the rules that generate acceptable behavior in a given culture. Cognitive anthropology has its roots in ethnoscience.

12. Cultural ecology seeks to understand the relationships between cultures and their physical and social environments. Cultural ecologists ask how a particular culture trait may be adaptive in its environment.

13. The theoretical orientation called political economy focuses on the impact of external political and economic processes, particularly as connected to colonialism and imperialism, on local events and cultures in the underdeveloped world. The political economy approach has reminded us that all parts of the world are interconnected for better or worse.

14. Evolutionary ecology involves the application of biological evolutionary principles to the social behavior of animals, including humans.

15. Feminist approaches were born from the realization that the study of women and women's roles in other cultures was relatively rare. Some feminist anthropologists take an overtly political stance, seeing their task as identifying ways in which women are exploited and working to overcome them. Others simply try to understand women's lives and how they differ from those of men.

16. For many interpretive anthropologists, the goal of anthropology is to understand what it means to be a person living in a particular culture, rather than to explain why cultures vary. The task of understanding meaning, these scholars claim, cannot be achieved scientifically, but can only be approached through forms of literary analysis.

17. Postmodernists take the interpretative idea that all knowledge is subjective, further arguing that knowledge is actively shaped by the political powers-that-be.

18. There are anthropologists who do not follow any particular theoretical orientation or prefer any particular subject matter or method of research. These anthropologists think of themselves as having a pragmatic orientation, using different methods and theories to answer different research questions.

GLOSSARY TERMS ○ ● ○

behavioral ecology   25
cultural ecology   23
dual-inheritance
    theory   25
ethnoscience   23
eugenics   19
evolutionary
    psychology   25
functionalism   21
general evolution   22

genus   16
group selection   25
hermeneutics   28
individual selection   25
political economy   24
sociobiology   25
specific evolution   22
structuralism   22
theoretical
    orientation   14

CRITICAL QUESTIONS ○ ○ ●

1. Does a theoretical orientation enhance one's way of looking at the world, or does it blind one to other possibilities? Explain your answer.

2. In anthropology, as in many other fields, one theoretical orientation will arise and may grow in popularity until another is proposed in opposition to it. Is this kind of rejection healthy for a discipline? If so, why? If not, why not?

3. Although anthropology is holistic in including the study of humans as both biological organisms and as cultural or social organisms, cultural and biological theories are rarely considered together. Why do you think? Explain why you think that this helps or hinders anthropology.

PEARSON
myanthrolab

Read Richard Scaglion, "Abelam: Giant Yams and Cycles of Sex, Warfare and Ritual" on MyAnthroLab and answer the following questions:

1. Describe what Scaglion means by the "ethnographic present." Does using that concept allow for studying cultural change?

2. Pick two of the theoretical orientations you have read about in this chapter, then indicate how they might point toward an explanation of some aspects of the yam-growing cycle."

Research Methods in Anthropology

The intellectuals who developed science in the mid-17th century understood very well that human knowledge of the world could be biased and incomplete. Rather than rejecting the possibility of objective understanding, as postmodern and interpretive anthropologists have argued, the founders of science created a way of generating understanding based on the rigorous testing of ideas. As anthropologist Philip Salzman explains:

> The scientific method, the heart of science, was invented because it was understood that human error, wish-fulfillment, duplicity, dishonesty, and weakness would commonly distort research findings. The scientific requirements that the procedures of all studies must be specified in detail so that others could repeat them, and the actual replication of findings by other scientists in other venues, were established to minimize the distorting effects of human subjectivity and moral weakness in the quest for knowledge.[1]

Many anthropologists continue to believe that objective knowledge is possible through science. Still, if the goal of anthropology is to understand what it means to be a human in a different cultural context, as interpretive anthropologists believe, then science and its pursuit of explanations may not be an appropriate method for all of anthropology. The task of interpretation is different from the task of explanation.

● ○ ●

EXPLANATION

An **explanation** is an answer to a *why* question. There are many types of explanations, some more satisfying than others. For example, suppose we ask why a society has a long postpartum sex taboo. We could guess that the people in that society want to abstain from sex for a year or so after the birth of a baby. Is this an explanation? Yes, because it does suggest that people have a purpose in practicing the custom; it therefore partly answers the *why* question. But such an explanation would not be very satisfying because it does not specify what the purpose of the custom might be. How about the idea that people have a long postpartum sex taboo because it is their tradition? That too is an explanation, but it is not satisfactory for a different reason. It is a *tautology*; that is, the thing to be explained (the taboo) is being explained by itself, by its prior existence. To explain something in terms of tradition is to say that people do it because they already do it, which is not informative. What kinds of explanations are more satisfactory, then? In science, investigators try to achieve two kinds of explanations: *associations* and *theories*.

Associations or Relationships

One way of explaining something (an observation, an action, a custom) is to say how it conforms to a general principle or relationship. So to explain why the water left outside in the basin froze, we say that it was cold last night and that water freezes at 32°F (0°C). The statement that water solidifies (becomes ice) at 32°F is a statement of a relationship or association between two **variables**—things or quantities that vary. In this case, variation in the

The statement that water becomes ice at 32°F (0°C) defines an association between two variables: water and temperature. A theory explains why an association exists.

state of water (liquid vs. solid) is related to variation in the temperature of the air (above vs. below 32°F). The truth of the relationship is suggested by repeated observations. In the physical sciences, such relationships are called **laws** when almost all scientists accept them. We find such explanations satisfactory because they allow us to predict what will happen in the future or to understand something that has happened regularly in the past.

In the social sciences, associations are usually stated *probabilistically*; that is, we say that two or more variables tend to be related in a predictable way, which means that there are usually some exceptions. For example, to explain why a society has a long postpartum sex taboo, we can point to the association (or correlation) that John Whiting found in a worldwide sample of societies: Societies with apparently low-protein diets tend to have long postpartum sex taboos.[2] We call the relationship between low-protein diets and the sex taboo a **statistical association,** which means that the observed relationship is unlikely to be due to chance.

Theories

Even though laws and statistical associations explain by relating what is to be explained to other things, we want to know more: why those laws or associations exist. Why does water freeze at 32°F? Why do societies with low-protein diets tend to have long postpartum sex taboos? Therefore, scientists try to formulate theories that will explain the observed relationships (laws and statistical associations).[3]

Theories—explanations of laws and statistical associations—are more complicated than the observed relationships they are intended to explain. It is difficult to be precise about what a theory is. By way of example, let us return to the question of why some societies have long

postpartum sex taboos. We have already seen that a known statistical association can be used to help explain it. In general (but not always), if a society has a low-protein diet, it will have a long postpartum sex taboo. But most people would ask additional questions: Why does a low-protein diet explain the taboo? What is the mechanism by which a society with such a diet develops the custom of a long postpartum sex taboo? A theory is intended to answer such questions.

John Whiting theorized that a long postpartum sex taboo may be an adaptation to certain conditions. Particularly in tropical areas, where the major food staples are low in protein, babies are vulnerable to the protein-deficiency disease called *kwashiorkor*. But if a baby could continue to nurse for a long time, it might have more of a chance to survive. The postpartum sex taboo might be adaptive, Whiting's theory suggests, because it increases the likelihood of a baby's survival. That is, if a mother puts off having another baby for a while, the first baby might have a better chance to survive because it can be fed mother's milk for a longer time. Whiting suggests that parents may be aware, whether unconsciously or consciously, that having another baby too soon might jeopardize the survival of the first baby, and so they might decide that abstaining from intercourse for more than a year after the birth of the first baby would be a good idea.

As this example of a theory illustrates, there are differences between a theory and an association. A theory is more complicated, containing a series of statements. An association usually states quite simply that there is a relationship between two or more measured variables. Another difference is that, although a theory may mention some things that are observable, such as the presence of a long postpartum sex taboo, parts of it are difficult or impossible to observe directly. For example, with regard to Whiting's theory, it would be difficult to find out if people had deliberately or unconsciously decided to practice a long postpartum sex taboo because they recognized that babies would thereby have a better chance to survive. Then, too, the concept of adaptation—that some characteristic promotes greater reproductive success—is difficult to verify because it is difficult to find out whether different individuals or groups have different rates of reproduction because they do or do not practice the supposedly adaptive custom. Thus, some concepts or implications in a theory are unobservable (at least at the present time), and only some aspects may be observable. In contrast, statistical associations or laws are based entirely on observations.[4]

Why Theories Cannot be Proved

Many people think that the theories they learned in physics or chemistry courses have been proved. Unfortunately, many students get that impression because their teachers present "lessons" in an authoritative manner. Scientists and philosophers of science now generally agree that no theory can be said to be proved or unquestionably true, although some theories may have considerable evidence supporting them. This is because many of the concepts and ideas in theories are not directly observable and therefore not directly verifiable. For example, scientists may try to explain how light behaves by postulating that it consists of particles called photons, but photons cannot be observed, even with the most powerful microscope. So, exactly what a photon looks like and exactly how it works remain in the realm of the unprovable. The photon is a **theoretical construct,** something that cannot be observed or verified directly. Because all theories contain such constructs, theories cannot be proved entirely or with absolute certainty.[5]

Why should we bother with theories, then, if we cannot prove that they are true? Perhaps the main advantage of a theory as a kind of explanation is that it may lead to new understanding or knowledge. A theory can suggest new relationships or imply new predictions that might be supported or confirmed by new research. For example, Whiting's theory about long postpartum sex taboos has implications that researchers could investigate. Because the theory discusses how a long postpartum sex taboo might be adaptive, we would expect that certain changes would result in the taboo's disappearance. For example, suppose people adopted either mechanical birth control devices or began to give supplementary high-protein foods to babies. With birth control, a family could space births without abstaining from sex, so we would expect the custom of postpartum abstinence to disappear. As well, we would expect it to disappear with protein supplements for babies, because kwashiorkor would then be less likely to afflict the babies. Whiting's ideas might also prompt investigators to try to find out whether parents are consciously or unconsciously aware of the problem of close birth spacing in areas with low supplies of protein.

Although theories cannot be proved, they are rejectable. The method of **falsification,** which shows that a theory seems to be wrong, is the main way that theories are judged.[6] Scientists derive implications or predictions that should be true if the theory is correct. So, for example, Whiting predicted that societies with long postpartum sex taboos would be found more often in the tropics than in temperate regions and that they would be likely to have low-protein food supplies. Such predictions of what might be found are called **hypotheses.** If the predictions turn out not to be correct, the researcher is obliged to conclude that something may be wrong with the theory or something wrong with the test of the theory. Theories that are not falsified are accepted for the time being because the available evidence seems to be con-

sistent with them. But remember that no matter how much the available evidence seems to support a theory, we can never be certain it is true. There is always the possibility that some implication of it, some hypothesis derivable from it, will not be confirmed in the future.

TESTING EXPLANATIONS

In any field of investigation, theories are generally the most plentiful commodity, apparently because of the human predisposition to try to make sense of the world. It is necessary, then, for us to have procedures that enable us to select from among the many available theories those that are more likely to be correct. "Just as mutations arise naturally but are not all beneficial, so hypotheses [theories] emerge naturally but are not all correct. If progress is to occur, therefore, we require a superfluity of hypotheses and also a mechanism of selection."[7] In other words, generating a theory or interpretation is not enough. We need some reliable method of testing whether or not that theory is likely to be correct. If a theory is not correct, it may detract from our efforts to achieve understanding by misleading us into thinking the problem is already solved.

The strategy in all kinds of testing in science is to predict what one would expect to find if a particular theory were correct, and then to conduct an investigation to see if the prediction is generally consistent with the data. If the prediction is not supported, the investigator is obliged to accept the possibility that the theory is wrong. If, however, the prediction holds true, then the investigator is entitled to say that evidence supports the theory. Thus, conducting research designed to test expectations derived from theory allows researchers to eliminate some theories and to accept others, at least tentatively.

Operationalization and Measurement

We test predictions derived from a theory to see if the theory may be correct, to see if it is consistent with observable events or conditions in the real world. A theory and the predictions derived from it are not useful if there is no way to measure the events or conditions mentioned in the predictions. If there is no way of relating the theory to

Yanomamö Indians of Brazil depend on root crops and thus have a relatively low-protein diet, whereas the Inuit of Nunavut depend largely on sea mammals and fish and thus have a relatively high-protein diet.

observable events, it does not matter how good the theory sounds; it is still not a useful scientific theory.[8] To transform theoretical predictions into statements that might be verified, a researcher provides an **operational definition** of each of the concepts or variables mentioned in the prediction. An operational definition is a description of the procedure that is followed to measure the variable.[9]

Whiting predicted that societies with a low-protein diet would have a long postpartum sex taboo. Amount of protein in the diet is a variable; some societies have more, others have less. Length of the postpartum sex taboo is a variable; a society may have a short taboo or a long taboo. Whiting operationally defined the first variable, *amount of protein*, in terms of staple foods.[10] For example, if a society depended mostly on root and tree crops (such as cassava and bananas), Whiting rated the society as having low protein. If the society depended mostly on cereal crops (such as wheat, barley, corn, oats), he rated it as having moderate protein, because cereal crops have more protein by weight than root and tree crops. If the society depended mostly on hunting, fishing, or herding for food, he rated it as having high protein. The other variable in Whiting's prediction, *length of postpartum sex taboo*, was operationalized as follows: A society was rated as having a long taboo if couples customarily abstained from sex for more than a year after the birth of a baby; abstention for a year or less was considered a short taboo.

Specifying an operational definition for each variable is extremely important because it allows other investigators to check a researcher's results.[11] Science depends on *replication*, the repetition of results. Only when many researchers observe a particular association can we call that association or relationship a law. Providing operational definitions is also extremely important because it allows others to evaluate whether a measure is appropriate. Only when we are told exactly how something was measured can we judge whether the measure reflects what it is supposed to reflect. Specifying measures publicly is so important in science that we are obliged to be skeptical of any conclusions offered by a researcher who fails to say how variables were measured.

To **measure** something is to say how it compares with other things on some scale of variation.[12] People often assume that a measuring device is always a physical instrument, such as a scale or a ruler, but physical devices are not the only way to measure something. *Classification* is also a form of measurement. When we classify people as male or female or employed versus unemployed, we are dividing them into *sets*. Deciding which set they belong to is a kind of measurement because doing so allows us to compare them. We can also measure things by deciding which cases or examples have more or less of something (e.g., more or less protein in the diet). The measures employed in physical science are usually based on scales that allow us to assign numbers to each case; we measure height in meters and weight in grams, for example. However we measure our variables, the fact that we can measure them means that we can test our hypotheses to see if the predicted relationships actually exist, at least most of the time.

Sampling

After deciding how to measure the variables in some predicted relationship, investigators must decide how to select which cases to study to see if the predicted relationship holds. If the prediction is about the behavior of people, the sampling decision involves which people to observe. If the prediction is about an association between societal customs, the sampling decision involves which societies to study. Investigators must decide not only which cases to choose but also how many to choose. No researcher can investigate all the possible cases, so choices must be made. Some choices are better than others. The best sample is almost always some kind of random sample. A **random sample** is one in which all cases selected have an equal chance of being included in the sample. Almost all statistical tests used to evaluate the results of research require random sampling, because only results based on a random sample can be assumed to be probably true for some larger set or universe of cases.

Before researchers can sample randomly, they must specify the **sampling universe,** that is, the list of cases to be sampled from. Suppose an anthropologist is doing fieldwork in a society. Unless the society is very small, it is usually not practical to use the whole society as the sampling universe. Because most fieldworkers want to remain in a community for a considerable length of time, the community usually becomes the sampling universe. If a cross-cultural researcher wants to test an explanation, it is necessary to sample the world's societies. But we do not have descriptions of all the societies—past and present—that have existed in the world. So, samples are usually drawn from published lists of described societies that have been classified or coded according to standard cultural variables,[13] or they are drawn from the *Human Relations Area Files (HRAF) Collection of Ethnography,* an indexed, annually growing collection of original full-text ethnographic books and articles on more than 400 societies—past and present—around the world.[14] Much of this collection is available online in *eHRAF World Cultures.* There is also a collection of archaeological traditions—*eHRAF Archaeology.*

Random sampling is not often employed in anthropology, but a nonrandom sample might still be fairly representative if the investigator has not personally chosen the cases for study. We should be particularly suspicious of any sample that may reflect the investigator's own biases or interests. For example, if investigators pick only the people with whom they are friendly, the sample is suspicious. If researchers select sample cases (i.e., societies, traditions) because books on them happen to be on their own bookshelves, such samples are also suspicious. A sampling procedure should be designed to get a fair, unbiased representation of the sampling universe. If we want to increase our chances of getting a representative sample, we have to use a random sampling procedure. To do so, we conventionally number the cases in the statistical universe and then use a table of random numbers to draw our sample cases.

Statistical Evaluation

When researchers have measured the variables of interest for all the sample cases, they are ready to see if the predicted relationship actually exists in the data. Remember, the results may not turn out to be what the theory predicts. Sometimes researchers construct a *contingency table*, like that shown in Table 3–1, to see if the variables are associated as predicted. In Whiting's sample of 172 societies, each case is assigned to a box, or cell, in the table, depending on how the society is measured on the two variables of interest. For example, a society that has a long postpartum sex taboo and a low-protein diet is placed in the third row of the Long Duration column. (In Whiting's sample [see Table 3–1], there are 27 such societies.) A society that has a short postpartum sex taboo and a low-protein diet is placed in the third row in the Short Duration column. (There are 20 such societies in the sample.) The statistical question is: Does the way the cases are distributed in the six central cells of the table generally support Whiting's prediction? If we looked just at the table, we might not know what to answer. Many cases appear to be in the expected places. For example, most of the high-protein cases (47 of 62) have short taboos, and most of the low-protein cases (27 of 47) have long taboos. But there are also many exceptions (e.g., 20 cases have low protein and a short taboo). So, although many cases appear to be in the expected places, there are also many exceptions. Do the exceptions invalidate the prediction? How many exceptions would compel us to reject the hypothesis? Here is where we resort to *statistical tests of significance*.

Statisticians have devised various tests that tell us how "perfect" a result has to be for us to believe that there is probably an association between the variables of interest, that one variable generally predicts the other. Essentially, every statistical result is evaluated in the same objective way. We ask: What is the chance that this result is purely accidental, that there is no association at all between the two variables? Although some of the mathematical ways of answering this question are complicated, the answer always involves a **probability value** (or *p-value*)—the likelihood that the observed result or a stronger one could have occurred by chance. The statistical test used by Whiting gives a *p*-value of less than .01 ($p < .01$) for the observed result. In other words, there is less than 1 chance out of 100 that the relationship observed is purely accidental. A *p*-value of less than .01 is a fairly low probability; most social scientists conventionally agree to call any result with a *p*-value of .05 or less (5 or fewer chances out of 100) a **statistically significant,** or probably true, result. When we describe relationships or associations in the rest of this book, we are almost always referring to results that have been found to be statistically significant.

But why should a probably true relationship have any exceptions? If a theory is really correct, shouldn't *all* the cases fit? There are many reasons why we can never expect a perfect result. First, even if a theory is correct (e.g., if a low-protein diet really does favor the adoption of a long postpartum sex taboo), there may still be other causes that we have not investigated. Some of the societies could have a long taboo even though they have high protein. For example, societies that depend mostly on hunting for their food, and would therefore be classified as having a high-protein diet, may have a problem carrying infants from one campsite to another and may practice a long postpartum sex taboo so that two infants will not have to be carried at the same time.

Exceptions to the predicted relationship might also occur because of *cultural lag*.[15] Cultural lag occurs when change in one aspect of culture takes time to produce change in another aspect. Suppose that a society recently changed crops and is now no longer a low-protein society but still practices the taboo. This society would be an exception to the predicted relationship, but it might fit the theory if it stopped practicing the taboo in a few years. Measurement inaccuracy is another source of exception. Whiting's measure of protein, which is based on the major sources of food, is not a very precise measure of protein in the diet. It does not take into account the possibility that a "tree crop" society might get a lot of protein from fishing or raising pigs. So it might turn out that some supposedly low-protein societies have been misclassified, which may be one reason why there are 20 cases in the lowest cell in the left-hand column of Table 3–1. Measurement error usually produces exceptions.

Significant statistical associations that are predictable from a theory offer tentative support for the theory. But much more is needed before we can be fairly confident about the theory. Replication is needed to confirm whether other researchers can reproduce the predictions using other samples. Other predictions should be derived from the theory to see if they too are supported. The theory should be pitted against alternative explanations to see which theory works better. We may have to combine theories if the alternative explanations also predict the relationship in question. The research process in science thus requires time and patience. Perhaps most important, it requires that researchers be humble. No matter how wonderful one's own theory seems, it is important to acknowledge that it may be wrong. If we don't acknowledge that possibility, we can't be motivated to test our theories. If we don't test our theories, we can never tell the difference between a better or worse theory, and we will be saddled forever with our present ignorance. In science, knowledge or understanding is explained variation. Thus, if we want to understand more, we have to keep testing

TABLE 3–1 Association Between Availability of Protein and Duration of Postpartum Sex Taboo			
AVAILABILITY OF PROTEIN	**DURATION OF POSTPARTUM SEX TABOO**		
	Short (0–1 Year)	Long (More Than 1 Year)	Total
High	47	15	62
Medium	38	25	63
Low	20	27	47
Total	105	67	172

Source: Based on Whiting 1964, 520.

our beliefs against sets of objective evidence that could contradict our beliefs.

TYPES OF RESEARCH IN ANTHROPOLOGY

Anthropologists use several methods to conduct research. Each has certain advantages and disadvantages in generating and testing explanations. The types of research in anthropology can be classified according to two criteria. One is the spatial scope of the study (for example, the analysis of a single society, analysis of societies in a region, or analysis of a worldwide sample of societies). The other criterion is the temporal scope of the study—historical versus nonhistorical. Combinations of these criteria are shown in Table 3–2.

In this section, we mostly discuss research strategies in cultural anthropology. However, most of these have parallels in archaeology and biological anthropology, as Table 3–2 makes clear. Archaeology and biological anthropology have special methods, and we devote the last section of the chapter to some of those methods.

Ethnography

Around the beginning of the 20th century, anthropologists realized that, if they were to produce anything of scientific value, they would have to study their subject in depth. To describe cultures more accurately, they started to live among the people they were studying. They observed, and even took part in, the important events of those societies and carefully questioned the people about their native customs. This method is known as **participant-observation.** Participant-observation always involves **fieldwork,** which is firsthand experience with the people being studied, but fieldwork may also involve other methods, such as conducting a census or a survey.[16]

Fieldwork, the cornerstone of modern anthropology, is the means by which most anthropological information is obtained. Regardless of other methods that anthropologists may use, participant-observation conducted usually

for a year or more is regarded as fundamental. In contrast to the casual descriptions of travelers and adventurers, anthropologists' descriptions record, describe, analyze, and eventually formulate a picture of the culture, or at least part of it.[17] After doing fieldwork, an anthropologist may prepare an *ethnography,* a description and analysis of a single society.

How an anthropologist goes about doing long-term participant-observation in another culture—and, more important, doing it well—is not so straightforward. Much of it depends on the person, the culture, and the interaction between the two. Without a doubt, the experience is physically and psychologically demanding, comparable often to a rite of passage. Although it helps enormously to learn the local language before going, often it is not possible to do so, and so most anthropologists find themselves struggling to communicate in addition to trying to figure out how to behave properly. Participant-observation carries its own dilemma. Participation implies living like the people who are being studied, trying to understand subjectively what they think and feel by doing what they do, whereas observation implies a certain amount of objectivity and detachment.[18] Because participant-observation is such a personal experience, it is not surprising that anthropologists have begun to realize that *reflecting* on their experiences and their personal interaction with the people they live with is an important part of understanding the enterprise.

An essential part of the participant-observation process is finding some knowledgeable people who are willing to work with you (anthropologists call them *informants*), to help you interpret what you observe and tell you about aspects of the culture that you may not have a chance to see, or may not be entitled to see. For example, it is not likely that you will see many weddings in a village of 200 people in a year or two of fieldwork. So how can you know who will be a good informant? It is obviously important to find people who are easy to talk to and who understand what information you need. But how do you know who is knowledgeable? You can't just assume that the people you get along with have the most knowledge. (Besides,

Scope	Nonhistorical	Historical
TABLE 3–2 **Types of Research in Anthropology**		
Single case	Ethnography/fieldwork * Archaeological site excavation * Single species study/fieldwork * Language study/fieldwork *	Ethnohistory * Culture history * Evolutionary history of a species * Language history
Region	Controlled comparison Regional comparison of archaeological or other sites Cross-species comparison Language family comparison	Controlled comparison Regional comparison of archaeological or other sites Cross-species comparison Language family comparison
Worldwide sample	Cross-cultural research Cross-archaeological research Cross-species comparison Cross-linguistic comparison	Cross-historical research Cross-archaeological research Cross-species comparison Comparative historical linguistics

*All of these can also involve comparisons within the research setting—of different individuals, social groups, or populations.

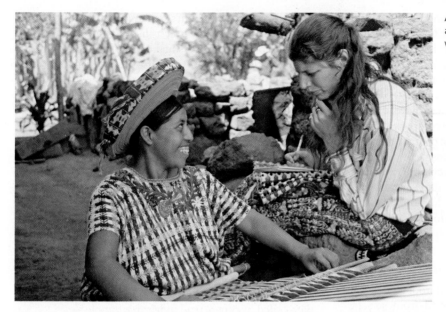

Anthropologist Margaret Kieffer conducts an ethnographic interview with a Mayan woman in Guatemala.

knowledge is often specialized; one person may know a whole lot more about some subjects than others.) At a minimum, you have to try out a few different people to compare what they tell you about a subject. What if they disagree? How do you know who is more trustworthy or accurate? Fortunately, formal methods have been developed to help anthropologists select the most knowledgeable informants. One method, called the "cultural consensus model," relies on the principle that those things that most informants agree on are probably cultural. After you establish which things appear to be cultural by asking a sample of informants the same questions about a particular cultural domain, it will be easy to discover which informants are very likely to give answers that closely match the cultural consensus. These individuals are your best bets to be the most knowledgeable in that domain.[19] It may seem paradoxical, but the most knowledgeable and helpful individuals are not necessarily "typical" individuals. Many anthropologists have pointed out that key informants are likely to feel somewhat marginal in their culture. After all, why would they want to spend so much time with the visiting anthropologist?[20]

Participant-observation is valuable for understanding some aspects of culture, particularly the things that are the most public, readily talked about, and most widely agreed upon. But more systematic methods are important too: mapping, house-to-house censuses, behavior observations (e.g., to determine how people spend their time), as well as focused interviews with a sample of informants.

Ethnographies and ethnographic articles on particular topics provide much of the essential data for all kinds of studies in cultural anthropology. To make a comparison of societies in a given region or worldwide, anthropologists would require ethnographic data on many societies. With regard to the goal of generating theory, ethnography—with its in-depth, firsthand, long-term observation—provides investigators with a wealth of descriptive material covering a wide range of phenomena. Thus, it may stimulate interpretations about the way different aspects of the culture are related to each other and to features of the

environment. Ethnographers in the field have the opportunity to get to know the context of a society's customs by directly asking the people about those customs and by observing the phenomena that appear to be associated with those practices. In addition, ethnographers who develop a possible explanation for some custom can test that hunch by collecting new information related to it. In this sense, ethnographers are similar to physicians who are trying to understand why a patient has certain symptoms of illness.

Although ethnography is extremely useful for generating explanations, a field study of a single site does not generally provide sufficient data to test a hypothesis. For example, an ethnographer may think that a particular society practices *polygyny* (one man married to two or more women simultaneously) because it has more women than men. But the ethnographer could not be reasonably sure that this explanation was correct unless the results of a comparative study of a sample of societies showed that most polygynous societies have more women than men. After all, the fact that one society has both these conditions could be a historical accident rather than a result of some necessary connection between the two conditions.

Within-Culture Comparisons

Ethnographers could test a theory within one society if they decide to compare individuals, families, households, communities, or districts. The natural variability that exists can be used to create a comparison. Suppose we want to verify Whiting's assumption that longer postpartum taboos enhance the survival of babies in a society with a low-protein diet. Although almost all couples might practice a long postpartum sex taboo because it is customary, some couples might not adhere to the taboo consistently and some couples might not conceive quickly after the taboo is lifted. So we would expect some variation in spacing between births. If we collected information on the births of each mother and the survival outcome of each birth, we would be able to compare the survival rates of children born a short time after the mother's last pregnancy with those of children born after longer intervals. A significantly higher survival rate for the births after longer intervals would support Whiting's theory. What if some communities within the society had access to more protein than others? If Whiting's theory is correct, those communities with more protein should also have a higher survival rate for babies. If there were variation in the length of the postpartum sex taboo, the communities with more protein should have shorter taboos.

Whether or not we can design intracultural tests of hypotheses depends on whether we have sufficient variability in the variables of the hypotheses. We do more often than not, and we can make use of that variation to test hypotheses within a culture.

Regional Controlled Comparisons

In a regional controlled comparison, anthropologists compare ethnographic information obtained from societies found in a particular region—societies that presumably have similar histories and occupy similar environments. Anthropologists who conduct a regional comparison are apt to be familiar with the complex of cultural features associated with that region. These features may provide a good understanding of the context of the phenomenon that is to be explained. An anthropologist's knowledge of the region under study, however, is probably not as great as the ethnographer's knowledge of a single society. Still, the anthropologist's understanding of local details is greater in a regional comparison than in a worldwide comparison. The worldwide comparison is necessarily so broad that the investigator is unlikely to know a great deal about any of the societies being compared.

The regional controlled comparison is useful not only for generating explanations but also for testing them. Because some of the societies being compared will have the characteristic that is to be explained and some will not, anthropologists can determine whether the conditions hypothesized to be related are in fact related, at least in that region. We must remember, however, that two or more conditions may be related in one region for reasons peculiar to that region. Therefore, an explanation supported in one region may not fit others.

Cross-Cultural Research

Anthropologists can generate interpretations on the basis of worldwide comparisons by looking for differences between those societies having and those lacking a particular characteristic. But the most common use of worldwide comparisons has been to test explanations. An example is Whiting's test of his theory about the adaptive functions of a long postpartum sex taboo. Recall that Whiting hypothesized that, if his theory were correct, variation in protein supplies in the adult diet should predict variation in the duration of the postpartum sex taboo. Cross-cultural researchers first identify conditions that should generally be associated if a particular theory is correct. Then they look at a worldwide sample of societies to see if the expected association generally holds true. Although it

is possible for cross-cultural researchers to choose any set of societies upon which to test theories and hypotheses, it is preferable to avoid personal bias in the selection of the sample societies. One of the worst possible samples would be to choose the ethnographies from your own bookshelf (you are unlikely to have collected them in a random way). As we indicated in the sampling section, most cross-culturalists choose a published sample of societies that was not constructed for any specific hypothesis test. Two of the most widely used samples are the Standard Cross-Cultural Sample (SCCS) of 186 societies and the annually growing HRAF Collection of Ethnography. Because HRAF actually contains full-text ethnographies that are subject-indexed by paragraph, researchers can fairly quickly find information to code a new variable across a large number of societies. In contrast, the SCCS sample contains pointers to ethnography, not ethnographies themselves. However, thousands of variables have now been coded by other researchers for this sample, so researchers who want to use data coded by others tend to use this sample.[21]

The advantage of cross-cultural research is that the conclusion drawn from it is probably applicable to most societies, if the sample used for testing has been more or less randomly selected and therefore is representative of the world. In other words, the results of a cross-cultural study are probably applicable to most societies and most regions, in contrast with the results of a regional comparison, which may or may not be applicable to other regions.

As we have noted, the greater the number of societies examined in a study, the less likely investigators will have detailed knowledge of the societies involved. So if a cross-cultural test does not support a particular explanation, the investigators may not know enough about the sample societies to know how to modify the interpretation or come up with a new one. In this situation, the anthropologists may reexamine the details of one or more particular societies to stimulate fresh thinking on the subject. Another limitation of cross-cultural research, as a means of both generating and testing explanations, is that only those explanations for which the required information is generally available in ethnographies can be tested. Investigators interested in explaining something that has not been generally described must resort to some other research strategy to collect data.

Historical Research

Ethnohistory consists of studies based on descriptive materials about a single society at more than one point in time. It provides the essential data for historical studies of all types, just as ethnography provides the essential data for all nonhistorical types of research. Ethnohistorical data may consist of sources other than the ethnographic reports prepared by anthropologists—accounts by explorers, missionaries, traders, and government officials. Ethnohistorians, like historians, cannot simply assume that all the documents they find are simply descriptions of fact; they were written by very different kinds of people with very different goals and purposes. So they need to separate carefully what may be fact from what may be speculative interpretation. To reconstruct how a culture changed over

Ethnohistorians need to analyze pieces of information from a variety of sources such as the accounts of European explorers. Pictured here is a group of Roanoke Native Americans fishing in the late 1500s. It provides ethnohistorians with good information on how these people harvested fish.

Source: John White/Copyright The British Museum.

hundreds of years, where the natives left few or no written accounts, anthropologists have to seek out travelers' accounts and other historical documents that were written by non-natives. Mary Helms had to do this when she decided to do fieldwork among the Miskito of Nicaragua, to reconstruct how their life had changed under the conditions of European colonialism. She was particularly interested in discovering why the Miskito were able to preserve a lot of political independence.[22]

In terms of generating and testing hypotheses, studies of single societies over time tend to be subject to the same limitations as studies of single societies confined to a single period. Like their nonhistorical counterparts, studies that concentrate on a single society observed through time are likely to generate more than one hypothesis, but they do not generally provide the opportunity to establish with reasonable certainty which of those hypotheses is correct. Cross-cultural historical studies (of which we have only a few examples thus far) suffer from the opposite limitation. They provide ample means of testing hypotheses through comparison, but, because of the necessity of working with secondhand data, they are severely constrained in their ability to generate hypotheses derived from the available data.

There is, however, one advantage to historical studies of any type. The goal of theory in cultural anthropology is to explain variation in cultural patterns, that is, to specify what conditions will favor one cultural pattern rather than another. Such specification requires us to assume that the supposed causal, or favoring, conditions antedated the pattern to be explained. Theories or explanations, then, imply a sequence of changes over time, which are the stuff of history. Therefore, if we want to come closer to an understanding of the reasons for the cultural variations we are investigating, we should examine historical sequences. They will help us determine whether the conditions we think caused various phenomena truly antedated those phenomena and thus might more reliably be said to have caused them. If we can examine historical sequences, we may be able to make sure that we do not put the cart before the horse.

The major impediment to historical research is that collecting and analyzing historical data—particularly when they come from the scattered accounts of explorers, missionaries, and traders—tends to be very time-consuming. It may be more efficient to test explanations nonhistorically first, to eliminate some interpretations. Only when an interpretation survives a nonhistorical test should we look to historical data to test the presumed sequence. Archaeological evidence is one answer to this problem, for many archaeological sites contain evidence from several cultures that lived in that location over time. Even when sites contain evidence for only one period of time, sites dating from different times can be compared to examine historical trends.

STUDYING THE DISTANT PAST

One goal of archaeological research is the description or reconstruction of what happened in the past. Archaeologists attempt to determine how people lived in a particular place at a particular time, and when and how their lifestyles changed. Also of interest, of course, is whether new populations carrying new cultures arrived, or whether people with a particular culture moved out of a given area. Creating histories of cultures and their changes over time is called, simply enough, **culture history.** Doing culture history was the primary goal of archaeology until the 1950s.[23]

A second major goal of archaeological research, and one that has become the primary goal since the 1950s, is testing specific explanations about human evolution and behavior. In part, this change in focus results from our increased knowledge about the past—the culture history of many areas is well known today. But this change is also due to changes going on in anthropology as a whole. As we discussed in the last chapter, historical particularism was dominant in American anthropology until the 1950s. It suggested that variation in human cultures was best explained by considering the specific historical developments of particular cultures. Like the purpose of historical particularism, the purpose of culture history was to trace historical developments. After the 1950s, a variety of new approaches arose in anthropology, most of them sharing

Vietnamese archaeologists expose the remains of the ancient citadel of Hanoi, preserved below the modern city.

the idea that the environment and how humans use it actively shapes cultures and mostly explains cultural variability. Archaeology became a key tool for anthropologists attempting to understand how changes in the ways humans used the environment explained variation in human cultures. One of the results of this focus on hypothesis testing and human use of the environment was research on agricultural origins, which we discuss in the chapter on the origins of food production and settled life. Another was a concern with the rise of cities and states, which radically transformed human use of the environment. We devote a separate chapter also to that subject.

In addition to testing explanations, archaeology has a primary role within anthropology in its attempt to identify and understand general trends and patterns in human biological and cultural evolution. As we discussed earlier, cross-cultural research (comparative ethnography) has this goal as well. But only archaeology is able to look through long stretches of time and directly examine evolutionary trends. In later chapters in this book, we trace the evolution of humans and human cultures from their beginnings. As we shall see, a major emphasis in paleoanthropology is demonstrating long-term trends and patterns in the biological evolution of humans. These trends and patterns help us understand how and why we have come to be the way we are.

Archaeologists and paleoanthropologists rely on four kinds of evidence to learn about the past: *artifacts, ecofacts, fossils,* and *features.*

Artifacts

Anything made or modified by humans is an **artifact.** The book you are reading now, the chair you are sitting in, the pen you are taking notes with are all artifacts. In fact, we are surrounded by artifacts, most of which we will lose or throw away. That is exactly how things enter what we call the "archaeological record." Think about it: How much garbage do you produce in a day? What kinds of things do you throw away? Mostly paper, probably, but also wood (from the ice cream bar you ate at lunch), plastic (like the pen that ran out of ink last night), and even metal (the

dull blade on your razor). Into the garbage they go and out to the dump or landfill. Under the right conditions, many of those items will survive for future archaeologists to find. Most of the artifacts that make up the archaeological record are just this kind of mundane waste—the accumulated garbage of daily life that archaeologists may recover and examine to reconstruct what daily life was like long ago. By far, the most common artifacts from the past are stone tools, which archaeologists call **lithics.** Indeed, lithics are the only kind of artifact available for 99 percent of human history.

Ecofacts

Ecofacts are natural objects that humans have used or affected. A good example is the bone from animals that people have eaten. These bones are somewhat like artifacts, but they haven't been made or modified by humans, just used and discarded by them. Another example is pollen found at archaeological sites. Because humans bring plants back to their houses to use, pollens from many plants are commonly found. These pollens may not have come from the same location. The only reason they are together is that they have been brought together by human use. Other examples are the remains of insect and animal pests that associate with humans, such as cockroaches and mice. Their remains are found in sites because they associate with humans and survive by taking advantage of the conditions that humans create. Their presence is in part caused by human presence, and thus they are also considered ecofacts.

Fossils

Fossils, although rare, are particularly informative about human biological evolution. **Fossils** may be impressions of an insect or leaf on a muddy surface that now is stone. A fossil may also consist of the actual hardened remains of an animal's skeletal structure. When an animal dies, the organic matter that made up its body begins to deteriorate. The teeth and skeletal structure are composed largely of inorganic mineral salts, and soon they are all that remains. Under most conditions, these parts eventually deteriorate too. But once

new perspectives on gender

Women in the Shell Mound Archaic

One of the main issues that archaeologists interested in gender address is how we can learn about and understand gender roles in prehistoric cultures. Gender roles might seem impossible to study in archaeological contexts. How is gender preserved in the archaeological record? How can knowledge about gender roles be recovered? Information about gender roles can be recovered if one is aware of how particular kinds of material culture are associated ethnographically with particular gender roles, and changes in them over time. Archaeologists argue that such an awareness leads not only to a better understanding of gender in prehistory but can also lead to a fuller understanding of prehistoric cultures overall.

An example is Cheryl Claassen's work on the Shell Mound Archaic culture of the Tennessee River valley. The Shell Mound Archaic represents the remains of people who lived in Tennessee and Kentucky between about 5,500 and 3,000 years ago. They were hunters and gatherers who lived in small villages, and probably moved seasonally between summer and winter communities. The most distinctive feature of the Shell Mound Archaic is the large mounds of mollusk shells they constructed for burying their dead. Tens of thousands of shells were piled together to create these mounds. Yet, around 3,000 years ago, shellfishing and thus the creation of shell burial mounds stopped abruptly. Claassen wondered why.

Suggested explanations include climate change, overexploitation of shellfish, and the migration of shellfishing peoples from the area. None has proven wholly satisfactory. In contemporary cultures, women and children typically do the shellfishing, and Claassen wondered whether an approach that considered gender roles might be more productive. She decided to approach the problem through the perspective of women's workloads, because women would have most likely been the ones shellfishing. The end of shellfishing would have meant that women would have had a lot of free time—free time that could have been put to use in some other way. What might have changed to lead women to stop shellfishing? Did some other activities become more important, so that women's labor was needed more for those other tasks?

Women's labor might have been redirected toward domesticated crops. There is archaeological evidence that about 3,000 years ago several productive crops that required intensive labor came into wide use. For example, *chenopodium*, one of the more plentiful and nutritious of these new crops, has tiny seeds that require considerable labor to harvest, clean, and process. Women were likely the ones burdened with such work. They not only would have harvested these crops but also would have been the ones to process and prepare meals from them. Thus, the

emergence of agricultural economies would have required women to undertake new labor in food production and processing that may well have forced them to stop engaging in other tasks, like shellfishing, especially if the new tasks produced a larger food supply.

The development of agricultural activities might also have brought about changes in ritual and ceremonialism. The shell burial mounds were clearly central to Shell Mound Archaic death ceremonies. Considerable labor, mostly by women, would have been required to collect the shells and to build these mounds. Later societies in the region buried their dead in earthen mounds. Could this be a reflection of the new importance dirt had in an emerging agricultural economy? If so, what role did women play in ceremonies of death and burial? If they were no longer the providers of the raw materials needed for burial, does that mean their status in society as a whole changed?

We may never know exactly why the Shell Mound Archaic disappeared, or how women's work and women's roles in society changed. But as Claassen points out, taking a gender perspective provides new avenues along which to pursue answers to these questions, and interesting new questions to pursue.

Sources: Cheryl Claassen 1991; 2009.

in a great while, conditions are favorable for preservation—for instance, when volcanic ash, limestone, or highly mineralized groundwater is present to form a high-mineral environment. If the remains are buried under such circumstances, the minerals in the ground may become bound into the structure of the teeth or bone, hardening the remains and thus making them less likely to deteriorate.

But we don't have fossil remains of everything that lived in the past, and sometimes we only have fragments from one or a few individuals. So the fossil record is very incomplete. For example, Robert Martin estimates that the earth has probably seen 6,000 primate species; remains of only 3 percent of those species have been found. It is

hardly surprising that primate paleontologists cannot identify most of the evolutionary connections between early and later forms. The task is particularly difficult with small mammals, such as the early primates, which are less likely than large animals to be preserved in the fossil record.[24] We discuss the fossil evidence for human evolution in detail in later chapters.

Features

Features are kinds of artifacts, but archaeologists distinguish them from other artifacts because they cannot be easily removed from an archaeological site. Hearths are good examples. When humans build a fire on bare ground, the soil becomes heated and is changed—all the water is driven out of it and its crystalline structure is broken down and reformed. When archaeologists find a hearth, what exactly is found? An area of hard, reddish, even slightly magnetic soil, often surrounded by charcoal and ash. Here, then, is an artifact—an object of human manufacture. But it would be very hard, if not impossible, for archaeologists to take the hearth back to the lab for study like a lithic or ceramic. A hearth is really an intrinsic feature of a site—hence the name *feature*.

Hearths are common features, but the most common features by far are called *pits*. Pits are simply holes dug by humans that are later filled with garbage or eroded soil. They are usually fairly easy to distinguish because the garbage or soil they are filled with is often different in color and texture from the soil the pit was dug into. *Living floors* are another common type of feature. These are the places where humans lived and worked. The soils in these locations are often compacted through human activity and are full of minute pieces of garbage—seeds, small stone flakes, beads, and the like—that became embedded in the floor. A large or very deep area of such debris is called a *midden*. Middens are often the remains of garbage dumps or areas repeatedly used over long periods of time, such as caves. Finally, *buildings* are common features on archaeological sites. These can range from the remains of stone rings that once held down the sides of tents to palaces built of stones that had been shaped and fitted together. Even the remains of wooden houses (or parts of them) have been preserved under some conditions. Features can be a diverse array of things that provide lots of information about the past.

Finding the Evidence of the Past

Evidence of the past is all around us, but finding it is not always easy or productive. Archaeologists and paleoanthropologists usually restrict their searches to what are called *sites*. **Sites** are known or suspected locations of human activity in the past that contain a record of that activity. Sites can be small, such as places where humans camped for perhaps only one night, to large ancient cities.

Sites are created when the remnants of human activity are covered or buried by some natural process. The most dramatic process is volcanic activity. The most impressive example of this must be Pompeii, an entire city that was buried in the eruption of Mount Vesuvius in A.D. 79. Today, archaeologists are digging out the city and finding the remains of ancient life just as it was left in the moments before the eruption.[25] Less dramatic processes are the natural processes of dirt accumulation and erosion. Wind- or water-borne soil and debris can cover a site either quickly (as in a flood) or over a long period of time, preserving intact the artifacts, ecofacts, fossils, and features left by humans. Finally, the processes through which soils are built up can also bury artifacts, ecofacts, fossils, and features in a way that allows archaeologists to uncover them later. In forests, for example, falling leaves cover the locations where humans camped. Over time, the leaves decay and build up soil, covering the remains of the human encampment slowly but completely over many years.

Because humans often reuse good locations to live and work in, many sites contain the remains of numerous human occupations. The most valuable sites to archaeologists and paleoanthropologists are those in which the burial processes worked quickly enough that each use of the site is clearly separated from the previous one. Such sites are called **stratified;** each layer, or *stratum,* of human occupation is separate like a layer in a layer cake. Not only do stratified sites allow archaeologists or paleoanthropologists to distinguish the sequence of site occupations, but the strata themselves provide a way to know the relative ages of the occupations—earlier occupations will always be below later ones.

There is no single method of finding sites, and indeed many sites are found by happenstance. But when archaeologists and paleoanthropologists want to go out and find

Archaeologists examine the wall of an excavation at Nippur, Iraq. The thick white line in the wall is the plastered floor of a building, and defines the division between two different strata. Items found on the floor can all be assumed to date from the same time, whereas items found below it can be assumed to date from an earlier time.

sites, they typically employ one of two basic methods: pedestrian survey and remote sensing. *Pedestrian survey* is what the name suggests—walking around and looking for sites. But archaeologists and paleoanthropologists can use sampling and systematic surveying methods to reduce the area to be covered on foot. *Remote sensing* techniques allow archaeologists and paleoanthropologists to find archaeological deposits from a remote location, usually the current surface of the ground beneath which the archaeological deposits are buried. Most remote sensing techniques are borrowed from exploration geology, and are the same ones geologists use to find mineral or oil deposits. They typically involve the measurement of minute variations in phenomena like the earth's magnetic or gravitational field, or changes in an electric current or pulse of energy directed into the ground. When these subtle changes, called *anomalies*, are located, more detailed exploration can be done to map the extent and depth of the buried archaeological deposits.

Whether they are identified by pedestrian survey or remote sensing, there is only one way to recover archaeological deposits once they are found them—by *excavation*. **Excavation** itself is a complex process with two goals: (1) to find every scrap of evidence (or a statistically representative sample) about the past that a given site holds, and (2) to record the horizontal and vertical location of that evidence with precision. Archaeologists and paleoanthropologists have developed many excavation strategies and techniques to accomplish these goals, but all of them involve the careful removal of the archaeological deposits; the recovery of artifacts, ecofacts, fossils, and features from the soil in which those deposits have been buried; and the detailed recording of where each artifact, ecofact, fossil, and feature was located on the site.

To date, no one has figured out a way to recover artifacts, ecofacts, fossils, and features from a site without destroying the site in the process, and this is one of the strange ironies of archaeological research. As we discuss shortly, the relationships between and among artifacts, ecofacts, fossils, and features are of most interest to archaeologists, and precisely these relationships are destroyed when archaeologists remove them from a site. For this reason, most excavation by professional archaeologists today is done only when a site is threatened with destruction, and then only by highly trained personnel using rigorous techniques. Archaeologists and paleoanthropologists collect data in basically the same ways, with one important difference. Archaeologists are most concerned with recovering intact features, whereas paleoanthropologists are most concerned with recovering intact fossils. This leads to some differences in approaches to collecting data, particularly where to look. So archaeologists tend to seek out undisturbed sites where intact features can be found. In contrast, disturbances are a plus for paleoanthropologists, because disturbed sites may make finding fossils easier—they may be eroding out of the surface of the ground and be easily visible without digging. This doesn't mean archaeologists never excavate disturbed sites, because they do. And paleoanthropologists have sometimes made important discoveries by excavating undisturbed sites.[26]

Putting It All in Context

You might have gained the impression from our discussion that archaeologists and paleoanthropologists analyze artifacts, ecofacts, fossils, and features as individual objects, separate from one another. Nothing could be farther from the truth. In fact, putting these materials in context with one another is really what archaeology and paleoanthropology are all about. **Context** is how and why the artifacts and other materials are related. Artifacts, ecofacts, fossils, and features in isolation may be beautiful or interesting by themselves, but only when they are placed in context with the other materials found on a site are we able to "read" and tell the story of the past.

To illustrate this point, let's consider a set of letters that were found separately: A E G I M N N. They are arranged here in alphabetical order, the way a set of beautiful artifacts might be arranged in a museum display in order of size. Do these arrangements tell us anything? No. What if we knew something about the relationships between and among these letters—their context? What if, for example, we knew that the *M* was the first letter found, and that the *A* and *E* were found next to the *M*, but in reverse order, that one *N* was found between the *E* and *I*, and that the other *N* was found between the *I* and the *G*? Knowing in what context the letters were found would tell us that the letters should be arranged like this: *M E A N I N G*. And meaning is exactly what context gives to artifacts, ecofacts, fossils, and features.

Dating the Evidence from the Past

An important, indeed vital, part of putting artifacts and other materials into context is putting them in chronological order. To reconstruct the evolutionary history of the primates, for example, one must know how old primate fossils are. For some time, relative dating methods were the only methods available. The last half century has seen important advances in absolute dating, including techniques that allow the dating of the earliest phases of primate evolution. **Relative dating** is used to determine the age of a specimen or deposit relative to another specimen or deposit. **Absolute dating,** or **chronometric dating,** is used to measure how old a specimen or deposit is in years.

Relative Dating Methods   The earliest, and still the most commonly used, method of relative dating is based on **stratigraphy,** the study of how different rock or soil formations are laid down in successive layers or strata (see Figure 3–1). Older layers are generally deeper or lower than more recent layers. Indicator artifacts or ecofacts are used to establish a stratigraphic sequence for the relative dating of new finds. These **indicator artifacts or ecofacts** are items of human manufacture or remains from animals and plants that spread widely over short periods of time, or that disappeared or changed fairly rapidly. Different artifacts and ecofacts are used as indicators of relative age in different areas of the world. In Africa, elephants, pigs, and horses have been particularly important in establishing stratigraphic sequences. Figure 3–1 shows the stratigraphy of Olduvai Gorge, an important site where early human fossils have been found. The stratigraphy here was

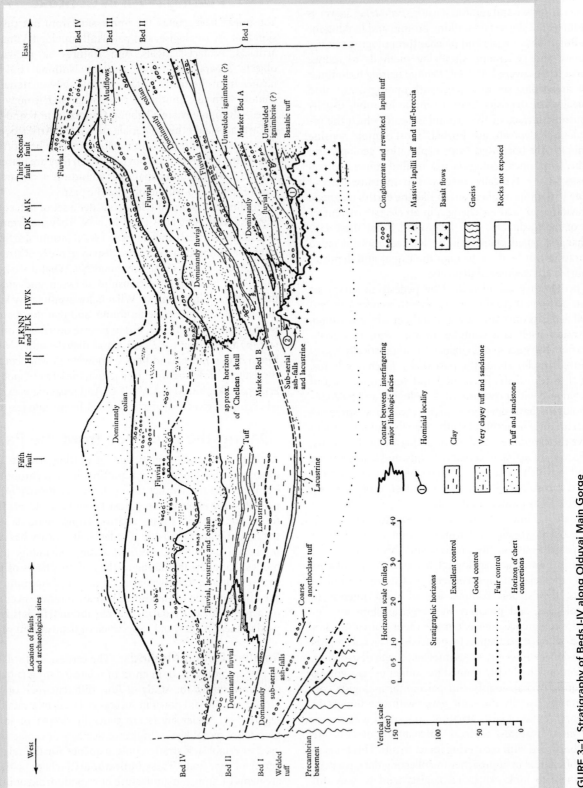

FIGURE 3–1 Stratigraphy of Beds I-IV along Olduvai Main Gorge

Notice how complex the four stratigraphic layers are—each has numerous layers of soil and rock within them. Index fossils, particularly pigs, along with a series of potassium-argon dates, allowed the researchers to identify the four major strata of the site, which correspond to four major periods of human occupation. Reprinted by permission of Cambridge University Press. Copyright © 1965.

Source: Leakey 1965.

established in part on the basis of fossil pigs.[27] The various species of pig in the successive strata are different, allowing archaeologists or paleoanthropologists to differentiate the strata based on the species found within them. Once the stratigraphy of an area is established, the relative ages of two different fossils, or features, in the same or different sites are indicated by the associated indicator artifacts or ecofacts. Major transitions in indicator artifacts or ecofacts define the epochs and larger units of geologic time. The dates of the boundaries between such units are estimated by absolute dating, described in the next section.

If a site has been disturbed, stratigraphy will not be a satisfactory way to determine relative age. As noted earlier, remains from different periods may be washed or blown together by water or wind. Or a landslide may superimpose an earlier layer on a later layer. Still, it may be possible using absolute, or chronometric, dating methods to estimate the relative age of the different fossils found together in a disturbed site.

Absolute, or Chronometric, Dating Methods

Many of the absolute dating methods are based on the decay of a radioactive isotope. Because the rate of decay is known, the age of the specimen can be estimated, within a range of possible error. **Radiocarbon,** or **carbon-14 (^{14}C), dating** is perhaps the most popularly known method of determining the absolute age of a specimen. It is based on the principle that all living matter possesses a certain amount of a radioactive form of carbon (carbon-14, or ^{14}C). Radioactive carbon, produced when nitrogen-14 is bombarded by cosmic rays, is absorbed from the air by plants and then ingested by animals that eat the plants (see Figure 3–2). After an organism dies, it no longer takes in any of the radioactive carbon. Carbon-14 decays at a slow but steady pace and reverts to nitrogen-14. (By *decays,* we mean that the ^{14}C gives off a certain number of beta radiations per minute.) The rate at which the carbon decays—its **half-life**—is known: ^{14}C has a half-life of 5,730 years. In other words, half of the original amount of ^{14}C in organic matter will have disintegrated 5,730 years after the organism's death; half of the remaining ^{14}C will have disintegrated after another 5,730 years; and so on. After about 50,000 years, the amount of ^{14}C remaining in the organic matter is too small to permit reliable dating.

To discover how long an organism has been dead—that is, to determine how much ^{14}C is left in the organism and therefore how old it is—we either count the number of beta radiations given off per minute per gram of material, or use a particle accelerator to measure the actual amount

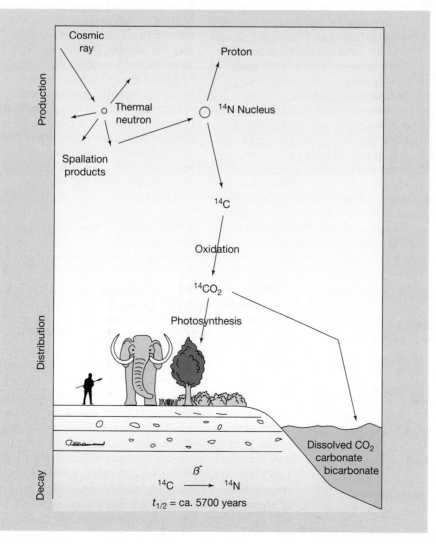

FIGURE 3–2 The Carbon-14 Cycle

Source: Taylor and Aitken 1997.

applied anthropology

Identifying Philip II of Macedon

The siege of Methone was going well, and King Philip II of Macedon—the man who had turned Macedon (what is now northern Greece) from a divided kingdom into a force that dominated the Greek world in the 4th century B.C.—decided to inspect the siege equipment. It turned out to be a near-fatal mistake. An enemy archer on the wall of the city took aim and struck him in the right eye. With the arrow stuck fast in his maxilla and his eyeball collapsed, Philip was rushed to the rear of the siege line where a well-known physician named Kritoboulos extracted the arrow and eye,

Stone bust of Philip II of Macedon.

and began treating the horrible wound. Kritoboulos saved Philip's life, but Philip was permanently disfigured, and apparently psychologically traumatized as well—it is said that he found mention of the word *eye* physically painful.

More than 1,600 years after Philip was wounded, a set of cremated bones were excavated from Tomb II of the royal cemetery at Vergina in central Macedonia. Whose bones were they? It was clear from the tomb that they were the remains of a noble, and an important one at that, but who? The bones had several strange features that might provide clues. First, the bones on the right side of the face appeared warped and perhaps shrunken—was this from the cremation? The right eye socket was clearly damaged, but when did the damage take place? Was it the cause of this individual's death, or did the damage perhaps occur after death? Clearly, these were questions for a forensic anthropologist.

A British group of anatomists and archaeologists took up the task of identifying the bones. First, they carefully examined them, and found that cremation was not likely to have caused the marked differences between the left and right sides of the skull—these differences were most likely due to some injury during life. The eye socket showed evidence of

such an injury, which included a large gouge in the upper margin of the eye and a crack in the lower socket. These had been healed for many years, and thus were certainly not the cause of death. It was concluded then that the bones clearly belonged to a man who had lost his right eye and sustained serious injury to the right side of his face many years before his death—just as Philip had.

Circumstantial evidence pointed to the cremated bones as being those of Philip II, but how could one be sure? A few images of Philip had been produced in antiquity, and the team decided that reconstructing the face of the individual in Tomb II might be the final piece of evidence to link the bones to Philip II. The reconstruction proved difficult. The combination of unusual anatomy caused by injury and burning made reconstruction of the skull a challenge. The forensic artist doing the reconstruction not only had to rebuild the soft tissues on the bone, but also attempted to model the damage that had been done prior to death. In the end, a carefully wrought face was produced, one that clearly resembled the surviving images of Philip II. It was the final piece of the puzzle. Philip II of Macedon had been found.

Sources: Musgrave, Neave, and Prag 1984; Prag 1990.

---

of ^{14}C in a sample. Modern ^{14}C emits about 15 beta radiations per minute per gram of material, but ^{14}C that is 5,730 years old emits only half that amount (the half-life of ^{14}C) per minute per gram. So, if a sample of some organism gives off 7.5 radiations a minute per gram, which is only half the amount given off by modern ^{14}C, the organism must be 5,730 years old. Similarly, because the amount of ^{14}C in a sample slowly declines over time, the atoms in a sample can be sent through a particle accelerator to separate them by weight (the lighter ^{12}C accelerates faster than the heavier ^{14}C) and measure the actual amount of each. This method, called accelerator mass spectrometry (AMS), is more accurate than the beta radiation method, requires only a very small sample of material, and provides a way to date specimens that are up to 80,000 years old.[28]

Another very common absolute dating technique based on radioactive decay uses potassium-40 (^{40}K), a radioactive form of potassium, that decays at an established rate and forms argon-40 (^{40}Ar). The half-life of ^{40}K is a known quantity, so the age of a material containing potassium can be measured by the amount of ^{40}K compared with the amount of ^{40}Ar it contains.[29] Radioactive potassium's (^{40}K's) half-life is very long—1,330 million years. This means that **potassium-argon (K-Ar) dating** may be used to date samples from 5,000 years up to 3 billion years old.

The K-Ar method is used to date potassium-rich minerals in rock, not the fossils that may be found in the rock. A very high temperature, such as occurs in a volcanic event, drives off any original argon in the material. The amount of argon that accumulates afterward from the decay of radioactive potassium is directly related to the amount of time since the volcanic event. This type of dating has been extremely useful in East Africa, where volcanic events have occurred frequently since the Miocene, which began 24 million years ago. If the material to be dated is not rich in potassium, or the area did not experience any high-temperature events, other methods of absolute dating are required.

One problem with the K-Ar method is that the amounts of potassium and argon must be measured on different rock samples; researchers must assume that the potassium and argon are evenly distributed in all the rock samples from a particular stratum. Researchers got around this problem by developing the ^{40}Ar-^{39}Ar dating method. After measuring the amount of ^{40}Ar, a nuclear reactor is used to convert another kind of argon, ^{39}Ar, to potassium so that the potassium–argon ratio can be measured from the same sample.[30]

There are many other methods of absolute dating; indeed, new methods are being developed all the time.

ETHICS IN ANTHROPOLOGICAL RESEARCH

Anthropologists have many ethical obligations—to the people they study, their anthropological colleagues, to the public and world community, and even to their employers and their own and host countries. But anthropologists agree that, should a conflict arise in ethical obligations, the most important obligation is to protect the interests of the people they study. According to the profession's code of ethics, anthropologists should tell people in the field site (or, if they are archaeologists, people who are direct descendants of the prehistoric people they are studying) about the research, and they should respect the right of people to remain anonymous if they so choose.[31] For this reason, informants are often given "pseudonyms" or fake names; many anthropologists have extended this principle to using a fake name for the community as well. But the decision to create a fake name for a community is questionable in many circumstances.[32] First, anthropologists "stick out," and it is not hard for anyone interested to figure out where they lived and worked. Governments may have to be asked for research clearance, which means that they know where the anthropologist is going to do the fieldwork. Second, people who are studied are often proud of their place and their customs and they may be insulted if their community is called something else. Third, important geographic information is often vital to understanding the community. You have to reveal if it is located at the confluence of two major rivers, or if it is the trading center of the region. And lastly, it may be difficult for future anthropologists to conduct follow-up studies if the community is disguised. Of course, if a community were truly in danger, there would be no question that an anthropologist has an obligation to try to protect it.

Honest, objective reporting is also an obligation to the anthropological profession, to the public at large, and to the observed community. But suppose a custom or trait that appears perfectly reasonable to the observed community is considered objectionable by outsiders? Such customs could range from acts that outsiders consider criminal, such as infanticide, to those that are considered repugnant, such as eating dogs. Archaeologists have caused outrage by presenting evidence of cannibalism in ancient populations.[33] An anthropologist may believe that publication of the information could bring harm to the population. Kim Hill and Magdalena Hurtado faced this situation when they realized that infanticide rates were high in the group they studied in South America. They did not want to play up their findings, nor did they want to dissimulate. After they met with community leaders to discuss the situation, they agreed not to publish their findings in Spanish to minimize the possibility that the local media or neighboring groups might learn of their findings.[34]

Everyday decisions like how to compensate people for their time are not easy either. Nowadays, many if not most informants expect to be paid or receive gifts. But in the early days of anthropology, in places where money was not an important part of the native economy, the decision to pay people was not a clear ethical choice. If money is rare, paying people increases the importance of money in that economy. Even nonmonetary gifts can increase inequalities or create jealousies. On the other hand, doing nothing by way of compensation doesn't seem right either. As an alternative, some anthropologists try to find some community project that they can help with—that way, everyone benefits. This is not to say that the anthropologists are necessarily a burden on the community. People often like to talk about their customs, and they may want others to appreciate their way of life. And anthropologists are often amusing. They may ask "funny" questions, and when they try to say or do customary things, they often do them all wrong. Probably every anthropologist has been laughed at sometimes in the field.

Archaeologists must always be concerned with the ethics of their work when undertaking or reporting the results of their research. Archaeology does not simply describe past cultures; it can also have a profound effect on living peoples. For example, many people find the idea of archaeologists excavating, cleaning, and preserving the remains of ancestors to be offensive. Therefore, archaeologists must be sensitive to the desires and beliefs of the populations that descend from the ones they are researching. In addition, artifacts from some ancient cultures are in great demand by art and antiquities collectors, and archaeological finds can lead to uncontrolled looting if archaeologists are not careful about how and to whom they report their discoveries. Wholesale ransacking of ancient cemeteries in some parts of China, for example, started because new archaeological discoveries led Chinese antiquities to become increasingly popular among collectors, and hence, increasingly valuable to those able to discover them.[35]

Although it is the ethical responsibility of archaeologists to consult with descendant populations and to be careful about how archaeological finds are reported, it is also an ethical responsibility of archaeologists to present the results of their work to the general public. Publishing

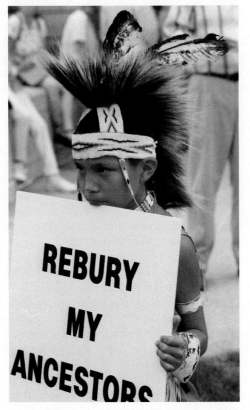

Archaeologists must be aware of the effects of their work on descendant communities. Many people, for example, find the excavation of ancestor's remains to be offensive.

archaeological results increases public awareness about the past and the importance of historic preservation. If people know how much can be learned from the archaeological record, they may be less likely to destroy it or to support those who destroy it for personal gain. Of course, when archaeologists excavate sites, they also destroy some of the context of the artifacts, ecofacts, fossils, and features found in the sites. But if they leave some of the sites unexcavated, they are preserving them (at least partially) for future investigation. To offset their partial destruction, archaeologists are ethically obligated to publish the results of their work. Reporting the results of archaeological research, therefore, plays a central role in both archaeological research and archaeological ethics.

SUMMARY ● ○ ○

1. Scientists try to achieve two kinds of explanations—associations (observed relationships between two or more variables) and theories (explanations of associations).

2. A theory is more complicated than an association. Some concepts or implications in a theory are unobservable; an association is based entirely on observations.

3. Theories can never be proved with absolute certainty. There is always the possibility that some implication,

some derivable hypothesis, will not be confirmed by future research.

4. A theory may be rejectable through the method of falsification. Scientists derive predictions that should be true if the theory is correct. If the predictions turn out to be incorrect, scientists are obliged to conclude that something may be wrong with the theory.

5. To make a satisfactory test, we have to specify operationally how we measure the variables involved in the relationships we expect to exist, so that other researchers can try to replicate, or repeat, our results.

6. Tests of predictions should employ samples that are representative. The most objective way to obtain a representative sample is to select the sample cases randomly.

7. The results of tests are evaluated by statistical methods that assign probability values to the results. These values allow us to distinguish between probably true and probably accidental results.

8. Anthropologists use several different methods to conduct research. Each has certain advantages and disadvantages in generating and testing explanations. The types of research in anthropology can be classified according to two criteria: the spatial scope of the study (analysis of a single case, analysis of several or more cases in a region, or analysis of a worldwide sample of cases), and the temporal scope of the study (historical vs. nonhistorical). The cases might be societies, archaeological traditions, languages, sites, or species. In cultural anthropology, the basic research methods, then, are ethnographic fieldwork and ethnohistory, historical and nonhistorical regional controlled comparisons, and historical and nonhistorical cross-cultural research.

9. Archaeologists and paleoanthropologists have four basic sources of evidence about the past: artifacts, ecofacts, fossils, and features. Artifacts are any objects made by humans. Ecofacts are natural objects that humans use or modify. Fossils are the preserved remains of ancient plants and animals. Features are artifacts that cannot be removed from archaeological sites.

10. Archaeological sites are locations where the evidence of the past has been buried and preserved. Sites are found through pedestrian survey or remote sensing, and artifacts, ecofacts, fossils, and features are recovered from sites through excavation. Key to excavation is the preservation of context (that is, the relationships between and among artifacts, ecofacts, fossils, and features).

11. Much information can be gained through the analysis of archaeological materials, but the materials themselves are not the primary focus of analysis. Rather, the context between and among artifacts, ecofacts, fossils, and features allows archaeologists or paleoanthropologists to gain insights about the past.

12. A key aspect of putting archaeological material into context is being able to date material accurately. Many kinds of dating techniques are used. Relative dating

techniques determine the age of archaeological materials relative to other materials of known ages. Absolute dating techniques determine the age of the archaeological deposits or materials themselves.

13. Ethics are important to all anthropologists. Anthropologists must inform the people they are studying (or the descendants of those people if they are studying an archaeological culture) about their work and its purpose. Anthropologists must ensure that their work does no harm, and that the confidentiality of people with whom they work is protected.

GLOSSARY TERMS ○ ● ○

absolute dating   **45**
^{40}Ar-^{39}Ar dating   **49**
artifact   **42**
chronometric dating   **45**
context   **45**
culture history   **41**
ecofacts   **42**
excavation   **45**
explanation   **32**
falsification   **35**
features   **43**
fieldwork   **38**
fossils   **42**
half-life   **47**
hypotheses   **35**
indicator artifacts or
   ecofacts   **45**
laws   **34**
lithics   **42**
measure   **36**

operational definition   **36**
participant-observation   **38**
potassium-argon (K-Ar)
   dating   **48**
probability value
   (*p*-value)   **37**
radiocarbon, or carbon-14
   (^{14}C), dating   **47**
random sample   **36**
relative dating   **45**
sampling universe   **36**
sites   **44**
statistical association   **34**
statistically significant   **37**
stratified   **44**
stratigraphy   **45**
theoretical construct   **35**
theories   **34**
variables   **32**

CRITICAL QUESTIONS ○ ○ ●

1. Are theories important? Explain why or why not.
2. Can a unique event be explained? Explain your answer.
3. How does measurement go beyond observation?
4. Why is scientific understanding always uncertain?
5. Why is context so important in archaeological research?

PEARSON myanthrolab

Read the chapter by Carol R. Ember and Melvin Ember, "On Cross-Cultural Research," on MyAnthroLab and answer the following questions:

1. Give a few examples of questions that can be answered by cross-cultural research.
2. What are the basic assumptions and steps in a cross-cultural study?

chapter 4

Genetics and Evolution

Astronomers estimate that the universe has been in existence for some 15 billion years, plus or minus a few billion. To make this awesome history more understandable, Carl Sagan devised a calendar that condenses this span into a single year.[1] Using 24 days for every billion years and 1 second for every 475 years as a scale, Sagan moves from the "big bang" or beginning of the universe on January 1, to the origin of the Milky Way on May 1. In this system, September 9 marks the beginning of our solar system, and September 25 the origin of life on earth. At 10:30 in the evening of December 31, the first humanlike primates appear. Sagan's compression of history provides us with a manageable way to compare the short span of human existence with the total time span of the universe. Humanlike beings have been around for only about 90 minutes out of a 12-month period. In this book, we are concerned with what has happened in the last few hours of that year.

Some 55 million to 65 million years ago, the first primates appeared. They were ancestral to all living primates, including monkeys, apes, and humans. The early primates may or may not have lived in trees, but they had flexible digits and could grasp things. Later, about 35 million years ago, the first monkeys and apes appeared. About 15 million years ago, some 20 million years after the appearance of monkeys and apes, the immediate apelike ancestors of humans probably emerged. About 4 million years ago, the first humanlike beings appeared. Modern-looking humans evolved only about 100,000 years ago.

How do we account for the biological and cultural evolution of humans? The details of the emergence of primates and the evolution of humans and their cultures are covered in subsequent chapters. In this chapter, we focus on how the modern theory of evolution developed and how it accounts for change over time. ● ○ ●

THE PRINCIPLES OF NATURAL SELECTION

In the chapter on theory in anthropology, we talked about Charles Darwin and the development of evolutionary theory. We noted that Darwin was not the first person to view the creation of new species in evolutionary terms, but he was the first to provide a comprehensive, well-documented explanation—natural selection—for the way evolution had occurred. **Natural selection** is the main process that increases the frequency of adaptive traits through time. The operation of natural selection involves three conditions or principles.[2] The first is *variation:* Every species is composed of a great variety of individuals, some of which are better adapted to their environment than others. The existence of variety is important. Without it, natural selection has nothing on which to operate; without variation, one kind of characteristic could not be favored over another. The second principle of natural selection is *heritability:* Offspring inherit traits from their parents, at least to some degree and in some way. The third principle of natural selection is *differential reproductive success:* Because better-adapted individuals generally produce more offspring over the generations than poorer-adapted individuals, the frequency of adaptive traits gradually increases in subsequent generations. A new species emerges when changes in traits or geographic barriers result in the reproductive isolation of the population.

When we say that certain traits are **adaptive** or advantageous, we mean that they result in greater reproductive success in a particular environment. The phrase "particular environment" is very important. Even though a species may become more adapted to a particular environment over time, we cannot say that one species adapted to its environment is "better" than another species adapted to a different environment. For example, we may like to think of ourselves as "better" than other animals, but humans are clearly less adapted than fish for living underwater, than bats for catching flying insects, or than raccoons for living on suburban garbage.

Although the theory of natural selection suggests that disadvantageous or **maladaptive** traits will generally decline in frequency or even disappear eventually, it does not necessarily follow that all such traits will do so. After all, species derive from prior forms that have certain structures. This means that not all changes are possible; it also means that some traits are linked to others that might have advantages that outweigh the disadvantages. Choking may be very maladaptive for any animal, yet all vertebrates are capable of choking because their digestive and respiratory systems cross in the throat. This trait is a genetic legacy, probably from the time when the respiratory system developed from tissue in the digestive system of some ancestral organism. Apparently, the propensity to choke has not been correctable evolutionarily.[3]

Changes in a species can be expected to occur as the environment changes or as some members of the species move into a new environment. With environmental change, different traits become adaptive. The forms of the species that possess the more adaptive traits will become more frequent, whereas those forms whose characteristics make continued existence more difficult or impossible in the modified environment will eventually become extinct.

Consider how the theory of natural selection would explain why giraffes became long-necked. Originally, the necks of giraffes varied in length, as happens with virtually any physical characteristic in a population. During a period when food was scarce, those giraffes with longer necks, who could reach higher tree leaves, might be better able to survive and suckle their offspring, and thus they would leave more offspring than shorter-necked giraffes. Because of heredity, the offspring of long-necked giraffes are more likely to have long necks. Eventually, the shorter-necked giraffes would diminish in number and the longer-necked giraffes would increase. The resultant population of giraffes would still have variation in neck length but on the average would be longer-necked than earlier forms.

Natural selection does not account for all variation in the frequencies of traits. In particular, it does not account for variation in the frequencies of neutral traits—that is, those traits that do not seem to confer any advantages or disadvantages on their carriers. Changes in the frequencies of neutral traits may result rather from random processes that affect gene frequencies in isolated populations—*genetic drift*—or from matings between populations—*gene flow*. We discuss these other processes later in the chapter.

Observed Examples of Natural Selection

Natural selection is a process we can see at work in the world today. It is a process that has been studied in both the laboratory and in nature, and it is a process that most scientists would argue is very well understood. However, as in all scientific endeavors, understanding grows and changes as new information is obtained. The understanding of natural selection we have today is quite different from that originally put forward by Darwin. A century and a half of research has added tremendously to the information Darwin had to work with, and entirely new fields, like population genetics, have emerged. With this new information, we know that Darwin was unaware of some things. For example, it seems clear that natural selection is not always a uniform process, but can act in jumps and starts. The fact that the ideas put forward by Darwin have changed, and are changing as new research is done, does not mean they were wrong. Darwin's ideas were simply incomplete. As we add to our knowledge base each day, we move closer to an even more complete understanding of natural selection. Because the process of natural selection may involve nearly imperceptible gradations over generations, it is often difficult to observe directly. Nevertheless, because some life forms reproduce rapidly, some examples of natural selection have been observed over relatively short periods in changing environments.

For example, scientists think they have observed natural selection in action in British moths. In 1850, an almost black moth was spotted for the first time in Manchester. That was quite unusual, for most of the moths were speckled gray. A century later, 95 percent of the moths in industrial parts of Britain were black; only in the rural areas were the moths mostly gray. How is this to be explained? It seems that, in the rural areas, the gray-speckled moth is hard to spot by bird predators against the lichen growing on the bark of trees. But in industrial areas, lichen is killed by pollution. The gray-speckled moths, formerly well adapted to blend into their environment, became clearly visible against the darker background of the lichen-free trees and were easier prey for birds. In contrast, the black moths, which previously would have had a disadvantage against the lighter bark, were now better adapted for survival. Their dark color was an advantage, and subsequently the darker moths became the predominant variety in industrial regions.

How can we be sure that natural selection was the mechanism accounting for the change? Consistent evidence comes from a series of experiments performed by H. B. D. Kettlewell. He deliberately released specially marked moths, black and gray, into two areas of England—one urban industrial and one rural—and then set light traps to recapture them subsequently. The proportions of the two kinds of moths recovered tell us about differential survival. Kettlewell found that proportionately more black moths compared with gray moths were recovered in the urban industrial area. Just the reverse happened in the rural area; proportionately more gray-speckled moths were recovered.[4] Questions have been raised recently about whether the Kettlewell experiments were properly conducted.[5] However, the basic conclusion has been replicated by subsequent research.[6] The same transformation—the switch to darker color—has occurred in 70 other species of moth, as well as in a beetle and a millipede. And the transformation did not just occur in Britain; it also happened in other highly polluted areas, including the Ruhr area of Germany and the Pittsburgh area of the United States. Moreover, in the Pittsburgh area, antipollution measures in the last 50 years have apparently caused the black moth to dwindle in number once again.[7]

The type of natural selection in the moth example is called **directional selection** because a particular trait seems to be positively favored and the average value shifts over time toward the adaptive trait. But there can also be **normalizing selection.** In this type of selection, the average value does not change, but natural selection removes the extremes. An example is the birth weight of babies. Both very low birth weights and very high birth weights are disadvantageous and would be selected against. Directional and normalizing selection both assume that natural selection will either favor or disfavor genes, but there is a third possibility—balancing selection. **Balancing selection** occurs when a *heterozygous* (varied) combination of *alleles* (genes) is positively favored, even though a *homozygous* (genes in the pairs are the same) combination is disfavored. In the chapter on human variation, we discuss a trait that apparently involves balancing selection—sickle-cell anemia—which is found in people of West African ancestry, among other populations.

Another well-known example of observed natural selection is the acquired resistance of houseflies to the insecticide DDT. When DDT was first used to kill insects, beginning in the 1940s, several new, DDT-resistant strains of housefly evolved. In the early DDT environment, many houseflies were killed, but the few that survived were the ones that reproduced, and their resistant characteristics became common to the housefly populations. To the chagrin of medical practitioners, similar resistances develop in bacteria. A particular antibiotic may lose its effectiveness after it comes into wide use because new, resistant bacterial strains emerge. These new strains will become more frequent than the original ones because of natural selection. In the United States now, a few strains are resistant to all antibiotics on the market, a fact that worries medical practitioners. One possible way to deal with the problem is to stop using antibiotics for a few years, so resistance to those antibiotics might not develop or develop only slowly.

The theory of natural selection answered many questions, but it also raised at least one whose answer eluded Darwin and others. The appearance of a beneficial trait may assist the survival of an organism, but what happens when the organism reproduces by mating with members that do not possess this new variation? Will not the new adaptive trait eventually disappear if subsequent generations mate with individuals that lack this trait? Darwin knew variations were transmitted through heredity, but he did not have a clear model of the mode of inheritance.

Gregor Mendel's pioneering studies in the science of genetics provided the foundation for such a model, but his discoveries did not become widely known until 1900.

HEREDITY
Gregor Mendel's Experiments

Mendel (1822–1884), a monk and amateur botanist who lived in what is now the Czech Republic, bred several varieties of pea plants and made detailed observations of their offspring. He chose as breeding partners plants that differed by only one observable trait. Tall plants were crossed with short ones, and yellow ones with green, for example.

When the pollen from a yellow pea plant was transferred to a green pea plant, Mendel observed a curious phenomenon: All of the first-generation offspring bore yellow peas. It seemed that the green trait had disappeared. But when seeds from this first generation were crossed, they produced both yellow and green pea plants in a ratio of three yellow to one green pea plant (see Figure 4–1). Apparently, Mendel reasoned, the green trait had not been lost or altered; the yellow trait was simply **dominant** and the green trait was **recessive.** Mendel observed similar results with other traits. Tallness dominated

FIGURE 4–1 When Mendel crossed a plant having two genes for yellow peas (YY) with a plant having two genes for green peas (yy), each offspring pea was yellow but carried one gene for yellow and one gene for green (Yy). The peas were yellow because the gene for yellow is dominant over the recessive gene for green. Crossing the first generation yielded three yellow pea plants for each green pea plant.

shortness, and the factor for smooth-skinned peas dominated the factor for wrinkled ones. In each cross, the three-to-one ratio appeared in the second generation. Self-fertilization, however, produced different results. Green pea plants always yielded green pea plants, and short plants always produced short plants.

From his numerical results, Mendel concluded that some yellow pea plants were pure (*homozygous*) for that trait, whereas others also possessed a green factor (the plants were *heterozygous*). That is, although two plants might both have yellow peas, one of them might produce offspring with green peas. In such cases, the genetic makeup, the **genotype,** differed from the observable appearance, or **phenotype.**

Genes: The Conveyors of Inherited Traits

Mendel's units of heredity were what we now call **genes.** He concluded that these units occurred in pairs for each trait and that offspring inherited one unit of the pair from each parent. Each member of a gene pair or group is called an **allele.** If the two genes, or alleles, for a trait are the same, the organism is **homozygous** for that trait; if the two genes for a characteristic differ, the organism is **heterozygous** for that trait. A pea plant that contains a pair of genes for yellow is homozygous for the trait. A yellow pea plant with a dominant gene for yellow and a recessive gene for green, although phenotypically yellow, has a heterozygous genotype. As Mendel demonstrated, the recessive green gene can reappear in subsequent generations. But Mendel knew nothing of the composition of genes or the processes that transmit them from parent to offspring. Many years of scientific research have yielded much of the missing information.

The genes of higher organisms (not including bacteria and primitive plants such as blue-green algae) are located on ropelike bodies called **chromosomes** within the nucleus of every one of the organism's cells. Chromosomes, like genes, usually occur in pairs. Each allele for a given trait is carried in the identical position on corresponding chromosomes. The two genes that determined the color of Mendel's peas, for example, were opposite each other on a pair of chromosomes.

Mitosis and Meiosis   The body cells of every plant or animal carry chromosome pairs in a number appropriate for its species. Humans have 23 pairs, or a total of 46 chromosomes, each carrying many times that number of genes. Each new body cell receives this number of chromosomes during cellular reproduction, or **mitosis,** as each pair of chromosomes duplicates itself.

But what happens when a sperm cell and an egg cell unite to form a new organism? What prevents the human baby from receiving twice the number of chromosomes characteristic of its species—23 pairs from the sperm and 23 pairs from the egg? The process by which the reproductive cells are formed, **meiosis,** ensures that this will not happen (see Figure 4–2). Each reproductive cell contains half the number of chromosomes appropriate for the species. Only one member of each chromosome pair is carried in every egg or sperm. At fertilization, the human embryo normally receives 23 separate chromosomes from its mother and the same number from its father, which add up to the 23 pairs.

DNA   As we have said, genes are located on chromosomes. Each gene carries a set of instructions encoded in its chemical structure. It is from this coded information carried in genes that a cell makes all the rest of its structural parts and chemical machinery. It appears that, in most living organisms, heredity is controlled by the same chemical substance, **DNA**—deoxyribonucleic acid. An enormous amount of research has been directed toward understanding DNA—what its structure is, how it duplicates itself in reproduction, and how it conveys or instructs the formation of a complete organism.

One of the most important keys to understanding human development and genetics is the structure and function of DNA. In 1953, American biologist James Watson, with British molecular biologist Francis Crick, proposed that DNA is a long, two-stranded molecule shaped like a double helix (see Figure 4–3). Genetic information is stored in the linear sequences of the bases; different species have different sequences, and every individual is slightly different from every other individual. Notice that each base in the DNA molecule always has the same opposite base; adenine and thymine are paired, as

Meiosis in a plant cell. The left image shows the metaphase stage. Note how the chromosomes (stained dark red) lie against and even on top of one another. The right image shows the anaphase stage, when the chromosomes separate and the cell is ready to divide.

FIGURE 4–2 Meiosis (sex cells)

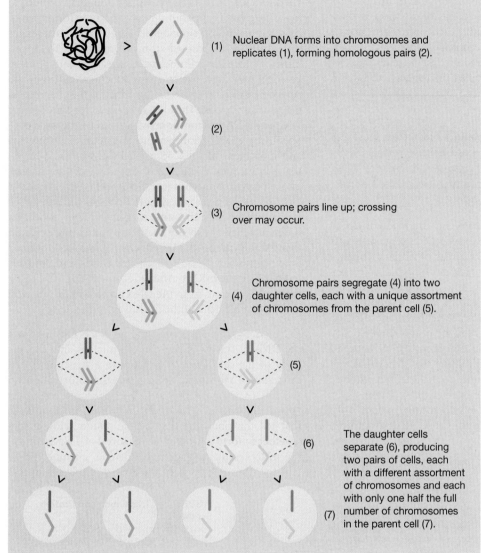

(1) Nuclear DNA forms into chromosomes and replicates (1), forming homologous pairs (2).

(2)

(3) Chromosome pairs line up; crossing over may occur.

(4) Chromosome pairs segregate (4) into two daughter cells, each with a unique assortment of chromosomes from the parent cell (5).

(5)

(6) The daughter cells separate (6), producing two pairs of cells, each with a different assortment of chromosomes and each with only one half the full number of chromosomes in the parent cell (7).

(7)

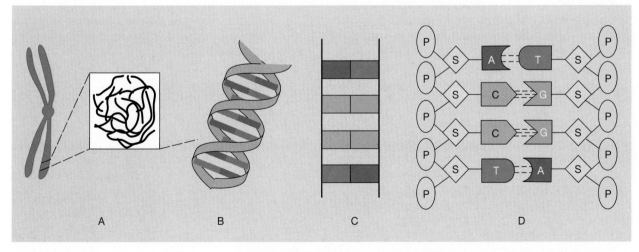

A   B   C   D

FIGURE 4–3 DNA

Chromosomes are built of DNA (A), which consists of two spiral sugar-phosphate strands (B) linked by the nitrogenous bases adenine, guanine, thymine, and cytosine (C). When the DNA molecule reproduces, the bases separate and the spiral strands unwind (D). Because adenine can only bond to thymine, and cytosine can only bond to guanine, each original strand serves as a mold along which a new complementary chain is formed.

are cytosine and guanine. The importance of this pattern is that the two strands carry the same information, so that, when the double helix unwinds, each strand can form a template for a new strand of complementary bases. Because DNA stores the information required to make up the cells of an organism, it has been called the language of life. As George and Muriel Beadle put it,

> the deciphering of the DNA code has revealed our possession of a language much older than hieroglyphics, a language as old as life itself, a language that is the most living language of all—even if its letters are invisible and its words are buried deep in the cells of our bodies.[8]

Once it was understood that genes are made of DNA, concerted efforts were begun to map DNA sequences and their locations on the chromosomes of different organisms. A project known as the Human Genome Project set out to assemble a complete genetic map for humans. In July 2000, the initial mapping of the human genome was completed.[9] This was a significant achievement and has already led to several breakthroughs in our understanding of how the genetic code functions.[10] For example, researchers recently reported finding two genes that appear to provide partial resistance to malaria, but without the damaging effects of the sickle-cell gene. These newly found genes appear to have evolved recently, perhaps only a few thousand years ago. If researchers can discover how these genes help to defend their carriers against malaria, that may help medical science discover how to prevent or treat this devastating disease.[11]

Messenger RNA   DNA stores the information to make cells, but it does not directly affect the formation of cells. One type of ribonucleic acid (RNA), **messenger RNA (mRNA),** is copied from a portion of DNA and moves outside the cell nucleus to direct the formation of proteins. Proteins have so many functions that they are considered to be responsible for most of the characteristics of an organism. They act as catalysts for synthesizing DNA and RNA and for the activities of cells; they also contribute many structural elements that determine the shape and movement of cells. Messenger RNA is like DNA in that it has a linear sequence of bases attached to a sugar-phosphate backbone, but it is slightly different chemically. One difference is that messenger RNA has the base uracil instead of the base thymine. Messenger RNA also has a different sugar-phosphate backbone and is single- rather than double-stranded. Messenger RNA is formed when a double-stranded DNA molecule unwinds and forms a template for the mRNA. After a section of DNA is copied, the mRNA releases from the DNA and leaves the nucleus, and the double helix of the DNA is reformed.

Protein Synthesis   Once the mRNA is released from the DNA, it travels out of the cell nucleus and into the body of the cell. There it attaches to a structure in the cell called a **ribosome,** which uses the information on the mRNA to make proteins. The ribosome essentially "reads" the chemical bases on the mRNA in commands that tell the ribosome the specific amino acids to join together to form a protein (see Figure 4–4). For example, the mRNA sequence adenine, adenine, guanine (AAG) tells the ribosome to place the amino acid lysine in that

FIGURE 4–4 Translation and Protein Synthesis
The mRNA copy of the cellular DNA is "read" by a ribosome that attaches the amino acid with the corresponding transfer RNA (tRNA) to a growing chain of amino acids (called a polypeptide chain because the amino acids are linked together by peptide bonds). A chain more than 100 amino acids long is called a protein.

applied anthropology

Who Owns Your DNA?

In this chapter, we have shown that your DNA is a blueprint for the proteins that form your body. In some ways, then, your DNA *is* you. What happens to your DNA when you give blood or have a biopsy? Does it stop being you or a blueprint for you? Have you given away a part of you, or do you always retain control of your DNA, because it is the essence of you? These questions have become increasingly important ethically, as DNA is now more easily extracted and sequenced from blood and body cells, and particularly because medical research has found some DNA sources valuable as experimental tools and structures for the design of new drugs.

Consider the case of Henrietta Lacks, who died of cervical cancer in 1951. Mrs. Lacks's cancer was particularly virulent; indeed, the cells grew more quickly than any human cells the Johns Hopkins University doctors had previously seen. Samples of her cancer were cultured and, because of their ability to reproduce so rapidly, were sent to researchers at other institutions where they became the targets of decades of medical research and the development of treatments. More than half a century after her death, the cells Henrietta Lacks

provided are still alive, growing in labs on every continent, and interacting daily with thousands of scientists. Are these cells Henrietta Lacks? Has she gained a type of immortality? Or are they simply samples of highly virulent cancer tissue? It is important to note that Mrs. Lacks did not give permission for her cells to be used in this way, nor did she need to. In 1951, as today, cells obtained through surgery or medical treatment are considered the property of the doctor or facility that obtained them.

For anthropologist Margaret Everett, the question of who controls an individual's DNA came to the forefront of her research when her infant son Jack was diagnosed with, and later died from, a genetic disorder. Samples of Jack's DNA were taken as part of his autopsy. Dr. Everett later learned these samples were being used in labs in England and Italy, and that several research papers had been published on them. As she relates about one of these publications, "I soon found myself combing through the article, looking for Jack in a handful of samples described in a series of tables." But was Jack there? From research conducted to explore the impact of an Oregon law that makes genetic

information the property of the individuals from which it is derived, Dr. Everett learned that her questions and concerns were widely held. Oregonians, she discovered, wanted to control access to their own DNA, and felt that privacy and consent needed to be assured when samples were taken.

In non-Western cultures, the situation may become even more complex. In the United States, we view the individual as autonomous and self-defining. We create ourselves through our work and contributions to our communities. But as we shall see in later chapters, who you are is defined by kinship and social class as well as by your work and activity. In many cultures, who you are may be mostly defined by others, not by you. In such situations, assuring privacy and consent may mean keeping private the location or identity of whole communities, or of gaining consent from kin group leaders in addition to individuals. As Dr. Everett puts it, "Property is never a thing—it is a bundle of rights, embedded in social relations." This is nowhere more true than when dealing with genetic property.

Sources: Everett 2007; Landecker 2000.

location, whereas the sequence adenine, adenine, cytosine (AAC) calls for the amino acid histidine. There are also mRNA commands that tell the ribosome when to begin and when to stop constructing a protein. Thus, the DNA code copied onto mRNA provides all the information necessary for ribosomes to build the proteins that make up the structures of organisms and drive the processes of life.

SOURCES OF VARIABILITY

Natural selection proceeds only when individuals within a population vary. There are two genetic sources of new variation: genetic recombination and mutation. There are also two processes through which variations are shuffled through populations: gene flow and genetic drift. Scholars have recently begun to consider one other potential source of variability: hybridization.

Genetic Recombination

The distribution of traits from parents to children varies from one offspring to another. Brothers and sisters, after all, do not look exactly alike, nor does each child resemble 50 percent of the mother and 50 percent of the father. This variation occurs because, when a sperm cell or an egg is formed, the single member of each chromosome pair it receives is a matter of chance. Each reproductive cell, then, carries a random assortment of chromosomes and their respective genes. At fertilization, the egg and sperm that unite are different from every other egg carried by the mother and every other sperm carried by the father. A unique offspring is thus produced by a shuffling of the parents' genes. One cause of this shuffling is the random **segregation,** or sorting, of chromosomes in meiosis. Conceivably, an individual could get any of the possible assortments of the paternal and maternal chromosomes. Another cause of the shuffling of parental genes is

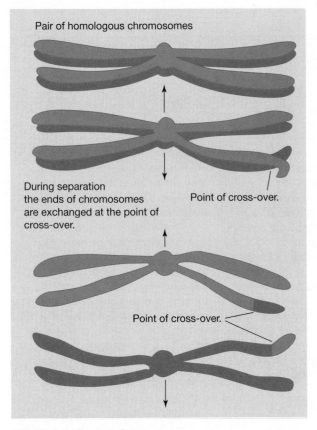

Pair of homologous chromosomes

During separation
the ends of chromosomes
are exchanged at the point of
cross-over.

Point of cross-over.

Point of cross-over.

FIGURE 4–5 Crossing-Over

Source: From Boaz and Almquist 1997.

The expression of these two characteristics depends on the sex of the organism.

Genetic recombination produces variety, which is essential for the operation of natural selection. Ultimately, however, the major source of variability is mutation. This is because mutation replenishes the supply of variability, which is constantly being reduced by the selective elimination of less fit variants. Mutation also produces variety in organisms that reproduce asexually.

Mutation

A **mutation** is a change in the DNA sequence. Such a change produces an altered gene. The majority of mutations are thought to occur because of occasional mismating of the chemical bases that make up DNA. Just as a typist will make errors in copying a manuscript, so will DNA, in duplicating itself, occasionally change its code. A mutation will result from such an error. Some mutations have more drastic consequences than others. Suppose the error is in one base on a DNA strand. The effect depends on what that portion of the DNA controls. The effect may be minimal if the product hardly affects the organism. On the other hand, if the change occurs at a place where the DNA regulates the production of many proteins, the effect on the organism can be serious.

Although it is very difficult to estimate the proportions of mutations that are harmful, neutral, or beneficial, there is no doubt that some mutations have lethal consequences. We can discuss the relative merits or disadvantages of a mutant gene only in terms of the physical, cultural, and genetic environment of that gene. Galactosemia, for example, is caused by a recessive mutant gene and usually results in

crossing-over, the exchange of sections of chromosomes between one chromosome and another (see Figure 4–5). Thus, after meiosis, the egg and sperm do not receive just a random mixture of complete paternal and maternal chromosomes; because of crossing-over, they also receive chromosomes in which some of the sections may have been replaced.

The traits displayed by each organism are not simply the result of combinations of dominant and recessive genes, as Mendel had hypothesized. In humans, most traits are influenced by the activity of many genes. Skin color, for example, is the result of several inherited characteristics. A brownish shade results from the presence of a pigment known as *melanin;* the degree of darkness in the hue depends largely on the amount of melanin present and how it is distributed in the layers of the skin. Another factor contributing to the color of all human skin is the blood that flows in blood vessels located in the outer layers of the skin. Humans carry at least five different genes for the manufacture of melanin and many other genes for the other components of skin hue. In fact, almost all physical characteristics in humans are the result of the concerted action of many genes. Some traits are sex-linked. The X chromosome, which together with the presence or absence of a Y chromosome determines sex, may also carry the gene for hemophilia or the gene for color blindness.

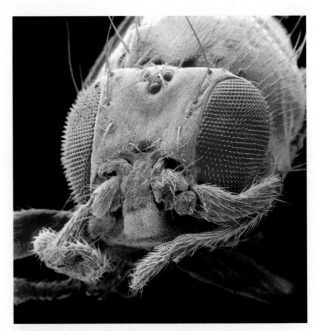

A mutation in a fruit fly causes legs to grow where antennae should be. Although most mutations are either neutral or harmful (like this one), some can be adaptive and spread rapidly through a population.

mental retardation and blindness. But it can be prevented by dietary restrictions begun at an early age. In this instance, the intervention of human culture counteracts the mutant gene and allows the afflicted individual to lead a normal life. Thus, some cultural factors can modify the effects of natural selection by helping to perpetuate a harmful mutant gene. People with the galactosemia trait who are enabled to function normally can reproduce and pass on one of the recessive genes to their children. Without cultural interference, natural selection would prevent such reproduction. Usually, natural selection acts to retain only those mutations that aid survival.

Even though most mutations may not be adaptive, those that are will multiply in a population relatively quickly, by natural selection. As Theodosius Dobzhansky has suggested:

> Consistently useful mutants are like needles in a haystack of harmful ones. A needle in a haystack is hard to find, even though one may be sure it is there. But if the needle is valuable, the task of finding it is facilitated by setting the haystack on fire and looking for the needle among the ashes. The role of the fire in this parable is played in biological evolution by natural selection.[12]

The black moth that was spotted in Manchester in 1850, probably resulted from a mutation. If the tree trunks had been light-colored, that moth or its offspring probably would have died out. But as industrialization increased and the tree trunks became darker, a trait that was once maladaptive became adaptive.

Genetic recombination and mutation are the sources of new variations, but evolutionary biologists have identified two other processes that are important in distributing those variations through populations: genetic drift and gene flow.

Genetic Drift

The term **genetic drift** refers to various random processes that affect gene frequencies in small, relatively isolated populations. Genetic drift is also known as the *Wright effect,* after geneticist Sewall Wright, who first directed attention to this process. Over time in a small population, genetic drift may result in a neutral or nearly neutral gene becoming more or less frequent just by chance.

One variety of genetic drift, called the *founder effect,* occurs when a small group of organisms recently derived from a larger population migrates to a relatively isolated location. If a particular gene is absent just by chance in the migrant group, the descendants are also likely to lack that gene, assuming that the group remains isolated. Similarly, if all members of the original migrant group just by chance carried a particular gene, their descendants would also be likely to share that gene. Isolation can occur for physical reasons, such as when a group moves to a previously uninhabited place and does not return. The populations that traveled over land when the Bering land bridge connected Asia to North America could not readily return when the sea level rose. This may explain why Native Americans have a higher proportion of individuals with type O blood than other populations—the first migrants may have had, by chance, a predominance of individuals with type O blood.

Isolation can also occur for social reasons. A religious sect of Anabaptists called "Dunkers" emigrated from Germany to the United States in the early 1700s. The fact that the 50 original families kept to themselves probably explains why some of their gene frequencies differ from what is found in both the German and general U.S. populations.[13]

Gene Flow

Gene flow is the process whereby genes pass from one population to another through mating and reproduction. Unlike the other processes of natural selection and genetic drift, which generally increase the differences between populations in different environments, gene flow tends to work in the opposite direction—it *decreases* differences between populations. Two populations at opposite ends of a region may have different frequencies of a particular gene, but the populations located between them have an intermediate gene frequency because of gene flow between them. The variation in gene frequency from one end of the region to the other is called a **cline.** In Europe, for example, there is a cline in the distribution of type B blood, which gradually diminishes in frequency from east to west.[14]

Most genetically determined characteristics in humans have gradually or clinally varying frequencies as one moves from one area to another. Neighboring regions have more similar gene frequencies than regions widely separated. But these clines do not always coincide, which makes the concept of "race" as applied to humans not very useful for understanding human biological variation.[15] We discuss this in more detail in the chapter on human variation.

Gene flow may occur between distant as well as close populations. Long-range movements of people, to trade or raid or settle, may result in gene flow. But they do not always do so.

Hybridization

A **species** is a population that consists of organisms able to interbreed and produce fertile and viable offspring. In general, individuals from one species do not successfully mate with members of a different species because of genetic and behavioral differences. If members of different species do mate, fertilization usually does not occur and, if it does, the embryo does not survive. In the cases where offspring are born, they are usually infertile. However, recent studies have suggested that **hybridization,** the creation of a viable offspring from two different species, may be more possible than once thought. Hybridization may be an important source of new variation in some populations.

current research and issues

Is Evolution Slow and Steady or Fast and Abrupt?

Darwin's evolutionary theory suggested that new species emerge gradually over time. Through the process of natural selection, frequencies of traits would slowly change, and eventually a new species would appear. But Darwin did not explain why so much speciation has occurred. If trait frequencies change only gradually over time, wouldn't descendant populations retain their ability to interbreed and wouldn't they, therefore, continue to belong to the same species?

In the 1930s and 1940s, biologists and geneticists advanced what came to be called the "modern synthesis" in evolutionary theory, adding what was known from genetics about heredity. Mutation and the recombination of genes now provided for genetic variety. The driving force of change was still adaptation to environments through natural selection; gene frequencies of a population presumably changed slowly as adaptive traits (because of existing genes or mutations) increased in prevalence and maladaptive traits decreased. As for speciation, the development and divergence of different species, the modern synthesis postulated that it would occur when subpopulations became isolated by geographic barriers or when different subpopulations encountered different climatic conditions or moved into new ecological niches; those environmental isolating processes would eventually result in the development of reproductive isolation and therefore new species.

Niles Eldredge and Stephen Jay Gould challenged this gradualist view of evolution in 1972. Their alternative model of evolution is referred to as "punctuated equilibrium." They still assume that natural selection is the primary mechanism of evolutionary change, but they see the pace of evolution quite differently. In their view, new species evolve quickly; but once a successful species emerges, its characteristics are likely to change very little over long periods of time. Thus, in contrast to the modern synthesis, Eldredge and Gould do not think it is common for the world's species to change gradually into descendant species. Rather, species are born more or less abruptly, they have lifetimes during which they do not change much, and they become extinct. As examples, Eldredge and Gould cite

Time

Morphological change

Gradualism

Punctuated equilibrium

FIGURE 4–6 A Graphical Depiction of Gradual Versus Punctuated Evolutionary Change

Hybridization is an important source of variation in some plant species, such as these South African Gazanias.

The finches of the Galápagos Islands that Darwin used as evidence for natural selection and that we refer to in the box "Is Evolution Slow and Steady or Fast and Abrupt?" also provide an example of hybridization in action. Many female cactus finches (*Geospiza scandens*) died during a period of severe drought, leaving an abundance of males. High competition for mates led some female ground finches (*Geospiza fortis*) to mate with the abundant male cactus finches, something that would not normally occur. The result was hybrid offspring with unique characteristics. These hybrids, both male and female, went on to mate only with cactus finches, because they imprinted on the male cactus finch song as infants. The end result was a one-time influx of ground finch genes into the cactus finch population, adding new variations upon which natural selection could work.[16]

THE ORIGIN OF SPECIES

One of the most controversial aspects of Darwin's theory was the suggestion that one species could, over time, evolve into another. How could one species evolve into the history of North American trilobites and Bermudan land snails. In both groups of animals, it looks as if the different species did not change for a long period of time—millions of years for some species—but then certain species seem to have been quickly replaced by related species from nearby areas. In short, Eldredge and Gould believe that the succession of one species after another involves replacement from outside more often than gradual change over time.

Evolution may or may not occur as the model of punctuated equilibrium specifies, but most evolutionists today agree that change could occur relatively quickly. Recent research suggests that some relatively quick climate changes in the earth's history helped bring about massive extinctions of species and families of species and exponential increases in the subsequent number of new families. For example, there is considerable evidence that a large meteorite collided with the earth at the end of the Cretaceous geological period, about 65 million years ago. Louis Alvarez and his colleagues proposed that so much dust was sent into the atmosphere by the collision that the earth was shrouded in darkness for months, if not longer. Some investigators now think that the meteorite impact may have also triggered a great deal of volcanic activity, even on the

opposite side of the world, which would also have reduced solar radiation to the earth's surface. Not only the dinosaurs disappeared about 65 million years ago, so also did many sea animals and plants. Afterward, the earth saw the proliferation of many other kinds of animals, such as fish, lizards, birds, and mammals, as well as flowering trees. As we shall see in the chapter on primate evolution, our own biological order, the Primates, is believed to have emerged around that time.

Peter Grant recently studied the same finches on the Galápagos Islands that partially inspired Darwin's theory. But, unlike Darwin, Grant had the chance to see natural selection in action. It was surprisingly quick. Central to the project was the attachment of colored bands to each individual bird, which allowed each bird to be identified at a distance. In the midst of the project, in 1977, when half the birds had been banded, there was a serious drought. Of the two main species of finch on one island, the cactus finch (*Geospiza scandens*) and the medium ground finch (*Geospiza fortis*), only the cactus finches were able to breed, but they had no surviving offspring. During the next 18 months, 85 percent of the adult medium ground finches disappeared. Those finches that survived tended to be larger and to have larger beaks than the ones that died. Why

larger beaks? Both species of finch eat seeds, but small seeds produced by grasses and herbs are scarce in a drought; bigger seeds are more available. So it seems that natural selection under conditions of drought favored finches with bigger beaks, which are better at cracking the husks of large seeds.

If it were not for the fact that wet years, which favor smaller finches, occur between years of drought, we might see the quick evolution of new finch species. An estimated 20 drought episodes would be sufficient to produce a new species of finch. Galápagos finches do not really provide an example of punctuated equilibrium (no replacement from outside occurred), but they do suggest that evolutionary change could be a lot quicker than Darwin imagined.

Controversy continues over whether evolution is slow and steady or fast and abrupt. But many scholars, including Gould, point out that there is no need to pit one model against the other. Both may be correct in different instances. In any case, much more investigation of evolutionary sequences is needed to help us evaluate the competing theoretical models.

Sources: Devillers and Chaline 1993; Grant 1991, 82–87; Tattersall 2009; Weiner 1994.

---

another? What is the explanation for this differentiation? How does one group of organisms become so unlike another group with the same ancestry that it forms a totally new species? **Speciation,** or the development of a new species, may occur if one subgroup of a species finds itself in a radically different environment. In adapting to their separate environments, the two populations may undergo enough genetic changes to prevent them from interbreeding, should they renew contact. Numerous factors can prevent the exchange of genes. Two species living in the same area may breed at different times of the year, or their behavior during breeding—their courtship rituals—may be distinct. The difference in body structure of closely related forms may in itself bar interbreeding. Geographic barriers may be the most common barriers to interbreeding.

Do new species diverge quickly or slowly from their ancestors? Paleontologists disagree about the pace of speciation. The traditional view is that evolution occurs very slowly over time; new species emerge gradually. Others who espouse what's called "punctuated equilibrium" believe that species are very stable over long periods of time, but when divergence occurs it is quick (see the box titled "Is Evolution Slow and Steady or Fast and Abrupt?")

Speciation Versus Creation

But some people, particularly those who call themselves "scientific creationists," argue that, although natural selection can produce variation within species (often referred to as *microevolution*), it cannot produce new species (often referred to as *macroevolution*). Creationists argue that God created all living things, and that evolution has only changed those living things in minor ways and has not created new kinds of living things. The major problem with the creationist view is that there is solid empirical evidence for speciation. For example, William Rice and George Salt demonstrated that, if they sorted fruit flies by their environmental preferences (such as light intensity and temperature) and then bred the sorted groups separately, they could produce flies incapable of interbreeding—separate species—in as little as 35 generations.[17] The fossil record contains numerous examples of speciation and even the development of entirely new kinds of creatures. For example, the evolution of birds from terrestrial creatures is clearly evidenced in the fossil record.[18] Although many creationists downplay the evidence for speciation, the evidence is plentiful, and can be seen by the public in museums all over the world.

With the abundant evidence for speciation found in both the fossil record and in experimental observations, creationists have recently developed a new argument to discount the role of natural selection in the process of speciation. The new argument is that life in general, and species in particular, are so complex that a random, undirected process like natural selection could never have created them. The complexity of life, these creationists argue, must stem from "intelligent design." This new appeal to intelligent design in the origin of species is actually an old, and widely discredited, one. In his 1802 book *Natural Theology*, William Paley wrote, "Suppose I had found a watch upon the ground, and it should be enquired how the watch happened to be in that place . . . the inference, we think, is inevitable; that the watch must have had a maker. . . ."[19] By this, Paley implied that if we find a complex mechanism at work in the world, like a watch, we must conclude that a maker exists. Paley extended the argument to the complexity of life, and concluded that life must stem from an intelligent designer—God.

Darwin wrote *On the Origin of Species* in part as a response to Paley, and Darwinists have been responding ever since. But in recent years, the "intelligent design" movement, or as proponents call it, the "wedge," has brought Paley's ideas back with force. Indeed, the force is an active political one, with the explicit purpose "to reverse the stifling dominance of the materialist world view, and to replace it with a science consonant with Christian and theistic convictions."[20] Intelligent design is, at the core, a political movement. The problem, however, is that intelligent design cannot explain speciation in a scientific way. The central argument made by proponents of intelligent design is simply that what we see in the world is too complex to be accounted for by natural selection, but they offer no alternative natural mechanism. They argue that, if natural selection may not account for all cases of speciation, then the only alternative is divine intervention. Clearly, this reasoning is flawed. Just because we do not understand something today does not mean we should toss out all we do know. Rather, the scientific approach is to continue to examine unexplained phenomena to learn more about them.

Intelligent design proponents also fail to answer critics who point out that natural selection can and has accounted for even the most complex of features—such as wings and eyes—and hence that intelligent design arguments lack a basis in fact. The key facts that intelligent design and other creationist scholars appeal to are biblical ones. But it is important to point out that most biblical scholars do not agree with creationist arguments. As theologian Ernan McMullin suggests, the Bible "ought to be understood as conveying fundamental theological truths about dependence of the natural and human worlds on their Creator, rather than explaining how exactly these worlds first took shape."[21] On the other hand, there is nothing in science that can absolutely rule out supernatural intervention in the natural world, because supernatural activities are beyond the realm of scientific explanation. For example, although we now know that people with a condition called hypertrichosis grow hair all over their faces because of a single mutation on the X chromosome, science cannot rule out the possibility that the mutation was caused by the "curse of the werewolf" or a divine punishment for sin.[22] Science cannot rule out such possibilities because they cannot be observed, measured, or experimentally tested. Science and religion should be regarded as different ways of understanding the world, the former relying on evidence, the latter relying on faith.

NATURAL SELECTION OF BEHAVIORAL TRAITS

Until now, we have discussed how natural selection might operate to change a population's physical traits, such as the color of moths or the neck length of giraffes. But natural selection can also operate on the behavioral characteristics of populations. Although this idea is not new, it is now receiving more attention. The approaches called **sociobiology**,[23] behavioral ecology,[24] evolutionary psychology,[25] and dual-inheritance theory[26] involve the application of evolutionary principles to the behavior of animals and humans. Behavioral ecology looks at how all kinds of behavior related to the environment; sociobiology looks at social organization and social behavior; evolutionary psychology looks at how evolution may have produced lasting variation in the way humans behave, interact, and perceive the world; and dual-inheritance theory looks at how beneficial cultural traits might be selected for and transmitted. The typical behaviors of a species are assumed to be adaptive and to have evolved by natural selection. For example, why do related species exhibit different social behaviors even though they derive from a common ancestral species?

Consider the lion, as compared with other cats. Although members of the cat family are normally solitary creatures, lions live in social groups called *prides*. Why? George Schaller has suggested that lion social groups may have evolved primarily because group hunting is a more successful way to catch large mammals in open terrain. He has observed that not only are several lions more successful in catching prey than are solitary lions, but several lions are more likely to catch and kill large and dangerous prey such as giraffes. Then, too, cubs are generally safer from predators when in a social group than when alone with their mothers. Thus, the social behavior of lions may have evolved primarily because it provided selective advantages in the lions' open-country environment.[27]

It is important to remember that natural selection operates on expressed characteristics, or the phenotype, of an individual. In the moth example, the color of the moth is part of its *phenotype,* subject to natural selection. Behavior is also an expressed characteristic. If hunting in groups, a behavioral trait, gets you more food, then individuals who hunt in groups will do better. But we must also remember that natural selection requires traits to be heritable. Can the concept of heritability be applied to learned behavior, not just genetically transmitted behavior? And, even more controversially, if the concept of heritability can include learning, can it also include cultural learning? Recent research on domesticated dogs suggests it may. Domesticated dogs appear to inherently understand social cues used by humans, such as pointing, whereas wolves do not. These findings suggest that some aspects of cultural learning in animals may be heritable.[28]

Early theorizing in sociobiology and behavioral ecology appeared to emphasize the genetic component of behavior. For example, Edward O. Wilson, in his book *Sociobiology,* defined sociobiology as "the systematic study of the biological causes of behavior."[29] But Bobbi Low points out that, although the term *biological* may have been interpreted to mean "genetic," most biologists understand that expressed or observable characteristics are the results of genes, environment, and life history, all interacting. Behavior is a product of all three. If we say that some behavior is

heritable, we mean that the child's behavior is more likely to resemble the parents' behavior than the behavior of others.[30] Learning from a parent could be an important part of why the offspring is like the parent. If the child is more like the parent than like others, then the likeness is heritable, even if it is entirely learned from the parent.

The sociobiological approach has aroused considerable controversy in anthropology, probably because of its apparent emphasis on genes, rather than experience and learning, as determinants of human behavior. Anthropologists have argued that the customs of a society may be more or less adaptive because cultural behaviors also have reproductive consequences. It is not just an individual's behavior that may have reproductive consequences. So, does natural selection also operate in the evolution of culture? Many biologists think not. They say there are substantial differences between biological and cultural evolution. How do cultural evolution and biological evolution compare? To answer this question, we must remember that the operation of natural selection requires three conditions, as we already noted: variation, heritability or mechanisms that duplicate traits in offspring, and differential reproduction because of heritable differences. Do these three requirements apply to cultural behavior?

In biological evolution, variability comes from genetic recombination and mutation. In cultural evolution, it comes from recombination of learned behaviors and from invention.[31] Cultures are not closed or reproductively isolated, as species are. A species cannot borrow genetic traits from another species, but a culture can borrow new things and behaviors from other cultures. The custom of growing corn, which has spread from the New World to many other areas, is an example of this phenomenon. As for the requirement of heritability, although learned traits obviously are not passed to offspring through purely genetic inheritance, parents who exhibit adaptive behavioral traits are more likely to "reproduce" those traits in their children, who may learn them by imitation or by parental instruction. Children and adults may also copy adaptive traits they see in people outside the family. Finally, as for the requirement of differential reproduction, it does not matter whether the trait in question is genetic or learned or both. As Henry Nissen emphasized, "behavioral incompetence leads to extinction as surely as does morphological disproportion or deficiency in any vital organ. Behavior is subject to selection as much as bodily size or resistance to disease."[32]

Many theorists are comfortable with the idea of applying the theory of natural selection to cultural evolution, but others prefer to use different terminology when dealing with traits that do not depend on purely genetic transmission from one generation to the next. For example, Robert Boyd and Peter Richerson discuss human behavior as involving "dual inheritance." They distinguish cultural transmission, by learning and imitation, from genetic transmission, but they emphasize the importance of understanding both and the interaction between them.[33] William Durham also deals separately with cultural

Domesticated dogs have evolved the ability to understand human social cues far better than wolves.

transmission, using the term *meme* (analogous to the term *gene*) for the unit of cultural transmission. He directs our attention to the interaction between genes and culture, calling that interaction "coevolution," and provides examples of how genetic evolution and cultural evolution may lead to changes in each other, how they may enhance each other, and how they may even oppose each other.[34]

So biological and cultural evolution in humans may not be completely separate processes. As we will discuss, some of the most important biological features of humans—such as our relatively large brains—may have been favored by natural selection because our ancestors made tools, a cultural trait. Conversely, the cultural trait of informal and formal education may have been favored by natural selection because humans have a long period of immaturity, a biological trait.

As long as the human species continues to exist and the social and physical environment continues to change, there is reason to think that natural selection of biological and cultural traits will also continue. However, as humans learn more about genetic structure, they will become more capable of curing genetically caused disorders and even altering the way evolution proceeds. Today, genetic researchers are capable of diagnosing genetic defects in developing fetuses, and parents can and do decide often whether to terminate a pregnancy. Soon, genetic engineering will probably allow humans to fix defects and even try to "improve" the genetic code of a growing fetus. Whether and to what extent humans should alter genes will undoubtedly be the subject of continuing debate. Whatever the decisions we eventually make about genetic engineering, they will affect the course of human biological and cultural evolution.

SUMMARY ● ○ ○

1. Charles Darwin and Alfred Wallace proposed the mechanism of natural selection to account for the evolution of species. Basic principles of the theory of natural selection are that (1) every species is composed of a great variety of individuals, some of which are better adapted to their environment than others; (2) offspring inherit traits from their parents at least to some degree and in some way; and (3) because better-adapted individuals generally produce more offspring over the generations than the poorer-adapted individuals, the frequency of adaptive traits increases in subsequent generations. In this way, natural selection results in increasing proportions of individuals with advantageous traits.

2. Mendel's and subsequent research in genetics and our understanding of the structure and function of DNA

and mRNA help us to understand the biological mechanisms by which traits may be passed from one generation to the next.

3. Natural selection depends on variation within a population. The primary sources of biological variation are genetic recombination, mutation, genetic drift, gene flow, and hybridization.

4. Speciation, the development of a new species, may occur if one subgroup becomes separated from other subgroups. In adapting to different environments, these subpopulations may undergo enough genetic changes to prevent interbreeding, even if they reestablish contact. Once species differentiation occurs, it is believed that the evolutionary process cannot be reversed.

5. So-called "creation scientists" and proponents of "intelligent design" theory argue that the origin of species cannot be accounted for through natural selection. This argument ignores the enormous body of evidence—experimental, fossil, and field data—that demonstrates how natural selection works to create new species.

6. Natural selection can also operate on the behavioral characteristics of populations. The approaches such as sociobiology and behavioral ecology involve the application of evolutionary principles to the behavior of animals. Much controversy surrounds the degree to which the theory of natural selection can be applied to human behavior, particularly cultural behavior. There is more agreement that biological and cultural evolution in humans may influence each other.

GLOSSARY TERMS ○ ● ○

adaptive 54
allele 56
balancing
   selection 55
chromosome 56
cline 61
crossing-over 60
directional selection 55
DNA 56
dominant 55
genes 56
gene flow 61
genetic drift 61
genotype 56
heterozygous 56
homozygous 56
hybridization 61

maladaptive 54
meiosis 56
messenger RNA
   (mRNA) 58
mitosis 56
mutation 60
natural selection 52
normalizing
   selection 55
phenotype 56
recessive 55
ribosome 58
segregation 59
sociobiology 64
speciation 63
species 61

CRITICAL QUESTIONS ○ ○ ●

1. Do you think the theory of natural selection is compatible with religious beliefs? Explain your reasoning.
2. How might the discovery of genetic cures and the use of genetic engineering affect the future of evolution?
3. Why do you think humans have remained one species?

PEARSON
myanthrolab

Read the chapter by Jonathan Marks titled "Genes, Bodies, and Species" on MyAnthroLab. Answer the following questions:

1. Compare Marks's discussion of the "Hardy-Weinberg Law" and Figure 4–1, which displays the distribution of genotypes in pea plants identified by Mendel. Explain how the Hardy-Weinberg Law relates to Mendel's discovery.
2. Marks argues that speciation requires a gene pool to be divided into isolated groups. Explain why this is the case. Given the enormous gene flow in human populations, is it likely (or even possible) that a new species of human will evolve under current conditions?
3. Marks concludes his essay by stating that genetic mutation is more complex than we had previously thought. In what ways does Marks's discussion of mutation and its effects differ from that we present in this text? Does Marks's discussion appear to make the process of mutation more complex than ours?

chapter 5

Human Variation and Adaptation

In any given human population, individuals vary in external features such as skin color or height and in internal features such as blood type or susceptibility to a disease. If you measure the frequencies of such features in different populations, you will typically find differences on average from one population to another. So, for example, some populations are typically darker in skin color than other populations.

Why do these physical differences exist? They may be largely the product of differences in genes. They may be largely due to growing up in a particular environment, physical and cultural. They are perhaps the result of an interaction between environmental factors and genes.

We turn first to the processes that may singly or jointly produce the varying frequencies of physical traits in different human populations. Then we discuss specific differences in external and internal characteristics and how they might be explained. Finally, we close with a critical examination of racial classification and whether it helps or hinders the study of human variation. ● ○ ●

PROCESSES IN HUMAN VARIATION AND ADAPTATION

Mutations—changes in the structure of a gene—are the ultimate source of all genetic variation. Because different genes make for greater or lesser chances of survival and reproduction, natural selection results in more favorable genes becoming more frequent in a population over time. We call this process **adaptation.** Adaptations are genetic changes that give their carriers a better chance to survive and reproduce than individuals without the genetic change who live in the same environment. It is the environment, of course, that favors the reproductive success of some traits rather than others.

How adaptive a gene or trait is depends on the specific environment; what is adaptive in one environment may not be adaptive in another. For example, in the chapter on genetics and evolution, we discussed the advantage that dark moths had over light moths when certain areas of England became industrialized. Predators could not easily see the darker moths against the newly darkened trees, and these moths soon outnumbered the lighter variety. Similarly, human populations live in a great variety of environments, so we would expect natural selection to favor different genes and traits in those different environments. As we shall see, variations in skin color and body build are among the many features that may be at least partly explainable by how natural selection works in different environments.

Adaptation through natural selection does not account for variation in frequencies of neutral traits—that is, traits that do not confer any advantages or disadvantages on their carriers. The sometimes different and sometimes similar frequencies of neutral traits in human populations may result, then, from genetic drift or gene flow. As we discussed in the chapter on genetics and evolution, genetic drift refers to variations in a population that appear because of random processes such as isolation (the "founder effect"), mating patterns, and the random segregation of chromosomes during meiosis. Gene flow involves the exchange of genes between populations. Neither genetic drift nor gene flow is an adaptive

process. Genetic drift may increase the differences between populations. Gene flow tends to work in the opposite direction—it tends to decrease differences between populations.

Acclimatization

Natural selection may favor certain genes because of certain physical environmental conditions, as in the case of the moths in England. But the physical environment can sometimes produce variation even in the absence of genetic change. As we shall see, climate may influence the way the human body grows and develops, and therefore some kinds of human variation may be explainable largely as a function of environmental variation. We call this process *acclimatization*. **Acclimatization** involves physiological adjustments to environmental conditions in individuals. Acclimatizations may have underlying genetic factors, but they are not themselves genetic. Individuals develop them during their lifetimes, rather than being born with them.

Many acclimatizations are simple physiological changes in the body that appear and disappear as the environment changes. For example, when we are chilled, our bodies attempt to create heat by making our muscles work, a physiological response to the environment that we experience as shivering. Longer exposure to cold weather leads our bodies to increase our metabolic rates so that we generate more internal heat. Both these physiological changes are acclimatizations, one short-term (shivering), one longer-term (increased metabolic rate).

As we discuss later in this chapter, some long-term acclimatizations are difficult to distinguish from adaptations because they become established as normal operating processes, and they may persist even after the individual moves into an environment that is different from the one that originally fostered the acclimatization. It also appears that some acclimatizations are closely related to genetic adaptations. For example, tanning, an acclimatization among light-skinned people when exposed to high levels of solar radiation, is likely in people where light skin color is adapted to environments with typically low solar radiation.

Influence of the Cultural Environment

Humans are not only influenced by their environments through adaptations and acclimatizations, but, as we shall see in the chapters on food production and on the state, humans can also dramatically affect their environments. Culture allows humans to modify their environments, and such modifications may lessen the likelihood of genetic adaptations and physiological acclimitizations. For example, the effects of cold may be modified by the culture traits of living in houses, harnessing energy to create heat, and clothing the body to insulate it. In these cultural ways, we alter our "microenvironments." Iron deficiency may be overcome by the culture trait of cooking in iron pots. If a physical environment lacks certain nutrients, people may get them by the culture trait of trading for them; trading

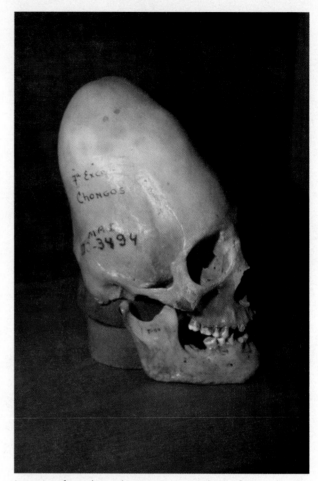

A cranium from the prehistoric Paracas culture of Peru, showing the effects of head binding.

for salt has been common in world history. Culture can also influence the direction of natural selection. As we shall see, the culture of dairying seems to have increased the frequency of genes that allow adults to digest milk.[1]

In addition, individual cultures sometimes practice behaviors that lead to physical variations between their members and between members of one culture and another. For example, elites in many highland Andean societies (the Inca, for example) practiced head binding. The heads of elite children were tightly bound with cloth. As the children grew, the binding forced the skull to take on an elongated, almost conical shape. This cultural practice, then, created physical variations among individuals that were intended to identify members of elite groups.[2] Many cultures have practices that are intended to create physical variations that distinguish members of their culture from members of other cultures. The Hebrew Bible, for example, tells the story of how Abraham was instructed by God to circumcise himself and all his male descendants as a sign of the covenant between them.[3] Thus, male descendants of Abraham traditionally share a culturally induced physical variation (lack of a foreskin) to identify themselves as a group.

In the next section, we discuss some aspects of human (physical) variation for which we have explanations that involve one or more of the processes just described.

PHYSICAL VARIATION IN HUMAN POPULATIONS

The most noticeable physical variations among populations are those that are external, on the surface—body build, facial features, skin color, and height. No less important are those variations that are internal, such as variation in susceptibility to different diseases and differences in the ability to produce certain enzymes.

We begin our survey with some physical features that appear to be strongly linked to variation in climate, particularly variation in temperature, sunlight, and altitude.

Body Build and Facial Construction

Scientists have suggested that the body build of many birds and mammals may vary according to the temperature of the environment in which they live. Bergmann and Allen, two 19th century-naturalists, suggested some general rules for animals, but researchers did not begin to examine whether these rules applied to human populations until the 1950s.[4] **Bergmann's rule** describes what seems to be a general relationship between body size and temperature: The slenderer populations of a species inhabit the warmer parts of its geographic range, and the more robust populations inhabit the cooler areas.

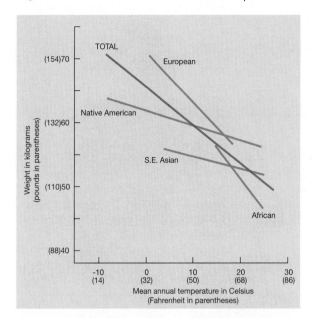

FIGURE 5–1 Relationship Between Body Weight of Males and Average Annual Temperature for Four Major Population Groups

Source: From Roberts 1953.

D. F. Roberts's studies of variation in mean body weight of human populations in regions with widely differing temperatures have provided support for Bergmann's rule.[5] Roberts discovered that the lowest body weights were found among residents of areas with the highest mean annual temperatures, and vice versa. Figure 5–1 shows the relationship between body weight of males and average annual temperature for four different geographic populations. Although the slope of the relationship is slightly different for each group, the trend is the same—with colder temperatures, weight is greater. Looking at the general trend across populations (see the "Total" line), we see that, where the mean annual temperatures are about freezing (32°F; 0°C), the average weight for males is about 143 pounds (65 kilograms); where the mean annual temperatures are about 77°F (25°C), men weigh, on the average, about 110 pounds (50 kilograms).

Allen's rule refers to another kind of variation in body build among birds and mammals: Protruding body parts (e.g., limbs) are relatively shorter in the cooler areas of a species' range than in the warmer areas. Research comparing human populations tends to support Allen's rule.[6]

The rationale behind these theories is that the long-limbed, lean body type often found in equatorial regions provides more surface area in relation to body mass and thus facilitates the dissipation of body heat. In contrast, the chunkier, shorter-limbed body type found among residents of cold regions promotes retention of body heat because the amount of surface area relative to body mass is lessened. The build of the Inuit (Eskimo) appears to exemplify Bergmann's and Allen's rules. The relatively large bodies and short legs of the Inuit may be adapted to the cold temperatures in which they live.

It is not clear whether differences in body build among populations are due solely to natural selection of different

These Samburu people from Kenya illustrate Bergmann's rule. They have the long-limbed, lean body type that is often found in equatorial regions. Such a body type provides more surface area in relation to body mass and thus may facilitate the dissipation of body heat.

This Inuit father and son illustrate Allen's rule. Both have relatively large bodies and short limbs, which help them maintain body heat in the cold climate they inhabit.

Human skin color varies dramatically, and Gloger's rule explains this variation as an adaptation to climate. In humans, the intensity of sunlight is a key factor in skin color variation.

genes under different conditions of cold or heat. Some of the variations may be acclimatizations induced during the life span of individuals.[7] Alphonse Riesenfeld provided experimental evidence that extreme cold can affect body proportions during growth and development. Rats raised under conditions of extreme cold generally showed changes that resemble characteristics of humans in cold environments. These cold-related changes included shortening of the long bones, consistent with Allen's rule.[8]

Like body build, facial structure may also be affected by environment. Riesenfeld found experimentally that the facial width of rats increased in cold temperatures and their nasal openings grew smaller.[9] Because the rats raised in cold environments were genetically similar to those raised in warmer environments, we can confidently conclude that the environment, not genes, brought about these changes in the rats. How much the environment directly affects variation in the human face is not clear. We do know that variation in climate is associated with facial variation. For example, people living in the humid tropics tend to have broad, short, flat noses, whereas people living in climates with low humidity (with cold or hot temperatures) tend to have long, thin noses. A narrow nose may be a more efficient humidifier of drier air than a broad nose.[10]

Skin Color

Human populations obviously differ in average skin color. Many people consider skin color the most important indicator of "race," and they sometimes treat others differently solely on this basis. But anthropologists, in addition to being critical of prejudice, also note that skin color is not a good indicator of ancestry. For example, dark skin is commonly found in sub-Saharan Africa. However, natives of southern India have skin as dark or darker than that of many Africans. Yet, these people are not closely related to Africans, either genetically or historically.

How can we explain the wide range of skin colors among the peoples of the world? The color of a person's skin depends on both the amount of dark pigment, or melanin, in the skin and the amount of blood in the small blood vessels of the skin.[11] Despite the fact that there is still much to understand about the genetics of skin color, we can explain much of the variation.

The amount of melanin in the skin seems to be related to the climate in which a person lives. **Gloger's rule** states that populations of birds and mammals living in warmer climates have more melanin and, therefore, darker skin, fur, or feathers, than do populations of the same species living in cooler areas. On the whole, this association with climate holds true for people as well as for other mammals and birds.

The populations of darker-skinned humans do live mostly in warm climates, particularly sunny climates (see Figure 5–2). Dark pigmentation seems to have at least one specific advantage in sunny climates. Melanin protects the sensitive inner layers of the skin from the sun's damaging ultraviolet rays; therefore, dark-skinned people living in sunny areas are safer from sunburn and skin cancers than are light-skinned people. Dark skin may also confer other important biological advantages in tropical environments, such as greater resistance to tropical diseases.[12]

What, then, might be the advantages of light-colored skin? Presumably, there must be some benefits in some environments; otherwise, all human populations would tend to have relatively dark skin. Although light-skinned people are more susceptible to sunburn and skin cancers, the ultraviolet radiation that light skin absorbs also facilitates the body's production of vitamin D. Vitamin D helps the body incorporate calcium and thus is necessary for the proper growth and maintenance of bones. Too much vitamin D,

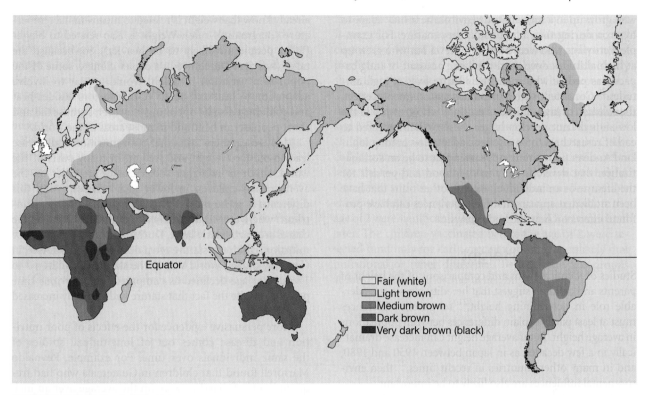

FIGURE 5–2 Variation in Skin Color

Source: From Robins 1991.

however, can cause illness. Thus, the light-colored skin of people in temperate latitudes maximizes ultraviolet penetration, perhaps ensuring production of sufficient amounts of vitamin D for good health, whereas the darker skin of people in tropical latitudes minimizes ultraviolet penetration, perhaps preventing illness from too much vitamin D.[13] Light skin may also confer another advantage in colder environments: It is less likely to be damaged by frostbite.[14]

We now have direct evidence that confirms the connection between solar radiation and skin pigmentation. Anthropologists Nina Jablonski and George Chaplin used data from NASA satellites to determine the average amount of ultraviolet radiation people were exposed to in different parts of the world. They compared these average radiation amounts to data on skin reflectance (the lighter one's skin, the more light it reflects) and found that dark skin is more prevalent where ultraviolet radiation is more intense. Interestingly, there seems to be one notable exception—Native Americans tend to be lighter-skinned than expected. Jablonski and Chaplin suggest that this is because they are recent migrants to the New World, and their skin colors have not adapted to the varying levels of ultraviolet radiation they encountered in the Americas, just as the skin colors of European colonizers have not.[15]

Adaptation to High Altitude

Oxygen constitutes 21 percent of the air we breathe at sea level. At high altitudes, the percentage of oxygen in the air is the same, but because the barometric pressure is lower, we take in less oxygen with each breath.[16] We breathe more rapidly, our hearts beat faster, and all activity is more

difficult. The net effects are discomfort and a condition known as **hypoxia,** or oxygen deficiency.

If high altitude presents such difficulties for many human beings, how is it that populations numbering in the millions can live out their lives, healthy and productive, at altitudes of 6,000, 12,000, or even 17,000 feet? Populations in the Himalayas and the Andes have adapted to their environments and do not display the symptoms that low-altitude dwellers suffer when they are exposed to high altitudes. Moreover, high-altitude dwellers have come to terms physiologically with extreme cold, deficient nutrition, strong winds, rough countryside, and intense solar radiation.[17]

Early studies of Andean high-altitude dwellers found that they differed in certain physical ways from low-altitude dwellers. Compared with low-altitude dwellers, high-altitude Andean Indians had larger chests and greater lung capacity, as well as more surface area in the capillaries of the lungs (which was believed to facilitate the transfer of oxygen to the blood).[18] Early researchers thought that genetic changes had allowed the Andeans to maximize their ability to take in oxygen at the lower barometric pressure of their high-altitude environment. Recent research, however, has cast some doubt on this conclusion. It appears now that other populations living at high altitudes do not show the Andean pattern of physical differences. In the Himalayas, for example, low-altitude dwellers and high-altitude dwellers do not differ in chest size or lung size, even though both groups show adequate lung functioning.[19]

Thus, current research does not suggest that high-altitude living requires biological adaptations that are purely genetic. In fact, some evidence suggests that humans

As we noted earlier, people have been getting taller in several areas of the world. What accounts for this recent trend toward greater height? Several factors may be involved. Some researchers think that it may be the result of improved nutrition and lower incidence of infectious diseases.[34] But it might also be that infant stress has increased as a result of giving birth in hospitals, which usually separate babies from mothers and also subject the newborns to medical tests, including taking blood. Various kinds of vaccinations have also become more common in infancy.[35]

In short, differences in human size seem to be the result of both adaptations and acclimatizations, with both of these, in turn, affected by cultural factors such as nutrition and stress.

Susceptibility to Infectious Diseases

Certain populations seem to have developed inherited resistances to particular infectious diseases. That is, populations repeatedly decimated by certain diseases in the past now have a high frequency of genetic characteristics that ameliorate the effects of these diseases. As Arno Motulsky pointed out, if there are genes that protect people from dying when they are infected by one of the diseases prevalent in their area, these genes will tend to become more common in succeeding generations.[36]

A field study of the infectious disease myxomatosis in rabbits supports this theory. When the virus responsible for the disease was first introduced into the Australian rabbit population, more than 95 percent of the infected animals died. But among the offspring of animals exposed to successive epidemics of myxomatosis, the percentage of animals that died from the disease decreased from year to year. The more epidemics the animals' ancestors had lived through, the smaller the percentage of current animals that died of the disease. Thus, the data

suggested that the rabbits had developed a genetic resistance to myxomatosis.[37]

Infectious diseases seem to follow a similar pattern among human populations. When tuberculosis first strikes a population that has had no previous contact with it, the disease is usually fatal. But some populations seem to have inherited a resistance to death from tuberculosis. For example, the Ashkenazi Jews in America (those whose ancestors came from central and eastern Europe) are one of several populations whose ancestors survived many years of exposure to tuberculosis in the crowded European ghettos where they had previously lived. Although the rate of tuberculosis infection is identical among American Jews and non-Jews, the rate of tuberculosis mortality is significantly lower among Jews than among non-Jews in the United States.[38] After reviewing other data on this subject, Motulsky thought it likely "that the present relatively high resistance of Western populations to tuberculosis is genetically conditioned through natural selection during long contact with the disease."[39]

We tend to think of measles as a childhood disease that kills virtually no one, and we now have a vaccine against it. But when first introduced into populations, the measles virus can kill large numbers of people. In 1949, the Tupari Indians of Brazil numbered about 200 people. By 1955, two-thirds of the Tupari had died of measles introduced into the tribe by rubber gatherers in the area.[40] Large numbers of people died of measles in epidemics in the Faeroe Islands in 1846, in Hawaii in 1848, in the Fiji Islands in 1874, and among the Canadian Inuit very recently. It is possible that, where mortality rates from measles are low, populations have acquired a genetic resistance to death from this disease.[41]

Why is a population susceptible to a disease in the first place? Epidemiologist Francis Black suggests that lack of genes for resistance is not the whole answer. A high degree of genetic homogeneity in the population may also increase

Permanent settlements and high population densities allow diseases to spread rapidly and produce epidemics. Shown here is Banda Aceh's Peunayong Market in Indonesia. Close contact between chickens and humans in markets like this one provided the opportunity for the deadly H5N1 strain of bird flu to evolve.

susceptibility.[42] A virus grown in one host is preadapted to a genetically similar new host and is therefore likely to be more virulent in the new host. For example, the measles virus adapts to a host individual; when it replicates, the viral forms that the host cannot kill are those most likely to survive and continue replicating. When the virus passes to a new host with similar genes, the preadapted virus is likely to kill the new host. On the other hand, if the next host is very different genetically, the adaptation process starts over again; the virus is not so virulent at first because the host can kill it.

Populations that recently came to an area, and that had a small group of founders (as was probably true for the first Native Americans and the Polynesian seafarers who first settled many islands in the Pacific), tended to have a high degree of genetic homogeneity. Therefore, epidemic diseases introduced by Europeans (such as measles) would be likely to kill many of the natives within the first few years after contact. Up to an estimated 56 million people died in the New World after contact with Europeans, mostly because of introduced diseases such as smallpox and measles. Similarly caused depopulation occurred widely in the Pacific.[43]

Some researchers suggest that nongenetic factors may also partly explain differential resistance to infectious disease. For example, cultural practices may partly explain the epidemics of measles among the Yanomamö Indians of Venezuela and Brazil. The Yanomamö frequently visit other villages, and that, together with the non-isolation of sick individuals, promoted a very rapid spread of the disease. Because many individuals were sick at the same time, there were not enough healthy people to feed and care for the sick; mothers down with measles could not even nurse their babies. Thus, cultural factors may increase exposure to a disease and worsen its effect on a population.[44]

Epidemics of infectious disease may occur only if many people live near each other. Hunter-gatherers, who usually live in small dispersed bands, do not have enough people in and near the community to keep an epidemic going. Without enough people to infect, short-lived microorganisms that cause or carry diseases die out. In contrast, among agriculturalists, there are larger numbers of people in and around the community to whom a disease can spread. Permanent settlements, particularly urban settlements, also are likely to have poor sanitation and contaminated water.[45] Tuberculosis is an example of an infectious disease that, although very old, began to kill large numbers of people only after the emergence of sedentary, larger communities.[46]

Sickle-Cell Anemia

Another biological variation is an abnormality of the red blood cells known as **sickle-cell anemia,** or **sicklemia.** This is a condition in which normal, disk-shaped red blood cells assume a crescent (sickle) shape when deprived of oxygen. The sickle-shaped red blood cells do not move through the body as readily as normal cells, and thus cause more oxygen deficiency and damage to the heart, lungs, brain, and other vital organs. In addition, the red blood cells tend to "die" more rapidly, and the anemia worsens still more.[47]

Sickle-cell anemia is caused by a variant form of the genetic instructions for hemoglobin, the protein that carries oxygen in the red blood cells.[48] Individuals who have sickle-cell anemia have inherited the same allele (Hb^S) from both parents and are therefore homozygous for that gene. Individuals who receive this allele from only one parent are heterozygous; they have one Hb^S allele and one allele for normal hemoglobin (Hb^A). Heterozygotes generally will not show the full-blown symptoms of sickle-cell disease, although a heterozygous individual may have a mild case of anemia in some cases. A heterozygous person has a 50 percent chance of passing on the sickle-cell allele to a child. And if the child later mates with another person who is also a carrier of the sickle-cell allele, the statistical probability is that 25 percent of their children will develop sickle-cell anemia. Without advanced medical care, most individuals with two Hb^S alleles are unlikely to live more than a few years.[49]

Why has the allele for sickle-cell persisted in various populations? If people with sickle-cell anemia do not usually live to reproduce, we would expect a reduction in the frequency of Hb^S to near zero through the process of *normalizing selection.* But the sickle-cell allele occurs fairly often in some parts of the world, particularly in the wet tropical belt of Africa, where frequencies may be between 20 percent and 30 percent, and in Greece, Sicily, and southern India.[50]

Because the sickle-cell gene occurs in these places much more often than expected, researchers in the 1940s and the 1950s began to suspect that heterozygous individuals (who carry one Hb^S allele) might have a reproductive advantage in a malarial environment.[51] If the heterozygotes were more resistant to attacks of malaria than the homozygotes for normal hemoglobin (who get the Hb^A allele from both parents), the heterozygotes would be more likely to survive and reproduce, and therefore the recessive Hb^S allele would persist at a higher-than-expected frequency in the population. This kind of outcome is an example of *balancing selection.*[52]

A number of pieces of evidence support the "malaria theory." First, geographic comparisons show that the sickle-cell allele tends to be found where the incidence of malaria is high (see Figure 5–3). Second, as land in the tropics is opened to yam and rice agriculture, the incidence of the sickle-cell allele also increases. Indeed, recent studies suggest malaria may have evolved alongside agriculture in these regions.[53] The reason seems to be that malaria, carried principally by the *Anopheles gambiae* mosquito, becomes more prevalent as tropical forest gives way to more open land where mosquitoes can thrive in warm, sunlit ponds. Indeed, even among peoples of similar cultural backgrounds, the incidence of the sickle-cell allele increases with greater rainfall and surpluses of water. Third, children who are heterozygous for the sickle-cell trait tend to have fewer malarial parasites in their bodies than do homozygous normal individuals, and they are more likely to survive.[54] The sickling trait does not necessarily keep people from contracting malaria, but it greatly

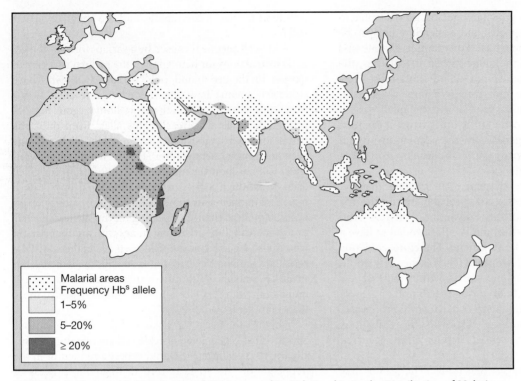

FIGURE 5–3 Geographic Distribution of Sicklemia and Its Relationship to the Distribution of Malaria

decreases the rate of mortality from malaria—and in evolutionary terms, the overall effect is the same.[55] Fourth, if there is no balancing selection because malaria is no longer present, we should find a rapid decline in the incidence of the sickle-cell allele. Indeed, we find such a decline in populations with African ancestry. Those who live in malaria-free zones of the New World have a much lower incidence of sicklemia than do those who live in malarial regions of the New World.[56]

Hb[S] is not the only abnormal hemoglobin to have a distribution related to malaria. It seems that a number of abnormal hemoglobins may be widespread because of the advantage that heterozygotes have against the disease. For example, another abnormal hemoglobin, Hb[E], occurs in populations from India through Southeast Asia and New Guinea where malaria occurs, but Hb[S] is not that common. Why should Hb[E] heterozygotes have resistance to malaria? One possibility is that malarial parasites are less able to survive in an individual's blood with some normal and some abnormal hemoglobin. Abnormal hemoglobin cells are more delicate and live less long, so they may not readily support malarial parasites.[57]

Lactase Deficiency

When American educators discovered that African American schoolchildren very often did not drink milk, they assumed that lack of money or education was the reason. These assumptions provided the impetus for establishing the school milk programs prevalent around the country. However, it now appears that, after infancy, many people lack the enzyme lactase, which is necessary for breaking down the sugar in milk—lactose—into simpler sugars that can be absorbed into the bloodstream.[58] Thus, a person without lactase cannot digest milk properly, and drinking it may cause bloating, cramps, stomach gas, and diarrhea. A study conducted in Baltimore among 312 African American and 221 European American children in grades 1 through 6 in two elementary schools indicated that 85 percent of the African American children and 17 percent of the European American children were milk-intolerant.[59]

More recent studies indicate that lactose intolerance occurs frequently in adults in many parts of the world.[60] The condition is common in Southeast and East Asia, India, the Mediterranean and the Near East, sub-Saharan Africa, and among Native North and South Americans. The widespread incidence of lactose intolerance should not be surprising. After infancy, mammals normally stop producing lactase.[61]

If lactose intolerance in adulthood in mammals is normal, we need to understand why only some human populations have the ability to make lactase in adulthood and digest lactose. Why would selection favor this genetic ability in some populations but not in others? In the late 1960s, F. J. Simoons and Robert McCracken noted a relationship between lactose absorption and dairying (raising cows for milk). They suggested that, with the advent of dairying, individuals with the genetic ability to produce lactase in adulthood would have greater reproductive success; hence, dairying populations would come to have a high proportion of individuals with the ability to break down lactose.[62]

(Top) Milking a cow in Barnstable, Massachusetts. Natural selection may favor production of the enzyme lactase, a genetic way of making milk digestible in dairying populations far from the equator. (Bottom) A Masai woman milking a cow in Kenya. Natural selection may favor the souring of milk, a cultural way of making it digestible in dairying populations close to the equator.

But people in some dairying societies do not produce lactase in adulthood. Rather, they seem to have developed a cultural solution to the problem of lactase deficiency; they transform their milk into cheese, yogurt, sour cream, and other milk products that are low in lactose. To make these low-lactose products, people separate the lactose-rich whey from the curds or treat the milk with a bacterium (*Lactobacillus*) that breaks down the lactose, thus making the milk product digestible by a lactase-deficient person.[63]

So, why did natural selection favor a biological solution (the production of the enzyme lactase in adulthood) in some dairying societies rather than the cultural solution? William Durham has collected evidence that natural selection may favor the biological solution in dairying societies farther from the equator. The theory is that lactose behaves biochemically like vitamin D, facilitating the absorption of calcium—but only in people who produce lactase so that they can absorb the lactose. Because people

in more temperate latitudes are not exposed to that much sunlight, particularly in the winter, and therefore make less vitamin D in their skin, natural selection may have favored the lactase way of absorbing dietary calcium.[64] In other words, natural selection may favor lactase production in adulthood, as well as lighter skin, at higher latitudes (where there is less sunlight).

This is an example of how culture may influence the way natural selection favors some genes over others. Without dairying, natural selection may not have favored the genetic propensity to produce lactase. This propensity is yet another example of the complex ways in which genes, environment, and culture interact to create human variation.

RACE AND RACISM

Fortunately, internal variations such as lactase deficiency have never been associated with intergroup tensions—perhaps because such differences are not immediately obvious. Unfortunately, the same cannot be said for some of the more obvious external human differences such as skin color.

For as long as any of us can remember, countless aggressive actions—from fistfights to large-scale riots and civil wars—have stemmed from tensions and misunderstandings between various groups commonly referred to by many as "races." *Race* has become such a common term that most of us take the concept for granted, not bothering to consider what it does and does not mean. We may talk about the "human race," which means that all humans belong to the same breeding population. Yet we are often asked to check a box to identify our particular "race." We discuss first how biologists sometimes use the term *race*; then we turn to why most biological anthropologists now conclude that the concept of race does not apply usefully to humans. We discuss how racial classifications are largely social constructions that have been used to justify discrimination, exploitation, and even the extermination of certain categories of people.

Race as a Construct in Biology

Biological variation is not uniformly distributed in any species. Although all members of a species can potentially interbreed with others, most matings take place within smaller groups or breeding populations. Through the processes of natural selection and genetic drift, populations inhabiting different geographic regions will come to exhibit some differences in biological traits. When differences within a species become sufficiently noticeable, biologists may classify different populations into different *varieties,* or *races.* If the term **race** is understood to be just a shorthand or classificatory way that biologists describe slight population variants within a species, the concept of race would probably not be controversial. Unfortunately, as applied to humans, racial classifications have often been confounded with **racism,** the belief that some "races" are innately inferior to others.

applied anthropology

The Use of Race in Forensic Anthropology

In this chapter, we have made the point that human "races" are not valid biological entities. There is more genetic variation within alleged "races" than between them, and the characteristics used to define "races" are primarily visual—skin color, hair form, eye form, and the like. Most anthropologists (over 70 percent according to a recent survey) disagree with the statement "There are biological races in the species *Homo sapiens*." Given this fact, it seems odd that many forensic anthropologists still employ "race" as one of the categories for identifying skeletal remains.

Diana Smay and George Armelagos argue that forensic anthropologists still employ the concept of "race" for three primary reasons. First, they suggest that some forensic anthropologists genuinely believe that "race" is a useful analytical tool. For these anthropologists, the fact that it is easy for anyone to categorize others into "races" must mean something is genuine about the concept. Indeed, some forensic anthropologists suggest that they can determine "race" with 80 percent accuracy from skeletal remains (although others argue that, without

clear information about the specific geographical location where the remains were found, accuracy drops to less than 20 percent). This leads to a second reason (according to Smay and Armelagos) that may lead forensic anthropologists to employ the "race" concept—it works for them. Within local areas, at least, a well-trained forensic anthropologist can determine whether a skeleton comes from one of the major "race" groups. But as forensic anthropologist Madeleine Hinkes explains: "sometimes it is only the anthropologist's experience that tells him there is an undefinable 'something' about the skeleton that suggests one race over another"—not a very convincing argument for the analytical utility of "race."

A third reason Smay and Armelagos give for why many forensic anthropologists continue to employ the concept of "race" is that they asked to do so. As Stanley Rhine points out, "The forensic anthropologist who can tell officials that an unknown skull is, for instance, Hispanic, provides a datum useful in narrowing search parameters. By contrast, the forensic anthropologist who delivers a

philosophical lecture to the sheriff on the non-existence of human races is unlikely to be consulted again." But is this a good reason to employ the concept of "race"? Might there be a better way to provide information to police and other officials to help them identify a set of human remains? Alice Brues thinks so. She argues that forensic anthropologists should focus on local, geographic variations among populations that we know do exist and avoid the large "race" categories that we know do not. In Alaska, for example, forensic anthropologists might be able to distinguish between Inuit and Aleut remains, or between Chinese, Japanese, and Polynesian in California. Brues argues that, by lumping the real variation that is present in these local populations into predefined "racial" categories, forensic anthropologists limit their ability to use the full range of variation to identify unique, local variations that might be useful in identifying human remains.

Sources: Brues 1992; Hinkes 1993, 51; Lieberman et al. 2003; Rhine 1993, 55; Smay and Armelagos 2000.

The misuse and misunderstanding of the term *race* and its association with racist thinking is one reason why many biological anthropologists and others have suggested that the term should not be applied to human biological differences.

A second reason for not applying racial classification to humans is that humans have exhibited so much interbreeding that different populations are not clearly classifiable into discrete groups that can be defined in terms of the presence or absence of particular biological traits.[65] Therefore, many argue that "race" is not scientifically useful for describing human biological variation. The difficulty in employing racial classification is evident by comparing the number of "races" that classifiers come up with. The number of "racial" categories in humans has varied from as few as 3 to more than 37.[66]

How can human groups be clearly divided into "races" if most adaptive biological traits show clines or gradual differences from one region to another?[67] Skin color is a

good example of clinal variation. In the area around Egypt, there is a gradient of skin color as one moves from north to south in the Nile Valley. Skin generally becomes darker closer to the equator (south) and lighter closer to the Mediterranean. But other adaptive traits may not have north-south clines, because the environmental predictors may be distributed differently. Nose shape varies with humidity, but clines in humidity do not particularly correspond to variation in latitude. So the gradient for skin color would not be the same as the gradient for nose shape. Because adaptive traits tend to be clinally distributed, there is no line you could draw on a world map that would separate "white" from "black" people or "whites" from "Asians."[68] Only traits that are neutral in terms of natural selection will tend (because of genetic drift) to cluster in regions.[69]

Racial classification is problematic also because there is sometimes more physical, physiological, and genetic diversity *within* a single geographic group that might be called a "race" (e.g., Africans) than there is *between* supposed "racial" groups. Africans vary more among themselves than they do in comparison with people elsewhere.[70] Analyses of all human populations have demonstrated that between 93 percent and 95 percent of genetic variation is due to individual differences within populations, whereas only 3 percent to 5 percent of genetic variation is due to differences between major human population groups.[71] "Race," when applied to humans, is a social category, not a scientific one.

Race and Civilization

Many people hold the racist viewpoint that the biological inferiority of certain groups, which they call "races," is reflected in the supposedly "primitive" quality of their cultures. They will argue that the "developed" nations are "white" and the "underdeveloped" nations are not. (We put terms like "white," which are used as racial categories, in quotes to indicate the problematic nature of the categories.) But to make such an argument ignores much of history. Many of today's so-called underdeveloped nations—primarily in Asia, Africa, and South America—had developed complex and sophisticated civilizations long before European nations expanded and acquired considerable power. The advanced societies of the Shang dynasty in China, the Mayans in Mesoamerica, and the

African empire of Ghana were all founded and developed by "nonwhites."

Between 1523 and 1028 B.C., China had a complex form of government, armies, metal tools and weapons, and production and storage facilities for large quantities of grain. The early Chinese civilization also had writing and elaborate religious rituals.[72] From A.D. 300 to 900, the Mayans were a large population with a thriving economy. They built many large and beautiful cities in which were centered great pyramids and luxurious palaces.[73] According to legend, the West African civilization of Ghana was founded during the 2nd century A.D. By A.D. 770, the time of the Sonniki rulers, Ghana had developed two capital cities—one Muslim and the other non-Muslim—each with its own ruler and both supported largely by Ghana's lucrative gold market.[74]

Considering how recently northern Europeans developed cities and central governments, it seems odd that some "whites" should label Africans, Native Americans, and others backward in terms of historical achievement, or biologically inferior in terms of capacity for civilization. But racists, both "white" and "nonwhite," choose to ignore the fact that many populations have achieved remarkable advances in civilization. Most significant, racists refuse to believe that they can acknowledge the achievements of another group without in any way downgrading the achievements of their own.

African metal workers created magnificent works of art like this golden head from Ghana long before Europeans arrived.

Race, Conquest, and the Role of Infectious Disease

There are those who would argue that Europeans' superiority accounted for their ability to colonize much of the world during the last few hundred years. But it now appears that Europeans were able to dominate at least partly because many native peoples were susceptible to diseases they introduced.[75] Earlier, we discussed how continued exposure to epidemics of infectious diseases, such as tuberculosis and measles, can cause succeeding generations to acquire a genetic resistance to death from such diseases. Smallpox had a long history in Europe and Africa; genetic resistance eventually made it mostly a survivable childhood disease. But in the New World, it was quite another story. Cortez and the conquistadores were inadvertently aided by smallpox in their attempt to defeat the Aztecs of Mexico. In 1520, a member of Cortez's army unwittingly transmitted smallpox to the natives. The disease spread rapidly, killing at least 50 percent of the population, and so the Aztecs were at a considerable disadvantage in their battling with the Spanish.[76]

Outbreaks of smallpox repeatedly decimated many Native American populations in North America a century or two later. In the early 19th century, the Massachusett and Narragansett Indians, with populations of 30,000 and 9,000, respectively, were reduced by smallpox to a few hundred members. Extremely high mortality rates were also noted among the Crow, the Blackfoot, and other

The conquest of the Aztecs was aided by smallpox contracted from the Spanish, which killed at least half the population.

Native American groups during the 19th century. The germ theory alone may not completely explain these epidemics; Europeans may have deliberately encouraged the spread of one new disease, smallpox, by purposely distributing infected blankets to the natives. Motulsky calls the spread of smallpox "one of the first examples of biological warfare."[77]

Race and Behavior

As an outgrowth of earlier attempts to show that inferior "races" have "primitive" cultures, some scholars have attempted to demonstrate behavioral differences between "races." One of the most active has been psychologist J. Philippe Rushton, whose 1995 book *Race, Evolution, and Behavior* purports to demonstrate behavioral differences between the "Negroid," "Caucasoid," and "Mongoloid" "races" in terms of sexual practices, parenting, social deviance, and family structure, among others.

Rushton argues that these behaviors have a genetic basis rooted in adaptations to particular environments. He suggests that "Negroids" are adapted to the warm environments of East Africa, where humans first evolved, through a reproductive strategy in which individuals have many offspring but put little energy into their children's upbringing and care. This strategy is known in evolutionary theory as *r-selected,* and is well documented among creatures such as fish, reptiles, and even some mammals (rabbits, for example).[78] Rushton further suggests that, as humans left Africa they adapted to the "colder" climates of Asia by adopting a more *K-selected* reproductive strategy, which involves having few offspring but putting lots of energy into their upbringing and care. K-selected strategies are also well documented in the animal world, and it is interesting to note that apes (and humans) are often presented as examples of highly K-selected species.[79]

The data Rushton uses to support his argument come almost entirely from modern nations, many with a history of racial discrimination (such as South Africa, Japan, and the United States). But if genetic differences in behavior do exist among these three "races," differences that have their origins in the exodus of modern humans from Africa more than 100,000 years ago, then those differences should be apparent both between and among all the cultures of the world. That is, "Negroid" cultures should all share behaviors that are clearly different from those of "Caucasoid" cultures; "Caucasoid" cultures should all share behaviors that are different from those of "Mongoloid" cultures; and so on. Do such differences exist?

The authors of this text used information about the 186 cultures composing the Standard Cross-Cultural Sample to test whether Rushton's ideas hold up.[80] We examined 26 separate behaviors that Rushton predicted would differ among the "races." Contrary to Rushton's predictions, most of the behaviors showed no differences between the supposed "racial" groups. Only one of them showed the differences that Rushton predicted, and five of them demonstrated a pattern that was the *opposite* of what Rushton predicted. So Rushton's gross division of humans into three "races" does not generally predict variation in human behavior. His ideas appear plainly wrong and do not support the belief that it is scientifically useful to distinguish human "races."[81]

Race and Intelligence

Attempts to document differences in intelligence among the so-called races have a fairly long history. In the 19th century, European white supremacists tried to find scientific justification for what they felt was the genetically inherited mental inferiority of "blacks." They did this by measuring skulls. It was believed that the larger the skull, the greater the cranial capacity and the bigger (hence, also better) the brain. Although the skull-measuring mania quickly disappeared and is no longer considered seriously as a way to measure intelligence, other "facts" may be used to demonstrate the presumed intellectual superiority of "white" people—namely, statistics from intelligence tests.

The first large-scale intelligence testing in the United States began with the nation's entry into World War I, in 1917. Thousands of draftees were given the so-called alpha and beta IQ tests to determine military assignments. Later, psychologists arranged the test results according to the "racial" categories of "white" and "black" and found what they had expected—"blacks" scored consistently lower than "whites." This result was viewed as scientific proof of the innate intellectual inferiority of "blacks" and was used to justify further discrimination against them, both in and out of the army.[82]

Otto Klineberg's subsequent statistical analyses of IQ test results demonstrated that "blacks" from northern states scored higher than "blacks" from the South. Although dedicated racists explained that this difference was due to the northward migration of innately intelligent "blacks," most academics attributed the result to the influence of superior education and more stimulating environments in the North. When further studies showed that northern "blacks" scored higher than southern "whites," the better-education-in-the-North theory gained support, but again racists insisted such results were due to northward migration by more intelligent "whites."

As a further test of his conclusions, Klineberg gave IQ tests to "black" schoolgirls born and partly raised in the South who had spent varying lengths of time in New York City. He found that the longer the girls had been in the North, the higher their average IQ. In addition to providing support for the belief that "blacks" are not inherently inferior to "whites," these findings suggested that cultural factors can and do influence IQ scores, and that IQ is not a fixed quantity.

The controversy about race and intelligence was fueled again in 1969 by Arthur Jensen.[83] He suggested that, although the IQ scores of American "blacks" overlapped considerably with the IQ scores of "whites," the average score for "blacks" was 15 points lower than the average for "whites." IQ scores presumably have a large genetic component, so the lower average score for "blacks" implied to Jensen that "blacks" were genetically inferior to "whites." Jensen's arguments were further developed by Richard Herrnstein and Charles Murray in their 1994 book, *The Bell Curve*. Herrnstein and Murray purported to show that the intelligence of an individual was largely inherited and unchangeable throughout the life span, that an individual's success was largely based on intelligence, and that African Americans were likely to remain at the bottom of society because they had less intelligence than European Americans.[84] Herrnstein and Murray appealed to a lot of studies to buttress their argument. But their argument was still faulty.

If you look at the average scores on many standard intelligence tests, you might conclude, as racists have, that African Americans are less intelligent than European Americans. The averages are different between the two groups; African Americans typically have lower scores. But what does this average difference mean? Herrnstein and Murray, like Jensen and others before them, fail to distinguish between a measure, such as a particular IQ test, and what is supposedly being measured, intelligence. If a test only imperfectly measures what it purports to measure, lower average IQ scores merely mean lower scores on that particular IQ test; they do not necessarily reflect lower intelligence.[85] There are many reasons why some smart people might not do well on particular kinds of IQ tests. For example, the way the tests are administered may affect performance, as may lack of familiarity with the format or the experiences and objects referred to. The test might also not measure particular kinds of intelligence such as social "smarts" and creativity.

If African Americans were really less intelligent, more than their average IQ scores would be lower. The whole frequency distribution of their individual scores should also be lower—they should have fewer geniuses and more retarded individuals. That is, the bell-shaped curve showing how their scores are distributed should range lower than the curve for other Americans, and African Americans should also have proportionately fewer scores at the very high end of the scale. But neither expectation is confirmed.[86] Critics have pointed to many other problems with the evidence presented in *The Bell Curve*. But the fundamental problem is the same as with all attempts to use differences in average IQ scores to make judgments about the capability of different groups. IQ tests may not adequately measure what they purport to measure.

First, there is widespread recognition now that IQ tests are probably not accurate measures of "intelligence" because they are probably biased in favor of the subculture of those who construct the tests. That is, many of the questions on the test refer to things that "white," middle-class children are familiar with, thus giving such children an advantage.[87] So far, no one has come up with a "culture-fair," or bias-free, test. There is more agreement that, although the IQ test may not measure "intelligence" well, it may predict scholastic success or how well a child will do in the primarily "white"-oriented school system.[88]

A second major problem with a purely genetic interpretation of the IQ difference is that many studies show that IQ scores can be influenced by the social environment. Economically deprived children, whether "black" or "white," will generally score lower than affluent "white" or "black" children. And training of children with low IQ scores clearly improves their test scores.[89] More dramatic evidence is provided by Sandra Scarr and her colleagues. "Black" children adopted by well-off "white" families have IQ scores above the average for "whites." And those "blacks" with more European ancestry do not have higher IQ scores.[90] So the average difference between "blacks" and "whites" in IQ cannot be attributed to a presumed genetic difference. For all we know, the 15-point average difference may be due completely to differences in environment or to test bias. New studies show very subtle effects of the social environment on test and school performance. Simply reminding "blacks" of their "race" before a test causes them to do worse. The difference on the Graduate Record Exam between "blacks" and "whites" disappeared after President Obama's election. These and other results strongly suggest that the pervasive stereotype of "blacks" not performing as well as "whites" (particularly potent prior to Obama's election) caused worse performance among "blacks."[91]

Geneticist Theodosius Dobzhansky reminded us that conclusions about the causes of different levels of achievement on IQ tests cannot be drawn until all people have equal opportunities to develop their potentials. He stressed the need for an open society operating under the democratic ideal, where all people are given an equal opportunity to develop whatever gifts or aptitudes they possess and choose to develop.[92]

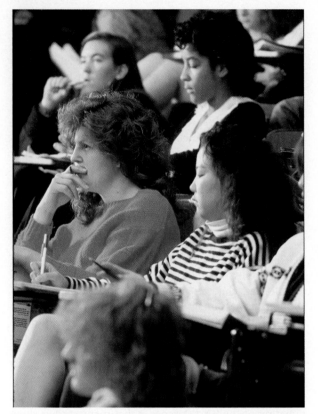

Until all people have an equal education and opportunities to achieve, there is no way we can be sure that some people are smarter than others.

THE FUTURE OF HUMAN VARIATION

Laboratory fertilization, subsequent transplantation of the embryo, and successful birth have been accomplished with humans and nonhumans. *Cloning*—the exact reproduction of an individual from cellular tissue—has been achieved with frogs, sheep, and other animals. *Genetic engineering*—the substitution of some genes for others—is increasingly practiced in nonhuman organisms. And *stem cells*, which can be induced to grow into any tissue type, are in clinical trials for human use. What are the implications of such practices for the genetic future of humans? Will it really be possible someday to control the genetic makeup of our species? If so, will the effects be positive or negative?

It is interesting to speculate on the development of a "perfect human." Aside from the serious ethical question of who would decide what the perfect human should be like, there is the serious biological question of whether such a development might in the long run be detrimental to the human species, for what is perfectly suited to one physical or social environment may be totally unsuited to another. The collection of physical, emotional, and intellectual attributes that might be "perfect" in the early 21st century might be inappropriate in the 22nd century.[93] Even defects such as the sickle-cell trait may confer advantages under certain conditions, as we have seen.

In the long run, the perpetuation of genetic variability is probably more advantageous than the creation of a "perfect" and invariable human being. In the event of dramatic changes in the world environment, absolute uniformity in the human species might be an evolutionary dead end. Such uniformity might lead to the extinction of the human species if new conditions favored genetic or cultural variations that were no longer present in the species. Perhaps our best hope for maximizing our chances of survival is to tolerate, and even encourage, the persistence of many aspects of human variation, both biological and cultural.[94]

SUMMARY ● ○ ○

1. Physical variation—variation in the frequencies of physical traits—from one human population to another is the result of one or more of the following factors: adaptation, acclimatization, and the influence of the social or cultural environment.

2. Some physical variations in human populations involve genetic variation; other variations, including body build, facial construction, and skin color, may be adapted to variation in climate. Still other variations, such as the ability to make lactase, may be adapted partially to variation in cultural environment.

3. Most biological anthropologists today agree that "race" is not a useful way of referring to human biological variation because human populations do not unambiguously fall into discrete groups defined by a particular set of biological traits. Physical traits that are adaptive vary clinally, which makes it meaningless to divide humans into discrete "racial" entities. Rather, it is suggested that "racial" classifications are mostly social categories that are presumed to have a biological basis.

4. Perhaps the most controversial aspect of racial discrimination is the relationship supposed between "racial" categories and intelligence. Attempts have been made to show, by IQ tests and other means, the innate intellectual superiority of one "racial" category over another. But there is doubt that IQ tests measure intelligence fairly. Because evidence indicates that IQ scores are influenced by both genes and environment, conclusions about the causes of differences in IQ scores cannot be drawn until all the people being compared have equal opportunities to develop their potentials.

GLOSSARY TERMS ○ ● ○

acclimatization **70**	hypoxia **73**
adaptation **68**	race **79**
Allen's rule **71**	racism **79**
Bergmann's rule **71**	sickle-cell anemia
Gloger's rule **72**	(sicklemia) **77**

CRITICAL QUESTIONS ○ ○ ●

1. Why is skin color used more often than hair or eye color or body proportions in "racial" classifications?
2. If Europeans had been more susceptible to New World and Pacific diseases, would the world be different today?
3. How might studies of natural selection help increase tolerance of other populations?

Read the chapter by C. Loring Brace titled "The Concept of Race in Physical Anthropology" on MyAnthroLab. Answer the following questions:

1. What does Brace mean when he states that "'race' is whatever people think it should be"?
2. How do geographic populations (or clines) differ from biological races?
3. How might the concept of "race" limit our ability to understand human variation?

The Living Primates

The goal of **primatology**, the study of primates, is to understand how different primates have adapted anatomically and behaviorally to their environments. The results of such studies may help us to understand the behavior and evolution of the human primate.

But how can living primates such as chimpanzees tell us anything about humans or the primates that were our ancestors? After all, each living primate species has its own history of evolutionary divergence from the earliest primate forms. All living primates, including humans, evolved from earlier primates that are now extinct. Nonetheless, by observing how humans and other primates differ from and resemble each other, we may be able to infer how and why humans diverged from the other primates.

In conjunction with fossil evidence, anatomical and behavioral comparisons of living primates may help us reconstruct what early primates were like. For example, if we know that modern primates that swing through the trees have a particular kind of shoulder bone structure, we can infer that similar fossil bones probably belonged to an animal that also swung through the trees. Differing adaptations of living primates may also suggest why certain divergences occurred in primate evolution. If we know what traits belong to humans, and to humans alone, this knowledge may suggest why the line of primates that led to humans branched away from the line leading to chimpanzees and gorillas.

In this chapter, we first examine the common features of the living primates. Next we introduce the different animals that belong to the order Primates, focusing on the distinctive characteristics of each major type. Then we discuss the traits that make humans different from all other primates. We close with a look at possible explanations of some of the varying adaptations exhibited by the different primate species. The purpose of this chapter is to help us understand more about humans. Therefore, we emphasize the features of primate anatomy and behavior that perhaps have the greatest bearing on human evolution.

● ○ ●

COMMON PRIMATE TRAITS

All primates belong to the class Mammalia, and they share all the common features of mammals. Except for humans, the bodies of primates are covered with dense hair or fur, which provides insulation. Even humans have hair in various places, though perhaps not always for insulation. Mammals are *warm-blooded*; that is, their body temperature is more or less constantly warm and usually higher than that of the air around them. Almost all mammals give birth to live young that develop to a considerable size within the mother and are nourished by suckling from the mother's mammary glands. The young have a relatively long period of dependence on adults after birth. This period is also a time of learning, for a great deal of adult mammal behavior is learned rather than instinctive. Play is a learning technique common to mammal young and is especially important to primates, as we shall see later in this chapter.

The primates have a number of physical and social traits that set them apart from other mammals.

Physical Features

No one of the primates' physical features is unique to primates; animals from other orders share one or more of the following described characteristics. But the complex of all these physical traits is unique to primates.[1]

Many skeletal features of the primates reflect an **arboreal** (tree-living) existence. All primate hind limbs are structured principally to provide support, but the "feet" in most primates can also grasp things (see Figure 6–1). Some primates—orangutans, for instance—can suspend themselves from their hind limbs. The forelimbs are especially flexible, built to withstand both pushing and pulling forces. Each of the hind limbs and forelimbs has one bone in the upper portion and two bones in the lower portion (with the exception of the tarsier). This feature has changed little since the time of the earliest primate ancestors. It has remained in modern primates (although many other mammals have lost it) because the double bones give great mobility for rotating arms and legs.

Another characteristic structure of primates is the clavicle, or collarbone. The clavicle also gives primates great freedom of movement, allowing them to move the shoulders both up and down and back and forth. Although humans obviously do not use this flexibility for arboreal activity, they do use it for other activities. Without a clavicle, we could not throw a spear or a ball; we could not make any fine tools or turn doorknobs if we did not have rotatable forearms.

Primates generally are **omnivorous;** that is, they eat all kinds of food, including insects and small animals, as well as fruits, seeds, leaves, and roots. The teeth of primates reflect this omnivorous diet. The chewing teeth—the **molars** and **premolars**—are unspecialized, particularly in comparison with those of other groups of animals, such as the grazers. The front teeth—the **incisors** and **canines**—are often very specialized, principally in the lower primates. For example, the slender, tightly packed lower incisors and canines in many prosimians form a "dental comb" that the animals use in grooming or for scraping hardened tree gum (which is a food for them) from tree trunks.[2]

Primate hands are extremely flexible. All primates have prehensile—grasping—hands, which can be wrapped around an object. Primates have five digits on both hands and feet (in some cases, one digit may be reduced to a stub), and their nails, with few exceptions, are broad and flat, not clawlike. This structure allows them to grip

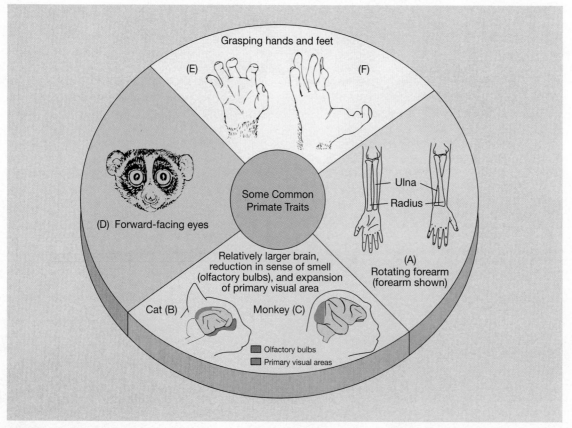

FIGURE 6–1 Some Common Primate Traits

Source: (A) From Wolff 1991, 255. Reprinted with permission of D.C. Heath; (B, C) from Deacon 1992, 110; (D) from Cartmill 1992b, 25; and (E, F) from Cartmill 1992b, 24.

objects; the hairless, sensitive pads on their fingers, toes, heels, and palms also help them to grip. Most primates have **opposable thumbs,** a feature that allows an even more precise and powerful grip.

Vision is very important to primate life. Compared with other mammals, primates have a relatively larger portion of the brain devoted to vision rather than smell. Primates are characterized by stereoscopic, or depth, vision. Their eyes are directed forward rather than sideways, as in other animals—a trait that allows them to focus on an object (insects or other food or a distant branch) with both eyes at once. Most primates also have color vision, perhaps to recognize when plant foods are ready to eat.

Another important primate feature is a large brain relative to body size. That is, primates generally have larger brains than animals of similar size, perhaps because their survival depends on an enormous amount of learning, as we discuss later. In general, animals with large brains seem to mature more slowly and to live longer than animals with small brains.[3] The more slowly an animal matures and the longer it lives, the more it can learn.

Finally, the primate reproductive system sets this order of animals apart from other mammals. Males of most primate species have a pendulous penis that is not attached to the abdomen by skin, a trait shared by a few other animals, including bats and bears. Females of most primate species have two nipples on the chest (a few prosimians have more than two nipples). The uterus is usually constructed to hold a single fetus (only the marmosets and tamarins typically give birth to twins), not a litter, as with most other animals. This reproductive system can be seen as emphasizing quality over quantity—an adaptation possibly related to the dangers of life in the trees, particularly the risk of falls.[4] Primate infants tend to be relatively well developed at birth, although humans, apes, and some monkeys have helpless infants. Most infant primates, except humans, can cling to their mothers from birth. Primates typically take a long time to mature. For example, the rhesus monkey is not sexually mature until about 3 years of age, and the chimpanzee is not until about age 9.

Social Features

For the most part, primates are social animals. Just as physical traits such as grasping hands and stereoscopic vision may have developed as adaptations to the environment, so may have many patterns of social behavior. For most primates, particularly those that are **diurnal**—that is, active during the day—group life may be crucial to survival, as we will see later in this chapter.

Dependency and Development in a Social Context
Social relationships begin with the mother and other adults during the fairly long dependency period of primates. (For the dependency period of primates, the

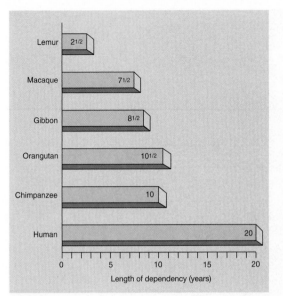

FIGURE 6–2 A Comparison of the Dependency Periods of Primate Offspring

Source: Data from Jolly 1985, 292.

infancy and juvenile phases, see Figure 6–2.) The prolonged dependency of infant monkeys and apes probably offers an evolutionary advantage in that it allows infants more time to observe and learn the complex behaviors essential to survival while enjoying the care and protection of mature adults.

Primates without a warm, social relationship with a mother or another individual do not appear to develop appropriate patterns of social interaction. In a series of classic experiments with rhesus monkeys, Harry Harlow investigated the effects of maternal neglect and isolation on offspring.[5] He found that, as a result of either inadequate mothering or isolation from other infants, some monkeys are unable to lead normal social lives. They develop aberrant sexual activities and may even become juvenile delinquents. Harlow mated socially deprived female monkeys with well-adjusted males. When these females gave birth, their behavior was not at all motherly, and they often rejected their babies entirely. Their abnormal behavior was offered as evidence that mothering is more than instinctive. Harlow's experiments underline the importance of maternal care and attention for monkeys and, as a corollary, for humans.

In many primate groups, the mother is not the only individual providing care to the dependent young. Among gray langur monkeys, the birth and subsequent rearing of a baby absorb the attention of most female members of the troop.[6] And in some primate species, the father may spend as much time caring for infants as the mother.[7]

Primates at Play Harlow's investigations have provided other information about social learning in young primates. The experiments that showed the importance of maternal care to baby rhesus monkeys also revealed that

A baby macaque clings to its (wire-and-cloth) "surrogate mother" during the Harry Harlow experiment. Harlow demonstrated that social interaction was necessary for primates to develop normally.

play is another crucial ingredient of normal development during the dependency period. Just as monkeys raised without mothers showed abnormal behavior as adults, so did monkeys raised with mothers but with no peers to play with. In fact, when some of the monkeys raised without mothers were allowed a regular playtime with peers, many of them behaved more normally. Subsequent work has supported Harlow's findings.[8]

Play is important for learning.[9] It provides practice for the physical skills necessary or useful in adulthood. For example, young monkeys racing through the trees at top speed are gaining coordination that may save their lives if predators chase them later on. Play is also a way of learning social skills, particularly in interacting and communicating with other members of the group. Some dominance relationships seem to be established partly through the rough-and-tumble games that older juveniles play, where winning depends on such factors as size, strength, and agility. These qualities, or the lack of them, may influence an individual's status throughout adult life. (Other factors also help determine an individual's status. For instance, the mother's status has been shown to be very important in some primates.[10])

Learning from Others   We know that primates, nonhuman and human alike, learn many things in social groups. Among humans, children often imitate others, and adults often deliberately teach the young. In English we say, "Isn't it cute how Tommy 'apes' his father?" But do apes (and monkeys) imitate others, or do they just learn to do similar things whether or not observing a model? There is controversy among researchers as to how much imitation versus independent learning occurs in nonhuman primates. Even more arguable is whether deliberate teaching occurs among nonhuman primates.[11]

Some fieldworkers have suggested that chimpanzees may learn by imitation to use tools. For example, Jane Goodall cited an occasion when a female with diarrhea picked up a handful of leaves to wipe her bottom. Her 2-year-old infant watched closely, and then twice picked up leaves to wipe its own, clean behind.[12] Termite "fishing," using a grass stalk to withdraw termites from a termite mound, is probably the best-known example of chimpanzee tool use. Immature chimpanzees in the wild have been observed to watch attentively and pick up stalks while others are "fishing." Mothers also let their infants hold on to the stalks while the mothers "fish." But some observers do not think these reports provide clear evidence of imitation or teaching. Even though the mother lets the infant hold on to the "fishing" stalk, the infant is doing the activity with her, not watching it and then independently repeating it soon after.[13]

CLASSIFICATION OF PRIMATES

Classification provides a useful way to refer to groups of species that are similar in biologically important ways. Sometimes classification schemes vary because the classifiers emphasize somewhat different aspects of similarity and difference. For instance, one type of classification stresses the evolutionary branching that led to the primates of today, another the quantity of shared features. A third approach considers the evolutionary lines as well as similarity and difference of features, but not all features are equally weighted. More "advanced" and specialized features that develop in an evolutionary line are emphasized.[14] Figure 6–3 gives a classification scheme that follows this last approach.[15]

Despite the different ways to classify, there is generally little disagreement about how the various primates should be classified. Most of the disagreement, as we shall see when we discuss the various primates, revolves around the classification of tarsiers and humans.

The order Primates is often divided into two suborders: the *prosimians*—literally, premonkeys—and the *anthropoids*. The prosimians include lemurs, lorises, and tarsiers. The anthropoid suborder includes New World monkeys, Old World monkeys, the lesser apes (gibbons, siamangs), the great apes (orangutans, gorillas, and chimpanzees), and humans.

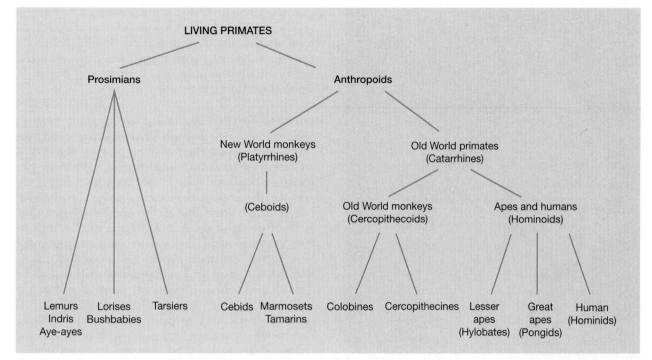

FIGURE 6–3 A Simplified Classification of the Living Primates

THE VARIOUS PRIMATES

Now that we have discussed their common features, let us focus on some of the ways in which the primates living in the world today vary. (The DK map titled "The Living Primates" at the end of the book shows some of the geographic variation among primates. A major division exists between those living in Europe, Asia, and Africa versus those living in the Americas.)

Prosimians

The **prosimians** resemble other mammals more than the anthropoid primates do. For example, the prosimians depend much more on smell for information than do anthropoids. Also in contrast with the anthropoids, they typically have more mobile ears, whiskers, longer snouts, and relatively fixed facial expressions. The prosimians also exhibit many traits shared by all primates, including grasping hands, stereoscopic vision, and enlarged visual centers in the brain.

Lemurlike Forms   Lemurs and their relatives, the indris and the aye-ayes, are found only on two island areas off the southeastern coast of Africa, Madagascar, and the Comoro Islands. These primates range in size from the mouse lemur to the 4-foot-long indri. Members of the lemur group

A ring-tailed lemur mother and its baby holding on. Prosimians such as ring-tailed lemurs depend much more on smell than do anthropoids. Prosimians also have more mobile ears, whiskers, longer snouts, and relatively fixed facial expressions.

The bush baby is a small arboreal prosimian that eats both fruit and insects. It is an energetic nocturnal animal that moves by vertical clinging and leaping.

usually produce single offspring, although twins and even triplets are common in some species. Many of the species in this group are **quadrupeds**—animals that move on all fours; they walk on all fours in the trees as well as on the ground. Some species, such as the indris, use their hind limbs alone to push off from one vertical position to another in a mode of locomotion called **vertical clinging and leaping.** Lemurs are mostly vegetarians, eating fruit, leaves, bark, and flowers. Lemur species vary greatly in their group size. Many lemur species, particularly those that are **nocturnal** (active during the night), are solitary during their active hours. Others are much more social, living in groups ranging in size from a small family to as many as 60 members.[16] An unusual feature of the lemurlike primates is that females often dominate males, particularly over access to food. In most primates, and in most other mammals, female dominance is rarely observed.[17]

Lorislike Forms   Members of the loris group, found in both Southeast Asia and sub-Saharan Africa, are all nocturnal and arboreal. They eat fruit, tree gum, and insects, and usually give birth to single infants.[18] There are two major subfamilies, the lorises and the bush babies (galagos), and they show wide behavioral differences. Bush babies are quick, active animals that hop between branches and tree trunks in the vertical-clinging-and-leaping pattern. On the ground, they often resort to a kangaroo-like hop. Lorises are much slower, walking sedately along branches hand over hand in the quadrupedal fashion.

With the use of searchlights and technical aids such as radio tracking, field researchers have learned a good deal about these nocturnal primates. For example, we know that among bush babies, females, particularly mothers and young adult daughters, stay together in small groups, whereas the males disperse. Newborns are born in nests or hollows of trees (which related females may share), and mothers return to nurse them regularly. A few days after birth, a mother may carry her infant in her mouth to nearby trees, "parking" it while she eats.[19]

Tarsiers   The nocturnal, tree-living tarsiers, found now only on the islands of the Philippines and Indonesia, are the only primates that depend completely on animal foods. They are usually insect eaters, but they sometimes capture and eat other small animals. They are well equipped for night vision, possessing enormous eyes, extraordinary eyesight, and enlarged visual centers in the brain. The tarsiers get their name from their elongated tarsal bones (the bones of the ankle), which give them tremendous leverage for their long jumps. Tarsiers are very skilled at vertical

Nocturnal tree-living tarsiers, like this one in the Philippines, are the only primates that depend completely on animal foods. Their enormous eyes equip them to find insects and other prey in the night. Their elongated anklebones (tarsals) make them very good at vertical clinging and leaping.

clinging and leaping. They live in family groups composed of a mated pair and their offspring. Like some higher primates, male and female tarsiers sing together each evening to advertise their territories.[20]

The classification of tarsiers is somewhat controversial. Instead of placing them with the suborder prosimians, as we have done here, some classifiers group tarsiers with anthropoids. In this other classification scheme, the suborders of primates are labeled *strepsirhines* (which includes lemurs and lorises) and *haplorhines* (which includes tarsiers and anthropoids). Tarsiers have chromosomes similar to those of other prosimians; they also have claws for grooming on some of their toes, more than two nipples, and a uterus shaped like that of other prosimians (two-horned). Like bush babies, tarsiers move about through vertical clinging and leaping. In other respects, tarsiers are more like the anthropoids. They have a reduced dependence on smell; not only are their noses smaller, but they lack the wet, doglike snout of lemurs. In common with the anthropoids, their eyes are closer together and are protected by bony orbits. Reproductively, the tarsier, like anthropoids, has a placenta that allows contact between the mother's blood and that of the fetus.[21]

Anthropoids

The anthropoid suborder includes humans, apes, and monkeys. Most **anthropoids** share several traits in varying degrees. They have rounded braincases; reduced, nonmobile outer ears; and relatively small, flat faces instead of muzzles. They have highly efficient reproductive systems. They also have highly dextrous hands.[22] The anthropoid order is divided into two main groups: **platyrrhines** and **catarrhines** (see Figure 6–4). These groups take their names from the nose shape of the different anthropoids, but they differ in other features as well, as we shall see. Platyrrhines have broad, flat-bridged noses, with nostrils facing outward; these monkeys are found only in the New World, in Central and South America. Catarrhines have narrow noses with nostrils facing downward. Catarrhines include monkeys of the Old World (Africa, Asia, and Europe), as well as apes and humans.

New World Monkeys Besides the shape of the nose and the position of the nostrils, other anatomical features distinguish the New World monkeys (platyrrhines) from the catarrhine anthropoids. The New World species have three premolars, whereas the Old World species have two. Some New World monkeys have a **prehensile** (grasping) tail; no Old World monkeys do. All the New World monkeys are completely arboreal; they vary a lot in the size of their groups; and their food ranges from insects to nectar and sap to fruits and leaves.[23]

Two main families of New World monkeys have traditionally been defined. One family, the *callitrichids,* contains marmosets and tamarins; the other family, the *cebids,* contains all the other New World monkeys. Although scholars recognize some problems with this division, it is a

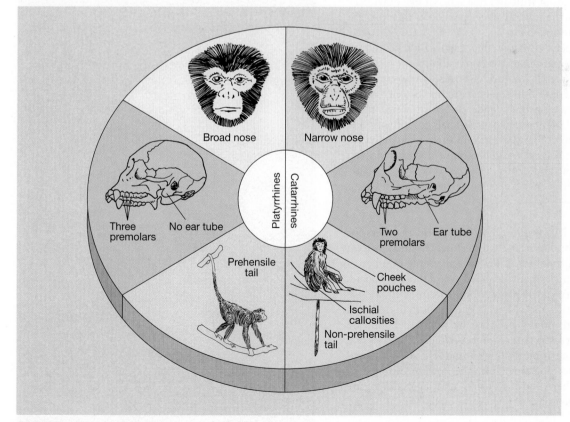

FIGURE 6–4 Features of Platyrrhines and Catarrhines

Source: Boaz and Almquist 1999.

The squirrel monkey, like all platyrrhines, almost never leaves the trees. It is well suited to an arboreal lifestyle; note how it uses both hands and feet to grasp branches.

useful one for gaining a basic understanding of the New World monkeys. The callitrichids are very small, have claws instead of fingernails, and give birth to twins who mature in about two years. Perhaps because twinning is so common and the infants have to be carried, callitrichid mothers cannot take care of them alone. Fathers and older siblings have often been observed carrying infants. Indeed, males may do more carrying than females. Callitrichid groups may contain a mated pair (monogamy) or a female mated to more than one male (polyandry). The callitrichids eat a lot of fruit and tree sap, but like other very small primates, they obtain a large portion of their protein requirements from insects.[24]

Cebids are generally larger than callitrichids, take about twice as long to mature, and tend to bear only one offspring at a time.[25] The cebids vary widely in size, group composition, and diet. For example, squirrel monkeys weigh about 2 pounds, whereas woolly spider monkeys weigh more than 16 pounds. Some cebids have small groups with one male-female pair; others have groups of up to 50 individuals. Some of the smallest cebids have a diet of leaves, insects, flowers, and fruits, whereas others are mostly fruit eaters with lesser dependence on seeds, leaves, or insects.[26]

Old World Monkeys   The Old World monkeys, or **cercopithecoids,** are related more closely to humans than to New World monkeys. They have the same number of teeth as apes and humans. The Old World monkey species are not as diverse as their New World cousins, but they live in a greater variety of habitats. Some live both in trees and on the ground; others, such as the gelada baboon, are completely **terrestrial,** or ground-living. Macaques are found both in tropical jungles and on snow-covered mountains, and they range from the Rock of Gibraltar to Africa to northern India, Pakistan, and Japan. There are two major subfamilies of Old World monkeys.

Colobine Monkeys   The colobine group includes Asian langurs, the African colobus monkeys, and several other species. These monkeys live mostly in trees, and their diet consists principally of leaves and seeds. Their digestive tracts are equipped to obtain maximum nutrition from a high-cellulose diet; they have pouched stomachs, which provide a large surface area for breaking down plant food, and very large intestinal tracts.

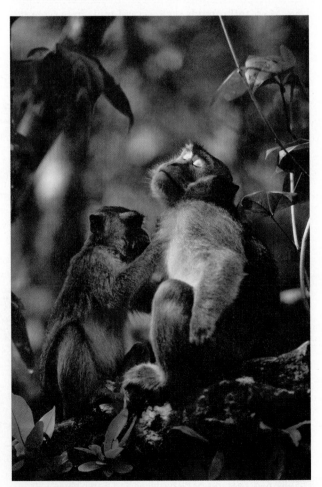

Grooming is an important activity among Old World primates. Here two macaques groom one another.

This langur, like all catarrhines, has a relatively narrow nose with nostrils that point downward. Langurs are Asian members of the colobine family and are primarily leaf eaters.

One of the most noticeable features of colobines is the flamboyant color typical of newborns. For example, in one species, dusky gray mothers give birth to brilliant orange babies.[27] Observational studies suggest that the colobines are also unusual among the primates (except for humans) in that mothers let other group members take care of their infants shortly after birth. But males who are not members of the group are dangerous for infants; males trying to enter and take over a group have been observed to kill infants. Although this description may suggest that a one-male group is the typical group structure, there does not appear to be a typical pattern for a given species. When more than one site of a species has been studied, both one-male and multiple-male groups have been found.[28]

Cercopithecine Monkeys The cercopithecine subfamily of monkeys includes more terrestrial species than any other subfamily of Old World monkeys. Many of these species are characterized by a great deal of **sexual dimorphism** (the sexes look very different); the males are larger, have longer canines, and are more aggressive than the females. Cercopithecines depend more on fruit than do colobines. They are also more capable of surviving in arid and seasonal environments.[29] Pouches inside the cheeks allow cercopithecines to store food for later eating and digestion. An unusual physical feature of these monkeys is the ischial callosities, or callouses, on their bottoms—an adaptation that enables them to sit comfortably in trees or on the ground for long periods of time.[30]

Studies of baboons and macaques suggest that closely related females form the core of a local group, or troop. In large groups, which are common among rhesus monkeys, many social behaviors seem to be determined by degree of biological relatedness. For example, an individual is most likely to sit next to, groom, or help an individual

A troop of baboons in Ethiopia spends most of its time on the ground.

need greater memory and brain capacity because their foods ripen at different times and in separate places that have to be remembered to be found.[79] The brain requires large supplies of oxygen and glucose. Because leaf-eating primates do not have as much glucose in their diets as fruit-eating primates, they may also not have the energy reserves to support relatively large brains.[80]

Group Size

Primate groups vary in size from solitary males and females with young (orangutans) to a few individuals and young (e.g., gibbons) to 100 or more individuals in some Old World monkey troops.[81] What factors might account for such variation?

Nocturnal activity is an important predictor not only of small body size but also of small group size. Nocturnal primates feed either alone or in pairs.[82] John Terborgh has noted that most nocturnal predators hunt by sound, so a nocturnal animal might best avoid attack by being silent.[83] Groups are noisy, and therefore nocturnal animals might be more likely to survive by living alone or in pairs.

On the other hand, a large group might provide advantages in the daytime. The more eyes, ears, and noses a group has, the more quickly a would-be predator might be detected—and perhaps avoided. Also, a larger group would have more teeth and strength to frighten or mob a predator that actually attacked.[84] But this line of reasoning would lead us to expect that all diurnal terrestrial species would have large groups. Yet, not all do. Other factors must be operating. One seems to be the amount and density of food. If food resources occur in small amounts and in separate places, only small groups can get enough to eat; but if food occurs in large patches, there will be enough to support large groups.[85] An additional factor may be competition over resources. One suggestion is that substantial but separated patches of resources are likely to be fought over, and therefore individuals living in larger groups might be more likely to obtain access to them.[86]

Having examined our distinctive traits, those traits we share with other primates, and some of the possible ways primates might have adapted to different environments, we need to ask what selective forces may have favored the emergence of primates, what forces may have favored the line of divergence leading to the first hominids, and what forces led to the emergence of the genus *Homo*. These questions are the subjects of the next several chapters.

SUMMARY ● ○ ○

1. Although no living primate can be a direct ancestor of humans, we do share a common evolutionary history with the other surviving primates. Studying the behavioral and anatomical features of our closest living relatives may help us make inferences about primate evolution. Studying distinctive human traits may help us understand why the line of primates that led to humans branched away from the line leading to chimpanzees and gorillas.

2. No one trait is unique to primates. However, primates do share the following features: two bones in the lower part of the leg and in the forearm, a collarbone, flexible prehensile (grasping) hands, stereoscopic vision, a relatively large brain, only one (or sometimes two) offspring at a time, long maturation of the young, and a high degree of dependence on social life and learning.

3. The order Primates is divided into two suborders: the prosimians and the anthropoids. Compared with the anthropoids, prosimians depend more on smell for information. They have mobile ears, whiskers, longer snouts typically, and relatively fixed facial expressions. Anthropoids have rounded braincases; reduced, nonmobile outer ears; and relatively small, flat faces instead of muzzles. They have highly dextrous hands.

4. The Anthropoid order is divided into two main groups: platyrrhines (monkeys of the New World) and catarrhines. The catarrhines are subdivided into cercopithecoids (Old World monkeys) and hominoids (apes and humans). The anthropoid apes consist of the hylobates, or lesser apes (gibbons and siamangs), and the pongids, or great apes (orangutans, gorillas, and chimpanzees).

5. Along with the gorilla, the chimpanzee has proteins and DNA remarkably similar to those of humans, as well as anatomical and behavioral similarities to humans. Wild chimpanzees have been seen to create and use tools, modifying a natural object to fulfill a specific purpose. High conceptual ability is also demonstrated by both the chimpanzee's and the gorilla's facility in learning sign language.

6. The differences between hominids and the other anthropoids show us what makes humans distinctive as a species. Hominids are totally bipedal; they walk on two legs and do not need the arms for locomotion. The hominid brain, particularly the cerebral cortex, is the largest and most complex. In contrast to females of almost all other primates, hominid females may engage in sexual intercourse at any time throughout the year. Hominid offspring have a proportionately longer dependency stage. And in comparison with other primates, more hominid behavior is learned and culturally patterned. Spoken, symbolic language and the use of tools to make other tools are uniquely modern human behavioral traits. Hominids also generally have a division of labor in food-getting and food-sharing in adulthood.

7. Variable aspects of the environment, differences in activity patterns, and variation in diet may explain many of the traits that vary in the primates. Nocturnal primates tend to be small and to live alone or in very small groups. Among diurnal species, the arboreal primates tend to be smaller and to live in smaller social groups than terrestrial primates. Fruit eaters have relatively larger brains than leaf eaters.

GLOSSARY TERMS ○ ● ○

anthropoids   93
arboreal   88
bilophodont   96
bipedalism   100
brachiators   97
canines   88
catarrhines   93
cercopithecoids   94
cerebral cortex   100
diastema   96
diurnal   89
hominids   96
hominoids   96
hylobates   96
incisors   88
knuckle walking   98

molars   88
nocturnal   92
omnivorous   88
opposable thumb   89
platyrrhines   93
pongids   96
prehensile   93
premolars   88
primatology   86
prosimians   91
quadrupeds   92
sexual dimorphism   95
terrestrial   94
vertical clinging and
   leaping   92
"Y-5" pattern   96

CRITICAL QUESTIONS ○ ○ ●

1. How could you infer that a fossil primate lived in the trees?
2. Under what conditions would the ability to communicate be adaptive?
3. Why are humans immature for so long?

PEARSON
myanthrolab

Read the chapter by Craig B. Stanford titled "Chimpanzee Hunting Behavior and Human Evolution" on MyAnthroLab. Answer the following questions:

1. How might the study of chimpanzee behavior, and particularly hunting behavior, benefit our understanding of early hominid behavior and of human evolution in general?
2. For many years chimpanzees were thought to be vegetarians. Why did it take so long for chimpanzee hunting to be identified and studied?
3. What do you think is the best answer to the question "Why do chimpanzees hunt"?

chapter 7

Primate Evolution: From Early Primates to Hominoids

Primate paleontologists and paleoanthropologists focus on various questions about primate evolution. How far back in time did the primates emerge? What did they look like? What conditions favored them? How did the early primates diverge after that point? What kinds of niches did the different primates occupy? Although our concern as anthropologists is largely with the emergence of humans, and with the primates that are in the ancestral line leading to humans, we must remember that evolution does not proceed with a purpose or to give rise to any particular species; rather, organisms adapt, or fail to adapt, to the environments in which they find themselves. Thus, the primate fossil record is full of diversity; it is also full of apparent extinctions. Probably most of the primate lineages of the past never left any descendants at all.[1]

● ○ ●

Although much of primate evolution is not yet known or is still controversial, we do know a lot. We know that, as of the early Eocene epoch, which began about 55 million years ago, primates with some of the features of modern prosimians had already emerged. Primates with monkey- and apelike features appeared in the Oligocene epoch, beginning about 34 million years ago. The Miocene epoch, beginning about 24 million years ago, saw the appearance of many different kinds of apes. The ancient primates we know from fossils had some of the features of today's primates, but none of the ancient primates looked like the primates of today.

In this and the following chapters, we describe the main features of current theory and evidence about primate evolution, from the origin of primates to the origin of modern humans. In this chapter, we deal with that part of the story before the emergence of definite bipedal hominids. Our overview in this chapter covers the period from about 65 million years ago to the end of the Miocene, a little over 5 million years ago (see Figure 7–1).

The reconstruction of primate evolution requires the finding of fossil remains. Although many fossils have been discovered and continue to be discovered, the fossil record is still very incomplete. If geological strata are not uplifted, exposed by erosion, or otherwise accessible in the areas where ancient primates lived, paleoanthropologists cannot recover their fossils. The fossils that are found are usually fragmented or damaged, and judgments about what the organism looked like may be based on one or just a few pieces. Piecing together the evolutionary history of the primates requires much more than recovering fossil remains. The knowledge gained from anatomical studies of living species can allow us to make inferences about physical and behavioral traits that are likely to have been associated with the fossil features. Dating techniques developed in geology, chemistry, and physics are used to estimate the age of fossil remains. And studies of ancient plants and animals, geography, and climate help us reconstruct the environments of ancient primates.

Paleontologists (studying humans or other species) can tell a great deal about an extinct animal from its fossilized bones or teeth, but that knowledge is based on much more than just the fossil record itself. Paleontologists rely on comparative anatomy to help reconstruct

Wilson

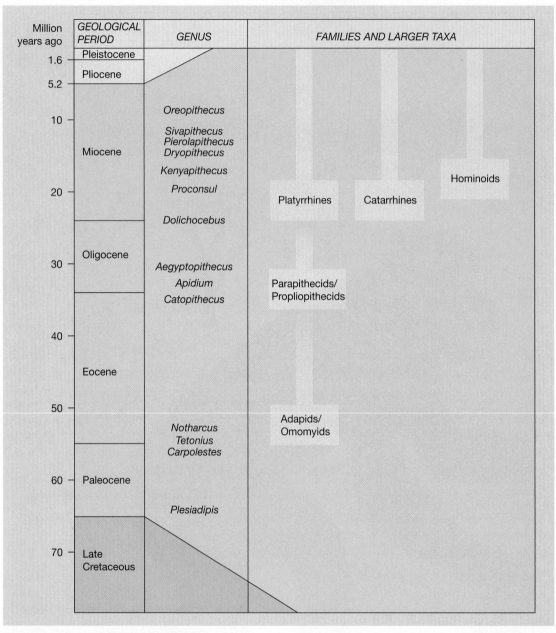

FIGURE 7–1 The Evolution of the Primates

missing skeletal pieces, as well as the soft tissues attached to bone. New techniques, such as electron microscopy, CAT scans, and computer-assisted biomechanical modeling, provide much information about how the organism may have moved about, the microstructure of bone and teeth, and how the organism developed. Chemical analysis of fossilized bone can suggest what the animal typically ate. Paleontologists are also interested in the surroundings of the fossil finds. With methods developed in geology, chemistry, and physics, paleontologists use the surrounding rocks to identify the time period in which the organism died. In addition, the study of associated fauna and flora can suggest what the ancient climate and habitat were like.

Still, much of the evidence for primate evolution comes from teeth, which are the most common animal parts (along with jaws) to be preserved as fossils. Animals vary in *dentition*—the number and kinds of teeth they have,

their size, and their arrangement in the mouth. Dentition provides clues to evolutionary relationships because animals with similar evolutionary histories often have similar teeth. For example, no primate, living or extinct, has more than two incisors in each quarter of the jaw. That feature, along with others, distinguishes the primates from earlier mammals, which had three incisors in each quarter. Dentition also suggests the relative size of an animal and often offers clues about its diet. For example, comparisons of living primates suggest that fruit eaters have flattened, rounded tooth cusps, unlike leaf- and insect eaters, which have more pointed cusps.[2] CAT scan methodology has helped paleontologists image the internal parts of teeth, such as the thickness of enamel, which can also suggest the diet (seed and nut eaters have thicker enamel). Electron microscopy has revealed different patterns of growth in bones and teeth; different species have different patterns.[3]

Paleontologists can tell much about an animal's posture and locomotion from fragments of its skeleton. Arboreal quadrupeds have front and back limbs of about the same length; because their limbs tend to be short, their center of gravity is close to the branches on which they move. They also tend to have long grasping fingers and toes. Terrestrial quadrupeds are more adapted for speed, so they have longer limbs and shorter fingers and toes. Disproportionate limbs are more characteristic of vertical clingers and leapers and *brachiators* (species that swing through the branches). Vertical clingers and leapers have longer, more powerful hind limbs; brachiators have longer forelimbs.[4] Even though soft tissues are not preserved, much can be inferred from the fossils themselves. For example, the form and size of muscles can be estimated by marks found on the bones to which the muscles were attached. The underside of the cranium may provide information about the proportions of the brain devoted to vision, smell, or memory. The skull also reveals information about characteristics of smell and vision. For example, animals that rely more on smell than on vision tend to have large snouts. Nocturnal animals tend to have large eye sockets.

THE EMERGENCE OF PRIMATES

When did the primates first emerge? This question turns out to be hard to answer with the current fossil record. Some paleoanthropologists have suggested that fossil finds from the **Paleocene** epoch, which began about 65 million years ago, are from archaic primates. These are the *plesiadapiforms.* They have been found in both Europe and North America, which were one connected landmass in the Paleocene. The most well-known of the plesiadapiforms is **Plesiadapis**. This squirrel-like animal had a large snout and large incisors. It also had a large nasal cavity and eye orbits located on the sides of the skull, suggesting a well-developed sense of smell and little or no stereoscopic vision (depth perception). The fingers of *Plesiadapis* had claws, and its hands and feet did not appear to allow for grasping. These features suggest that *Plesiadapis* was not a primate. However, the elbow and ankle joints suggest great mobility, and the teeth suggest a primatelike omnivorous diet despite the large incisors. The structure of their inner ears also resembled that of modern primates. Because it had these primatelike features, some scholars believe that the plesiadapiforms were archaic primates.[5]

Other paleoanthropologists find so few similarities between the plesiadapiforms and later obvious primates that they do not include the plesiadapiforms in the order Primates.[6] There is no dispute, however, about fossils dating from the early **Eocene**, about 55 million years ago. These oldest definite primates appear in two major groups of prosimians—*adapids* and *omomyids.* Because these two kinds of primate are different from each other in major ways, and because they both appeared rather abruptly at the border of the Paleocene and Eocene, there presumably was an earlier common primate ancestor. One strong candidate for the common primate ancestor is *Carpolestes simpsoni*, a mouse-sized arboreal creature

Reconstruction of *Carpolestes simpsoni*, an arboreal creature from the late Paleocene that may be the common ancestor of the primates.

from Wyoming dating to about 56 million years ago. *Carpolestes* has an interesting mix of primate and nonprimate characteristics. Although it lacks stereoscopic vision, *Carpolestes* has nails instead of claws on its big toes, and it has grasping hands and feet.[7] Not all scholars are convinced that *Caropolestes* is the common ancestor of all primates, and in Figure 7–2, the circled P represents where paleontologist Robert D. Martin placed the common ancestor of primates, in the late Cretaceous.

Now we turn to the conditions that may have favored the emergence of the primates.

The Environment

It is generally agreed that the earliest primate may have emerged by the Paleocene, 65 million to 55 million years ago, and perhaps earlier, in the late **Cretaceous**. What was the environment like in those times? The beginning of the Paleocene marked a major geological transition, what geologists call the transition from the Mesozoic to the Cenozoic era. About 75 percent of all animal and plant life that lived in the last part of the Cenozoic (the late Cretaceous) vanished by the early Paleocene. The extinction of the dinosaurs is the most famous of these disappearances.[8]

The climate of the Cretaceous period was almost uniformly damp and mild, but temperatures began falling at the end of the Cretaceous. Around the beginning of the Paleocene epoch, both seasonal and geographic fluctuations in temperature began to develop. The climate became much drier in many areas, and vast swamplands disappeared. The climate of the Paleocene was generally somewhat cooler than in the late Cretaceous, but by no means cold. Forests and savannas thrived in fairly high latitudes. Subtropical climates existed as far north as latitude 62 in Alaska.[9]

One important reason for the very different climates of the past is **continental drift** (Figure 7–3). In the early

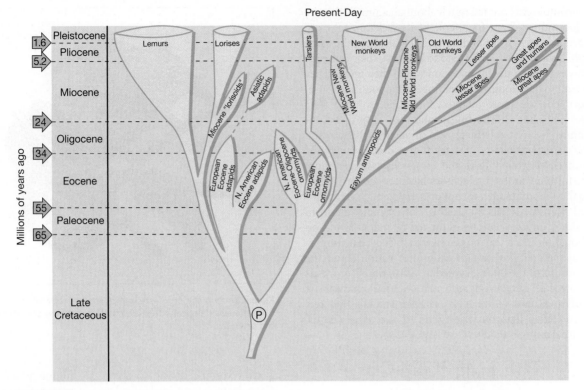

FIGURE 7–2

A view of the evolutionary relationships between early primates and living primates, adapted from one suggested by R. D. Martin. The primate lineages that do not extend to the present day indicate presumed extinctions. Branching from a common "stalk" suggests divergence from a common ancestor. P represents the unknown common ancestor of all primates.

Source: From Martin 1990. The dates for the Paleocene, Eocene, Oligocene, and the beginning of the Miocene are from Berggren et al. 1992, 29–45. The dates for the end of the Miocene, Pliocene, and Pleistocene are from Jones et al. 1992.

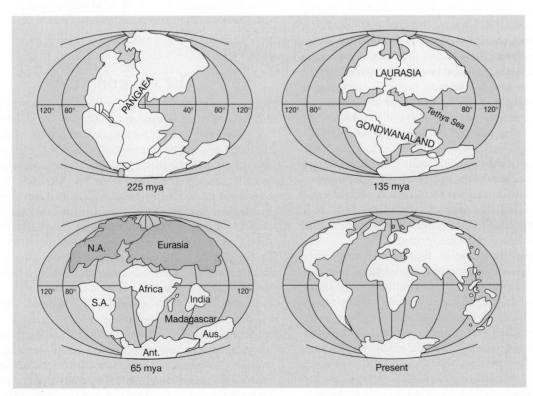

FIGURE 7–3 Continental Drift

The supercontinent Pangea split into Laurasia and Gondwanaland 135 million years ago (mya). These further divided into the continents as we know them today.

Source: Boaz and Almquist 1999.

Cretaceous (circa 135 million years ago), the continents were actually clumped into two large landmasses or "supercontinents"—*Laurasia,* which included North America and Eurasia, and *Gondwanaland,* which included Africa, South America, India, Australia, and Antarctica. By the beginning of the Paleocene (circa 65 million years ago), Gondwanaland had broken apart, with South America drifting west away from Africa, India drifting east, and Australia and Antarctica drifting south. As the continents changed position, they moved into locations with different climatic conditions. More importantly, however, the very movement of the continents affected the climate, sometimes on a global scale.[10]

Large landmasses affect wind and weather patterns differently than smaller landmasses, so weather patterns across Laurasia would have been different from weather in the subsequently separated continents. When continents collide, mountain ranges are formed, and mountains can also have a profound effect on weather patterns. Clouds drop their moisture as they meet a mountain range, and therefore the side away from the prevailing movement of weather systems is often very dry (a condition called a *rain shadow*), whereas the other side (called the *windward side*) is often wet. When the location of continents prevents the movement of ocean currents from the tropics to the poles, the earth's climate becomes colder. Continental drift and climate change had profound effects on the evolution of the primates.[11]

With changes in climate come changes in vegetation. Although the first deciduous trees (that lose their leaves in winter) and flowering plants (called *angiosperms*) arose during the Cretaceous, large trees with large fruits and seeds also became common during the late Paleocene and early Eocene.[12] New species of animals evolved as the climate and environment changed. Although some mammals date from the Cretaceous, the Paleocene saw the evolution and diversification of many different types of mammals, and the expansion and diversification of deciduous trees and flowering plants probably played a large role in mammalian expansion and diversification. Indeed, primate paleontologists think primates evolved from one of these mammalian *radiations,* or extensive diversifications, probably from the **insectivore** order of mammals, including modern shrews and moles, that is adapted to eating insects—insects that would have lived off the new deciduous trees and flowering plants.

To put it simply, the new kinds of plant life opened up sources of food and protection for new animal forms. Of most interest to us is that the new plant life provided an abundant food supply for insects. The result was that insects proliferated in both number and variety, and in turn there was an increase in *insectivores*—the mammals that ate the insects. The insectivores were very adaptable and were able to take advantage of many different habitats—under the ground, in water, on the ground, and above the ground, including the woody habitat of bushes, shrubs, vines, and trees. It was the last kind of adaptation, above the ground, that may have been the most important for primate evolution. The woody habitat had been exploited only partially in earlier periods. But then several different kinds, or taxa, of small animals, one of which may have been the archaic primate, began to take advantage of the woody habitat.

What in Particular May Have Favored the Emergence of Primates?

The traditional explanation of primate origins is called the *arboreal theory.* According to this view, the primates evolved from insectivores that took to the trees. Different paleoanthropologists emphasized different possible adaptations to life in the trees. In 1912, G. Elliot Smith suggested that taking to the trees favored vision over smell. Searching for food by sniffing and feeling with the snout might suit terrestrial insectivores, but vision would be more useful in an animal that searched for food in the maze of tree branches. With smaller snouts and the declining importance of the sense of smell, the eyes of the early primates would have come to face forward. In 1916, Frederic Wood Jones emphasized changes in the hand and foot. He thought that tree climbing would favor grasping hands and feet, with the hind limbs becoming more specialized for support and propulsion. In 1921, Treacher Collins suggested that the eyes of the early primates came to face forward not just because the snout got smaller. Rather, he thought that three-dimensional binocular vision would be favored because an animal jumping from branch to branch would be more likely to survive if it could accurately judge distances across open space.[13] In 1968, Frederick Szalay suggested that a shift in diet—from insects to seeds, fruits, and leaves—might have been important in the differentiation of primates from insectivores.[14]

Arboreal theory still has some proponents, but Matt Cartmill highlighted some crucial weaknesses in the theory.[15] He argued that tree living is not a good explanation for many of the primate features because there are living mammals that dwell in trees but seem to do very well without primatelike characteristics. One of the best examples, Cartmill says, is the tree squirrel. Its eyes are not front-facing, its sense of smell is not reduced in comparison with other rodents, it has claws rather than nails, and it lacks an opposable thumb. Yet these squirrels are very successful in trees. They can leap accurately from tree to tree, they can walk over or under small branches, they can go up and down vertical surfaces, and they can even hang from their hind legs to get food below them. Furthermore, other animals have some primate traits but do not live in trees or do not move around in trees as primates do. For example, carnivores, such as cats, hawks, and owls, have forward-facing eyes, and the chameleon, a reptile, and some Australian marsupial mammals that prey on insects in bushes and shrubs have grasping hands and feet.

Cartmill thinks, then, that some factor other than moving about in trees may account for the emergence of the primates. He proposes that the early primates may have been basically insect eaters, and that three-dimensional vision, grasping hands and feet, and reduced claws may have been selectively advantageous for hunting insects on full stereoscopic vision and a reduced muzzle. It appears to have lived in the forest and had long, powerful hind legs for leaping from tree to tree.[23]

There was a great deal of diversity among all mammals during the Eocene epoch, and the primates were no exception. Evolution seems to have proceeded rapidly during those years. Both the omomyids and adapids had a few features that suggest links between them and the anthropoids that appear later, in the Oligocene, but there is no agreement that either group gave rise to the anthropoids.[24] Although the omomyids had some resemblances to modern tarsiers and the adapids had some resemblances to lemurs and lorises, paleoanthropologists are not sure that either group was ancestral to modern prosimians. But it is generally thought that the populations ancestral to lemurs and lorises as well as tarsiers did emerge in the Eocene or even earlier, in the late Paleocene.[25]

THE EMERGENCE OF ANTHROPOIDS

The anthropoids of today—monkeys, apes, and humans—are the most successful living primates and include well over 150 species. Unfortunately, the fossil record documenting the emergence of the anthropoids is extremely spotty, and there is no clear fossil record of the Old World forms (the catarrhines) in the two areas where they are most abundant today—the rain forests of sub-Saharan Africa and Southeast Asia.[26] Some paleoanthropologists think that recent Eocene primate finds from China, Southeast Asia, and Algeria have anthropoid affinities, but there is no clear agreement on their evolutionary status.[27]

Undisputed remains of early anthropoids date from a somewhat later period, the late Eocene and early Oligocene, about 34 million years ago, in the **Fayum** area, southwest of Cairo, Egypt. One of the earliest fossil primates at Fayum is *Catopithecus*, dating to around 35 million years ago. Several recent finds have made it one of the best-known late Eocene primates. *Catopithecus* was about the size of a modern marmoset or squirrel monkey. Its dentition suggests a mixed diet of fruit and insects. Its eyes were small, suggesting it was active during the day (diurnal). The few skeletal remains of *Catopithecus* suggest it was an agile arboreal quadruped. It may be the best candidate for the earliest anthropoid, though how it was related to other primates is still debated.[28]

Oligocene Anthropoids

The Fayum is an uninviting area of desert badlands, but it has yielded a remarkable array of early anthropoid fossils. During the **Oligocene** epoch, 34 million to 24 million years ago, the Fayum was a tropical rain forest very close to the shores of the Mediterranean Sea. The area had a warm climate, and it contained many rivers and lakes. The Fayum, in fact, was far more inviting than the northern continents then, for the climates of both North America and Eurasia were beginning to cool during the Oligocene.

The general cooling seems to have resulted in the virtual disappearance of primates from the northern areas, at least for a time.

Oligocene anthropoids from the Fayum are grouped into two main types: the monkeylike **parapithecids** and the apelike **propliopithecids**. Dating from 35 million to 31 million years ago, the parapithecids and the propliopithecids had enough features to be unquestionably classified as anthropoids.

Parapithecids The monkeylike parapithecids had three premolars (in each quarter), as do most prosimians and the New World monkeys. They were similar to modern anthropoids, with a bony partition behind the eye sockets, broad incisors, projecting canines, and low, rounded cusps on their molars. But they had prosimianlike premolars and relatively small brains. The parapithecids were small, generally weighing less than 3 pounds, and resembled the squirrel monkeys living now in South and Central America.[29] Their relatively small eye sockets suggest that they were not nocturnal. Their teeth suggest that they ate mostly fruits and seeds. Locomotion is best known from one of the parapithecids, *Apidium*, an arboreal quadruped that also did a considerable amount of leaping.[30] The parapithecids are the earliest definite anthropoid group, and although there is still disagreement among paleoanthropologists, most believe that the emergence of the anthropoids preceded the split between the New World monkeys (platyrrhines) and the Old World monkeys (catarrhines).[31]

That parapithecids may be ancestral to New World monkeys (platyrrhines) raises an interesting puzzle in primate evolution: the origin of the New World monkeys. Anthropoidal primates such as *Dolichocebus*, a small fruit-eating monkey similar to the modern squirrel monkey,[32] appear suddenly and without any apparent ancestors in South America around 25 million years ago. Because the parapithecids predate the appearance of anthropoids in South America, and resemble them in many ways, it seems reasonable to view them as part of the population ancestral to the New World monkeys.[33]

But how did anthropoidal primates get from Africa to South America? Although the continents were closer together in the late Oligocene, when primates first appear in South America, at least 1,864 miles (3,000 kilometers) separated South America and Africa. An extended continental shelf and islands created by lower sea levels in the late Oligocene may have made it possible to "island-hop" from Africa to South America over ocean stretches as short as 125 miles (200 kilometers), but that is still a long distance for an arboreal primate.

Going from Africa to Europe and North America, which were still joined in the late Oligocene, is not a likely route either. North America and South America were not joined until some 5 million years ago, so even if the ancestors of the New World monkeys made it to North America, they would still have needed to make a long ocean crossing to reach South America. One suggestion is that the ancestors of the New World monkeys "rafted" across the Atlantic on large mats of vegetation. Such "rafts" of matted plants, roots, and soil break away from the mouths of major rivers today, and they can be quite large. It seems an unlikely scenario, but many scholars believe such drifting vegetation must have been the means of bringing anthropoids to South America.[34]

Propliopithecids The other type of anthropoid found in the Fayum, the propliopithecids, had the dental formula of modern catarrhines. This trait clearly places the propliopithecids with the catarrhines.[35] In contrast with the parapithecids, which had three premolars (in each quarter of the jaw), the propliopithecids had only two premolars, as do modern apes, humans, and Old World monkeys. Propliopithecids shared with the parapithecids the anthropoid dental characteristics of broad lower incisors, projecting canines, and lower molars with low, rounded cusps. And, like parapithecids, propliopithecids had a bony partition behind the eye socket.

Aegyptopithecus, the best-known propliopithecid, probably moved around quadrupedally in the trees, and weighed about 13 pounds. Its molars were low with large cusps, and it had relatively large incisors, suggesting that *Aegyptopithecus* ate mostly fruit. Its eyes were relatively small, and thus it was probably active during the day. It had a long muzzle and a relatively small brain. Endocasts of the brain cavity suggest *Aegyptopithecus* had a relatively large area of the brain dedicated to vision and a relatively small area dedicated to smell. The skulls of *Aegyptopithecus* show considerable sexual dimorphism, and individuals also changed dramatically as they aged, developing bony ridges along the top and across the back of the skull, much like modern great apes. Although its teeth, jaws, and some aspects of the skull were apelike, the rest of *Aegyptopithecus*'s skeleton was monkeylike,[36] and most scholars classify them as primitive catarrhines. Because the propliopithecids lack the specialized characteristics of living Old World monkeys and apes (catarrhines), but share the dental formula of the catarrhines, some paleoanthropologists think that the propliopithecids included the ancestor of both the Old World monkeys and the hominoids (apes and humans).[37]

The fossil skull of an *Aegyptopithecus* from the Fayum. Its dentition, small bony eye sockets, and relatively large brain make it an unambiguous ancestor of Old World monkeys and apes.

THE MIOCENE ANTHROPOIDS: MONKEYS, APES, AND HOMINIDS (?)

During the **Miocene** epoch, 24 million to 5.2 million years ago, monkeys and apes clearly diverged in appearance, and numerous kinds of apes appeared in Europe, Asia, and Africa. In the early Miocene, the temperatures were considerably warmer than in the Oligocene. From early to late Miocene, conditions became drier, particularly in East Africa. The reasons for this relate again to continental drift. By about 18 million years ago, Africa came into contact with Eurasia, ending the moderating effect that the Tethys Sea, which separated Africa from Eurasia, had on the climates of both continents. The contact of Africa and, more significantly, India with the Eurasian continent also initiated mountain building, changing established weather patterns. The overall effect was that southern Eurasia and eastern Africa became considerably drier than they had been. Once again, these changes appear to have significantly influenced primate evolution.

We can infer that late, in the Miocene, between about 8 million and 5 million years ago, the direct ancestor of humans—the first hominid—may have emerged in Africa. The inference about where hominids emerged is based on the fact that undisputed hominids lived in East Africa after about 5 million years ago. The inference about when hominids emerged is based not as much on fossil evidence as it is on comparative molecular and biochemical analyses of modern apes and humans. As we will see in the next chapter, the effect of a drier climate and the creation of more open, grassland environments may have directly influenced the evolution of the hominids.

One of the Miocene apes (known or unknown) was ancestral to hominids, so our discussion here deals mostly with the *proto-apes*—anthropoids with some apelike characteristics—of the early Miocene and the definite apes of the middle and late Miocene. But before we get to the apes, we should say something about monkeys and prosimians in the Miocene. Unfortunately, monkey fossils from the early Miocene are rare. In the New World, the whole Miocene fossil record is quite small. Only a few primate fossils have been found in Colombia and Argentina; they show close affinities with present-day South American monkeys. In the Old World, early Miocene monkey fossils have been found only in northern Africa. The situation is different for the middle and late Miocene: Old World monkey fossils become much more abundant than ape fossils.[38] As for prosimians, fossils from the Miocene are scarce, but we know that at least some adapids survived into the middle Miocene in India and the late Miocene in China.[39] Some loris-like prosimians appear in East Africa, Pakistan, and India during the Miocene.[40]

Early Miocene Proto-Apes

Most of the fossils from the early Miocene are described as proto-apes. They have been found mostly in Africa. The best-known genus is **Proconsul**, found in sites in Kenya and Uganda that are about 20 million years old.[41]

current research and issues

What Happened to *Gigantopithecus?*

In studying human evolution, we tend to focus on the primate lineages that presumably are ancestral to modern humans and our closest primate cousins. There were, however, other primate lineages that left no apparent descendants but were very successful in the sense that they persisted for millions of years. The first definite primates, the omomyids and the adapids, first appeared early in the Eocene and stayed for more than 20 million years, much longer than bipedal hominids have been around! Why some primates were successful for so long is an important question, so is why they became extinct. To understand evolution, we need to investigate not only why some form may have survived for a while; we need also to investigate why it died out. For example, what happened to the largest primate that ever lived, *Gigantopithecus?*

A paleoanthropologist, Russell Ciochon, and an archaeologist, John Olsen, have searched for clues to understanding the extinction of "Giganto," as they call it, which apparently left no descendants living in the world today. Ciochon and Olsen think that the largest form of *Gigantopithecus*, *G. blacki*, persisted for at least 5 million years and did not

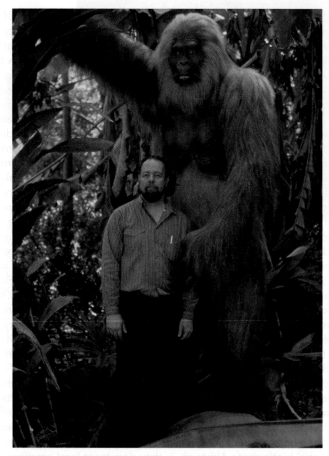

Gigantopithecus probably lived mostly on bamboo. It is the largest primate known to us. The genus survived for about 10 million years and only became extinct 250,000 years ago. Bill Munns is shown here with the model of Giganto that he and Russell Ciochon reconstructed.

over the nearly 10 million years of its existence.[52] (See the box "What Happened to *Gigantopithecus?*") *Gigantopithecus* was restricted to the forests of Southeast Asia, and is thought to have had a diet focused on bamboo.

Dryopithecids *Dryopithecus*, which appears about 15 million years ago, was a chimpanzee-sized ape that lived in the forests of Eurasia. It was mainly arboreal and apparently omnivorous. *Dryopithecus* had thinner tooth enamel than *Sivapithecus*, lighter jaws, and pointed molar cusps. In the palate, jaw, and mid face, *Dryopithecus* looked like the African apes and humans. In contrast to later hominoids, however, *Dryopithecus* had a very short face and a relatively small brow ridge.[53]

The fingers and elbows of *Dryopithecus* and *Sivapithecus* suggest that they were much more capable of suspending

themselves than were earlier hominoids. *Sivapithecus* may have moved about more on the ground than *Dryopithecus*, but both were probably mostly arboreal.[54] Indeed, recent finds of *Dryopithecus* hand, arm, shoulder, and leg bones strongly suggest that *Dryopithecus* was highly efficient at suspensory locomotion and probably moved through the trees like modern orangutans do.

It is still very difficult to identify the particular evolutionary lines leading from the Miocene apes to modern apes and humans. Only the orangutans have been linked to a late Miocene ape genus, *Sivapithecus*, so presumably that lineage continued into modern times.[55] *Dryopithecus* disappears from the fossil record after about 10 million years ago, leaving no descendants, perhaps because less rainfall and more seasonality reduced the forests where they lived.[56]

become extinct until about 250,000 years ago. If you count earlier *Gigantopithecus* forms, the genus may have been around for nearly 10 million years. Ciochon and Olsen think it likely that Giganto and *Homo erectus*, a hominid that looked very much like modern humans from the head down, met up about a quarter of a million years ago in at least two Asian locations—now parts of China and Vietnam. The possible contact with *H. erectus* may have been partly responsible for the demise of Giganto.

What did Giganto look like? Reconstruction requires some guesswork, particularly with Giganto, because the only remains we have are teeth and jaw fragments. But we can reasonably infer some of Giganto's features and measurements from the body proportions of existing apes and the more complete fossil remains of extinct apes. Thus, it is estimated that Giganto was 10 feet tall and weighed over 600 pounds.

What did Giganto eat? Ciochon's guess is that Giganto ate mostly bamboo from the then-plentiful bamboo forests. The large size of the jaw, the wear patterns on the teeth, and the fact that large primates eat mostly foods with a lot of cellulose all suggest a diet of bamboo or something like it. Another kind of evidence suggests the same conclusion. A student had suggested to Ciochon that he look for phytoliths on the fossil teeth of Giganto. Phytoliths are microscopic granules of silicon

dioxide that enter a plant's cells and take their shape. When the plants decompose, the phytoliths remain. Different plants have phytoliths of different shapes.

So, on the chance that phytoliths were on the fossil teeth from Giganto, the researchers looked microscopically at the teeth. They found phytoliths that belong to a family of grasses as well as phytoliths from a kind of fruit. Bamboo is a kind of grass, so the phytoliths found on the Giganto teeth are consistent with both bamboo and fruit eating. The teeth revealed something else too. Many showed pitting of the tooth enamel (hypoplasias), which suggests that Giganto suffered periodically from malnutrition. (Hypoplasias are produced by dietary insufficiencies.)

Bamboo forests are found almost everywhere in China and Southeast Asia, but for reasons not yet understood, they dwindle every 20 years or so. If Giganto ate bamboo, it would have had a serious problem every so often, which is consistent with the hypoplasias. Could the extinction of Giganto be linked to something that happened to the bamboo forests? Perhaps. Giant pandas, which are bamboo eaters almost exclusively, are now at risk of extinction because of the spread of humans throughout China and Southeast Asia. Humans use bamboo for shelter, boats, tools, and food (bamboo shoots), and the bamboo forests are now drastically

reduced. In their time, *H. erectus* may also have reduced the bamboo forests, thus contributing to the demise of Giganto. It is also possible that *H. erectus* hunted Giganto for food. This possibility is very speculative, but many recent human societies have hunted nonhuman primates for food. Like the giant panda, Giganto was probably very slow-moving and easy to hunt, as are most megaherbivores.

Humans in different places tell stories about huge, hairy, humanlike creatures—"bigfoot" or Sasquatch in northwestern North America, the "abominable snowman" or yeti of the Himalayas. Is it possible that Giganto is still around? Ciochon and Olsen point out that no recent Giganto bones have been found, so it is very unlikely that Giganto is still out there. But perhaps humans continue to believe it because they encountered Giganto in the not-so-distant past. After all, Australian aborigines still tell stories referring to events that happened more than 30,000 years ago.

What we do know is that *Gigantopithecus* persisted for a very long time, until humans came on the scene. Researchers have learned a lot about Giganto from very fragmentary remains. If more fossils are found in the future, we can expect that more will come to be known about the gigantic ape.

Source: Ciochon, Olsen, and James 1990.

THE DIVERGENCE OF HOMINIDS FROM THE OTHER HOMINOIDS

The later Miocene apes are best known from Europe and Asia. Until recently, there has been an almost complete lack of African fossil hominoids dating between 13.5 million and 5 million years ago.[57] Recently, two species, *Orrorin tugenensis*, from Kenya and dated to about 6 million years ago, and *Sahelanthropus tchadensis*, from Chad and dated to perhaps 7 million years ago, have provided a glimpse of hominoid evolution during this time period, which we discuss in the next chapter. Still, this scarcity of fossils from 13.5 to 5 million years ago is unfortunate for our understanding of human evolution because the earliest unambiguous bipedal primates (hominids) appear in Africa near

the beginning of the Pliocene, after 5 million years ago. To understand the evolutionary links between the apes of the Miocene and the hominids of Africa, we need more fossil evidence from late Miocene times in Africa.

However, we do have some idea about the transition to hominids beyond the few fossil remains. The molecular biology of the various modern primates suggests when the last common ancestor of humans and our closest primate relatives, chimpanzees, probably lived.

The Molecular Clock

In 1966, on the basis of biochemical comparisons of blood proteins in the different surviving primates, Vincent Sarich and Allan Wilson estimated that gibbons diverged from the other hominoids about 12 million years ago, orangutans 10 million years ago, and the other apes (gorillas and chimps) from hominids only 4.5 million years ago. These estimates depended on the assumption that the more similar in chemistry the blood proteins of different primates are—for instance, comparing chimpanzees and humans—the closer those primates are in evolutionary time. In other words, the more similar the blood proteins of related species, the more recently they diverged.[58]

But knowing that species are close molecularly does not translate into evolutionary time unless it is assumed that molecular changes occur at a constant rate. After all, a reliable "molecular clock" should not slow down or speed up from one period of time to another. To maximize the likelihood of molecular change at a constant rate, researchers try to examine molecular characteristics that are probably neutral in terms of adaptation. (Natural selection can speed up the rate of molecular change in the case of a characteristic that is very advantageous or very disadvantageous.) The rate of change in a neutral characteristic is calculated from the time of some divergence that is absolutely dated. For example, if we know that two lineages split 20 million years ago, and we know the degree of molecular difference between a contemporary representative of each, we can estimate the rate of change that produced that degree of difference. Given such an estimated rate of change (in a particular characteristic), we can estimate the amount of time that has elapsed since other pairs of related species diverged from each other.[59]

In 1987, Rebecca Cann and colleagues used genetic differences between living peoples to determine how long ago modern humans separated from our closest ancestors (we talk more about this in a later chapter). Cann relied on the genes within a tiny structure found in all of our eukaryotic cells called *mitochondria*. Mitochondria produce enzymes needed for energy production, and they have their own DNA, which replicates when a cell replicates but is not thought to be under any pressure from natural selection.[60]

The only source of change in mitochondrial DNA (usually referred to as *mt*DNA) is random mutation. Mitochondrial DNA is inherited only from mothers in animals; it is not carried into an egg cell by sperm, but is left with the sperm's tail on the outside of the egg. These unique characteristics make it possible to use mtDNA to measure the degree of relatedness between two species, and even to say how long ago those species diverged.[61] The longer two species have been separated, the more differences there will be in their mtDNA, which is thought to mutate at a fairly constant rate of about 2 percent per million years. Thus, the number of differences between the mtDNA of two organisms can be converted into an estimated date in the past when those organisms stopped being part of the same breeding population. Although controversy remains over many of the details of how and why mtDNA mutates and about its accuracy for determining absolute dates of divergence, most scholars agree that it is a powerful tool for examining relative degrees of relatedness between species.[62]

The results of mtDNA analyses place the split between hominids and the other hominoids at about 5 million years ago.[63] More recently, the chimpanzee and macaque genomes have been sequenced, and comparison of their nuclear DNA with those of humans have confirmed the probable recency of the hominid divergence from chimpanzees and gorillas.[64] Although the different techniques yield slightly different estimates, the results are not that divergent. Most of the recent comparisons place the split somewhat earlier than the Sarich and Wilson estimates, but not by much.[65]

So what does the fossil evidence tell us about where and when hominids first emerged? *Sahelanthropus tchadensis* and *Orrorin tugenensis* appear to support the molecular data. Both show mixed hominid and hominoid traits, both are from Africa, and both date to between 6 and 7 million years ago. We turn to the early hominids in the next chapter.

SUMMARY ● ○ ○

1. We cannot know with certainty how primates evolved. But fossils, a knowledge of ancient environments, and an understanding of comparative anatomy and behavior give us enough clues to have a tentative idea of when, where, and why primates emerged and diverged.

2. The surviving primates—prosimians, New World monkeys, Old World monkeys, apes, and humans—are thought to be descendants of small, originally terrestrial insectivores (the order, or major grouping, of mammals, including modern shrews and moles, that is adapted to feeding on insects). However, exactly who the common ancestor was and when it emerged are not yet known.

3. Fossils dating from the early Eocene, about 55 million years ago, are definitely primates. They appear to fall into two major groups of prosimians—adapids and omomyids. These two kinds of primates are different from each other in major ways, and they both appeared rather abruptly at the border of the Paleocene and Eocene, so their common ancestor would have had to emerge earlier, probably in the Paleocene.

4. What conditions may have favored the emergence of the primates? The proliferation of insects led to an increase in insectivores—the mammals that ate the insects, some of which lived above ground, in the woody habitat of bushes, shrubs, vines, and trees. Eventually, trees with large flowers and fruits evolved. The exploitation of resources in the woody habitat was probably the key adaptation in the emergence of the primates.

5. The traditional view of primate evolution was that arboreal (tree) life would have favored many of the common primate features, including distinctive dentition, greater reliance on vision over smell, three-dimensional binocular vision, and grasping hands and feet. A second theory proposes that some of the distinctive primate characteristics were selectively advantageous for hunting insects on the slender vines and branches that filled the undergrowth of forests. A third theory suggests that the distinctive features of primates (including reliance more on vision than on smell) were favored because the early primates were nocturnal and ate flowers, fruits, and seeds, which they had to locate on slender branches in dim light.

6. Undisputed remains of early anthropoids unearthed in Egypt date from the early Oligocene (after 34 million years ago). They include the monkeylike parapithecids and the propliopithecids with apelike teeth.

7. During the Miocene epoch (24 million to 5.2 million years ago), monkeys and apes clearly diverged in appearance, and numerous kinds of apes appeared in Europe, Asia, and Africa. Most of the fossils from the early Miocene are described as proto-apes. From the end of the middle Miocene into the late Miocene, the apes diversified and spread geographically. Most paleoanthropologists divide the later Miocene apes into at least two main groups: dryopithecids, found primarily in Europe, and sivapithecids, found primarily in western and southern Asia.

8. The fossil record does not tell us much about the first hominids, but biochemical and genetic analyses of modern apes and humans suggest that the hominid-ape split occurred during the late Miocene (after about 5 million years ago). Because undisputed hominids lived in East Africa after about 4 million years ago, the first hominid probably emerged in Africa.

GLOSSARY TERMS ○ ● ○

adapid **113**

Aegyptopithecus **115**

Carpolestes **109**

continental drift **109**

Cretaceous **109**

Dryopithecus **118**

Eocene **109**

Fayum **114**

insectivore **111**

Kenyapithecus **116**

Miocene **115**

Oligocene **114**

omomyid **113**

Paleocene **109**

parapithecids **114**

Pierolapithecus **116**

Plesiadapis **109**

Proconsul **115**

propliopithecids **114**

Sivapithecus **117**

CRITICAL QUESTIONS ○ ○ ●

1. What an animal eats and how it gets its food are suggested by its skeletal anatomy. Discuss possible examples in the evolution of the primates.

2. Why do you suppose there are more monkey than ape species?

3. We like to think of the human lineage as biologically unique, which of course it is (like all evolutionary lineages). But some paleoanthropologists say that humans, chimpanzees, and gorillas are so similar that all three should be grouped as hominids. What do you think, and why do you think so?

PEARSON
myanthrolab

Read the chapter by David Begun titled "Miocene Apes" on MyAnthroLab. Answer the following questions:

1. Begun begins his essay describing the area where he looks for fossils of ancient primates. Why are so many important primate fossil deposits in what are today arid, windswept landscapes like southern Spain and the Fayum Depression in Egypt?

2. Begun suggests that the modern African apes—chimpanzees and gorillas—should be placed in the same taxonomic family as humans, and that the Asian apes—orangutans—should be in a different family. Why does he suggest this? Does the fossil record of Miocene apes support his suggestion?

chapter 8

The First Hominids

ipedal locomotion is a defining feature of the hominids. Undisputed bipedal hominids lived in East Africa about 4 million years ago (see Figure 8–1). These hominids, and some others who may have lived later in eastern and southern Africa, are generally classified in the genus *Australopithecus*. In this chapter, we discuss what we know or suspect about the transition from hominoids to hominids, the emergence of australopithecines, and their relationship to later hominids, including ourselves.

● ○ ●

THE EVOLUTION OF BIPEDAL LOCOMOTION

Perhaps the most crucial change in early hominid evolution was the development of *bipedal locomotion,* or walking on two legs. We know from the fossil record that other important physical changes—including the expansion of the brain, modification of the female pelvis to allow bigger-brained babies to be born, and reduction of the face, teeth, and jaws—did not occur until about 2 million years after the emergence of bipedalism. Other human characteristics, such as an extended period of infant and child dependency and increased meat-eating, may also have developed after that time.

We do not know whether bipedalism developed quickly or gradually, because the fossil record for the period between 8 million and 4 million years ago is very skimpy. We do know, on the basis of their skeletal anatomy, that many of the Miocene anthropoids were capable of assuming an upright posture. For example, *brachiation,* swinging by the arms through the trees, puts an animal in an upright position; so does climbing up and down trees with the use of grasping hands and feet.[1] It is also likely that the protohominids were capable of occasional bipedalism, just as many modern monkeys and apes are.[2]

Definitely bipedal hominids emerged in Africa, judging by the available fossil record. The emergence of bipedal hominids coincides with a change from extensive tropical forest cover to more discontinuous patches of forest and open country.[3] About 16 million to 11 million years ago, a drying trend set in that continued into the Pliocene. Gradually, the African rain forests, deprived of intense humidity and rainfall, dwindled in extent; areas of **savanna** (grasslands) and scattered deciduous woodlands became more common. The tree-dwelling primates did not completely lose their customary habitats, because some tropical forests remained in wetter regions, and natural selection continued to favor the better-adapted tree dwellers in those forested areas. But the new, more open country probably favored characteristics adapted to ground living in some primates as well as other animals. In the evolutionary line leading to humans, these adaptations included bipedalism.

Theories for the Evolution of Bipedalism

What in particular may have favored the emergence of bipedal hominids? There are several possible explanations for this development. One idea is that bipedalism was adaptive for life amid the tall grasses of the savannas because an erect posture may have made it easier to spot ground predators as well as potential prey.[4] This theory does not adequately account for the development of bipedalism, however. Baboons and some other Old World monkeys also live in savanna environments, yet, although they can stand erect and occasionally do so, they have not evolved fully bipedal locomotion. And recent evidence suggests that the area where early hominids lived in East Africa was not predominantly savanna; rather, it seems to have been a mix of woodland and open country.[5]

Other theories stress the importance of freeing the hands. If some hand activity is critical while an animal is moving, selection may favor bipedalism because it frees the hands to perform other activities at the same time. What hand activities might have been so critical?

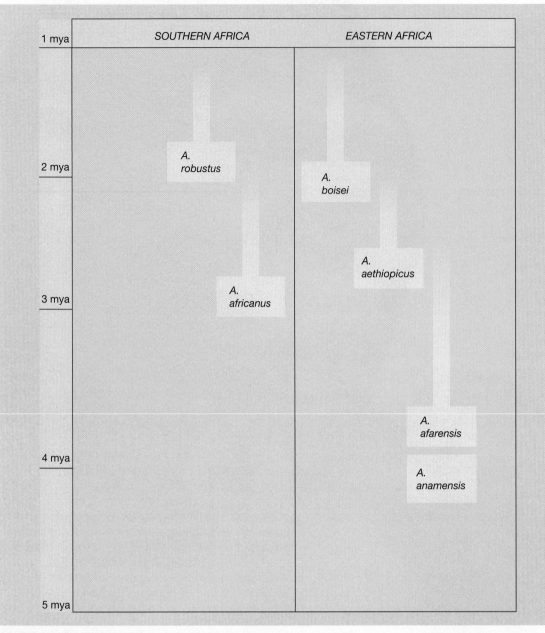

FIGURE 8–1 The Evolution of the Australopithecines

Gordon Hewes suggested that carrying food in the hands was the critical activity; if it were necessary to carry food from one locale to another, moving about only on the hind limbs would have been adaptive.[6] Hewes emphasized the importance of carrying hunted or scavenged meat, but many paleoanthropologists now question whether early hominids hunted or even scavenged.[7] However, the ability to carry any food to a place safe from predators may have been one of the more important advantages of bipedalism. C. Owen Lovejoy has suggested that food carrying might have been important for another reason. If males provisioned females and their babies by carrying food back to a home base, the females would have been able to conserve energy by not traveling and therefore might have been able to produce and care for more babies.[8] Thus, whatever the advantages of carrying food, the more bipedal a proto-hominid was, the more it might reproduce.

But carrying food or provisioning families might not have been the only benefit of freeing the hands; feeding itself may have been more efficient. Clifford Jolly has argued that bipedalism would have allowed early hominids to efficiently harvest small seeds and nuts because both hands could be used to pick up food and move it directly to the mouth.[9] Natural selection would not have favored bipedalism just for locomotion, but also for more efficient foraging. In the changing environments of East Africa, where forests were giving way to more open woodlands and savannas, an advantage in foraging for small seeds and nuts might well have proven important for survival, and thus have been favored by natural selection.

Bipedalism might also have been favored by natural selection because the freeing of the hands would allow proto-hominids to use, and perhaps even make, tools that they could carry with them as they moved about. Consider how

applied anthropology

Anthropometry

An interesting fact about physical anthropology is that the same types of measurements used to understand the appearance and behavior of our most distant ancestors are also used to understand variation in the appearance and behavior of humans today. Physical anthropologists who practice **osteology,** the study of bones, often focus on the remains or fossils left by ancient humans. But physical anthropologists who practice anthropometry use many of the same measurements and techniques to study living humans.

The term **anthropometry** refers to measurement of the human body, but the field of anthropometry is much broader, encompassing topics from the identification of individuals to the creation of efficient workplaces. What kinds of work do physical anthropologists use anthropometry for today? To dress soldiers, for one thing. The U.S. military does extensive anthropometric studies to help them design helmets, boots, gloves, and other items to fit well. They also use anthropometric data to design aircraft seats and to ensure that tools are easy to use. Businesses use anthropometry for many of the same reasons. A clothing manufacturer, for example, might create different sizes of clothes for sale in the United States (where people are relatively large) and Japan (where people are relatively small).

Many companies undertake studies to ensure that tasks performed by their employees, or by people using the goods they manufacture, do not cause harm through repetitive use. Such research, often called ergonomics, is also done to improve the efficiency or comfort of tasks. So, anthropometry is used today whenever there is a need to know how people vary in size and movement.

Anthropometry is also important in understanding growth and development. Humans grow in regular ways, and by measuring and charting growth in populations around the world, physical anthropologists are able to aid medical doctors in assessing nutrition, health, disease, and stress. Many potentially debilitating diseases are discovered in young children because the children do not grow according to established patterns, which informs medical doctors that something may be wrong with the child.

Basic anthropometric measurements are of two kinds: typological and metric. Typological measurements identify the form or type of feature in an individual. One common example is the absence or presence of earlobes that attach more tightly to the skin of the jaw. Physical anthropologists have also devised many typological systems to classify the form of features such as noses, ears,

eyes, and even breasts and buttocks! The interest in classification derived from the expectation that appearance and behavior were linked. But such a link has not been demonstrated, and typological measurements are infrequently used today. More common, and more useful, are metric measurements—measurements that record the length or size of a feature. Finger length, leg length, sitting height, and standing height are examples of metric measurements. These tend to be more useful than typological measurements because they reveal variation in greater detail, and they can be used to create indices that provide a description of the shape or form of a feature in mathematical terms. As we have noted, physical anthropologists have found that metric measures of variation are useful for applications such as charting child growth or designing tools. Anthropometric measurements and indices are thus used widely in physical anthropology, and are particularly important in the field of osteology, because, as we demonstrate in this chapter and those that follow, the same measurements can be used to examine and compare ancient humans of different species.

Sources: Gay 1986; Gordon and Friedl 1994; Larsen 1997; White and Folkens 2000.

advantageous such tool use might have been. Sherwood Washburn noted that some contemporary ground-living primates dig for roots to eat, "and if they could use a stone or a stick they might easily double their food supply."[10] David Pilbeam also suggests why tool use by the more open-country primates may have appreciably increased the number and amount of plant foods they could eat: In order to be eaten, many of the plant foods in the grassy areas probably had to be chopped, crushed, or otherwise prepared with the aid of tools.[11] Tools may also have been used to kill and butcher animals for food. Without tools, primates in general are not well equipped physically for regular hunting or even scavenging. Their teeth and jaws are not sharp and strong enough, and their speed afoot is not fast enough. So the use of tools to kill and butcher game might have enlarged even further their ability to exploit the available food supply.

Finally, tools may have been used as weapons against predators, which would have been a great threat to the relatively defenseless ground-dwelling protohominids. In Milford Wolpoff's opinion, it was the advantage of carrying weapons *continuously* that was responsible for transforming occasional bipedalism to completely bipedal locomotion.[12] In particular, Sue Savage-Rumbaugh has suggested that the ability to abduct or snap the wrist would have permitted early humans "to perfect both throwing and rock-striking skills [for toolmaking] and consequently to develop throwing as a much more effective predator defense system than apes could ever manage."[13]

But some anthropologists question the idea that tool use and toolmaking favored bipedalism. They point out that the first clear evidence of stone tools appears more than 2 million years *after* the emergence of bipedalism. So

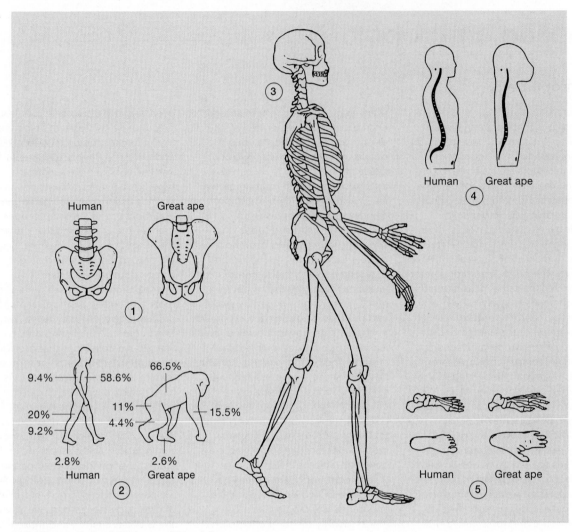

FIGURE 8–2 Skeletal Evidence of Bipedalism
Because humans move about on their legs only, the human skeleton differs from the skeleton of the great ape. The human head is more or less balanced on the backbone (see the feature marked 3 in the figure). There is no need for powerful muscles at the back of the neck, as in the great ape. The human vertebral column (see 4 in the figure) has a forward curvature in the neck and lower back regions. These two extra curves, along with the curvature in the middle back region, allow the backbone to act more like a spring, which is advantageous given that the legs have to bear all the weight and given the need to balance on one leg with each stride. Bipedal locomotion has favored a human pelvis (see 1 in the figure) that is lower and broader than the ape pelvis. In contrast to the apes, the legs in humans are longer than the arms and represent a larger proportion of the body weight (see 2 in the figure); this change lowers the body's center of gravity and is advantageous with bipedalism. The most obvious adaptation to bipedalism is the human foot (see 5 in the figure). The big toe is not opposed to the other toes, as in the other primates, and the foot can no longer grasp. When we walk, the big toe is the last point of contact with the ground before the leg swings forward, which explains why the big toe has become aligned with the other toes.

Source: From Jones, Martin, and Pilbeam 1992, 78.

how could toolmaking be responsible for bipedalism? Wolpoff suggests an answer. Even though bipedalism appears to be at least 2 million years older than stone tools, it is not unlikely that protohominids used tools made of wood and bone, neither of which would be as likely as stone to survive in the archaeological record. Moreover, unmodified stone tools present in the archaeological record might not be recognizable as tools.[14]

Some researchers have taken a closer look at the mechanics of bipedal locomotion to see if it might be a more efficient form of locomotion in the savanna-woodland environment, where resources are likely to be scattered. Compared with the quadrapedal locomotion of primates such as chimpanzees, bipedalism appears to be more efficient for long-distance travel (see Figure 8–2).[15] But why travel long distances? If the ancestors of humans had the manipulative ability and tool-using capability of modern chimpanzees (e.g., using stones to crack nuts), and those ancestors had to move around in a more open environment, then those individuals who could efficiently travel longer distances to exploit those resources might do better.[16]

Finally, bipedalism might have been favored by natural selection as a way of regulating body temperature, particularly in the increasingly hot and dry environments of East Africa at the end of the Miocene and the beginning of the Pliocene. Peter Wheeler has argued that a bipedal posture limits the area of the body directly exposed to the sun, especially when the sun is at its hottest, at midday.[17] Bipedal posture would also facilitate convective heat loss by allowing heat to rise up and away from the body rather than being trapped underneath it. (We radiate a lot of body heat through the head.) Cooling through the evaporation of sweat would also be facilitated by a bipedal posture, as more skin area would be exposed to cooling winds. Thus, natural selection may have favored bipedalism because it reduced heat stress in the warming environments of East Africa.

All theories about the origin of bipedalism are speculative. We do not yet have direct evidence that any of the factors we have discussed were actually responsible for bipedalism. Any or all of the factors may explain the transformation of an occasionally bipedal protohominid to a completely bipedal hominid.

The "Costs" of Bipedalism

We must remember that there are also "costs" to bipedal walking. Bipedalism makes it harder to overcome gravity to supply the brain with sufficient blood,[18] and the weight of the body above the pelvis and lower limbs puts greater stress on the hips, lower back, knees, and feet. As Adrienne Zihlman points out, the stresses on the lower body are even greater for females.[19] Females have to support extra weight during pregnancy, and as mothers they usually are responsible for carrying nursing infants. So whatever the advantages of bipedalism, they must be greater than the disadvantages—or our ancestors never would have become bipedal.

We must also remember that the evolution of bipedalism required some dramatic changes in the ancestral ape skeleton. Although apes today can and do walk bipedally, they cannot do so efficiently or for long periods of time. To be habitually bipedal, the ancestral ape skeleton had to be modified, and the major changes that allowed the early hominids to become fully bipedal occurred primarily in the skull, pelvis, knees, and feet.[20] Let's take a look at each of these changes (see Figure 8–2).

In both ancient and modern apes, the spinal column enters the skull toward the back, which makes sense because apes generally walk on all fours, with the spine roughly parallel to the ground. In bipedal hominids, the spinal column enters the skull at the bottom, through a hole called the **foramen magnum.** Thus, when hominids became bipedal, the skull ended up on top of the spinal column.

The shape of ancient and modern ape pelvises is considerably different from that of a bipedal hominid. Ape pelvises are long and flat, forming a bony plate in the lower back to which the leg muscles attach. In bipedal hominids, the pelvis is bowl-shaped, which supports the internal organs and also lowers the body's center of gravity, allowing better balance on the legs. The hominid pelvis also provides a different set of muscle attachments and shifts the orientation of the femurs (the upper leg bones) from the side of the pelvis to the front. These changes allow hominids to move their legs forward in a bipedal stride (and do things like kick a soccer ball). Apes, in comparison, move their legs forward (when they walk bipedally) by shifting their pelvis from side to side, not by kicking each leg forward alternately as we do.[21]

Another change associated with the hominid ability to kick the leg forward is our "knock-kneed" posture. Ape legs hang straight down from the pelvis. Bipedal hominid legs, on the other hand, angle inward toward one another. This configuration not only helps us move our legs forward but also helps us maintain a center of gravity in the midline of our bodies, so that our center of gravity does not shift from side to side when we walk or run.

Finally, the feet of bipedal hominids have two major changes compared to those of apes. First, hominid feet have an enlarged group of ankle bones forming a robust heel that can withstand the substantial forces placed on them as a result of habitual bipedalism. Second, hominid feet have an arch, which also aids in absorbing the forces endured by the feet during bipedal locomotion. We know this arch is vital to our ability to be habitually bipedal because "flat-footed" people who lack it have chronic problems in their feet, ankles, knees, and back.[22]

When did these changes take place? We don't know for sure, but fossils from East Africa—Ethiopia, Tanzania, and Kenya—clearly show that bipedal hominids lived there between 4 million and 5 million years ago, perhaps even earlier.

THE TRANSITION FROM HOMINOIDS TO HOMINIDS

Western Chad, in north-central Africa, and its windswept deserts do not seem a likely place to find fossil apes or hominids, but paleoanthropologist Michel Brunet thinks it might be.[23] Western Chad was covered by an ancient lake, and for several million years was a location where forest-dwelling mammals, including primates, congregated. Around 7 million years ago, a primate called **Sahelanthropus tchadensis** lived on the shores of the lake, where Brunet and his colleagues recovered its fossilized bones in 2001. *Sahelanthropus,* represented by an almost complete skull, has a unique mix of hominid and hominoid traits. Although the skull itself is hominoid, with a small brain, large brow ridges, and wide face, the teeth seem more hominidlike, especially the canines, which do not project below the tooth row.[24]

Reconstructed skull of *Sahelanthropus tchadensis,* possibly the earliest hominid, dating to almost 7 million years ago.

Unfortunately, there is no evidence that *Sahelanthropus* was bipedal. For now, we have to wait for additional evidence to know whether *Sahelanthropus* was the first bipedal ape.

There is, however, tantalizing evidence that another possible early hominid, **Orrorin tugenensis**, was bipedal. Discovered in western Kenya by Brigitte Senut and colleagues in 1998, *Orrorin tugenensis* consists of 19 specimens of jaw, teeth, finger, arm, and leg bones, including the top of a femur.[25] The femur in *Orrorin,* according to Brian Richmond and William Jungers, shows adaptations to bipedalism, including a long, angled "head" (or top).[26] *Orrorin* dates between 5.8 and 6 million years, so it may turn out to be the earliest hominid if further research supports *Orrorin* bipedalism.

In 1992, a team of researchers led by anthropologist Tim White began surveying a 4.4-million-year-old fossil deposit at Aramis, in the Middle Awash region of Ethiopia. There, they discovered 17 fossils of what may be the earliest hominid (more have been found since, including some fragments dating perhaps as early as 5.8 million years ago). Although initially suggested to be a new australopithecine species, White and his colleagues decided that *ramidus,* the species name given to the new fossils, was distinct enough from the australopithecines to warrant a new genus: *Ardipithecus.*[27]

What makes **Ardipithecus ramidus** unique is the combination of apelike dentition along with evidence of bipedal locomotion and an overall hominidlike skeleton. Like apes, *Ardipithecus* has relatively small cheek teeth with thin enamel and relatively large canines. However, its arm bones seem hominidlike, and the base of its skull shows the foramen magnum positioned underneath the skull, just as in definitely bipedal hominids.[28] The feet of *Ardipithecus* also seem adapted to bipedalism.[29] Although more evidence is needed to be sure, *Ardipithecus* may be the earliest hominid yet found.

AUSTRALOPITHECUS: THE FIRST DEFINITE HOMINID

Although some doubt remains about the status of *Ardipithecus* as a hominid genus, there is no doubt that the australopithecines (members of the genus **Australopithecus**) were hominids. (Figure 8–3 shows australopithecine sites.) Their teeth share the basic hominid characteristics of small canines, flat and thickly enameled molars, and a parabolic dental arch, and there is unambiguous evidence that even the earliest australopithecines were fully bipedal. Not only do their skeletons reflect bipedal locomotion, but at Laetoli, Tanzania, more than 50 hardened humanlike footprints about 3.6 million years old give striking confirmation that the hominids there were fully bipedal. The bipedalism of the australopithecines does not mean that these earliest definite hominids were terrestrial all of the time. All of the

FIGURE 8–3 Australopithecine Sites

Source: From Ciochon and Fleagle 1993.

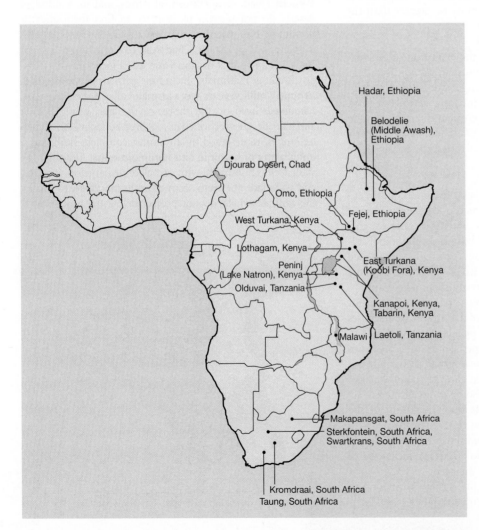

australopithecines, including the later ones, seem to have been capable of climbing and moving in trees, judging by arm versus leg length and other skeletal features.[30]

Most scholars divide the various australopithecine species into two groups, the "gracile" australopithecines and the "robust" australopithecines.[31]

The **gracile australopithecines** include *A. anamensis, A. afarensis,* and *A. africanus.* All of them have smaller dentition and lighter facial and dental musculature than the robust australopithecines. ***Australopithecus anamensis,*** which may be 4.2 million years old, is the earliest australopithecine, and has been found only in northern Kenya. Other hominids found in East Africa from 4 million to 3 million years ago are classified by most paleoanthropologists as belonging to the species ***Australopithecus afarensis.*** A few paleoanthropologists do not think that these hominids should be placed in a separate species, because they resemble the later hominid species ***Australopithecus africanus,*** which lived between about 3 million and 2 million years ago, primarily in southern Africa. But the temporal and spatial separation of these forms leads many paleoanthropologists to argue that they were different species.

New fossils from eastern Africa found in the last two decades suggest there may have been other species of gracile australopithecine as well. Most scholars consider two groups of fossils in particular to represent new australopithecine species, named ***Australopithecus bahrelghazali*** and ***Australopithecus garhi.*** *A. bahrelghazali* is currently represented by a single, fragmentary jaw, and only a handful of skull and limb fragments represent *A. garhi.* Although the finds are intriguing, we will not know how important either species is, or how they may change our understanding of early hominid evolution, until more fossils from them are found.

Australopithecus garhi, found in rock dating to approximately 2.5 million years ago, is particularly interesting, as it is similar to, but is not clearly a member of, any of the other australopithecine species. *A. garhi* has larger molars than *A. afarensis,* yet does not have the huge face and jaws of the robust australopithecines. It also lacks the enlarged brain of early *Homo.* Several limb bones were found in the same rock layers, and these do resemble *A. afarensis. A. garhi,* then, looks to be an *afarensis*-like creature but with greatly enlarged molars.[32] It may represent one end of the range of variation in *afarensis,* or it may represent an adaptation to eating tough foods, similar to that made by the robust australopithecines, whom we will discuss shortly.

It is interesting, however, that the remains of butchered animals were found in the same rock layer as the *A. garhi* remains. Several bones found near the *A. garhi* fossils show unambiguous cut marks and signs of having been broken with a stone tool. Unfortunately, no stone tools have been found, but the evidence for butchery suggests they must have been used. And since no other species of hominid have been found in the area, it is reasonable to think that *A. garhi* was the toolmaker and butcher. The fossil's discoverer, Berhane Asfaw, suggests that *A. garhi* is in the right place, at the right time, and has the right physical and behavioral traits to be the direct ancestor of early *Homo.*[33]

Equally intriguing is *Australopithecus bahrelghazali,* not so much because of its physical features, but because it was

Reconstructed skull of *Australopithecus garhi.* Note the large molars but relatively small face.

found further west, in what is now central Chad. *A. bahrelghazali* is the first early hominid to be found outside of the Rift Valley (a long valley in East Africa where the earth is pulling apart, exposing fossils from millions of years ago), and until *A. bahrelghazali* surfaced, few thought early hominids were present anywhere else. *A. bahrelghazali* dates to about 3 million years ago, and is very similar to contemporary *A. afarensi's* fossils from the Rift Valley. It differs from *A. afarensis* in some distinct ways (its premolars, for example, have thinner enamel and more well-defined roots), but the important difference is where *A. bahrelghazali* lived. Most scholars assume the early hominids represent a specific adaptation to the Rift Valley. The discovery of an early australopithecine some (1,550 or so miles) 2,500 kilometers west of the Rift Valley calls this assumption into question.[34]

A related hominid genus, ***Kenyanthropus platyops,*** is thought by some scholars to be yet another australopithecine (and hence should not be regarded as a separate genus). The nearly complete 3.5-million-year-old skull of *Kenyanthropus platyops* from western Kenya shows traits that Meave Leakey and her colleagues suggest separate it from the australopithecines that lived at the same time. Its face is smaller and flatter, and its molars are smaller than those of the australopithecines. Leakey believes *Kenyanthropus* may be a direct link to *Homo,* but others are not so sure. The skull is distorted, and scholars are not convinced that its features lie outside the range of the australopithecines.[35] The debate over the relation of *Kenyanthropus* to *Australopithecus* will continue until more fossils are found.

The **robust australopithecines** have larger dentition than the gracile species, and massive faces and jaws. Some robust individuals had a ridge of bone called a **sagittal crest** on the top of their heads; the ridge anchored the heavy musculature for their large teeth and jaws. The earliest robust species is ***Australopithecus aethiopicus,*** which lived in eastern Africa between 2.7 and 2.3 million years ago. Most paleoanthropologists think that the later robust australopithecines, who lived between 2.3 and

1 million years ago, consist of two species: the East African species **Australopithecus boisei** and the South African species **Australopithecus robustus.**

The picture that emerges from this brief overview of the australopithecines is one of diversity. There seem to have been many different species of australopithecine, and even within species there seems to be a relatively high level of variation.[36] All shared similar environments in eastern and southern Africa, but those environments were diverse and changing. Forests were giving way to open woodlands and grasslands. Large lakes were formed and then broken apart through uplifting and volcanic activity in the Rift Valley of eastern Africa. And the climate continued to warm until the end of the **Pliocene,** some 1.6 million years ago. The apparent diversity of the australopithecines may reflect an *adaptive radiation* (a dispersal and divergence) of bipedal hominids to these dynamic environmental conditions.[37] On the other hand, Tim White has suggested that we really do not know enough about the australopithecines to judge how many species there are. He also suggests some variations may be the result of differences in the fossilization process itself.[38] Whatever the cause, *diversity* seems to be the key word when thinking about the australopithecines. Let's take a closer look at the diverse gracile species of *Australopithecus,* and then the robust species.

Gracile Australopithecines

Australopithecus Anamensis   The earliest australopithecine species is *A. anamensis,* which has been found in several locations in northern Kenya and is dated between 3.9 million and 4.2 million years ago.[39] Although there is controversy about some of the specimens included in *A. anamensis,* the general picture is that it was a small bipedal hominid with teeth similar to those of the later *A. afarensis.*[40] The more controversial specimens have long bones, suggesting well-developed bipedalism, but their elbow and knee joints look more like those of the later *Homo* genus than like those of any other species of *Australopithecus.* It has been said that *A. anamensis* is "*afarensis*-like from the neck up and *Homo*-like from the neck down."[41]

Australopithecus Afarensis   *A. afarensis* is perhaps the most well-represented australopithecine species. Remains from at least two dozen individuals were unearthed at Laetoli, Tanzania.[42] Although the remains there consisted largely of teeth and jaws, there is no question that the Laetoli hominids were bipedal, because the now-famous trail of footprints was found at the Laetoli site. Two hominids walking erect and side by side left their tracks in the ground 3.6 million years ago. The remains of at least 35 individuals have been found at another site, Hadar, in Ethiopia. The Hadar finds are remarkable for their completeness. Whereas paleoanthropologists often find just parts of the cranium and jaws, many parts of the skeleton were also found at Hadar. For example, paleoanthropologist Donald Johanson found 40 percent of the skeleton of a female hominid he named Lucy, after the Beatles's song "Lucy in the Sky with Diamonds."[43]

Dating of the hominid remains at Laetoli suggests that the hominids there lived between 3.8 million and

3.6 million years ago.[44] Although Lucy and the other hominids at Hadar were once thought to be about as old as those at Laetoli, recent dating suggests that they are somewhat younger—less than 3.2 million years old. Lucy probably lived 2.9 million years ago.[45] The environment Lucy lived in was semiarid, upland savanna with rainy and dry seasons.[46]

The existence of such extensive fossil collections has allowed paleoanthropologists such as Donald Johanson and Tim White to develop a portrait of this ancient hominid species. *A. afarensis* was a small hominid, but, like most of the living great apes, was sexually dimorphic. Females weighed perhaps 65 pounds and stood a little more than 3 feet tall; males weighed more than 90 pounds and stood about 5 feet tall.[47]

A. afarensis teeth were large compared to their body size, and they had thick molar enamel. They also had large, ape-like canines, which, on some specimens, projected beyond the adjacent teeth. However, even the longer canines did not rub against the lower teeth or fit into a diastema (a space between the teeth), and thus did not prevent side-to-side movement of the lower jaw.[48] This is important, because side-to-side movement of the lower jaw allowed *A. afarensis* to efficiently chew small seeds and nuts. The thick enamel on the molars and wear patterns on the molar crowns suggest that such small, hard materials made up a significant part of the diet of *A. afarensis.*[49] The cranium of *A. afarensis* reflects its dentition. The face juts forward because of the large teeth and jaws, and the base of the skull flares out to provide attachment areas for large neck muscles to support the heavy face. The brain is small, about 400 cubic centimeters (cc), but relatively large for an animal this size.[50]

The arms and legs of *A. afarensis* were about the same length, and the fingers and toe bones are curved, suggesting

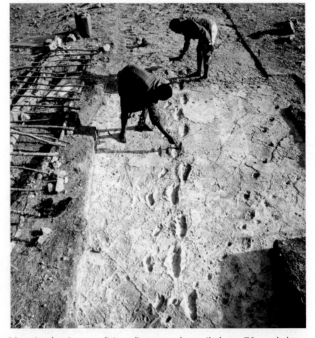

Mary Leakey's expedition discovered a trail about 70 yards long of 3.8-million-year-old fossilized footprints at Laetoli, Tanzania. Shown here is one part of the trail left by two adults who were clearly upright walkers. The footprints shows a well-developed arch and forward-facing big toe.

A reconstruction of a female *Australopithecus afarensis* skeleton. Note how long the arms are relative to the legs, and the long fingers. Both suggest *A. afarensis* was at least partially arboreal.

they were heavily muscled. Most scholars believe these limb proportions and strong hands and feet point to a partially arboreal lifestyle.[51] In other words, it appears that *A. afarensis* spent a lot of time in the trees, probably feeding, sleeping, and avoiding terrestrial predators. The pelvis and leg bones of *A. afarensis*, however, demonstrate that it moved bipedally when on the ground. The pelvis is wide and flaring, but has the bowl-like shape of all later hominids. The legs angle inward, and the feet have an arch and an ankle much like later hominids.[52] Detailed analyses of the Laetoli footprints suggest that *A. afarensis* may have had a shorter and less efficient stride than modern humans.[53]

Although *A. afarensis* is the most well-represented australopithecine species, it was not the first one discovered. That distinction rests with *Australopithecus africanus*.

Australopithecus Africanus In 1925, Raymond Dart, professor of anatomy at the University of Witwatersrand in Johannesburg, South Africa, presented the first evidence that an erect bipedal hominid existed in the Pliocene epoch. As he separated bones from a matrix of material found in the Taung cave on the edge of the Kalahari Desert, Dart realized he was looking at more than the remains of an ape. He described the experience:

> On December 23, [1924,] the rock parted. I could view the face from the front, although the right side was still embedded. The creature that had contained this massive brain was no giant anthropoid such as a gorilla. What emerged was a baby's face, an infant with a full set of milk teeth and its permanent molars just in the process of erupting.[54]

By the teeth, Dart identified the fossil as the remains of a 5- to 7-year-old child (although recent analysis by electron microscope suggests that the child was no more than 3 1/2[55]). He named the specimen *Australopithecus africanus*, which means "southern ape of Africa." Dart was certain the skull was that of a bipedal animal. He based his conclusion on the fact that the foramen magnum faced downward, indicating that the head was carried directly over the spine. Furthermore, the Taung child's incisors and canine teeth were short, and therefore definitely more human- than apelike.

Dart's conclusion met with widespread skepticism and opposition. Not the least of the problems was that scientists at the time believed hominids had originated in Asia. But there were probably other reasons: Dart had found only one fossil; it was an infant rather than an adult; and no other hominid fossils had yet been found in Africa. Other australopithecines were not discovered until the 1930s, when Robert Broom recovered some fossils from the Sterkfontein cave near Johannesburg. Dart's and Broom's conclusions did not begin to be accepted until after 1945, when Wilfred Le Gros Clark, a professor of anatomy at Oxford, supported the hominid status of their finds.[56]

Since the Taung child's discovery 80 years ago, the remains of hundreds of other similar australopithecines have been unearthed from caves at Sterkfontein and Makapansgat in South Africa. From this abundant evidence, a fairly complete picture of *A. africanus* can be drawn: "The brain case is rounded with a relatively well-developed forehead. Moderate brow ridges surmount a rather projecting face."[57] The estimated cranial capacity for the various finds from Taung and Sterkfontein is between 428 and 485 cc.[58]

Like *A. afarensis*, *A. africanus* was very small; the adults were 3 1/2 to 4 1/2 feet tall, weighed 60 to 90 pounds, and were sexually dimorphic.[59] The large, chinless jaw of *A. africanus* resembles that of *A. afarensis*, but some of the dental features of *A. africanus* are similar to those of modern humans—broad incisors and small, short canines. And, although the premolars and molars were larger than in modern humans, their form was very similar. Presumably, function and use were also similar.

Fossil skull of an *Australopithecus africanus* (STS 5) nicknamed "Mrs. Ples" found by Robert Broom at Sterkfontein cave in 1947.

A reconstruction of an *Australopithecus africanus* mother and child picking berries in a tree. Like *A. afarensis*, *A. africanus* probably spent time in trees both feeding and avoiding predators.

Dating of the australopithecine finds from the South African limestone caves is somewhat difficult because none of the absolute dating techniques can be applied. But relative dating is possible. Comparisons of the fauna found in the strata with fauna found elsewhere suggest that the South African *A. africanus* lived between 3 million and 2 million years ago. The climate was probably semi-arid, not too different from the climate of today.[60]

Robust Australopithecines

The robust australopithecines lived in eastern Africa and in southern Africa from about 2.7 million to 1 million years ago, and are quite distinct from the gracile australopithecines. Indeed, some paleoanthropologists think these fossils are so different that they deserve to be classified in a different genus, which they call *Paranthropus*, literally, "beside humans." Robust australopithecines were found first in South African caves, in Kromdraai and in Swartkrans, and later in East Africa, in the Omo Basin in Ethiopia, on the east and west sides of Lake Turkana in Kenya, and Olduvai Gorge in Tanzania.[61] Most paleoanthropologists classify the South African robust australopithecines from about 1.8 million to 1 million years ago as *A. robustus* and the East African robust forms from 2.3 million to 1.3 million years ago as *A. boisei*.[62] The third

robust species, *A. aethiopicus,* is even earlier, dating back more than 2.5 million years ago, and may have been ancestral to *A. boisei* (see the box "Early 'Robust' Australopithecines Are Puzzling").

In contrast to the gracile australopithecines, the robust australopithecines had thicker jaws, with larger molars and premolars but smaller incisors, more massive muscle attachments for chewing, and well-developed sagittal crests and ridges to support heavy chewing.[63] In addition, *A. robustus* and *A. boisei* have somewhat larger cranial capacities (about 490–530 cc) than any of the gracile species.

It used to be thought that the robust australopithecines were substantially bigger than the other australopithecines—hence, the term *robust*. But recent calculations suggest that these australopithecines were not substantially different in body weight or height from the other australopithecines. The robustness is primarily in the skull and jaw, most strikingly in the teeth. If the robust forms were larger in body size, their slightly bigger brain capacity would not be surprising, because larger animals generally have larger brains. However, the body of the robust forms is similar to that of *A. africanus,* so the brain of the robust australopithecines was relatively larger than the brain of *A. africanus.*[64]

Australopithecus Aethiopicus *A. aethiopicus* is the earliest and also the least known of the robust australopithecines. *A. aethiopicus* is represented by a small group of fossils found in northern Kenya and southern Ethiopia dating between 2.3 million and 2.7 million years ago, including one spectacular find—a nearly complete skull (known as the "Black Skull" because of its dark color) found in 1985.[65] Even though we have only a few fossils, it seems clear that *A. aethiopicus* was quite different from other australopithecines. They differ from *A. afarensis* specimens from roughly the same region and perhaps even the same time period by having much larger dentition, particularly molars, huge cheekbones, projecting and dish-shaped (round and flat) faces, and large sagittal crests. But they are similar to *A. afarensis* in most other ways. Overall, *A. aethiopicus* resembles *A. afarensis* with a massively "scaled-up" dental apparatus.[66]

Australopithecus Robustus In 1936, Robert Broom, then curator of vertebrate paleontology at the Transvaal Museum in South Africa, began visiting quarries seeking fossils for the museum, particularly hominids that might support Raymond Dart's earlier discovery of the Taung child. In 1938, a quarry manager gave Broom a hominid jaw that had been found in a nearby cave called Kromdraai. Broom immediately began excavating in the cave, and within days was able to piece together the skull of what would prove to be a new australopithecine species—*Australopithecus robustus.*[67]

Although Broom had expected another example of *Australopithecus africanus* (he had found an *A. africanus* skull in 1936), this one was different. It had larger teeth, a massive jaw, and a flatter face than *A. africanus.*[68] Indeed, after further study, Broom decided that the fossil represented an entirely new hominid genus: *Paranthropus.*

current research and issues

Early "Robust" Australopithecines Are Puzzling

Where do the robust australopithecines, with their big jaws and bony skull ridges, fit into the evolution of humans? Paleoanthropologists agree that the robust australopithecines are a side branch of human evolution, but when did they diverge from the *Homo* line? The very early date of some robust australopithecine fossils in East Africa presents a puzzle, according to paleoanthropologist Henry McHenry. These fossils, classified as *Australopithecus aethiopicus,* date apparently from about 2.7 million years ago. If the late robust forms— *A. robustus* and *A. boisei*—descend from *A. aethiopicus,* and if the line leading to *Homo* had already split off from an earlier australopithecine, then why do the late robust australopithecines resemble *Homo erectus* more than they resemble the australopithecines who were their presumed ancestors?

The late robust australopithecines are like *H. erectus* in having a relatively large brain (as compared with *A. africanus*), reduced prognathism (lower face projection), and a deep jaw joint. If they diverged recently from the *Homo* line, similarity to *Homo* would not present a puzzle. But if the robust line diverged earlier, as the 2.7 million-year-old *A. aethiopicus* suggests, the late robust forms should be much more divergent from *Homo.* After all, the further back in time the two lines diverge, the more you would expect the later examples in each to differ.

What could explain some of the similarities between the late robust australopithecines and the *Homo* line? McHenry suggests two possible explanations, both involving convergence. He points out that convergence, the independent appearance of similar structures in different lines of descent, can obscure the issue of how far back there was common ancestry. Bats, birds, and butterflies have wings, but they are not closely related—their common ancestor is way back in evolutionary time. One possible explanation for the similarities between the late robust australopithecines and the *Homo* line is that the late robust forms descend from the early robust forms but resemble *H. erectus* because of convergence. A second possibility is that the late robust forms and *Homo* share a recent, not yet found ancestor; if they do, then the early robust forms were not ancestral to the late robust forms. Convergence, not close common ancestry, might then explain the resemblance between the late and early robust forms.

McHenry prefers the second possibility. On the basis of his analysis of trait similarities, McHenry thinks that the two late robust australopithecine species (*A. robustus* and *A. boisei*) share a common ancestor but that ancestor was not the early robust form, *A. aethiopicus.* In many ways, the late robust forms are not that similar to *A. aethiopicus.* One of the best examples of *A. aethiopicus* is a nearly complete skull (the "Black Skull"). It is no doubt robust. It has huge premolars and molars and an enormous sagittal crest. But in other ways, it resembles *A. afarensis:* protruding muzzle, shallow jaw joint, and small braincase. McHenry thinks that convergent evolution produced the resemblances between the early and late robust australopithecines, and the convergence happened because of strong selective pressure for heavy chewing. Features good for heavy chewing have evolved in other primates as well, in evolutionary lines far removed from the human line. *Gigantopithecus,* with its enormous premolars and molars, was one such primate. Thus, although McHenry still considers the late robust australopithecines to constitute a side branch to the *Homo* line, his analysis suggests that *A. robustus* and *A. boisei* were not as far from *Homo* as previously thought.

Timothy Bromage, who has studied fossil facial growth, and Randall Susman, who has studied the hominid thumb, have other suggestions about the robust australopithecines. Bromage has used the scanning electron microscope to study images of fossil faces, particularly to see how the face would have grown from infancy to adulthood. The maturing face changes in shape by a combination of deposition of bone in some locations and resorption of bone in other locations. So, for instance, a jaw becomes more protruding when bone deposits on the forward-facing surfaces and resorbs on the opposite surfaces. Scanning electron microscopy can reveal whether bone is deposited or resorbed. Bromage found differences between the growth patterns of the robust australopithecines and *A. africanus. Australopithecus africanus* and even early *Homo* finds are more apelike in their growth pattern than the later robust australopithecines.

Susman has studied thumb bones and attached musculature to see what traits would be needed to make tools. Modern humans have longer but stouter thumbs than apes, so they can perform the kind of precision grasping needed for toolmaking. Did any early hominids have such precision-grasping ability? Susman thinks that all the australopithecines after about 2.5 million years ago, including the robust ones, had toolmaking hand capabilities. This doesn't mean that they made tools, only that they could have.

The robust australopithecines, with their small foreheads, extremely flat cheeks, and enormous jaws, may have looked very different from the forms in the *Homo* line, but they could be closer to us evolutionarily than we once thought.

Sources: McHenry 2009; Susman 1994, 1570–73.

Broom's genus designation was not widely accepted at the time (scholars thought the specimen represented a species of *Australopithecus*), but as we noted earlier, many scholars today believe the robust australopithecines are unique enough to warrant classification in a separate *Paranthropus* genus.

During the 1940s, Broom added many new fossils of *A. robustus* and *A. africanus* to the collections of the Transvaal Museum. But his discoveries also raised a problem. How did two strikingly different hominid species evolve in the same environment? In 1954, John T. Robinson proposed that *A. africanus* and *A. robustus* had different dietary adaptations—*A. africanus* being an omnivore (dependent on meat and plants) and *A. robustus* a vegetarian, with a need for heavy chewing. Robinson's view was hotly debated for many years. Evidence from electron microscopy supports Robinson's view that *A. robustus* ate mostly small, hard objects such as seeds, nuts, and tubers. But how different was *A. africanus* in this respect? Recent analyses suggest that *A. africanus* also practiced fairly heavy chewing.[69]

The idea that *A. robustus* was just a vegetarian is also questioned by a relatively new chemical technique that analyzes strontium–calcium ratios in teeth and bones to estimate the proportion of plant versus animal food in the diet. This new kind of analysis suggests that *A. robustus* was an omnivore.[70] Thus *A. robustus* may have needed large teeth and jaws to chew seeds, nuts, and tubers, but that doesn't mean that it didn't eat other things too.

Was *A. robustus* adapted, then, to a drier, more open environment than *A. africanus?* This is a possibility, but the evidence is controversial. At any rate, most paleoanthropologists think that *A. robustus* died out shortly after 1 million years ago[71] and is not ancestral to our own genus, *Homo.*[72]

Australopithecus Boisei Legendary paleoanthropologist Louis Leakey began his search for a human ancestor in 1931, at Olduvai Gorge in western Tanzania. It was not until 1959 that his efforts paid off with the discovery of *Australopithecus boisei* (named after a benefactor, Charles Boise). The nearly 30 years that Leakey, his wife, Mary Leakey, and their children (including paleoanthropologist Richard Leakey) worked at Olduvai before finding *A. boisei* were not wasted. The Leakeys assembled a rich collection of nonhominid fossils and established a detailed understanding of the ancient environment of the region.[73] As we discuss in the next chapter, they also amassed a remarkable collection of ancient stone tools. So, on a hot July morning, when Mary Leakey rushed to tell Louis, who was sick in bed, that she had discovered the hominid they had long been searching for, the Leakeys were able immediately to place their find into a rich environmental and perhaps cultural context.

The discovery of *A. boisei* was particularly important because it demonstrated that early hominids were present in East Africa. Until the Leakeys found *A. boisei*, it was thought that South Africa was the homeland of the hominids. Indeed, Leakey initially assigned *A. boisei* to a new genus—*Zinjanthropus*—to highlight its location (*Zinj* means "East Africa" in Arabic). Today, we know that the most ancient fossil hominids are all found in East Africa,

Fossil skull of *Australopithecus boisei* found by Louis and Mary Leakey in 1959. Note its huge face and teeth and its sagittal crest.

but, in 1959, simply finding a fossil hominid in East Africa was remarkable.

What did *A. boisei* look like? Compared with *A. robustus*, *A. boisei* had even more extreme features that reflected a huge chewing apparatus—enormous molar teeth and expanded premolars that look like molars; a massive, thick and deep jaw; thick cheekbones; and a more pronounced sagittal crest.[74] Indeed, *A. boisei* has been called a "hyper-robust" australopithecine—a name that definitely captures the species.

A. boisei lived between about 2.3 million and 1.3 million years ago. Like *A. robustus,* it seems to have lived in a dry, open environment and ate a lot of coarse seeds, nuts, and roots. And, like *A. robustus,* most paleoanthropologists think *A. boisei* is not ancestral to our genus, *Homo.*[75] We don't know for sure whether *A. boisei* was the maker of the stone tools the Leakeys found at Olduvai for, as we will learn in the next chapter, it lived alongside at least two other hominid species—*Homo habilis* and *Homo erectus*—who are perhaps the more likely toolmakers.

ONE MODEL OF HUMAN EVOLUTION

At this point, you may well be wondering how all these species fit together. Figure 8–4 shows one model entertained by paleoanthropologists about how the known fossils may be related. The main disagreement among paleontologists concerns which species of *Australopithecus* were ancestral to the line leading to modern humans. For example, the model shown in Figure 8–4 suggests that *A. africanus* is not ancestral to *Homo,* only to one line of robust australopithecines. *Australopithecus afarensis* is viewed as ancestral to both lines of robust australopithecines and to the line leading to modern humans. Those who think that *A. afarensis* was the last common ancestor of all the hominid lines shown in Figure 8–4 think the split to *Homo* occurred over 3 million years ago.[76]

Despite the uncertainty and disagreements about what species was ancestral to the *Homo* line, paleoanthropologists widely agree about other aspects of early hominid evolution: (1) There were at least two separate hominid lines

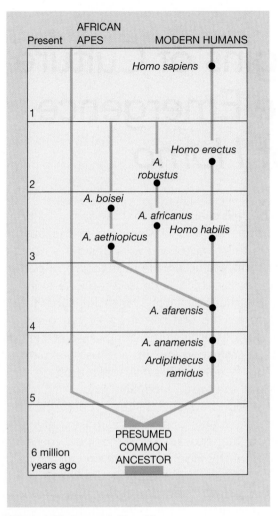

FIGURE 8–4 Phylogenetic Time Lines

Source: Adapted from *The New York Times,* September 5, 1995, p. C9. Dates changed slightly to reflect recent redating.

between 3 million and 1 million years ago; (2) the robust australopithecines were not ancestral to modern humans but became extinct about 1 million years ago; and (3) *Homo habilis* (and successive *Homo* species) were in the direct ancestral line to modern humans. In the next chapter, we turn to our direct ancestors, the first members of the *Homo* genus.

SUMMARY ● ○ ○

1. The drying trend in climate that began about 16 million to 11 million years ago diminished the extent of African rain forests and gave rise to areas of savanna (grasslands) and scattered deciduous woodlands. The new, more open country probably favored characteristics adapted to ground living in some primates. In the evolutionary line leading to humans, these adaptations included bipedalism.

2. One of the crucial changes in early hominid evolution was the development of bipedalism. There are several theories for this development: It may have increased the emerging hominid's ability to see predators and potential prey while moving through the tall grasses of the savanna; by freeing the hands for carrying, it may

have facilitated transferring food from one place to another; tool use, which requires free hands, may have favored two-legged walking; and bipedalism may have made long-distance traveling more efficient.

3. *Sahelanthropus, Orrorin,* and *Ardipithecus* are likely candidates for the first hominid. They date as early as 6 million years ago, and may have walked bipedally. Undisputed hominids dating before 4 million years ago have been found in East Africa. These definitely bipedal hominids are now generally classified in the genus *Australopithecus.*

4. At least six species of australopithecine have been identified, and these are generally divided into two types: gracile and robust. The gracile australopithecines have relatively smaller teeth and jaws, and include *A. anamensis, A. afarensis,* and *A. africanus.* The robust australopithecines have relatively larger teeth and jaws, and are more muscular than the gracile australopithecines. They include *A. aethiopicus, A. robustus,* and *A. boisei.*

GLOSSARY TERMS ○ ● ○

anthropometry **125**
Ardipithecus ramidus **128**
Australopithecus **128**
Australopithecus aethiopicus **129**
Australopithecus afarensis **129**
Australopithecus africanus **129**
Australopithecus anamensis **129**
Australopithecus bahrelghazali **129**
Australopithecus boisei **130**
Australopithecus garhi **129**

Australopithecus robustus **130**
foramen magnum **127**
gracile australopithecines **129**
Kenyanthropus platyops **129**
Orrorin tugenensis **128**
osteology **125**
Pliocene **130**
robust australopithecines **129**
sagittal crest **129**
Sahelanthropus tchadensis **127**
savanna **122**

CRITICAL QUESTIONS ○ ○ ●

1. How could there have been more than one species of hominid living in East Africa at the same time?

2. What may have enabled australopithecines to survive in the face of many ground predators?

3. What evolutionary processes can you envision that may have led the genus *Australopithecus* to divide into two major types: gracile and robust?

PEARSON
myanthrolab

Read the chapter by Scott Simpson titled "*Australopithecus afarensis* and Human Evolution" on MyAnthroLab. Answer the following questions:

1. Why is the Afar region of Ethiopia such a rich and important area for finding early hominid fossils?

2. How does Simpson come to the conclusion that only one species, *A. afarensis,* is represented in the collections from Hadar and Laetoli?

chapter 9

The Origins of Culture and the Emergence of *Homo*

e discussed the origins of bipedalism and how that fundamental hominid means of locomotion first appeared and was refined in the australopithecines in the last chapter. In this chapter, we will consider a number of other trends in hominid evolution, including the routine use of patterned or nearly standardized stone tools, which is considered one sign of the emergence of culture. It is assumed, but not known for sure, that patterned stone tools were made by the first members of our own genus, *Homo,* for we first see a number of trends in the genus *Homo* that probably started because of habitual stone toolmaking and use—expansion of the brain, modification of the female pelvis to accommodate bigger-brained babies, and reduction in the teeth, face, and jaws.

Even though stone tools are found at various sites in East Africa before the time early *Homo* appeared, most anthropologists surmise that members of early *Homo* species, rather than the australopithecines, made those tools (see Figure 9–1). After all, early *Homo* had a brain capacity almost one-third larger than that of the australopithecines. But the fact is that none of the earliest stone tools is clearly associated with early *Homo,* so it is impossible as yet to know who made them.[1] We turn now to a discussion of those earliest stone tools and what archaeologists and paleoanthropologists infer about the lifestyles of their makers, the hominids (whoever they were) who lived between about 2.5 million and 1.5 million years ago.

● ○ ●

EARLY HOMINID TOOLS

The earliest identifiable stone tools found so far come from various sites in East Africa and date from about 2.5 million years ago,[2] and maybe earlier. The oldest tools, some 3,000 in number, were discovered at Gona, Ethiopia. They range from very small flakes (thumb-size) to cobble or core tools that are fist-size.[3] These early tools were apparently made by striking a stone with another stone, a technique called **percussion flaking.** Both the sharp-edged flakes and the sharp-edged cores (the pieces of stone left after flakes are removed) were probably used as tools.

What were those earliest stone tools used for? What do they tell us about early hominid lifestyles? Unfortunately, little can be inferred about lifestyles from the earliest tool sites because little else was found with the tools. In contrast, finds of later tool assemblages at Olduvai Gorge in Tanzania have yielded a rich harvest of cultural information. The Olduvai site was uncovered accidentally in 1911, when a German entomologist followed a butterfly into the gorge and found fossil remains. As we discussed in the last chapter, Louis and Mary Leakey searched the gorge for clues to the evolution of early humans beginning in the 1930s. Of the Olduvai site, Louis Leakey wrote,

> [It] is a fossil hunter's dream, for it shears 300 feet through stratum after stratum of earth's history as through a gigantic layer cake. Here, within reach, lie countless fossils

Artist's reconstruction of a group of *Homo erectus* driving a predator away from an antelope carcass.

and artifacts which but for the faulting and erosion would have remained sealed under thick layers of consolidated rock.[4]

The oldest cultural materials from Olduvai (Bed I) date from Lower Pleistocene times (about 1.6 million years ago). The stone artifacts include core tools and sharp-edged flakes. Flake tools predominate. Among the core tools, so-called choppers are common. Choppers are cores that have been partially flaked and have a side that might have been used for chopping. Other core tools, with flaking along one side and a flat edge, are called scrapers. Whenever a stone has facets removed from only one side of the cutting edge, we call it a **unifacial tool**. If the stone has facets removed from both sides, we call it a **bifacial tool.** Although there are some bifacial tools in the early stone tool assemblages, they are not as plentiful or as elaborated as in later tool traditions. The kind

of tool assemblage found in Bed I and to some extent in later (higher) layers is referred to as **Oldowan** (see Figure 9–2).[5]

EARLY HOMINID LIFESTYLES

Archaeologists have speculated about the lifestyles of early hominids from Olduvai and other sites. Some of these speculations come from analysis of what can be done with the tools, microscopic analysis of wear on the tools, and examination of the marks the tools make on bones; other speculations are based on what is found with the tools.

Archaeologists have experimented with what can be done with Oldowan tools. The flakes appear to be very versatile; they can be used for slitting the hides of animals, dismembering animals, and whittling wood into sharp-pointed sticks (wooden spears or digging sticks). The larger stone tools (choppers and scrapers) can be used to hack off branches or

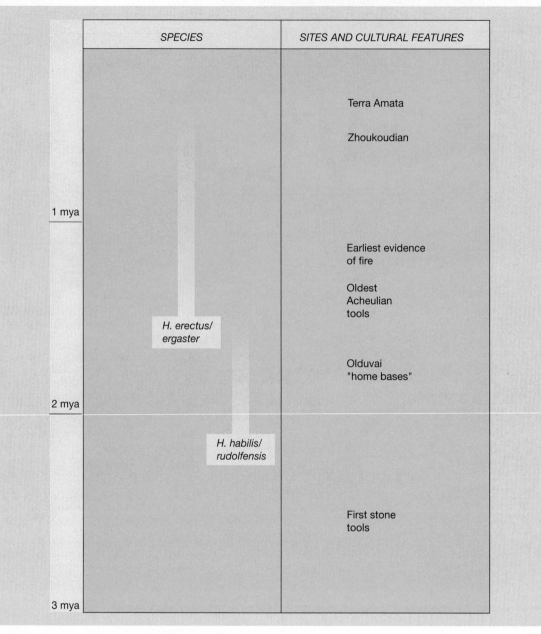

FIGURE 9–1 **Early Evolution of the Genus** *Homo*

cut and chop tough animal joints.[6] Those who have made and tried to use stone tools for various purposes are so impressed by the sharpness and versatility of flakes that they wonder whether most of the core tools were really used as tools. The cores could mainly be what remained after wanted flakes were struck off.[7]

Archaeologists surmise that many early tools were also made of wood and bone, but these do not survive in the archaeological record. Present-day populations use sharp-pointed digging sticks for extracting roots and tubers from the ground; stone flakes are very effective for sharpening wood to a very fine point.[8]

None of the early flaked stone tools can plausibly be thought of as weapons. So, if the toolmaking hominids were hunting or defending themselves with weapons, they had to have used wooden spears, clubs, or unmodified stones as missiles. Later, Oldowan tool assemblages also include stones that were flaked and battered into a rounded shape. The unmodified stones and the shaped stones might have been lethal projectiles.[9]

Experiments may indicate what can be done with tools, but they cannot tell us what was *actually* done with them. Other techniques, such as microscopic analysis of the wear on tools, are more informative. Early studies looked at the microscopic scratches formed when a tool was used in different ways. Scratches parallel to the edge of a tool often occur when a tool is used in a sawing motion; perpendicular scratches suggest whittling or scraping.[10] Lawrence Keeley used high-powered microscopes in his experimental investigations of tools and found that different kinds of "polish" develop on tools when they are used on different materials. The polish on tools used for cutting meat is different from the polish on tools used for woodworking. On the basis of microscopic investigation of the

Olduvai Gorge, Tanzania. Bed I, where evidence of early human culture was found, is at the very bottom of the gorge.

1.5-million-year-old tools from the eastern side of Lake Turkana, Keeley and his colleagues concluded that at least some of the early tools were probably used for cutting meat, others for cutting or whittling wood, and still others for cutting plant stems.[11]

In the 1950s and 1960s, Olduvai Gorge revealed the presence of both Oldowan tools and the remains of broken

Figure 9–2 The Production of a Simple Oldowan Chopper Core and the Resultant Flakes

Source: Freyman 1987. Reprinted by permission of the artist, Ed Hanson.

bones and teeth from many different animal species. For many years, it seemed plausible to assume that hominids were the hunters and the animals their prey. But, archaeologists had to reexamine this assumption with the emergence of the field of *taphonomy*, which studies the processes that can alter and distort an assemblage of bones. So, for example, flowing water can bring bones and artifacts together, which may have happened at Olduvai Gorge about 1.8 million years ago. (The area of what is now the gorge bordered the shores of a shallow lake at that time.) Other animals such as hyenas could have also brought carcasses to some of the same places that hominids spent time. Taphonomy requires archaeologists to consider all the possible reasons things may be found together.[12]

But there is little doubt that hominids were cutting up animal carcasses for meat shortly after 2 million years ago. Microscopic analyses show that cut marks on animal bones were unambiguously created by stone flake tools, and microscopic analyses of the polish on stone tools indicate that the polish is consistent with butchering. We still do not know for sure whether the hominids around Olduvai Gorge were just scavenging meat (taking meat from the kills of other animals) or actually hunting the animals.

On the basis of her analysis of cut marks on bone from Bed I in Olduvai Gorge, Pat Shipman suggested that scavenging, not hunting, was the major meat-getting activity of the hominids living there between 2 million and 1.7 million years ago. For example, the cut marks made by the stone tools usually (but not always) overlie teeth marks made by carnivores. This suggests that the hominids were often scavenging the meat of animals killed and partially eaten by nonhominid predators. The fact that the cut marks were sometimes made first, however, suggested to Shipman that the hominids were also sometimes the hunters.[13] On the other hand, prior cut marks may indicate only that the hominids scavenged before carnivores had a chance to consume their prey.

The artifact and animal remains from Bed I and the lower part of Bed II at Olduvai suggest a few other things

A replica of an Oldowan stone tool is used to chop into a large bone to extract the nutrient-rich marrow. Few animals have jaws powerful enough to break open the bones of large mammals, but stone tools would have allowed early humans to do so.

about the lifestyles of the hominids there. First, it seems that the hominids moved around during the year; most of the sites in what is now the Olduvai Gorge appear to have been used only in the dry season, as indicated by an analysis of the kinds of animal bones found there.[14] Second, whether the early Olduvai hominids were hunters or scavengers, they apparently exploited a wide range of animals. Although most of the bones are from medium-sized antelopes and wild pigs, even large animals such as elephants and giraffes seem to have been eaten.[15] It is clear, then, that the Olduvai hominids scavenged or hunted for meat, but we cannot tell yet how important meat was in their diet.

There is also no consensus about how to characterize the Olduvai sites that contain concentrations of stone tools and animal bones. In the 1970s, there was a tendency to think of them as home bases to which hominids (presumably male) brought meat to share with others (presumably nursing mothers and young children). Indeed, Mary Leakey identified two locations where she thought early hominids had built simple structures (Figure 9–3).

One was a stone circle that she suggested formed the base of a small brush windbreak. The other was a circular area of dense debris surrounded by an area virtually without debris. Leakey suggested that the area lacking debris may represent the location of a ring of thorny brush with which early hominids surrounded their campsite in order to keep out predators—much like pastoralists living in the region do today.[16] But archaeologists today are not so sure that these sites were home bases. For one thing, carnivores also frequented the sites. Places with meaty bones lying around may not have been so safe for hominids to use as home bases. Second, the animal remains at the sites had not been completely dismembered and butchered. If the sites had been hominid home bases, we would expect more complete processing of carcasses.[17] Third, natural processes as simple as trees growing through a site can create circular areas of debris such as the ones Leakey identified as structures, and without better evidence that early hominids made them, one cannot be sure that the circles of debris were indeed structures.[18]

If these sites were not home bases, what were they? Some archaeologists are beginning to think that these early sites with many animal bones and tools may just have been places where hominids processed food but did not live. Why would the hominids return repeatedly to a particular site? Richard Potts suggests one possible reason—that hominids left caches of stone tools and stones for toolmaking at various locations to facilitate recurrent food-collecting and processing activities.[19] Future research may tell us more about early hominid life. Did they have home bases, or did they just move from one processing site to another? How did they protect themselves from predators? They apparently did not have fire to keep the predators away. Did they climb trees to get away or to sleep?

Stone Tools and Culture

Regardless of the answers to these questions, the presence of patterned stone tools means that these early hominids had

FIGURE 9–3 Olduvai "Hut"
A ring of stones and bones found in Bed I of Olduvai Gorge that Mary Leakey interpreted as the remains of an ancient hut.

applied anthropology

Stone Tools and Historic Preservation

Historic preservation laws protect archaeological materials in most countries of the world today. What this means is that people cannot remove artifacts, ecofacts, or fossils from the country without permission, nor can they excavate sites or features. Many professional archaeologists and paleoanthropologists work for governments as applied anthropologists protecting and, when necessary, excavating archaeological deposits to prevent them from being destroyed. In our discussion of early hominid sites in Olduvai Gorge and elsewhere, we have touched upon a difficult question in historic preservation—how can one tell a site from a natural disturbance? More specifically, how can paleoanthropologists distinguish early stone tools from ordinary rocks? It is not always easy.

To tell that a core tool is not a naturally flaked rock, paleoanthropologists typically look for three distinct features. First, the tool has to be made of the *right kind of rock*. The rock must be both flakable and durable. You can flake shale, for example, but it is not durable. Many metamorphic rocks are durable, but you cannot flake them because there are too many flaws in the rock. Most stone tools are made from obsidian, quartz, flint, or chert. Second, paleoanthropologists look for *bilateral flaking*. Bilateral flaking occurs when flakes are struck from two sides of a stone to form a cutting edge. Natural processes may knock a couple of flakes from one side of a stone but will rarely knock them off from opposite sides. Third, paleoanthropologists look for *retouching*. Retouching occurs when additional flakes are removed from an existing tool in order to resharpen it. Again, natural processes may knock a series of flakes from one side of a rock but will rarely create something resembling a retouched cutting edge.

Paleoanthropologists may also look for a distinct *striking platform* on flakes. A striking platform is the place where the blow landed that knocked the flake from the core. When a flake is struck from a core, it leaves a clean scar that can be used as a striking platform to knock a flake from the opposite side of the core. On flakes made by humans, the striking platform is often the scar left by a previous flake. Just as bilateral flaking is rare in nature, so too is a flake scar with a clearly prepared striking platform.

With these features, paleoanthropologists can usually distinguish naturally flaked rocks from stone tools. But this is not always the case, and many paleoanthropologists have made mistakes. Indeed, one of the most famous mistakes was made by Louis Leakey, one of the first paleoanthro-pologists to identify early hominid tools. In the late 1960s, Leakey claimed that a site in California called Calico Hills contained early human tools. This claim was met with disbelief, as no evidence of premodern humans has ever been found in North America, and, as we discuss in the chapter on the Upper Paleolithic world, there is good evidence that modern-looking humans were the continent's first inhabitants. However, because Leakey made the claim, it had to be taken seriously. A group of respected paleoanthropologists met at the site upon Leakey's request to make a determination. Their finding? The alleged stone tools were natural objects, not made by humans.

Calico Hills is an important cautionary tale. How do you know a stone was modified by a hominid, and thus requires protection under historic preservation laws? In addition to the tool's physical features, paleoanthropologists must also consider the context in which it is found. When alleged tools are found in the absence of hominids or with no other clear evidence of stone tool use, as in the case of Calico Hills, and the context does not suggest the possibility of tools, paleoanthropologists should question their presence.

Sources: Andrefsky 1998; Haynes 1973; Patterson 1983.

---

probably developed *culture*. Archaeologists consider a pattern of behavior, such as a particular way to make a tool that is shared and learned by a group of individuals, to be a sign of cultural behavior. To be sure, toolmaking does not imply that early humans had anything like the complex cultures of humans today. Chimpanzees have patterns of tool use and toolmaking that appear to be shared and learned, but they do not have that much in the way of cultural behavior.

What, exactly, makes human culture so different from other forms of animal behavior? Anthropologists have spent more than a century trying to answer this question, and there is still no widely accepted answer. One thing is clear, however: Culture must be understood as a set of interrelated processes, not as a thing.[20] What are the processes that make up culture? Let's consider some of the more important ones.

First, culture is *learned* as well as *shared*. This is the fundamental difference between culture and most other forms of animal behavior. Culture is not a set of innate behaviors but, rather, a set of learned ones. Culture is something individuals acquire during their lifetimes as they mature and interact with others. Interaction is key here, because not only are cultural behaviors learned, they are learned through interaction with others, through education, and through shared experiences. Culture, then, is a social process, not an individual one. It also includes attitudes, values, and ideals as well as behavior.

Second, culture is generally *adaptive*. What this means is that most of the learned and shared behaviors that make up a culture are thought to have developed and spread through a group of people because they help that group of people survive in a given environment. Thus, cultural behaviors may be favored by natural selection just as genes are. The extent to which human culture is a product of natural selection is hotly debated, but few anthropologists would argue that culture is not a key aspect of human adaptation. What makes culture quite different from the behavioral systems of other animals is that, because culture is learned and shared rather than innate, humans can develop new behaviors quickly and adapt to diverse and changing conditions with relative ease. Adaptation, then, is perhaps the most significant process of culture.

Change is the third major process of culture, for culture is always *changing*. Culture change regularly occurs as new and beneficial means of adaptation are developed and shared. But anthropologists also assume that, when new behaviors or ideas are developed, they tend to become integrated with existing behaviors or ideas. That is, new items that conflict with established ones may lead to one or the other changing. For example, a group of early humans could not have both scavenged meat and, at the same time, prohibited eating meat that they did not themselves kill. Such a situation would create a contradiction, and something would probably have to change. Working out contradictions between new, highly beneficial behaviors and established but less beneficial ones may be one of the reasons that cultures are so dynamic. (For more on the concept of culture, see a later chapter that discusses it in more detail.)

It seems clear that the early hominids, like other primates, were social beings. It also seems clear from the archaeological record that early hominids were making and using stone tools on a regular basis. Tools are frequently found in discrete concentrations, and often in association with animal bones and other debris from human activity. And, as we have already noted, a number of paleoanthropologists have argued that such concentrations of debris may represent campsites or even small shelters. Home bases of some sort may have been a part of early hominid culture.

Whether they reflect home bases or not, large numbers of animal bones and tools are found in discrete locations, and these accumulations suggest that groups of individuals used the areas over periods of time. In such a situation, sharing of food is very likely. It seems counterintuitive to think that individuals would have purposely brought food to a common location only to keep it to themselves. Although we must move into the realm of pure speculation, it does seem reasonable to think that closely related individuals, like parents, children, and siblings, would be more likely to associate and share food with one another than more distantly related individuals. This speculation is supported by the fact that, when food sharing takes place among chimpanzees, it is usually among closely related individuals.[21] Thus, the ancient locations of early hominid social activity may be evidence of family groups. How would such a system of social behavior—the creation of a common meeting, resting, and living place for a group of related individuals to share food—have evolved? Let's consider one model.

One Model for the Evolution of Culture

Early *Homo* had a brain almost one-third larger than that of the australopithecines. As we discuss later in the section on trends in hominid evolution, one of the possible consequences of brain expansion was the lessening of maturity at birth. The fact that babies were born more immature may at least partly explain the lengthening of the period of infant and child dependency in hominids. Compared with other animals, we spend not only a longer proportion of our life span, but also the longest absolute period, in a dependent state. Prolonged infant dependency has probably been of great significance in human cultural evolution. According to Theodosius Dobzhansky,

> it is this helplessness and prolonged dependence on the ministrations of the parents and other persons that favors . . . the socialization and learning process on which the transmission of culture wholly depends. This may have been an overwhelming advantage of the human growth pattern in the process of evolution.[22]

It used to be thought that the australopithecines had a long period of infant dependency, just as modern humans do, but the way their teeth apparently developed suggests that the early australopithecines followed an apelike pattern of development. Thus, prolonged maturation may be relatively recent, but just how recent is not yet known.[23]

Although some use of tools for digging, defense, or scavenging may have influenced the development of bipedalism, full bipedalism may have made possible more efficient toolmaking and consequently more efficient foraging and scavenging. As we have seen, there are archaeological signs that early hominids may have been scavenging (and perhaps even hunting) animals as far back as the late Pliocene. Indeed, we have fairly good evidence that early hominids were butchering and presumably eating big game some 2 million years ago.

Whenever it was that hominids began to scavenge for game and perhaps hunt regularly, the development of scavenging would have required individuals to travel long distances frequently in search of suitable carcasses. Among groups of early *Homo,* longer infant and child dependency may have fostered the creation of home bases or at least established meeting places. The demands of childbirth and caring for a newborn might have made it difficult for early *Homo* mothers to travel for some time after the birth. Certainly, it would have been awkward for a mother carrying a nursing child to travel long distances to hunt. Although carrying an infant might be possible with a sling, successful hunting might not be so likely with a needy and potentially noisy child along. Because early *Homo* males (and perhaps females without young children) would have been freer to roam farther from home, they probably became the scavengers or hunters. Women with young children may have gathered wild plants within a small area that could be covered without traveling far from the home base or meeting place.

The creation of home bases or meeting places among early *Homo* groups may have increased the likelihood of food sharing. If mothers with young children were limited to gathering plant foods in a relatively small area, the only way to ensure that they and their children could obtain a complete diet would have been to share the other foods obtained elsewhere. With whom would such sharing take place? Most likely with close relatives. Sharing with them would have made it more likely that their offspring would survive to have offspring. Thus, if early *Homo* had home bases and families, those characteristics could have encouraged the development of the learned and shared behaviors we call culture.[24] Obviously this is a "just-so" story—a tale that we may never be able to prove really happened. However, it is a tale that is consistent with the archaeological record.[25]

TRENDS IN HOMINID EVOLUTION

Patterned stone tools do not appear until early *Homo* comes on the scene. With early *Homo*, we see the start of several trends in hominid evolution that appear to reflect the manufacture and use of patterned stone tools—the expansion of the brain, the modification of the female pelvis to accommodate bigger-brained babies, and a general reduction in the size of teeth, face, and jaws.

Expansion of the Brain

The australopithecines had relatively small cranial capacities, about 380–530 cubic centimeters (cc)—not much larger than that of chimpanzees. But around 2.3 million years ago, close to the time that patterned stone tools first appeared, some hominids show evidence of enlarged brain capacity. These hominids, early *Homo*, had cranial capacities averaging about 630–640 cc, which is about 50 percent of the brain capacity of modern humans (which averages slightly more than 1,300 cc). (See Figure 9–4.) A later member of our genus, *Homo erectus,* which may have first appeared about 1.8 million years ago, had a cranial capacity averaging about 895–1,040 cc, or about 70 percent of the brain capacity of modern humans.[26]

The australopithecines were small, and the earliest *Homo* finds were hardly bigger, so much of the increase in brain size over time might have been a result of later hominids' bigger bodies. When we correct for body size,

however, it turns out that brain size increased not only absolutely but also relatively after 2 million years ago. Between about 4 million and 2 million years ago, relative brain size remained just about the same. Only in the last 2 million years has the hominid brain doubled in relative size and tripled in absolute size.[27]

What may have favored the increase in brain size? As we noted earlier, many anthropologists think that the increase is linked to the emergence of stone toolmaking about 2.5 million years ago. The reasoning is that stone toolmaking was important for the survival of our ancestors, and therefore natural selection would have favored bigger-brained individuals because they had motor and conceptual skills that enabled them to be better toolmakers. According to this view, the expansion of the brain and more sophisticated toolmaking would have developed together. Other anthropologists think that the expansion of the brain may have been favored by other factors, such as warfare, hunting, longer life, and language.[28] One intriguing theory is that life in complex social groups requires increased intelligence and memory, and that the creation of home bases and family groups may have fostered the expansion of the hominid brain.[29] Whatever the factors favoring bigger brains, they also provided humans with an expanded capacity for culture. Thus, along with bipedalism, the expansion of the brain marks a watershed in human evolution.

As the hominid brain expanded, natural selection also favored the widening of the female pelvis to allow larger-brained babies to be born.[30] But there was probably a limit to how far the pelvis could widen and still be adapted to bipedalism. Something had to give, and that something was the degree of physical development of the human infant at birth—for instance, the human infant is born with cranial bones so plastic that they can overlap. Because birth takes place before the cranial bones have hardened, the human infant with its relatively large brain can pass through the opening in the mother's pelvis. Human infants are born at a relatively early stage of development, and are wholly dependent on their parents for many years. As we have noted, this lengthy period of infant dependency may have been an important factor in the evolution of culture.

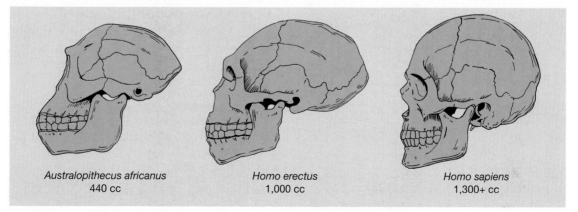

Australopithecus africanus
440 cc

Homo erectus
1,000 cc

Homo sapiens
1,300+ cc

FIGURE 9–4
Comparison of the estimated cranial capacities of *Australopithecus africanus, Homo erectus,* and *Homo sapiens,* demonstrating the expansion of the brain in hominid evolution.

Source: Estimated cranial capacities from Tattersall et al. 2000. Reproduced by permission of Routledge, Inc., part of The Taylor & Francis Group.

Reduction of the Face, Teeth, and Jaws

As in the case of the brain, substantial changes in the face, teeth, and jaws do not appear in hominid evolution until after about 2 million years ago. The australopithecines all have cheek teeth that are very large relative to their estimated body weight, perhaps because the diet of the australopithecines was especially high in plant foods,[31] including small, tough objects such as seeds, nuts, and tubers. The australopithecines have thick jawbones, probably also related to their chewing needs. The australopithecines have relatively large faces that project forward below the eyes. But when we get to the *Homo* forms, we see reduction in the size of the face, cheek teeth, and jaws (see Figure 9–5). It would seem that natural selection in favor of a bigger and stronger chewing apparatus was relaxed. One reason might be that members of the *Homo* genus started to eat foods that were easier to chew. Such foods might have included roots, fruits, and meat. As we discuss later, it may have been the development of habitual tool use and the control of fire that allowed members of the *Homo* genus to change their diet to include foods that are easier to chew, including meat. If food is cooked and easy to chew, individual humans with smaller jaws and teeth would not be disadvantaged, and therefore the face, cheek teeth, and jaw would get smaller on average over time.[32]

The expansion of the brain and reduction of the face occurred at about the same time, and were probably related. A recent discovery in human genetics appears to provide direct evidence of a connection. Researchers studying muscle diseases in modern humans discovered that humans have a unique myosin gene called MYH16

(myosin is a protein in muscle tissue) that is only present in jaw muscles. Comparing MYH16 to related genes in primates, the researchers determined that MYH16 evolved about 2.4 million years ago—around the time the brain began to enlarge and the face and jaw began to shrink. So, the expansion of the brain appears to have been aided by a mutation in myosin that caused jaw muscles to shrink.[33]

Other Evolved Traits

The fossil evidence, which we discuss later in this chapter and in the next chapter, suggests when, and in which hominids, changes occurred in brain size and in the face, teeth, and jaws. Other changes in the evolution of hominids cannot yet be confidently dated with regard to time and particular hominid. For example, we know that modern humans are relatively hairless compared with the other surviving primates. But we do not know when hominids became relatively hairless, because fossilized bones do not tell us whether their owners were hairy. On the other hand, we suspect that most of the other characteristically human traits developed after the brain began to increase in size, during the evolution of the genus *Homo*.

What is the evidence that the physical and behavioral changes we have been discussing occurred during the evolution of the *Homo* genus? We shall now consider the earliest *Homo* fossils and how they are associated with brain expansion and the reduction of the face, jaws, and teeth.

EARLY *HOMO*

Hominids with a brain absolutely and relatively larger than that of the australopithecines appear about 2.3 million years ago. These hominids, classified in our own genus,

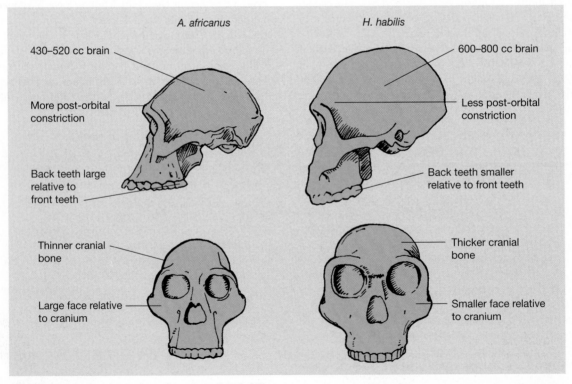

FIGURE 9–5 Comparison of *A. africanus* and *H. habilis*

Homo, are generally divided into two species: **Homo habilis** and **Homo rudolfensis**. Both are known primarily from the western parts of Kenya and Tanzania, but remains have been found elsewhere in eastern and southern Africa, including the Omo Basin of Ethiopia and Sterkfontein cave in South Africa. Both lived in the same place and time as the robust australopithecine, *Australopithecus boisei*, and may later have lived at the same time as *Homo erectus*.

Homo habilis appears to be the earlier of these two species, appearing around 2.3 million years ago. Compared with the australopithecines, *H. habilis* had a significantly larger brain, averaging 630–640 cc,[34] and reduced molars and premolars.[35] The rest of the skeleton is reminiscent of the australopithecines, including the presence of powerful hands and relatively long arms, suggesting that *H. habilis* was at least partially arboreal. *H. habilis* may also have been sexually dimorphic like the australopithecines, as individuals seem to have greatly differed in size.

Homo rudolfensis is roughly contemporary with *Homo habilis*, and shares many of its features. Indeed, many paleoanthropologists make no distinction between the two species, putting *H. rudolfensis* into *H. habilis*. Those who do see them as distinct species point to the larger and more thickly enameled cheek teeth of *H. rudolfensis*, its flatter and broader face, and its more modernlike limb proportions. Even with its larger teeth and broader face, the dentition of *H. rudolfensis* is considerably reduced over the australopithecines and, as in *H. habilis*, its brain is at least a third larger.

We have little postcranial skeletal material for either early *Homo* species, so it is impossible to tell whether the female pelvis had changed. But, with brains averaging a third larger than that of the australopithecines, it seems likely that some modifications must have developed to allow bigger-brained babies to be born. We do know that changes in the female pelvis to accommodate bigger-brained babies can be seen in *Homo erectus*, and it is this species that we turn to next.

HOMO ERECTUS

Homo erectus evolved very shortly after *Homo habilis*, probably about 1.8 million years ago. **Homo erectus** was the first hominid species to be widely distributed in the Old World. Examples of *H. erectus* were found first in Java, later in China, and still later in Africa (see the box "The First Migrants"). Most paleoanthropologists agree that some human ancestor moved from Africa to Asia at some point. Until recently, it was assumed that it was *H. erectus* who moved, because *H. erectus* lived in East Africa about 1.6 million years ago but not until after about 1 million years ago in Asia.[36] Recent redating, however, suggests that *H. erectus* in Java may be somewhat older, dating to perhaps 1.8 million years ago.[37] And *H. erectus* fossils from Dmanisi, in the southeastern European nation of Georgia, have recently been dated to at least 1.7 million years ago.[38] If this last dating is accurate, early hominids may have moved out of Africa earlier. Indeed, one well-preserved skull found at Dmanisi in 2001 has some features that are reminiscent of *H. habilis*—a brain only about 600 cc, relatively large canines, and a relatively thin browridge.[39] Although the excavators classify the skull as *H. erectus*, it does make one wonder whether *H. habilis* or transitional *habilis-erectus* individuals were the first to leave Africa.

The skull of a Homo habilis/rudolfensis (ER-1470) found by Richard Leakey in 1972. Note its high forehead and large braincase.

The skull of the *Homo erectus/ergaster* boy found at Nariokotome, Kenya. Though an adolescent when he died, he already stood five and a half feet tall.

migrants and immigrants

The First Migrants

Hominids evolved in Africa, yet today hominids are found on every continent. Who were the first hominids to leave Africa, and when did they first leave? For many years, the clear answer was that *Homo erectus* were the first to leave Africa, and they did so perhaps 700,000 to 1 million years ago. In recent years, new findings and sources of evidence have led scholars to question this established answer.

The first new information came from geochemist Carl Swisher, who in the mid-1990s redated the Java sites where *Homo erectus* fossils had been found and determined they dated to perhaps 1.8 million years ago. Because the earliest *H. erectus* fossils in Africa share a similar date, this created a problem—how did *H. erectus* appear in Java at about the same time they appeared in Africa? As this question was being pondered, a remarkable set of new *H. erectus* fossils were being uncovered in Dmanisi, Georgia. Dated at 1.7 million years ago, these fossils made it clear that *H. erectus* left Africa almost as soon

as they had evolved. The discovery of a *Homo habilis*-like fossil at Dmanisi, and of Oldowan-like tools at Riwat, Pakistan and Longgupo, China, suggested that *H. habilis* may have been the first to leave Africa, and *H. erectus* followed a path their predecessors blazed. If they were following an earlier migration, it could explain how *H. erectus* were able to move so quickly across Asia.

A more unusual source of information on when hominids first left Africa comes from the parasites that accompanied them. All hominoids are plagued by lice, but humans host a distinct species, *Pediculus humanus*. Geneticist David Reed and his colleagues found that *P. humanus* diverged from other lice about 5.6 million years ago—about the time the first hominids appeared. More interesting, however, Reed and colleagues discovered that there are two subspecies of *P. humanus* that appear to have diverged about 1.2 million years ago. One subspecies is found worldwide today; the other is restricted to the New World. Reed and

colleagues suggest this is evidence that at least some hominid migrants (probably *H. erectus*) became isolated in Asia by at least 1.2 million years ago, where their lice diverged from that of other hominid populations, only to be picked up much later by modern human migrants who ended up colonizing the New World.

So, who were the first hominid migrants? They may have been *H. habilis,* or they may have been very early *H. erectus*. When did the first hominid migrations out of Africa take place? Probably slightly less than 2 million years ago, but once these hominids left, they moved quickly, and they moved long distances. By 1.6 million years ago, *H. erectus* was in both western and southern Asia, and by 1.2 million years ago, their populations had moved far enough to have become isolated from one another. Whether or not they were the first migrants out of Africa, *H. erectus* migrated fast and far.

Sources: Reed et al. 2004; Tattersall 1997.

Neandertals, but resembles that of the great apes and australopithecines (unfortunately, no wrists of *H. erectus* or *H. habilis* have been found, so no comparison can be made to them).[53] Similarly, the foot of *H. floresiensis* resembles that of *H. erectus* and earlier hominids more than that of modern humans.[54] Once again, *H. floresiensis* appears to be a tiny version of *H. erectus*.

How might a miniature version of *H. erectus* have evolved? The answer is that both dwarfism and gigantism are common phenomena in isolated populations. Dwarfism appears to be an adaptation that occurs when there are few predators—a species in isolation can become smaller, and have a large population, if there are no predators threatening them. This may be what happened on Flores.[55] It is interesting that the island also hosted a number of dwarf species in addition to *H. floresiensis*, including a dwarf elephant that appears to have been one of the favorite foods of *H. floresiensis*. Perhaps even more interesting is the fact that *H. floresiensis* may have survived until as recently as 12,000 years ago—well into the time period when modern humans were living in Indonesia. Could modern humans

and the tiny *H. floresiensis* have met some time in the distant past? It is an intriguing possibility, but there is no evidence to tell us.

The Evolution of *Homo erectus*

The evolution of *Homo erectus* reflects a continuation of the general evolutionary trends we discussed previously. The brain continued to expand, increasing more than a third over early *Homo* (just as early *Homo* had increased more than a third over the australopithecines). The face, teeth, and jaws continued to shrink, taking on an almost modern form. An increasing use and variety of tools may have led to a further development of the brain. *Homo erectus* was eating and probably cooking meat, and this may have led to further reduction in the teeth and jaws.

One additional change in *Homo erectus* is an apparent reduction in the extent of sexual dimorphism to almost modern levels. Recall that the australopithecines and early *Homo* were quite sexually dimorphic. *Homo erectus* does not appear to be as sexually dimorphic as these earlier hominids. What might have caused this change? In other primates, sexual dimorphism appears to be linked to social systems in which males are at the top of dominance hierarchies due to physical size and prowess and such males control sexual access to multiple females in the group. In contrast, lack of sexual dimorphism seems most pronounced in the animals where *pair bonding* exists—that is, where a male and a female form a breeding pair that lasts for a long period of time (as we will learn in later chapters, there are several distinct variations of male-female bonding in modern human cultures).[56] Could male-female bonding have developed in *Homo erectus*? It seems possible.

Recall that early *Homo* may have established some of the basic elements of human culture, including home bases or meeting places, family groups, and sharing. Another basic element of recent human culture, one that is present in almost all known cultures, is *marriage*. Marriage is a socially recognized sexual and economic bond between two individuals, typically a male and a female, that is intended to continue throughout the lifetimes of the individuals and to produce socially accepted children. It is a specific kind of pair bond with a set of behaviors, expectations, and obligations that extend beyond the pair to those individuals' families. With marriage, then, the competition between males for access to females may have diminished, lessening the importance of sexual dimorphism. But why might marriage have developed in *Homo erectus*?

In animal species where females can feed themselves and their babies after birth, pair bonding is rare. But in species where females cannot feed both themselves and their babies, pair bonding is common. Why? We think it is because a strong male-female bond provides a good solution to the problem of incompatibility between a mother's feeding requirements and tending a newborn baby. A male partner can bring food and/or watch the newborn while the mother gets food.[57] But most primates lack pair bonding. This may be because primate infants are able to cling to their mother's fur soon after birth, so that the mother's hands are free to forage. Human infants demonstrate a residual form of this innate ability to cling during their first few weeks of life. This is called the *Moro reflex*. If a human infant feels it is falling backward, it will automatically stretch out its arms and clench its fists.[58]

This infant chimpanzee has no problem traveling with its mother, as it can cling tightly to her fur. *Homo erectus* mothers probably had no fur to hold on to and had to carry their infants.

We have no way of knowing if *Homo erectus* had fur like other primates, but we think probably not, because we think they may have worn clothing, as we discuss later. The brain in *Homo erectus* may also have already expanded enough that *Homo erectus* infants, like modern human infants, could not adequately support their heads even if they could hold onto their mother's fur. In any case, when early hominids began to depend on scavenging and hunting for food (and for skins to be used in clothing), it would have been difficult and hazardous for a parent with a newborn baby to engage in these activities with a baby along. Marriage would have been an effective solution to this problem because each parent could help protect the baby while the other was away getting food. (For further discussion of this theory, see the chapter on marriage.)

Another important aspect of the evolution of *Homo erectus* was the movement of populations out of eastern and southern Africa. As with the lessening of sexual dimorphism, it seems likely that cultural innovations were the key to allowing *Homo erectus* to move into new environments. Why? Because upon entering new environments, *Homo erectus* would have been faced with new (and generally colder) climatic conditions, new and different sources of raw material for tools, and new plants and animals to rely on for food. All animals adapt to such changes through natural selection, but natural selection typically takes a relatively long time and requires physical changes in the adapting organisms. *Homo erectus* was able to adapt to new environments very quickly and without apparent physical changes. This suggests that the primary mechanisms of adaptation for *Homo erectus* were cultural rather than biological.

What cultural adaptations might *Homo erectus* have made? Fire might have been the crucial cultural adaptation to colder climates. As we discuss later, there is tantalizing evidence that *Homo erectus* used fire. But fire can only warm people when they are stationary; it doesn't help when people are out collecting food. To be mobile in colder climates, *Homo erectus* may have begun to wear animal furs for warmth. Some *Homo erectus* tools look like the hide-processing tools used by more recent human groups,[59] and it seems unlikely that *Homo erectus* could have survived in the colder locations where they have been found, in eastern Europe and Asia, without some form of clothing. And if *Homo erectus* was wearing furs for warmth, they must have been hunting. *Homo erectus* could not have depended on scavenging to acquire skins—the skin is the first thing predators destroy when they dismember a carcass. *Homo erectus* needing skins would have had to kill fur-bearing animals themselves if they wanted intact skins and furs for clothing.

As we mentioned earlier, fossil remains themselves cannot provide evidence for whether or not *H. erectus* was hairless. But scientists have found that the genes of modern peoples may offer clues to when our ancestors became hairless. For example, one of the primary genes responsible for hair and skin color, called MC1R, demonstrates uniformity among modern dark-skinned African populations, but diversity among non-Africans. Alan Rogers and colleagues have recently argued that the uniformity in this gene among Africans demonstrates recent, powerful selective pressure in favor of darker skin, and that protection against the tropical sun after the loss of body hair is the likely reason. When did this selective pressure start? Rogers and colleagues estimate it was at least 1.2 million years ago.[60]

It is interesting to consider that, in eastern Africa, *Homo erectus* coexisted with at least one other species of hominid (*A. boisei*), and possibly with as many as three others (*A. boisei, A. africanus,* and *H. habilis/rudolfensis*). Why did *Homo erectus* survive and flourish while these other species went extinct? Again, culture may be the answer. *A. boisei* seems to have been a specialized grasslands species. Their large molars and powerful dental architecture would have allowed them to eat hard grass seeds and other coarse materials that other hominids could not chew. However, they had to compete with the many other grassland animals that also relied on these plants, but reproduced faster and had speed to help them escape from predators. Early *Homo* was apparently a tool user and relied at least in part on scavenging and hunting, but compared to *Homo erectus,* early *Homo* technology was crude and early *Homo* populations may not have been as well organized to scavenge, hunt, and to defend themselves against predators. These differences in culture may have provided advantages to *Homo erectus* that drove early *Homo* to extinction.

This scenario, just like the one we suggested for the evolution of early *Homo,* is a "just-so" story that may or may not be true. But it does fit the facts we now have about *Homo erectus* and the area in which it evolved. Regardless of this story's particular details, there seems no doubt that the development of a more complex culture was vital to the evolution of *Homo erectus.*

LOWER PALEOLITHIC CULTURES

The stone tool traditions of *Homo erectus* are traditionally called **Lower Paleolithic**. These stone tool traditions involve "core" tool techniques, in which a core of stone, rather than a flake, is used as the basic raw material for finished tools (we will talk more about Lower Paleolithic stone tool technology shortly). Because stone tools are the most common cultural material in the archaeological record of these ancient peoples, the entire culture of *Homo erectus* is often termed *Lower Paleolithic,* a practice we follow here.

The archaeological finds of tools and other cultural artifacts dating from 1.5 million years to about 200,000 years ago are assumed to have been produced by *Homo erectus.* But hominid fossils are not usually associated with these materials. Therefore some of the tools during this period were possibly produced by hominids other than *H. erectus,* such as australopithecines earlier and *H. sapiens* later. But the so-called *Acheulian* tool assemblages dating from 1.5 million years ago to more than a million years later are very similar to each other, and *H. erectus* is the only hominid that spans the entire period. Thus, it is conventionally assumed that *H. erectus* was responsible for most if not all of the Acheulian tool assemblages we describe.[61]

The Acheulian Tool Tradition

The stone toolmaking tradition known as the **Acheulian** was named after the site at St. Acheul, France, where the first examples were found. But the oldest Acheulian tools recovered are from East Africa, on the Peninj River, Tanzania, dating back about 1.5 million years.[62] In contrast to Oldowan, Acheulian assemblages have more large tools created according to standardized designs or shapes. Oldowan tools have sharp edges made by a few blows. Acheulian toolmakers shaped the stone by knocking more flakes off most of the edges. Many of these tools were made from very large flakes that had first been struck from very large cores or boulders.

One of the most characteristic and common tools in the Acheulian tool kit is the so-called **hand axe**, which is a teardrop-shaped, bifacially flaked tool with a thinned sharp tip. Other large tools resemble cleavers and picks. There were also many kinds of flake tools, such as scrapers with a wide edge.

Early Acheulian tools appeared to have been made by blows with a hard stone, but later tools are wider and flatter and may have been made with a **soft hammer** of bone or antler.[63] This soft hammer technique of making stone tools was an important innovation. Tools made by a **hard hammer** technique, rock against rock, have limits in terms of their sharpness and form, because only large and thick flakes can be made with a hard hammer technique (unless the flintknapper is very skillful and the stone being used has unique qualities). Flakes created by soft hammer flaking are much thinner and longer than hard hammer flakes, and the flintknapper generally has better control over their size and shape. This means that thinner and sharper tools can be made, as well as tools with complex shapes. Hand axes can be made with either technique, as their shape is simple, but those made using a soft hammer have much thinner and sharper edges.[64]

Were hand axes made for chopping trees, as their name suggests? We cannot be sure what they were used for, but experiments with them suggest that they are not good for cutting trees; they seem more suited for butchering large animals.[65] Lawrence Keeley microscopically examined some Acheulian hand axes, and the wear on them is more consistent with animal butchery. They may also have been used for woodworking, particularly hollowing and shaping wood, and they are also good for digging.[66] William Calvin has even suggested that a hand axe could be used as a projectile thrown like a discus into a herd of animals in the hope of injuring or killing an animal.[67]

Acheulian tools are found widely in Africa, Europe, and western Asia, but bifacial hand axes, cleavers, and picks are not found as commonly in eastern and southeastern Asia.[68] Because *H. erectus* has been found in all areas of the Old World, it is puzzling that the tool traditions seem to differ from west to east. Some archaeologists have suggested that large bifacial tools may be lacking in eastern and southeastern Asia because *H. erectus* in Asia had a better material to make tools out of— bamboo. Bamboo has been used recently in Southeast Asia for many purposes, including incredibly sharp

Homo erectus ate—and probably hunted—large game animals, and they probably also learned to control fire.

arrows and sticks for digging and cutting. Geoffrey Pope has shown that bamboo is found precisely in those areas of Asia where hand axes and other large bifacial tools are largely missing.[69]

Big Game Eating

Some of the Acheulian sites have produced evidence of big game eating. F. Clark Howell, who excavated sites at Torralba and Ambrona, Spain, found a substantial number of elephant remains and unmistakable evidence of human presence in the form of tools. Howell suggests that the humans at those sites used fire to frighten elephants into muddy bogs from which they would be unable to escape.[70] To hunt elephants in this way, the humans would have had to plan and work cooperatively in fairly large groups.

But do these finds of bones of large- and medium-sized animals, in association with tools, tell us that the humans definitely were big game hunters? Some archaeologists who have reanalyzed the evidence from Torralba think that the big game may have been scavenged. Because the Torralba and Ambrona sites are near ancient streams, many of the elephants could have died naturally, their bones accumulating in certain spots because of the flow of water.[71] What seems fairly clear is that the humans did deliberately butcher different kinds of game—different types of tools are found with different types of animals.[72] Thus, whether the humans hunted big game at Torralba and Ambrona is debatable; all we can be sure of, as of now, is that they consumed big game and probably hunted smaller game.

Control of Fire

One way in which *H. erectus* is thought to have hunted is by using *fire drives*—a technique still used by hunting and gathering peoples in recent times. It is highly effective: Animals are driven out of their hiding places and homes by fire and dispatched by hunters positioned downwind of the oncoming flames. Most peoples who use this technique today set fires deliberately, but fires caused by lightning strikes may have also been utilized. Did *H. erectus* set these fires? Because *H. erectus* was the first hominid to be found throughout the Old World and in areas with

freezing winters, most anthropologists presume that *H. erectus* had learned to control fire, at least for warmth. There is archaeological evidence of fire in some early sites, but fires can be natural events. Thus, whether fire was under deliberate control by *H. erectus* is not definitely established.[73]

Suggestive but not conclusive evidence of the deliberate use of fire comes from Kenya in East Africa and is over 1.4 million years old.[74] More persuasive evidence of human control of fire, dating from nearly 800,000 years ago, comes from the site of Gesher Benot Ya'aqov in Israel. Here, researchers found evidence of burned seeds, wood, and stone, as well as concentrations of burned items suggestive of hearths.[75] Evidence of the deliberate use of fire comes from Europe somewhat later. Unfortunately, the evidence of control of fire at Gesher Benot Ya'aqov and European sites is not associated with *H. erectus* fossils, so the link between deliberate use of fire and *H. erectus* cannot definitely be established yet.[76] The lack of clear evidence does not, of course, mean that *H. erectus* did not use fire. After all, *H. erectus* did move into cold areas of the world, and it is hard to imagine how that could have happened without the deliberate use of fire. Such a move is also hard to imagine if *H. erectus* were relatively hairless and did not get warm skins and furs from hunting.

Clothing, therefore, may have been necessary, but fire might have been even more important, and not only for warmth. Cooking would be possible. The control of fire was a major step in increasing the energy under human control. Cooking would have made all kinds of food (not just meat) more safely digestible and therefore more usable.[77] Fires would also have kept predators away, a not inconsiderable advantage given that there were many.

Campsites

Acheulian sites were usually located close to water sources, lush vegetation, and large stocks of herbivorous animals. Some camps have been found in caves, but most were in open areas surrounded by rudimentary fortifications or windbreaks. Several African sites are marked by stony rubble brought there by *H. erectus,* possibly for the dual purpose of securing the windbreaks and providing ammunition in case of a sudden attack.[78]

The presumed base campsites display a wide variety of tools, indicating that the camp was the center of many group functions. More specialized sites away from camp have also been found. These are marked by the predominance of a particular type of tool. For example, a butchering site in Tanzania contained dismembered hippopotamus carcasses and rare heavy-duty smashing and cutting tools. Workshops are another kind of specialized site encountered with some regularity. They are characterized by tool debris and are located close to a source of natural stone suitable for toolmaking.[79]

A camp has been excavated at the Terra Amata site near Nice, on the French Riviera. The camp appears to have been occupied in the late spring or early summer, judging by the pollen found in fossilized human feces. The excavator describes stake holes driven into the sand, paralleled by lines of stones, presumably marking the spots where the people constructed huts of roughly 30 feet by 15 feet (see Figure 9–8). A basic feature of each hut was a central hearth that seems to have been protected from drafts by a small wall built just outside the northeast corner of the hearth. The evidence suggests that the Terra Amata occupants gathered seafood such as oysters and mussels, did some fishing, and hunted in the surrounding area. The animal remains suggest that they obtained both small and large animals but mostly got the young of larger animals such as stags, elephants, boars, rhinoceroses, and wild oxen. Some of the huts contain recognizable toolmakers' areas, scattered with tool debris; occasionally, the impression of an animal skin shows where the toolmaker actually sat.[80]

Religion and Ritual

Thus far, we have discussed the lifestyles of Lower Paleolithic and, in the last chapter, of late Pliocene peoples, but we have not talked about the less material aspects of life, such as religion and ritual. What beliefs did *Homo erectus* hold about the world around them? Did they take part in rituals? Did *H. erectus* have religion? The data we have to answer these questions are limited, but there are some hints that ritual and religion may have been a part of Lower Paleolithic culture.

Remains of *red ochre* (oxidized clay) have been found on a number of Lower Paleolithic sites.[81] This may be significant because, in many later cultures, even modern ones, red ochre has been used in rituals of various types to represent blood or, more generally, life. Ochre seems to be particularly important in burial rituals, and human remains sprinkled with red ochre have been found in many parts of the world and dating as far back as the Middle Paleolithic (about 200,000 years ago). However, there is no evidence that *Homo erectus* buried their dead, nor any evidence that ochre was used in rituals. It may have been used for body decoration, or simply for protection against insects or sunburn.

More significant, and even more controversial, is the suggestion made by the excavators of Zhoukoudian (in northern China) that some of the *H. erectus* remains there showed evidence of ritual cannibalism.[82] The foramen magnum of some specimens had been deliberately enlarged and the facial bones had been deliberately broken away from the cranium on others. A possible reason may have been to remove the brain for ritual consumption. Ritual cannibalism has been widely reported among living peoples, so its presence among ancient peoples is not impossible. But scholars point out that the parts of the skull that seem to have been

FIGURE 9–8 A Reconstruction of the Oval Huts Built at Terra Amata.
These huts were approximately 30 feet by 15 feet.

Source: Copyright © 1969 by Eric Mose.

purposely enlarged (to remove the brain) are those that are also the weakest points on the skull, and may have broken away because of decay or disturbance over the millennia.

At this point, we simply cannot say whether religion and ritual were parts of Lower Paleolithic culture.

SUMMARY ● ○ ○

1. The earliest identifiable stone tools found so far come from various sites in East Africa and date from about 2.5 million years ago. Flake tools predominate, but choppers are also common. Choppers are cores that have been partially flaked and have a side that might have been used for chopping. These early stone tools are referred to as Oldowan.

2. Archaeologists have experimented with what can be done with Oldowan tools. The flakes appear to be very versatile; they can be used for slitting the hides of animals, dismembering animals, and whittling wood. The choppers can be used to hack off branches or cut and chop tough animal joints. Hominids shortly after 2 million years ago were cutting up animal carcasses for meat, mostly obtained through scavenging rather than hunting.

3. There are archaeological sites dating as early as 2 million years ago that contain concentrations of stone tools and animal bones. Some scholars think these might have been early hominid home bases, others do not. If these sites were not home bases, what were they? Some archaeologists are beginning to think that these early sites with many animal bones and tools may just have been places where hominids processed food but did not live.

4. The presence of stone tools and perhaps home bases suggests that early hominids had culture. Culture is a dynamic, adaptive process of learned, shared, and integrated behaviors and ideas.

5. Important physical changes in early hominids that led to the evolution of our genus, *Homo*, include the expansion of the brain, the modification of the female pelvis to allow bigger-brained babies to be born, and the reduction of the face, teeth, and jaws. These physical changes are seen in the species *Homo habilis* and *Homo rudolfensis*, both of which date to around 2.3 million years ago. Early *Homo* appears to have used tools and scavenged or possibly hunted meat, so culture, or the evolution of cultural behavior, seems to have played a role in these physical changes as well.

6. *Homo erectus* emerged about 1.8 million to 1.6 million years ago. It had a larger brain capacity than *Homo habilis* and an essentially modern postcranial skeleton. What differentiates *Homo erectus* most from modern humans is the shape of the skull, which is long, low, and has prominent browridges.

7. *Homo erectus* was the first hominid species to be widely distributed in the Old World. Some of the locations where *Homo erectus* lived in eastern Europe and Asia were quite cold, and *Homo erectus* was able to adapt to these new and often colder environments through culture. Some scholars reserve *Homo erectus* for those populations living outside of Africa, and call the African populations *Homo ergaster*. Outside of Africa, there was at least one additional species of hominid, *Homo floresiensis*.

8. Lower Paleolithic tools and other cultural artifacts from about 1.6 million to about 200,000 years ago were probably produced by *H. erectus*. Acheulian is the name given to the most well-known tool tradition of this period. Acheulian tools include both small flake tools and large tools, but hand axes and other large bifacial tools are characteristic.

9. Although it is presumed that *H. erectus* had learned to use fire to survive in areas with cold winters, there is no definite evidence of the control of fire by *H. erectus*. There is evidence in some sites of big game eating, but whether *H. erectus* hunted those animals is debated. There is little evidence of ritual behavior among *H. erectus*.

GLOSSARY TERMS ○ ● ○

Acheulian **150**	Lower Paleolithic **150**
bifacial tool **137**	occipital torus **147**
hand axe **150**	Oldowan **137**
hard hammer **150**	percussion
Homo **136**	flaking **136**
Homo erectus **145**	prognathic **147**
Homo ergaster **146**	sagittal keel **147**
Homo floresiensis **147**	soft hammer **150**
Homo habilis **145**	taurodontism **147**
Homo rudolfensis **145**	unifacial tool **137**

CRITICAL QUESTIONS ○ ○ ●

1. Why might early hominids have begun to make stone tools? How would stone tools have been more useful than wood or bone tools?

2. How do the physical changes that occur in early hominids correlate with the apparent changes in their behavior?

3. How did *Homo erectus* culture differ from the culture of earlier hominids?

4. When compared to earlier hominids, *Homo erectus* is larger, has a larger brain, and smaller teeth. How might these physical changes correlate with apparent behavioral changes in *Homo erectus*?

5. *Homo erectus* lived in many places in the Old World. What may have enabled them to spread so widely?

PEARSON
myanthrolab

Read the chapter by Andrew Kramer titled "The Natural History and Evolutionary Fate of Homo erectus" on MyAnthroLab. Answer the following questions:

1. What is the primary question Kramer attempts to answer in his article? Why is this question important?

2. What methods does Kramer use to determine whether different populations of H. erectus were different species?

3. Describe the difference between "lumpers" and "splitters." How might this difference affect the way each group of scholars views human evolution?

chapter 10

The Emergence of *Homo sapiens*

Recent finds in Africa indicate the presence of *Homo sapiens* perhaps 160,000 years ago (see Figure 10–1). Completely modern-looking humans, ***Homo sapiens sapiens,*** appeared by 50,000 years ago. One paleoanthropologist, Christopher Stringer, characterizes the modern human, *Homo sapiens sapiens,* as having "a domed skull, a chin, small eyebrows, browridges, and a rather puny skeleton."[1] Some of us might not like to be called puny, but except for our larger brain, most modern humans definitely are puny compared with *Homo erectus* and even with earlier forms of our own species, *H. sapiens.* We are relatively puny in several respects, including our thinner and lighter bones, as well as our smaller teeth and jaws.

In this chapter, we discuss the fossil evidence, as well as the controversies, about the transition from *H. erectus* to modern humans, which may have begun 500,000 years ago. We also discuss what we know archaeologically about the Middle Paleolithic cultures between about 300,000 and 40,000 years ago. ● ○ ●

THE TRANSITION FROM *HOMO ERECTUS* TO *HOMO SAPIENS*

Most paleoanthropologists agree that *H. erectus* evolved into *H. sapiens,* but they disagree about how and where the transition occurred. There is also disagreement about how to classify some fossils from about 500,000 years to 200,000 years ago that have a mix of *H. erectus* and *H. sapiens* traits.[2] A particular fossil might be called *H. erectus* by some anthropologists and "archaic" *Homo sapiens* by others. And, as we shall see, still other anthropologists see so much continuity between *H. erectus* and *H. sapiens* that they think it is completely arbitrary to call them different species. According to these anthropologists, *H. erectus* and *H. sapiens* may just be earlier and later varieties of the same species and therefore all should be called *H. sapiens.* (*H. erectus* would then be *H. sapiens erectus.*)

Homo heidelbergensis

In recent years, some scholars have suggested that the "transitional" fossils share common traits and may actually represent a separate species—***Homo heidelbergensis***, named after a jaw found in 1907, in the village of Mauer near Heidelberg, Germany.[3] Other specimens that have been suggested as members of this species have been found in many parts of the world: Bodo, Hopefield, Ndutu, Elandsfontein, and Rabat in Africa; Bilzingsleben, Petralona, Arago, Steinheim, and Swanscombe in Europe; and Dali and Solo in Asia. More recently discovered "transitional" specimens from the Atapuerca region of Spain have been classified as a different species, ***Homo antecessor***, but many scholars believe these specimens should be classified as *H. heidelbergensis.*[4] To simplify things, we will call all these "transitional" specimens *H. heidelbergensis.*

Homo heidelbergensis differs from *Homo erectus* in having smaller teeth and jaws, a much larger brain (on the order of 1,300 cc), a skull that lacks a sagittal keel and occipital torus, a browridge that divides into separate arches above each eye, and a more robust skeleton (see Figure 10–2). *Homo heidelbergensis* differs from *Homo sapiens* in retaining a large and prognathic face with relatively large teeth and jaws, a browridge, a long, low cranial vault with a sloping forehead, and in its more robust skeleton.[5]

Skull of *Homo neandertalensis.*

Many scholars question whether *Homo heidelbergensis* represents one or several species of Middle Pleistocene hominid, or whether it is indeed a separate species at all. Many would argue that *Homo heidelbergensis* should be considered an archaic *Homo sapiens.* As noted, some scholars also argue that *Homo erectus* should be included in the *Homo sapiens* species.

Neandertals: *Homo sapiens* or *Homo neandertalensis?*

There may be disagreement about how to classify the mixed-trait fossils from 500,000 to 200,000 years ago, but recently an outright battle has emerged about many of the fossils that are less than 200,000 years old. Some anthropologists argue that they were definitely *Homo sapiens* and classify them as *Homo sapiens neandertalensis.* Other anthropologists argue

that they were part of a distinct species, ***Homo neandertalensis,*** more commonly referred to as the **Neandertals.** The Neandertals have been a confusing hominid fossil group since the first specimen was found in 1856. Somehow through the years, the Neandertals have become the victims of their cartoon image, which usually misrepresents them as burly and more ape than human. Actually, they might go unnoticed in a cross-section of the world's population today. Were they part of our species? For a while, the answer seemed to be yes. But recent archaeological and genetic evidence has led most to question the relationship between Neandertals and modern humans, and today the tide seems to have turned against those who would group them together. Let's take a look at some of the history of research on the Neandertals.

In 1856, three years before Darwin's publication of *Origin of Species,* a skullcap and other fossilized bones were

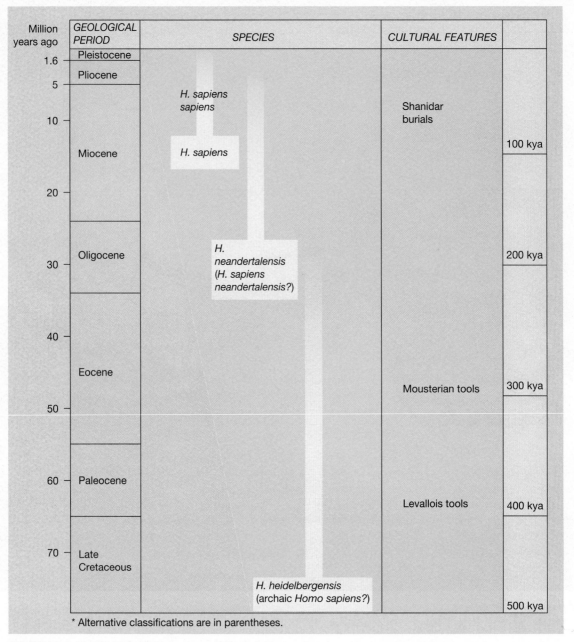

Million years ago	GEOLOGICAL PERIOD	SPECIES	CULTURAL FEATURES	
1.6	Pleistocene			
5	Pliocene	*H. sapiens sapiens*	Shanidar burials	
10		*H. sapiens*		100 kya
	Miocene			
20				
30	Oligocene	*H. neandertalensis* (*H. sapiens neandertalensis?*)		200 kya
40				
	Eocene			
50			Mousterian tools	300 kya
60	Paleocene		Levallois tools	400 kya
70	Late Cretaceous			
		H. heidelbergensis (archaic *Homo sapiens?*)		500 kya

* Alternative classifications are in parentheses.

FIGURE 10–1 Timeline for the Emergence of Modern Humans*

discovered in a cave in the Neander Valley (*tal* is the German word for "valley"), near Düsseldorf, Germany. The fossils in the Neander Valley were the first that scholars could tentatively consider as an early hominid. (The fossils classified as *Homo erectus* were not found until later in the 19th century, and the fossils belonging to the genus *Australopithecus* were not found until the 20th century.) After Darwin's revolutionary work was published, the Neandertal find aroused considerable controversy. A few evolutionist scholars, such as Thomas Huxley, thought that the Neandertal was not that different from modern humans. Others dismissed the Neandertal as irrelevant to human evolution; they saw it as a pathological freak, a peculiar, disease-ridden individual.

However, similar fossils turned up later in Belgium, Yugoslavia, France, and elsewhere in Europe, which meant that the original Neandertal find could not be dismissed as an oddity.[6]

The predominant reaction to the original and subsequent Neandertal-like finds was that the Neandertals were too "brutish" and "primitive" to have been ancestral to modern humans. This view prevailed in the scholarly community until well into the 1950s. A major proponent of this view was Marcellin Boule, who between 1908 and 1913, claimed that the Neandertals would not have been capable of complete bipedalism. Boule, however, misinterpreted the bowed legs and bent spine in the Neandertal skeleton he examined—these were not normal in

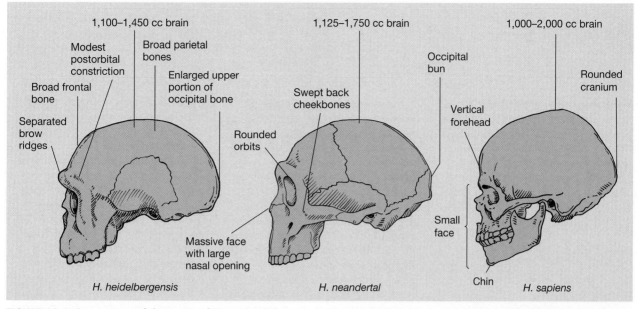

FIGURE 10–2 Comparison of the crania of *Homo heidelbergensis*, *Homo neandertalensis*, and *Homo sapiens*, showing important differences.

Neandertals, but were the result of disease in this particular individual. It is now universally agreed that the skeletal traits of the Neandertals are completely consistent with bipedalism.

Perhaps more important, when the much more ancient australopithecine and *H. erectus* fossils were accepted as hominids in the 1940s and 1950s, anthropologists realized that the Neandertals did not look that different from modern humans—despite their sloping foreheads, large browridges, flattened braincases, large jaws, and nearly absent chins (see Figure 10–2).[7] After all, they did have larger brains (averaging more than 1,450 cc) than modern humans (slightly more than 1,300 cc).[8] Some scholars believe that the large brain capacity of Neandertals suggests that they were capable of the full range of behaviors characteristic of modern humans. Their skeletons did, however, attest to one behavioral trait markedly different from behaviors of most modern humans: Neandertals apparently made very strenuous use of their bodies.[9]

It took almost 100 years for scholars to accept the idea that Neandertals were not that different from modern humans and perhaps should be classified as *Homo sapiens neandertalensis*. But in the last decade, there has been a growing debate over whether the Neandertals in western Europe were ancestral to modern-looking people who lived later in western Europe, after about 40,000 years ago. Neandertals lived in other places besides western Europe. A large number of fossils from central Europe strongly resemble those from western Europe, although some features, such as a projecting midface, are less pronounced.[10] Neandertals have also been found in southwestern Asia (Israel, Iraq) and Central Asia (Uzbekistan). One of the largest collections of Neandertal fossils comes from Shanidar cave in the mountains of northeastern Iraq, where Ralph Solecki unearthed the skeletons of nine individuals (see Figure 10–3).[11]

A comparison of a Neandertal and a modern human skeleton. Note how similar they are, yet the Neandertal appears more stocky and robust.

What has changed scholars' opinions of the Neandertals so that they are now most commonly seen as not belonging to the *Homo sapiens* group?

In 1997, a group of researchers from the United States and Germany published findings that forced a reconsideration of the Neandertals and their relationship to modern

applied anthropology

Facial Reconstruction

Have you ever wondered how we know what early humans looked like? We have pictures of them throughout this book, but how did the artists determine what to sculpt or draw? The answer lies in the field of forensic anthropology and more particularly in the field of facial reconstruction.

Boule's reconstruction of a Neandertal, as displayed at Chicago's Field Museum in 1929, illustrates how subjective fossil reconstructions can be. It falsely implies that Neandertals could not stand upright or straighten their knees, and that they were more primitive than we know today that they actually were.

Facial reconstruction is based on knowledge of skull musculature and the thickness of soft tissue, determined over many years (the first such analysis was done in 1895) from cadavers and, more recently, magnetic resonance images of living people. From these measurements, forensic anthropologists have established a standard set of 21 to 34 locations on the skull where the average soft tissue thicknesses are known. The first step in facial reconstruction is to mark these locations on a cast of the skull to be reconstructed, using pegs that are the same length as the thickness of muscle and soft tissue at that location. Clay is then used to cover the skull cast to the depth of these pegs (the musculature of the face is first modeled in more sophisticated reconstructions, then clay is used to represent the soft tissues, up to the depth of the pegs).

The size and shape of the nose are reconstructed based on the size and shape of the nasal opening. The size and shape of lips and ears are more difficult to determine, and the skull itself can tell the forensic anthropologist almost nothing about hair or eye color, whether the person had facial hair, or how the person's hair was cut. Those aspects of facial reconstruction require some artistic intuition, and it is helpful to know something about the person, such as sex, age, and ethnicity.

But what about ancient humans? The standard measurements used to reconstruct faces from modern human skulls cannot be assumed to work for ancient skulls. For those, the forensic anthropologists have to go back to

the basis of facial reconstruction—muscle and soft tissue. When reconstructing the faces of ancient humans, forensic anthropologists begin with a careful reconstruction of skull musculature, often aided by the comparative anatomy of modern great apes. Once the muscles are in place, glands, fatty tissue, and skin are added, and the face begins to take shape. The size and shape of the nose are determined much like that for modern humans, from the size and shape of the nasal opening. Lips, ears, eyes, and hair are, however, subject to almost pure guesswork—we really have no way of knowing how hairy our ancestors were, whether they had full lips like ours or thin lips like other great apes, or whether their ears were large or small.

Though based on study of the likely muscular anatomy in fossils and the comparative anatomy of modern humans and great apes, it is important to realize that the reconstruction of ancient faces is in part an artistic exercise. We can never know for sure what, for example, *Homo erectus* really looked like. We do not know how hairy they were or how they "styled" their hair. We do not know if their ears were like ours. We do not know the color of their eyes or skin. This is why reconstructions vary in the ways they depict ancient humans. We need to keep in mind when we look at reconstructions that they are educated, perhaps biased, guesses, and not necessarily true depictions of ancient people.

Sources: Prag and Neave 1997; Moser 1998.

humans. These scholars reported that they had been able to extract mitochondrial DNA (mtDNA) from the original Neandertal specimen found in 1856.[12] How similar is Neandertal mtDNA to modern human mtDNA? Not as similar as many scholars would have expected. Among individual modern humans, there are usually five to ten differences in the sequence of mtDNA examined by the U.S.

and German researchers. Between modern humans and the Neandertal specimen, there tend to be about 25 differences—more than three times that among modern humans (see Figure 10–4). This suggested to the researchers that the ancestors of modern humans and the Neandertal must have diverged about 600,000 years ago.[13] If the last common ancestor of ours and the Neandertal

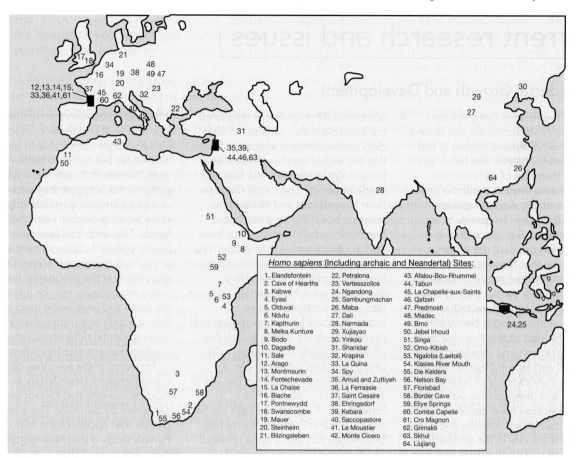

FIGURE 10–3 *Homo sapiens* Sites

Source: Ciochon and Fleagle 1993.

Homo sapiens (Including archaic and Neandertal) Sites:

1. Elandsfontein
2. Cave of Hearths
3. Kabwe
4. Eyasi
5. Olduvai
6. Ndutu
7. Kapthurin
8. Melka Kunture
9. Bodo
10. Dagadle
11. Sale
12. Arago
13. Montmaurin
14. Fontechevade
15. La Chaise
16. Biache
17. Pontnewydd
18. Swanscombe
19. Mauer
20. Steinheim
21. Bilzingsleben
22. Petralona
23. Vertesszollos
24. Ngandong
25. Sambungmachan
26. Maba
27. Dali
28. Narmada
29. Xujiayao
30. Yinkou
31. Shanidar
32. Krapina
33. La Quina
34. Spy
35. Amud and Zuttiyeh
36. La Ferrassie
37. Saint Cesaire
38. Ehringsdorf
39. Kebara
40. Saccopastore
41. Le Moustier
42. Monte Cicero
43. Afalou-Bou-Rhummel
44. Tabun
45. La Chapelle-aux-Saints
46. Qafzeh
47. Predmosti
48. Miadec
49. Brno
50. Jebel Irhoud
51. Singa
52. Omo-Kibish
53. Ngaloba (Laetoli)
54. Klasies River Mouth
55. Die Kelders
56. Nelson Bay
57. Florisbad
58. Border Cave
59. Eliye Springs
60. Combe Capelle
61. Cro Magnon
62. Grimaldi
63. Skhul
64. Liujiang

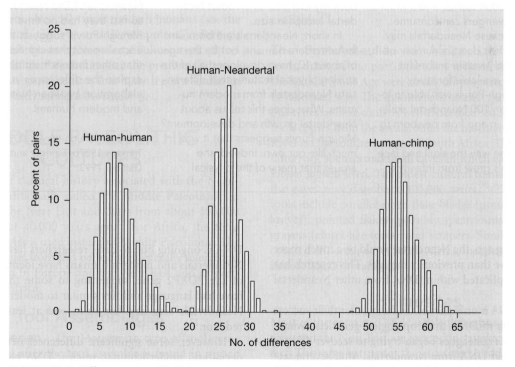

FIGURE 10–4 Differences in mtDNA Sequences among Humans, the Neandertal, and Chimpanzees
The *x*-axis shows the number of sequence differences; the *y*-axis shows the percent of individuals that share that number of sequence differences.

Source: Krings 1997, 25.

group of scholars has argued that an Upper Paleolithic skeleton from Portugal demonstrates a combination of modern human and Neandertal features.[67] The finding remains controversial, however, because it is a child's skeleton (approximately 4 years old) and its Neandertal-like features have not been corroborated by other scholars. More significantly, if the interbreeding hypothesis is correct, then the mtDNA analysis we have discussed several times in this chapter must be wrong. On the other hand, recent research on Neandertal tools suggests that some Neandertal groups adopted new techniques of tool manufacture that are thought to be uniquely associated with modern humans (we discuss these in more detail in the next chapter).[68] If Neandertals were learning from modern humans, then the idea that they could have interbred and perhaps been absorbed within the modern human population gains credibility.

Genocide The genocide scenario, that modern humans killed off Neandertals, has appeal as a sensational story, but little evidence. Not a single "murdered" Neandertal has ever been found, and one might wonder, in a fight between the powerful Neandertals and the more gracile modern humans, who might get the better of whom.

Extinction Finally, the extinction scenario, that Neandertals simply could not compete with modern humans, seems to have the best archaeological support. As we discussed earlier, there appear to be "refugee" populations of Neandertals in Iberia as recently as perhaps 30,000 years ago. The "retreat" of Neandertals from the Near East, eastern Europe, and finally western Europe following the movement of modern humans into the region seems to support the "refugee" interpretation.[69] More importantly, physical anthropologist Erik Trinkaus has argued, based on both physical characteristics of the Neandertal skeleton and their apparent patterns of behavior, that Neandertals were less efficient hunters and gatherers than modern humans.[70] And not only may Neandertals have been less efficient than modern humans in getting food, they may have needed more of it. Steve Churchill has suggested that Neandertals' stocky bodies and great muscle mass might have required 25 percent more calories than modern humans.[71] If this is true, a modern human group would have been able to live and reproduce more easily than a Neandertal group in the same territory, and this would likely drive the Neandertals away. When there were no new territories to run to, the Neandertals would go extinct—precisely what the archaeological record seems to suggest.[72]

But were modern humans and their cultures really that much more efficient than Middle Paleolithic cultures? As we will see in the next chapter, the Upper Paleolithic does seem to mark a watershed in the evolution of human culture, allowing humans to expand their physical horizons throughout the world and their intellectual horizons into the realms of art and ritual.

SUMMARY ● ○ ○

1. Most anthropologists agree that *Homo erectus* began to evolve into *Homo sapiens* after about 500,000 years ago. But there is disagreement about how and where the transition occurred. The mixed traits of the transitional fossils include large cranial capacities (well within the range of modern humans), together with low foreheads and large browridges, which are characteristic of *H. erectus* specimens. The earliest definite *H. sapiens*, who did not look completely like modern humans, appeared about 160,000 years ago.

2. *Homo sapiens* have been found in many parts of the Old World—in Africa and Asia as well as in Europe. Some of these *H. sapiens* may have lived earlier than the Neandertals of Europe. There is still debate over whether the Neandertals in western Europe became extinct or survived and were ancestral to the modern-looking people who lived in western Europe after about 40,000 years ago.

3. The period of cultural history associated with the Neandertals is traditionally called the Middle Paleolithic in Europe and the Near East and dates from about 300,000 years to about 40,000 years ago. For Africa, the term *Middle Stone Age* is used. The assemblages of flake tools from this period are generally referred to as Mousterian in Europe and the Near East and as post-Acheulian in Africa. Compared with an Acheulian assemblage, a Mousterian tool assemblage has a smaller proportion of large hand axes and cleavers and a larger proportion of small flake tools such as scrapers. Some Mousterian sites show signs of intentional burial.

4. Fossil remains of fully modern-looking humans, *Homo sapiens sapiens*, have been found in Africa, the Near East, Asia, and Australia, as well as in Europe. The oldest of these fossils have been found in East Africa and may be 160,000 years old.

5. Two theories about the origins of modern humans continue to be debated among anthropologists. One, the *single-origin theory*, suggests that modern humans emerged in just one part of the Old World—the Near East and, more recently, Africa have been the postulated places of origin—and spread to other parts of the Old World, superseding Neandertals. The second theory, the *multiregional theory*, suggests that modern humans emerged in various parts of the Old World, becoming the varieties of humans we see today.

GLOSSARY TERMS ○ ● ○

Cro-Magnon **164**	Levalloisian method **161**
Homo antecessor **154**	Middle Paleolithic **161**
Homo heidelbergensis **154**	Mousterian tool
Homo neandertalensis **155**	assemblage **161**
Homo sapiens sapiens **154**	Neandertal **155**

CRITICAL QUESTIONS ○ ○ ●

1. If the single-origin or "out-of-Africa" theory were correct, by what mechanisms could *Homo sapiens* have been able to replace *Homo erectus* and *Homo neandertalensis* populations?

2. If modern human traits emerged in *Homo erectus* populations in different areas more or less at the same time, what mechanisms would account for similar traits emerging in different regions?

3. How do Middle Paleolithic cultures differ from Lower Paleolithic cultures?

PEARSON myanthrolab

Read the chapter by David Frayer titled "Testing Theories and Hypotheses about Modern Human Origins" on MyAnthroLab. Answer the following questions:

1. What does Frayer identify as the key elements of debate between the "Out of Africa" (or, as he calls it, "Noah's Ark") and "Multiregional" models of modern human origins?

2. What problems does Frayer identify with mitochondrial DNA evidence of modern human origins?

3. Frayer is in the minority among physical anthropologists today in supporting the multiregional model of human evolution. What reasons does he give for rejecting the more broadly accepted "Out of Africa" model?

The Upper Paleolithic World

The period of cultural history in Europe, the Near East, and Asia known as the Upper Paleolithic (see Figure 11–1) dates from about 40,000 years ago to the period known as the *Neolithic* (beginning about 10,000 years ago, depending on the area). In Africa, the cultural period comparable to the Upper Paleolithic is known as the *Later Stone Age* and may have begun much earlier. In North and South America, the period begins when humans first entered the New World, some time before 12,000 years ago (these colonizers are typically called *Paleo-Indians*) and continues until what are called *Archaic traditions* emerged some 10,000 years ago. To simplify terminology, we use the term *Upper Paleolithic* to refer to cultural developments in all areas of the Old World during this period.

In many respects, lifestyles during the Upper Paleolithic were similar to lifestyles before. People were still mainly hunters, gatherers, and fishers who probably lived in small mobile bands. They made their camps out in the open in skin-covered huts and in caves and rock shelters. And they continued to produce smaller and smaller stone tools.

But the Upper Paleolithic is also characterized by a variety of new developments. One of the most striking is the emergence of art—painting on cave walls and stone slabs, and carving tools, decorative objects, and personal ornaments out of bone, antler, shell, and stone. (Perhaps for this as well as other purposes, people began to obtain materials from distant sources.) Because more archaeological sites date from the Upper Paleolithic than from any previous period and some Upper Paleolithic sites seem larger than any before, many archaeologists think that the human population increased considerably during the Upper Paleolithic.[1] And new inventions, such as the bow and arrow, the spear thrower, and tiny replaceable blades that could be fitted into handles, appear for the first time.[2]

● ○ ●

THE LAST ICE AGE

The Upper Paleolithic world had an environment very different from today's. The earth was gripped by the last ice age, with glaciers covering Europe as far south as Berlin and Warsaw, and North America as far south as Chicago. To the south of these glacial fronts was a tundra zone extending in Europe to the Alps and in North America to the Ozarks, Appalachians, and well out onto the Great Plains (see Figure 11–2). Environmentally, both Europe and North America probably resembled contemporary Siberia and northern Canada. Elsewhere in the world conditions were not as extreme, but were still different from conditions today.[3]

For one thing, the climate was different. Annual temperatures were as much as 50 degrees Fahrenheit (10 degrees Celsius) below today's, and changes in ocean currents would have made temperature contrasts (i.e., the differences between summer and winter months) more extreme as well. The changing ocean currents also changed weather patterns, and Europe experienced heavy annual snowfall. Not all the world was cold, however;

Artist's reconstruction of early modern humans painting the walls of a cave.

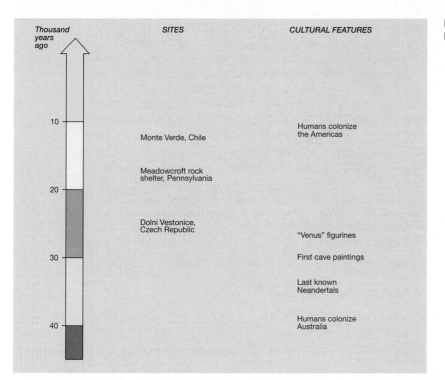

Thousand years ago	SITES	CULTURAL FEATURES
10	Monte Verde, Chile	Humans colonize the Americas
	Meadowcroft rock shelter, Pennsylvania	
20		
	Dolni Vestonice, Czech Republic	"Venus" figurines
30		First cave paintings
		Last known Neandertals
40		Humans colonize Australia

FIGURE 11–1 Places and Events in the Upper Paleolithic

still, the presence of huge ice sheets in the north changed the climate throughout the world. North Africa, for example, appears to have been much wetter than today, and South Asia was apparently drier. And everywhere the climate seems to have been highly variable.[4]

The plants and animals of the Upper Paleolithic world were adapted to these extreme conditions. Among the most important, and dramatic, were the large game animals collectively known as *Pleistocene megafauna*.[5] These animals, as their name suggests, were huge compared to their contemporary descendants. In North America, for example, giant ground sloths stood some 8 feet to 10 feet tall and weighed several thousand pounds. Siberian mammoths were the largest elephants ever to live—some standing more than 14 feet tall. In East Asia, species such as the woolly rhinoceros and giant deer were present.

171

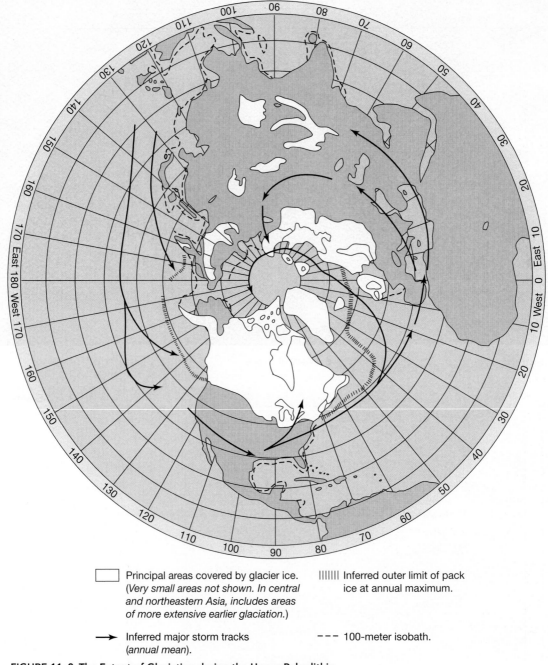

FIGURE 11–2 The Extent of Glaciation during the Upper Paleolithic

Source: Stein and Rowe 2000.

Legend:

☐ Principal areas covered by glacier ice. (*Very small areas not shown. In central and northeastern Asia, includes areas of more extensive earlier glaciation.*)

||||||| Inferred outer limit of pack ice at annual maximum.

→ Inferred major storm tracks (*annual mean*).

– – – 100-meter isobath.

UPPER PALEOLITHIC EUROPE

With the vast supplies of meat available from megafauna, it is not surprising that many Upper Paleolithic cultures relied on hunting, and this was particularly true of the Upper Paleolithic peoples of Europe, on whom we focus here. Their way of life represents a common pattern throughout the Old World. But as people began to use more diverse resources in their environments, the use of local resources allowed Upper Paleolithic groups in much of the Old World to become more sedentary than their predecessors. They also began to trade with neighboring groups to obtain resources not available in their local territories.[6]

As was the case in the known Middle Paleolithic sites, most of the Upper Paleolithic remains that have been excavated were situated in caves and rock shelters. In southwestern France, some groups seem to have paved parts of the shelter floors with stones. Tentlike structures were built in some caves, apparently to keep out the cold.[7] Some open-air sites have also been excavated.

The site at Dolni Vestonice in what is now the Czech Republic, dated to around 25,000 years ago, is one of the first for which there is an entire settlement plan.[8] The settlement seems to have consisted of four tentlike huts, probably made from animal skins, with a great open hearth in the center. Around the outside were mammoth bones, some rammed into the ground, which suggests that the huts were surrounded by a wall. All told, there were bone heaps from about 100 mammoths. Each hut probably housed a group of related families—about 20 to 25 people. (One hut was approximately 27 feet by 45 feet and had five hearths distributed inside it, presumably one for each family.) With 20 to 25 people per hut, and assuming that all four huts were occupied at the same time, the population of the settlement would have been 100 to 125 people.

Up a hill from the settlement was a fifth and different kind of hut. It was dug into the ground and contained a bake oven and more than 2,300 small, fired fragments of animal figurines. There were also some hollow bones that may have been musical instruments. Another interesting feature of the settlement was a burial find, of a woman with a disfigured face. She may have been a particularly important personage; her face was found engraved on an ivory plaque near the central hearth of the settlement.

Upper Paleolithic Tools

Upper Paleolithic toolmaking appears to have had its roots in the Mousterian and post-Acheulian traditions, because flake tools are found in many Upper Paleolithic sites. But the Upper Paleolithic is characterized by a preponderance of blades; there were also burins, bone and antler tools, and microliths. In addition, two new techniques of toolmaking appeared—*indirect percussion* and *pressure flaking*. Blades were found in Middle Paleolithic assemblages, but they were not widely used until the Upper Paleolithic. Although blades can be made in a variety of ways, **indirect percussion** using a hammer-struck punch was common in the Upper Paleolithic. After shaping a core into a pyramidal or cylindrical form, toolmakers put a punch of antler, wood, or other hard material into position and struck it with a hammer. Because the force is readily directed, toolmakers were able to strike off consistently shaped **blades,** which are more than twice as long as they are wide[9] (see Figure 11–3).

The Upper Paleolithic is also noted for the production of large numbers of bone, antler, and ivory tools; needles, awls, and harpoons made of bone appear for the first time.[10] The manufacture of these implements may have been made easier by the development of many varieties of burins. **Burins** are chisel-like stone tools used for carving; bone and antler needles, awls, and projectile points could be produced with them.[11] Burins have been found in Middle and Lower Paleolithic sites but are present in great number and variety only in the Upper Paleolithic.

Pressure flaking also appeared during the Upper Paleolithic. Rather than using percussion to strike off flakes as in previous technologies, pressure flaking works by employing pressure with a bone, wood, or antler tool at the edge of the tool to remove small flakes. Pressure flaking would usually be used in the final stages of retouching a tool.[12]

As time went on, all over the Old World, smaller and smaller blade tools were produced. The very tiny ones, called **microliths,** were often hafted or fitted into handles, one blade at a time or several blades together, to serve as spears, adzes, knives, and sickles. The hafting required

FIGURE 11–3
One way to remove blades from a core is to hit them with a punch using indirect percussion. The object being struck is the punch, which is made of bone or horn.

Source: Fagan 1972.

Upper Paleolithic bone needle and spear or harpoon points. Upper Paleolithic peoples made a much wider variety of tools than their predecessors.

inventing a way to trim the blade's back edge so that it would be blunt rather than sharp. In this way, the blades would not split the handles into which they might be inserted; the blunting would also prevent the users of an unhafted blade from cutting themselves.[13]

Some archaeologists think that the blade technique was adopted because it made for more economical use of flint. André Leroi-Gourhan of the Musée de l'Homme in Paris calculated that, with the old Acheulian technique, a 2-pound lump of flint yielded 16 inches of working edge and produced only two hand axes. If the more advanced Mousterian technique were used, a lump of equal size would yield 2 yards of working edge. The indirect percussion method of the Upper Paleolithic would yield as much as 25 yards of working edge.[14] With the same amount of material, a significantly greater number of tools could be produced. Getting the most out of a valuable resource may have been particularly important in areas lacking large flint deposits. Then again, if the population were increasing, that by itself would require more tools and more working edges to be produced.

Jacques Bordaz suggested that the evolution of toolmaking techniques, which continually increased the amount of usable edge that could be gotten out of a lump of flint, was significant because people could then spend more time in regions where flint was unavailable. Another reason for adopting the blade toolmaking technique may have been that it made for easy repair of tools. For example, the cutting edge of a tool might consist of a line of razorlike microliths set into a piece of wood. The tool would not be usable if just one of the cutting edge's microliths broke off or was chipped. But if the user carried a small prepared core of flint from which an identical-sized microlith could be struck off, the tool could be repaired easily by replacing the lost or broken microlith. A spear whose point was lost could be repaired similarly. Thus, the main purpose of the blade toolmaking technique may not have been to make more economical use of flint but rather to allow easy replacement of damaged blades.[15]

How Were the Tools Used?   Ideally, the study of tools should reveal not only how the implements were made but also how they were used. One way of suggesting what a particular tool was used for in the past is to observe the manner in which similar tools are used by members of recent or contemporary societies, preferably societies with subsistence activities and environments similar to those of the ancient toolmakers. This method of study is called reasoning from **ethnographic analogy.** The problem with such reasoning, however, is obvious: We cannot be sure that the original use of a tool was the same as the present use. When selecting recent or contemporary cultures that may provide the most informative and accurate comparisons, we should try to choose those that derive from the ancient culture in which we are interested. If the cultures being compared are historically related—prehistoric and recent Pueblo cultures in the southwestern United States, for example—there is a greater likelihood that the two

groups used a particular kind of tool in similar ways and for similar purposes.[16]

Another way of suggesting what a particular kind of tool was used for is to compare the visible and microscopic wear marks on the prehistoric tools with the wear marks on similar tools made and experimentally used by contemporary researchers. The idea behind this approach is that different uses leave different wear marks. A pioneer in this research was S. A. Semenov, who re-created prehistoric stone tools and used them in a variety of ways to find out which uses left which kinds of wear marks. For example, by cutting into meat with his re-created stone knives, he produced a polish on the edges that was like the polish found on blades from a prehistoric site in Siberia. This finding led Semenov to infer that the Siberian blades were probably also used to cut meat.[17]

The tools made by Upper Paleolithic peoples suggest that they were much more effective hunters and fishers than their predecessors.[18] During the Upper Paleolithic, and probably for the first time, spears were shot from a spear thrower rather than thrown with the arm. We know this because bone and antler **atlatls** (the Aztec word for "spear thrower") have been found in some sites. A spear propelled off a grooved board could be sent through the air with increased force, causing it to travel farther and hit harder, and with less effort by the thrower. The bow and arrow was also used in various places during the Upper Paleolithic; and harpoons, used for fishing and perhaps for hunting reindeer, were invented at this time.

These new tools and weapons for more effective hunting and fishing do not rule out the possibility that Upper Paleolithic peoples were still scavenging animal remains. Olga Soffer suggests that Upper Paleolithic peoples may have located their settlements near places where many mammoths died naturally in order to make use of the bones for building (see Figure 11–4). For example, in Moravia, the mammoths may have come to lick deposits of calcite and other sources of magnesium and calcium, particularly during the late spring and early summer when resources were short and mortality was high. Consistent with the idea that humans may not have killed so many of the enormous mammoths is the fact that in some places there are few human-made cut marks on mammoth bones. For example, at Dolni Vestonice, where bones of 100 mammoths were found, few bones show cut marks from butchering and few bones were found inside the huts. In contrast, the site is littered with bison, horse, and reindeer bones, suggesting that these other animals were deliberately killed and eaten by humans. If the people had been able to kill all the mammoths we find the remains of, why would they have hunted so many other animals?[19]

Upper Paleolithic Art

The earliest discovered traces of art are beads and carvings, and then paintings, from Upper Paleolithic sites. We might expect that early artistic efforts were crude, but the cave paintings of Spain and southern France show a marked degree of skill. So do the naturalistic paintings

FIGURE 11-4
Here we see the type of mammoth-bone shelters constructed about 15,000 years ago on the East European Plain. Often mammoth skulls formed part of the foundation for the tusk, long bone, and wooden frame, covered with hide. As many as 95 mammoth mandibles were arranged around the outside in a herringbone pattern.

on slabs of stone excavated in southern Africa. Some of those slabs appear to have been painted as much as 28,000 years ago, which suggests that painting in Africa is as old as painting in Europe.[20] But painting may be even older than that. The early Australians may have painted on the walls of rock shelters and cliff faces at least 30,000 years ago and maybe as much as 60,000 years ago.[21] And at Blombos Cave in South Africa, engraved pieces of red ochre date back to more than 77,000 years ago.[22]

Peter Ucko and Andrée Rosenfeld identified three principal locations of paintings in the caves of western Europe: (1) in obviously inhabited rock shelters and cave entrances—art as decoration or "art for art's sake"; (2) in "galleries" immediately off the inhabited areas of caves; and (3) in the inner reaches of caves, whose difficulty of access has been interpreted by some as a sign that magical-religious activities were performed there.[23]

The subjects of the paintings are mostly animals. The paintings are on bare walls, with no backdrops or environmental trappings. Perhaps, like many contemporary peoples, Upper Paleolithic men and women believed that the drawing of a human image could cause death or injury. If that were indeed their belief, it might explain why human figures are rarely depicted in cave art. Another explanation for the focus on animals might be that these people sought to improve their luck at hunting. This theory is suggested by evidence of chips in the painted figures, perhaps made by spears thrown at the drawings. But if hunting magic was the chief motivation for the paintings, it is difficult to explain why only a few show signs of having been speared.

Paintings of wild horses from Chauvet cave in France. Cave paintings like this demonstrate the remarkable skill of Upper Paleolithic artists.

THE END OF THE UPPER PALEOLITHIC

After about 10,000 years ago, the glaciers began to disappear, and with their disappearance came other environmental changes. The melting of the glacial ice caused the oceans to rise, and, as the seas moved inland, the waters inundated some of the richest fodder-producing coastal plains, creating islands, inlets, and bays. Other areas were opened up for human occupation as the glaciers retreated and the temperatures rose.[55] The cold, treeless plains, tundras, and grasslands eventually gave way to dense mixed forests, mostly birch, oak, and pine, and the Pleistocene megafauna became extinct. The warming waterways began to be filled with fish and other aquatic resources.[56]

Archaeologists believe that these environmental changes induced some populations to alter their food-getting strategies. When the tundras and grasslands disappeared, hunters could no longer obtain large quantities of meat simply by remaining close to large migratory herds of animals, as they probably did during Upper Paleolithic times. Even though deer and other game were available, the number of animals per square mile (density) had decreased, and it became difficult to stalk and kill animals sheltered in the thick woods. Thus, in many areas, people seemed to have turned from a reliance on big game hunting to the intensive collecting of wild plants, mollusks, fish, and small game to make up for the extinction of the large game animals they had once relied upon.

The Maglemosian Culture of Northern Europe

Some adaptations to the changing environment can be seen in the cultural remains of the settlers in northern Europe who archaeologists call *Maglemosians*. Their name derives from the peat bogs (*magle mose* in Danish means "great bog") where their remains have been found.

To deal with the new, more forested environment, the Maglemosians made stone axes and adzes to chop down trees and form them into various objects. Large timbers appear to have been split for houses; trees were hollowed out for canoes; and smaller pieces of wood were made into paddles. The canoes presumably were built for travel and perhaps for fishing on the lakes and rivers that abounded in the postglacial environment.

We do not know to what extent the Maglemosians relied on wild plant foods, but there were a lot of different kinds available, such as hazelnuts. However, we do know many other things about the Maglemosians' way of life. Although fishing was fairly important, as suggested by the frequent occurrence of bones from pike and other fish, as well as fishhooks, these people apparently depended mainly on hunting for food. Game included elk, wild ox, deer, and wild pig. In addition to many fishing implements and the adzes and axes, the Maglemosians' tool kit included the bow and arrow. Some of their tools were ornamented with finely engraved designs. Ornamentation

independent of tools also appears in amber and stone pendants and small figurines representing, for example, the head of an elk.[57]

Like the Maglemosian finds, many of the European post–Upper Paleolithic sites are along lakes, rivers, and oceanfronts. But these sites probably were not inhabited year-round; there is evidence that at least some groups moved seasonally from one place of settlement to another, perhaps between the coast and inland areas.[58] Finds such as kitchen *middens* (piles of shells) that centuries of post–Upper Paleolithic seafood eaters had discarded, and the remains of fishing equipment, canoes, and boats indicate that these people depended much more heavily on fishing than had their ancestors in Upper Paleolithic times.

The Archaic Cultures of Eastern North America

A related set of adaptations to the changing environment can be seen among the peoples who inhabited eastern North America at the end of the ice age. As the climate became warmer and drier, the flora and fauna of North America changed. Megafauna, as elsewhere in the world, went extinct, and were replaced by smaller mammals, particularly deer. The availability of meat was greatly reduced—hunters could count on coming home with pounds, not tons, of meat. Warmer-adapted plants replaced cold-adapted plants, and were used for food to replace the meat that was no longer available. Warmer-adapted plants had advantages as food resources for humans over cold-adapted ones because edible seeds, fruits, and nuts were more common, and often more plentiful and accessible, on the warmer-adapted plants. Thus, the Archaic peoples came to use a much greater diversity of plants and animals.[59]

The Archaic peoples of North America, like the Maglemosian peoples in Europe, began to follow a more sedentary lifestyle. Two forms of Archaic settlement appear to have been typical. One was a residential base camp, which would have been inhabited seasonally by several, probably related, families. The other was a special-purpose camp, which would have been a short-term habitation near a particular resource or perhaps used by a group of hunters for a short period of time.[60] On the Atlantic coast, for example, individual groups apparently moved seasonally along major river valleys, establishing summer base camps in the piedmont and winter camps near the coast. Special-purpose camps were created year-round as groups went out from the base camp to hunt and collect particular resources, such as stone for making tools.[61]

One of the innovations of the Archaic peoples was the development of ground stone woodworking tools. Axes, adzes, and tools for grinding seeds and nuts become more and more common in the tool kit.[62] This probably reflects the emergence of greater areas of forest following the retreat of the glaciers from North America, but it also demonstrates a greater reliance on forest products and, most likely, a greater use of wood and wood products. Fish and shellfish also came to be relied upon in some areas, and this too reflects the adjustment made by the Archaic peoples to the changing conditions they faced at the end of the last ice age.

Some examples of Archaic ground stone woodworking tools from eastern North America (wooden handles are reproductions). Archaic peoples apparently used wood more extensively than the Paleo-Indians.

The innovation of most lasting importance in both the New and Old Worlds, however, was the development of domesticated plants and animals. In both parts of the world, peoples at the end of the ice age began to experiment with plants. By around 14,000 years ago in the Old World, and 10,000 years ago in the New World, some species had been domesticated. We turn to this fundamental change in food-getting—the invention of agriculture—in the next chapter.

SUMMARY ● ○ ○

1. The period of cultural history known as the Upper Paleolithic in Europe, the Near East, and Asia or the Later Stone Age in Africa dates from about 40,000 years ago to about 14,000 to 10,000 years ago. During this time, the world was locked in an ice age, with glaciers covering much of northern Europe and North America, and annual temperatures as much as 50 degrees Fahrenheit (10 degrees Celsius) below today's temperatures.

2. The Upper Paleolithic tool kit is characterized by the preponderance of blades; there were also burins, bone and antler tools, and (later) microliths. In many respects, lifestyles were similar to lifestyles before. People were still mainly hunters, gatherers, and fishers who probably lived in highly mobile bands. They made their camps out in the open and in caves and rock shelters.

3. The Upper Paleolithic is also characterized by a variety of new developments: new techniques of toolmaking, the emergence of art, population growth, and new inventions such as the bow and arrow, the spear thrower (atlatl), and the harpoon.

4. Only *Homo sapiens sapiens* remains have been found in the New World. The prevailing opinion is that humans migrated to the New World over a land bridge between Siberia and Alaska in the area of what is now the Bering Strait. Until recently, it was thought that humans were not present south of Alaska until after 11,500 years ago. Now it appears from an archaeological site called Monte Verde in Chile that modern humans arrived in southern South America by at least 12,500 years ago and perhaps as much as 33,000 years ago.

5. At the end of the ice age, around 14,000 years ago, the climate began to become more temperate. Many large animals that Upper Paleolithic peoples relied upon for food went extinct, and at the same time new, warmer-adapted plants provided a rich, new food source. Around the world, people began to use more plant foods and a broader range of resources overall. In many parts of the world, people began experimenting with domesticating plants and animals.

GLOSSARY TERMS ○ ● ○

atlatl **174**	indirect percussion **173**
blade **173**	microlith **173**
burin **173**	pressure flaking **173**
ethnographic analogy **174**	Upper Paleolithic **170**

CRITICAL QUESTIONS ○ ○ ●

1. How do Upper Paleolithic tools differ from Middle Paleolithic tools? What is the significance of these differences in terms of human culture?

2. Upper Paleolithic cave paintings arouse our imaginations. We have described some research that tested ideas about what these paintings might mean. Can you think of other ways to understand the significance of cave art?

3. What factors might have led humans to colonize the New World?

PEARSON
myanthrolab

Read the chapter by William Parry titled "When and How Did Humans Populate the New World?" on MyAnthroLab. Answer the following questions:

1. Why is the issue of when and how humans first colonized the Americas such a vibrant and important topic in archaeology?

2. Parry states that the following is the key question needing to be answered: "Is there any evidence of pre-Clovis people in the Americas, or were the Clovis people the first immigrants?" What is Parry's answer, and why did he have such difficulty developing it?

houses, they constructed plastered storage pits. In addition to wild grains, the Natufians exploited a wide range of other resources.[10] The remains of many wild animals are found in Natufian sites; Natufians appear to have concentrated on hunting gazelle, which they would take by surrounding whole herds.[11]

The Natufians, as well as foragers in other areas at the time, show many differences as compared with foragers in earlier periods.[12] Not only was Natufian foraging based on a more intensive use of stationary resources such as wild grain, but the archaeological evidence suggests increasing social complexity. Natufian sites on the average were five times larger than those of their predecessors. Communities were occupied for most of the year, if not year-round. Burial patterns suggest more social differences between people. Although the available wild cereal resources appear to have enabled the Natufians to live in relatively permanent villages, their diet seems to have suffered. Their tooth enamel shows signs of nutritional deficiency, and their stature declined over time.[13]

Mesoamerica

A similar shift toward more broad-spectrum hunting and gathering occurred in the New World at the end of the Paleo-Indian period, about 10,000 years ago. Climate change seems to have been vital here too, as it was in the Old World. The retreat of glacial ice from North America and overall warmer and wetter climate brought dramatic changes to plant and animal communities throughout North America and Mesoamerica. Pleistocene megafauna, such as mammoths, mastodon, rhinoceros, giant ground sloth, and others, as well as a variety of smaller game animals, such as the horse, all went extinct in a relatively short period of time.[14] Hunting strategies shifted toward a broader range of game species, particularly deer, antelope, bison, and small mammals. At the same time, deciduous woodlands and grasslands expanded, providing a range of new plants to exploit. Ground stone woodworking tools such as axes and adzes first appeared, as did nut-processing tools such as mortars and pestles. Shellfish began to be exploited in some areas. Throughout North America and Mesoamerica, people began to expand the range of plants and animals they relied upon.[15]

The Archaic Peoples of Highland Mesoamerica In Highland Mesoamerica, the mountainous regions of central and southern Mexico, we also see a shift from big game hunting to a broader use of resources, in part due to a change in climate more like today's. Altitude became an important factor in the hunting and collecting regime, as different altitudes have different plant and animal resources. Valleys tend to have scrubby, grassland vegetation, whereas foothills and mountains have "thorn forests" of cactuses and succulents, giving way to oak and pine forests at higher altitudes, where there is more moisture. This vertical zonation means that a wide range of plants and animals were available in relatively close proximity—different environments were close by—and the Archaic peoples took advantage of these varied conditions to hunt and collect a broad range of resources.[16]

About 8,000 years ago, the Archaic peoples in Mesoamerica appear to have moved seasonally between communities of two different sizes: camps with 15 to 30 residents (*macrobands*) and camps with only 2 to 5 residents (*microbands*). Macroband camps were located near seasonally abundant resources, such as acorns or mesquite pods. Several families would have come together when these resources were in season, both to take advantage of them and to work together to harvest them while they were plentiful, perhaps to perform rituals, and simply to socialize. Microband camps were also inhabited seasonally, probably by a single family, when groups were not assembled into macroband camps. Remains of these microband camps are often found in caves or rock shelters from which a variety of environments could be exploited by moving either upslope or downslope from the campsite.[17]

Unlike the Natufians of the Near East, there is no evidence of social differences among the Archaic peoples of Highland Mesoamerica. The largest social unit, the macroband camp, was probably composed of related family groups, and leadership in these groups was probably informal. There is little evidence of ritual behavior beyond the presence of what may have been a ceremonial dance floor at Gheo-Shih, a macroband campsite in the Valley of Oaxaca. In short, lifestyles remained much like the simple and egalitarian ones of the Paleo-Indians, despite the transition to a much broader strategy of foraging.

Other Areas

People in other areas of the world also shifted from hunting big game to collecting many types of food before they began to practice agriculture. The still-sparse archaeological record suggests that such a change occurred in Southeast Asia, which may have been one of the important centers of original plant and animal domestication.[18] The faunal remains in inland sites there indicate that many different sources of food were being exploited from the same base camps. For example, at these base camps, we find the remains of animals from high mountain ridges as well as lowland river valleys, birds and primates from nearby forests, bats from caves, and fish from streams. The few coastal sites indicate that many kinds of fish and shellfish were collected and that animals such as deer, wild cattle, and rhinoceros were hunted.[19] The preagricultural developments in Southeast Asia probably were responses to changes in the climate and environment, including a warming trend, more moisture, and a higher sea level.[20]

In Africa, too, the preagricultural period was marked by a warmer, wetter environment. The now-numerous lakes, rivers, and other bodies of water provided fish, shellfish, and other resources that apparently allowed people to settle more permanently than they had before. For example, there were lakes in what is now the southern and central Sahara Desert, where people fished and hunted hippopotamuses and crocodiles. This pattern of broad-spectrum food-collecting seems also to have been characteristic of the areas both south and north of the Sahara.[21] One area showing increased sedentarism is the Dakhleh Oasis in the Western Desert of Egypt. Between 9,000 years and 8,500 years ago, the inhabitants lived in circular stone

These young Fulbe-Waila girls in Chad are collecting seeds much like preagricultural peoples did.

huts on the shores of rivers and lakes. Bone harpoons and pottery are found there and in other areas from the Nile Valley through the central and southern Sahara westward to what is now Mali. Fishing seems to have allowed people to remain along the rivers and lakes for much of the year.[22]

Why Did Broad-Spectrum Collecting Develop?

It is apparent that the preagricultural switch to broad-spectrum collecting was fairly common throughout the world. Climate change was probably at least partly responsible for the exploitation of new sources of food. For example, the worldwide rise in sea level because of glacial melting may have increased the availability of fish and shellfish. Changes in climate may have also been partly responsible for the decline in the availability of big game, particularly the large herd animals. In addition, it has been suggested that another possible cause of that decline was human activity, specifically overkilling of some of these animals.[23] The evidence suggesting overkill is that the extinction in the New World of many of the large Pleistocene animals, such as the mammoth, coincided with the movement of humans from the Bering Strait region into the Americas.[24]

The overkill hypothesis has been questioned on the basis of bird as well as mammal extinctions in the New World. An enormous number of bird species also became extinct during the last few thousand years of the North American Pleistocene, and it is difficult to argue that human hunters caused all of those extinctions. Because the bird and mammal extinctions occurred simultaneously, it is likely that most or nearly all the extinctions were due to climatic and other environmental changes.[25] Then again, the example of the New Zealand moas, which went extinct soon after humans colonized the islands, may be instructive. Moas had low reproductive rates; computer simulations suggest their population would have been very sensitive to increases in adult mortality. Because many large animals have low reproductive rates like moas,

human overhunting may have been responsible for their extinction.[26]

The decreasing availability of big game may have stimulated people to exploit new food resources. But they may have turned to a broader spectrum of resources for another reason—population growth (see Figure 12–3). As Mark Cohen has noted, hunter-gatherers were "filling up" the world, and they may have had to seek new, possibly less desirable sources of food.[27] (We might think of shellfish as more desirable than mammoths, but only because we don't have to do the work to get such food. A lot of shellfish have to be collected, shelled, and cooked to produce the amount of animal protein obtainable from one large animal.)

Broad-spectrum collecting may have involved exploitation of new sources of food, but that does not necessarily mean that people were eating better. A decline in stature often indicates a poorer diet. During the preagricultural period, height apparently declined by as much as two inches in many parts of the Old World (Greece, Israel, India, and northern and western Europe).[28] This decline may have been a result of decreasing nutrition, but it could also be that natural selection for greater height was relaxed because leverage for throwing projectiles such as spears was not so favored after the decline of big game hunting. (Greater limb-bone length, and therefore greater height, would enable a hunter to throw a spear with more force and farther.[29]) In other areas of the world, such as Australia and what is now the midwestern United States, skeletal evidence also suggests a decline in the general level of health with the rise of broad-spectrum collecting.[30]

Broad-Spectrum Collecting and Sedentarism

Does the switch to broad-spectrum collecting explain the increasingly sedentary way of life we see in various parts of the world in preagricultural times? The answer seems to be both yes and no. In some areas of the world—some sites in Europe, the Near East, Africa, and Peru—settlements

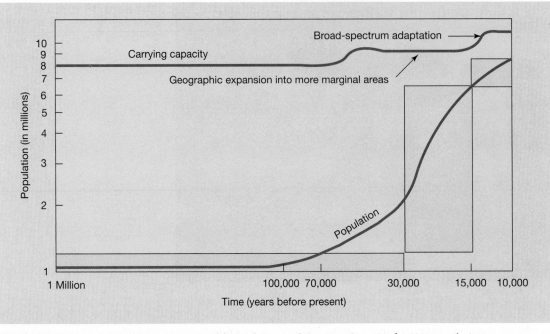

FIGURE 12–3 Reconstructed Increases in World Population and Carrying Capacity for Humans during the Pleistocene
Estimates of human population suggest that substantial increases preceded the movement of humans into more marginal areas. Further population increase preceded the emergence of broad-spectrum collecting.

Source: Hassan 1981.

became more permanent. In other areas, such as the semi-arid highlands of Mesoamerica, the switch to broad-spectrum collecting was not associated with increasing sedentarism. Even after the Highland Mesoamericans began to cultivate plants, they still did not live in permanent villages.[31] Why?

It would seem that it is not simply the switch to broad-spectrum collecting that accounts for increasing sedentarism in many areas. Rather, a comparison of settlements on the Peruvian coast suggests that the more permanent settlements were located nearer, within three and a half miles, to most, if not all, of the diverse food resources exploited during the year. The community that did not have a year-round settlement seems to have depended on more widely distributed resources. What accounts for sedentarism may thus be the nearness[32] or the high reliability and yield[33] of the broad-spectrum resources, rather than the broad spectrum itself.

Sedentarism and Population Growth

Although some population growth undoubtedly occurred throughout the hunting and gathering phase of world history, some anthropologists have suggested that populations would have increased dramatically when people began to settle down. The evidence for this suggestion comes largely from a comparison of recent nomadic and sedentary !Kung populations.

The settling down of a nomadic group may reduce the typical spacing between births.[34] Nomadic !Kung have children spaced four years apart on the average; in contrast,

recently sedentarized !Kung have children about three years apart. Why might birth spacing change with settling down? There are several possibilities.

The spacing of children far apart can occur in a number of ways. One way, if effective contraceptives are not available, is prolonged sexual abstinence after the birth of a child—the postpartum sex taboo—which is common in recent human societies. Another way is abortion or infanticide.[35] Nomadic groups may be motivated to have children farther apart because of the problem of carrying small children. Carrying one small child is difficult enough; carrying two might be too burdensome. Thus, sedentary populations could have their children spaced more closely because carrying children would not always be necessary.

Although some nomadic groups may have deliberately spaced births by abstinence or infanticide, there is no evidence that such practices explain why four years separate births among nomadic !Kung. There may be another explanation, involving an unintended effect of how babies are fed. Nancy Howell and Richard Lee have suggested that the presence of baby foods other than mother's milk may be responsible for the decreased birth spacing in sedentary agricultural !Kung groups.[36] It is now well established that the longer a mother nurses her baby without supplementary foods, the longer it is likely to be before she starts ovulating again. Nomadic !Kung women have little to give their babies in the way of soft, digestible food, and the babies depend largely on mother's milk for two to three years. But sedentary !Kung mothers can give their babies soft foods such as cereal (made from cultivated grain) and milk from domesticated animals. Such changes in feeding

A !Kung group moving camp. When hunters and gatherers move, they have to carry their children and all their possessions with them. Spacing births an average of four years apart helps to ensure that a woman will not have to carry more than two children at a time.

practices may shorten birth spacing by shortening the interval between birth and the resumption of ovulation. In preagricultural sedentary communities, it is possible that baby foods made from wild grains might have had the same effect. For this reason alone, therefore, populations may have grown even before people started to farm or herd.

Another reason sedentary !Kung women may have more babies than nomadic !Kung women has to do with the ratio of body fat to body weight. Some investigators suspect that a critical minimum of fat in the body may be necessary for ovulation. A sedentary !Kung woman may have more fatty tissue than a nomadic !Kung woman, who walks many miles daily to gather wild plant foods, often carrying a child with her. Thus, sedentary !Kung women might resume ovulating sooner after the birth of a baby, and so for that reason alone may be likely to have more closely spaced children. If some critical amount of fat is necessary for ovulation, that would explain why many women who have little body fat in our own society—long-distance runners, gymnasts, and ballet dancers are examples—do not ovulate regularly.[37]

Microlithic Technology

Technologically, these preagricultural cultures did not differ radically from Upper Paleolithic cultures.[38] The trend toward smaller and lighter tools continued. Microliths, small blades half an inch to two inches long, which were made in late Upper Paleolithic times, were now used in quantity. In place of the one-piece flint implement, the preagricultural peoples in Europe, Asia, and Africa equipped themselves with *composite* tools—that is, tools made of more than one material.

Microliths, too small to be used one at a time, could be fitted into grooves in bone or wood to form arrows, harpoons, daggers, and sickles. A sickle, for example, was made by inserting several microliths into a groove in a wooden or bone handle. Resin held the blades in place. A broken mi-

A sickle made with microliths.

crolith could be replaced like a blade in a modern razor. Besides being adaptable for many uses, microliths could be made from many varieties of available stone. Because they did not need the large nodules to make large core and flake tools, people using microliths could work with smaller nodules to make the small blades.[39]

THE DOMESTICATION OF PLANTS AND ANIMALS

Neolithic means "of the new stone age"; the term originally signified the cultural stage in which humans invented pottery and ground-stone tools. We now know, however, that both were present in earlier times, so we cannot define a Neolithic state of culture purely on the basis of the presence of pottery and ground-stone tools. At present,

FIGURE 12–4 Seed Heads of Wild and Domesticated Wheat
Note the larger and more numerous seeds on domesticated wheat.

Source: Feder 2000.

archaeologists generally define the **Neolithic** in terms of the presence of domesticated plants and animals. In this type of culture, people began to produce food rather than merely collect it.

The line between food-collecting and food-producing occurs when people begin to plant crops and to keep and breed animals. How do we know when this transition occurred? In fact, archaeologically we do not see the beginning of food production; we can see signs of it only after plants and animals show differences from their wild varieties. When people plant crops, we refer to the process as cultivation. It is only when the crops cultivated and the animals raised are *modified*—different from wild varieties—that we speak of plant and animal **domestication.**

We know, in a particular site, that domestication occurred if plant remains have characteristics different from those of wild plants of the same types (see Figure 12–4). For example, wild grains of barley and wheat have a fragile **rachis**—the seed-bearing part of the stem—which shatters easily, releasing the seeds. Domesticated grains have a tough rachis, which does not shatter easily. In addition, the grain of wild barley and wheat has a tough shell protecting the seed from premature exposure, whereas domesticated grain has a brittle shell that can be easily separated, which facilitates preparing the seed for grinding into flour.

How did the domesticated plants get to be different from the wild varieties? Artificial or human selection, deliberate or accidental, obviously was required. Consider how the rachis of wheat and barley may have changed. As we said, when wild grain ripens in the field, the rachis shatters easily, scattering the seed. This trait is selectively advantageous under wild conditions; it is nature's method of propagating the species. Plants with a tough rachis, therefore, have only a slight chance of reproducing themselves under natural conditions, but they are more desirable for planting. When humans arrived with sickles and flails to collect the wild stands of grain, the seeds harvested

probably contained a high proportion of tough-rachis mutants, because these could best withstand the rough treatment of harvest processing. If planted, the harvested seeds would be likely to produce tough-rachis plants. If, in each successive harvest, seeds from tough-rachis plants were the least likely to be lost, tough-rachis plants would come to predominate.[40]

Domesticated species of animals also differ from the wild varieties. For example, the horns of wild goats in the Near East are shaped differently from those of domesticated goats.[41] But differences in physical characteristics may not be the only indicators of domestication. Some archaeologists believe that imbalances in the sex and age ratios of animal remains at particular sites also suggest that domestication had occurred. For example, at Zawi Chemi Shanidar in Iraq, the proportion of young to mature sheep remains was much higher than the ratio of young to mature sheep in wild herds. One possible inference to be drawn is that the animals were domesticated, the adult sheep being saved for breeding purposes whereas the young were eaten. (If mostly young animals were eaten, and only a few animals were allowed to grow old, most of the bones found in a site would be from the young animals that were killed regularly for food.[42])

Domestication in the Near East

For some time, most archaeologists have thought that the Fertile Crescent (see Figure 12–5), the arc of land stretching up from Israel and the Jordan Valley through southern Turkey and then downward to the western slopes of the Zagros Mountains in Iran, was one of the earliest centers of plant and animal domestication. We know that several varieties of domesticated wheat were being grown there after about 8000 B.C., as were oats, rye, barley, lentils, peas, and various fruits and nuts (apricots, pears, pomegranates, dates, figs, olives, almonds, and pistachios).[43] It appears that animals were first domesticated in the Near East. Dogs were first domesticated before the rise of agriculture, around 13,000 B.C. (see the box "Did Dogs (and Cats) Domesticate Themselves?"), goats and sheep around 7000 B.C., and cattle and pigs around 6000 B.C.[44]

Let us look at two early Neolithic sites in the Near East to see what life there may have been like after people began to depend on domesticated plants and animals for food.

Ali Kosh   At the stratified site of Ali Kosh in what is now southwestern Iran (see Figure 12–5), we see the remains of a community that started out about 7500 B.C., living mostly on wild plants and animals. Over the next 2,000 years, until about 5500 B.C., agriculture and herding became increasingly important. After 5500 B.C., we see the appearance of two innovations—irrigation and the use of domesticated cattle—that seem to have stimulated a minor population explosion during the following millennium.

From 7500 to 6750 B.C., the people at Ali Kosh cut little slabs of raw clay out of the ground to build small, multi-room structures. The rooms excavated by archaeologists are seldom more than 7 feet by 10 feet, and there is no evidence that the structures were definitely houses where

current research and issues

Did Dogs (and Cats) Domesticate Themselves?

Early evidence of a close relationship between dogs and people comes from an archaeological site in northern Israel dating to nearly 12,000 years ago. At that site, archaeologists found the grave of an elderly woman, lying on her right side with her legs folded up, with a dog under her left hand.

The Embers' dog was always happy to greet them when they came home. She also was a retriever, an alarm system, could follow a scent, and ate everything that dropped on the floor. Do any of these attributes explain why humans all over the world have had domesticated descendants of wolves around the house for the last 10,000 to 15,000 years?

Dogs were probably the first animals domesticated by humans, probably about 15,000 years ago, and several thousand years before plants, sheep, and goats were domesticated in the Near East. Humans were starting to settle down in semipermanent camps and villages, as they began to depend less on big game (which they would have had to follow over long distances) and more on relatively stationary food resources, such as fish, shellfish, small game, and wild plants rich in carbohydrates, proteins, and oils.

Why would humans have been interested in taming wolves at that time? One theory is that humans were shifting their prey from large animals to small, and they needed dogs for tracking wounded game or for retrieving killed game from bodies of water or underbrush. Dogs might also have been useful as alarm-givers in case predators came close. Finally, dogs might have helped to keep a camp clean by scavenging garbage.

The Embers think that this last use of dogs suggests an alternative theory of dog domestication. Perhaps it wasn't so much that humans domesticated dogs, but that some wolves domesticated themselves by hanging around human camps. Why would wolves be interested in those humans who were first settling down? It couldn't have been the possibility of a human dinner, because that would have been a possibility for millions of years before. So perhaps something else lured wolves to those early settled camps and villages. What was different about those early settlements? For the first time in human history, people were staying put for considerable periods of time—months at a time, year after year—because they could count on being able to "harvest" and live on the wild resources of the area. If they lived in a place for years, even if only seasonally, they would eventually have a problem with garbage.

The residues of meals, in particular, would have been a problem. They might not only come to stink; they might also attract rodents and bigger threats to health and children. What could the people do about this problem? Well, as any camper nowadays realizes, they could have buried the garbage so that its scent would not attract unwelcome visitors. But eventually they would have run out of room for garbage pits in or close to the settlement. Of course, they could have moved the settlement. But maybe they didn't want to. After all, they had spent a lot of time and effort building a permanent house that was warm in the winter and dry in the rains. And they had a lot of things stored there. So what could they do?

Maybe people didn't have to do anything. Maybe those wolves hanging around the neighborhood solved the problem for our ancestors. How? By scavenging, which is something most dogs (particularly larger ones, like the first domesticated dogs) do quite naturally and efficiently. The Embers' dog ate anything (except maybe undressed lettuce). So even a few tame wolves or domesticated dogs could have kept a garbage pit or pile from stinking and growing. And the people "feeding" that pit or pile could stay put in one place for a long time, safe from smells, vermin, and disease. Dogs may have mostly domesticated themselves because it was good for some of them as well as for those preagricultural humans.

A similar theory may explain the domestication of cats. Cats are especially good at catching and killing mice. Masses of mice skeletons (of the house mouse) begin to appear in basements of Near East dwellings after the emergence of agriculture. It is possible that humans purposely tried to domesticate cats to catch mice, but it is more likely that cats would have domesticated themselves by adapting to life near or in a granary or storage cellar. Of course, humans might have helped the process of domestication a little, by killing the more ferocious wild cats that were attracted to the settlement. The same was probably true for the wolves attracted to garbage. Even if you didn't at first want to "pet" the canids or felids that were hanging around, you wouldn't want them to attack humans. Wolves in the wild have a dominance-submission hierarchy, so they would be preadapted to heeding a "dominant" human; those that were not sufficiently submissive could be killed.

How could these theories of dog and cat domestication be tested? If dogs domesticated themselves as scavengers, archaeologists should find evidence of dog domestication (e.g., changes in anatomy) only in sites that were occupied for a good part of the year over a period of years. Only under those circumstances would garbage be a problem and dogs a solution. Similarly, evidence of cat domestication should be found only in sites that show signs of year-to-year grain storage. Only then would rodents be a problem and cats a solution. We hope archaeologists will make these tests in the future.

Sources: Budiansky 1992; Driscoll et al. 2007; 2009; Clutton-Brock 1984; Robinson 1984.

FIGURE 12–5 Early Agricultural Settlements in the Near East
Modern cities are represented by a dot, early settlements by a square. The yellow color indicates the area known as the Fertile Crescent.

people actually spent time or slept. Instead, they may have been storage rooms. On the other hand, house rooms of even smaller size are known in other areas of the world, so it is possible that the people at Ali Kosh in its earliest phase were actually living in those tiny, unbaked, "brick" houses. There is a bit of evidence that the people at Ali Kosh may have moved for the summer (with their goats) to the grassier mountain valleys nearby, which were just a few days' walk away.

We have a lot of evidence about what the people at Ali Kosh ate. They got some of their food from cultivated emmer wheat and a kind of barley and a considerable amount from domesticated goats. We know the goats were domesticated because wild goats do not seem to have lived in the area. Also, the fact that virtually no bones from elderly goats were found in the site suggests that the goats were domesticated and herded rather than hunted. Moreover, it would seem from the horn cores found in the site that mostly young male goats were eaten, so the females probably were kept for breeding and milking. But with all these signs of deliberate food production, there is an enormous amount of evidence—literally tens of thousands of seeds and bone fragments—that the people at the beginning of Ali Kosh depended mostly on wild plants (legumes and grasses) and wild animals (including gazelles, wild

oxen, and wild pigs). They also collected fish, such as carp and catfish, and shellfish, such as mussels, as well as waterfowl that visited the area during part of the year.

The flint tools used during this earliest phase at Ali Kosh were varied and abundant. Finds from this period include tens of thousands of tiny flint blades, some only a few millimeters wide. About 1 percent of the chipped stone that archaeologists found was **obsidian,** or volcanic glass, which came from what is now eastern Turkey, several hundred miles away. Thus, the people at Ali Kosh during its earliest phase definitely had some kind of contact with people elsewhere. This contact is also suggested by the fact that the emmer wheat they cultivated did not have a wild relative in the area.

From 6750 to 6000 B.C., the people increased their consumption of cultivated food plants; 40 percent of the seed remains in the hearths and refuse areas were now from emmer wheat and barley. The proportion of the diet coming from wild plants was much reduced, probably because the cultivated plants have the same growing season and grow in the same kind of soil as the wild plants. Grazing by the goats and sheep that were kept may also have contributed to the reduction of wild plant foods in the area and in the diet. The village may or may not have grown larger, but the multiroom houses definitely had. The rooms were now larger than 10 feet by 10 feet; the walls were much thicker; and a mud mortar now held the clay-slab bricks together. Also, the walls now often had a coat of smooth mud plaster on both sides. The stamped-mud house floors were apparently covered with rush or reed mats (you can see the imprints of them). There were courtyards with domed brick ovens and brick-lined roasting pits. Understandably, considering the summer heat in the area, none of the ovens found was inside a house.

Even though the village probably contained no more than 100 individuals, it participated in an extensive trading network. Seashells were probably obtained from the Persian Gulf, which is some distance to the south; copper may have come from what is now central Iran; obsidian was still coming from eastern Turkey; and turquoise somehow made its way from what is now the border between Iran and Afghanistan. Some of these materials were used as ornaments worn by both sexes—or so it seems from the remains of bodies found buried under the floors of houses.

After about 5500 B.C., the area around Ali Kosh began to show signs of a much larger population, apparently made possible by a more complex agriculture employing irrigation and plows drawn by domesticated cattle. In the next thousand years, by 4500 B.C., the population of the area probably tripled. This population growth was apparently part of the cultural developments that culminated in the rise of urban civilizations in the Near East,[45] as we will see in the next chapter.

Population growth may have occurred in and around Ali Kosh but did not continue in all areas of the Near East after domestication. For example, one of the largest early villages in the Near East, 'Ain Ghazal (on the outskirts of what is now Amman, Jordan), suffered a decline in population and standard of living over time, perhaps because the environment around 'Ain Ghazal could not permanently support a large village.[46]

Catal Hüyük On a windswept plateau in the rugged, mountainous region of southern Turkey stand the remains of a mud-brick town known as Catal Hüyük. *Hüyük* is the Turkish word for a mound formed by a succession of settlements, one built on top of another.

About 5600 B.C., Catal Hüyük was an adobe town. Some 200 houses have been excavated, and they are interconnected in *pueblo fashion* (each flat-roofed structure housed a number of families). The inhabitants decorated the walls of the houses with imaginative murals, and their shrines with symbolic statuary. The murals depict what seem to be religious scenes and everyday events. Archaeologists peeling away frescoes found layer upon layer of murals, indicating that old murals were plastered over to make way for fresh paintings. Several rooms are believed to have been shrine rooms. They contain many large bull murals and clay bull figurines and have full-sized clay heads of cattle on the walls. Other "shrine room" murals depict scenes of life and death, painted in red and black, respectively. Clay statuettes of a pregnant woman and of a bearded man seated on a bull have also been found in these rooms.

Farming was well advanced at Catal Hüyük. Lentils, wheat, barley, and peas were grown in quantities that produced a surplus. Archaeologists were astonished at the richly varied handicrafts, including beautifully carved wooden bowls and boxes that the people of the town produced. These people also had obsidian and flint daggers, spearheads, lance heads, scrapers, awls, and sickle blades. Bowls, spatulas, knives, ladles, and spoons were made from bone. The houses contained belt hooks, toggles, and pins carved from bone. Evidence also suggests that men and women wore jewelry fashioned from bone, shell, and copper, and that they used obsidian mirrors.[47]

Because Catal Hüyük is located in a region with few raw materials, the town evidently depended on exchange with other areas to secure the rich variety of materials it used. Shells were procured from the Mediterranean, timber from the hills, obsidian from 50 miles away, and marble from western Turkey.

Excavation in the pueblo-like structures of Neolithic Catal Hüyük.

Sophisticated ceramics like this 5,000-year-old Chinese funeral urn first appeared in the Neolithic era as part of the elaboration of material possessions.

Source: Dagli Orti/Picture Desk, Inc./Kobal Collection

became more artistic. Designers shaped the clay into graceful forms and painted colorful patterns on the vessels.

It is probable that virtually none of these architectural and technological innovations could have occurred until humans became fully sedentary. Nomadic hunting and gathering peoples would have found it difficult to carry many material goods, especially fragile items such as pottery. Only when humans settled in one place would these goods have provided advantages, enabling villagers to cook and store food more effectively and to house themselves more comfortably.

There is also evidence of long-distance trade in the Neolithic, as we have noted. Obsidian from southern Turkey was being exported to sites in the Zagros Mountains of Iran and to what are now Israel, Jordan, and Syria in the Levant. Great amounts of obsidian were exported to sites about 190 miles from the source of supply; more than 80 percent of the tools that residents of those areas used were made of this material.[98] Marble was being sent from western to eastern Turkey, and seashells from the coast were traded to distant inland regions. Such trade suggests a considerable amount of contact among various Neolithic communities.

About 3500 B.C., cities first appeared in the Near East. These cities had political assemblies, kings, scribes, and specialized workshops. The specialized production of goods and services was supported by surrounding farming villages, which sent their produce to the urban centers. A dazzling transformation had taken place in a relatively short time. People had not only settled down, but they had also become "civilized," or urbanized. (The word *civilized* literally means to make "citified.") Urban societies seem to have developed first in the Near East and somewhat later

around the eastern Mediterranean, in the Indus Valley of northwestern India, in northern China, and in Mexico and Peru. In the next chapter, we turn to the rise of these earliest civilizations.

SUMMARY ● ○ ○

1. In the period immediately before plants and animals were domesticated, there seems to have been a shift in many areas of the world to less dependence on big game hunting and greater dependence on what is called broad-spectrum collecting. The broad spectrum of available resources frequently included aquatic resources such as fish and shellfish and a variety of wild plants, deer, and other game. Climatic changes may have been partly responsible for the change to broad-spectrum collecting.

2. In some sites in Europe, the Near East, Africa, and Peru, the switch to broad-spectrum collecting seems to be associated with the development of more permanent communities. In other areas, such as the semiarid highlands of Mesoamerica, permanent settlements may have emerged only after the domestication of plants and animals.

3. The shift to the cultivation and domestication of plants and animals has been referred to as the Neolithic revolution, and it occurred, probably independently, in a number of areas. To date, the earliest evidence of domestication comes from the Near East at about 8000 B.C. Dating for the earliest domestication in other areas of the Old World is not so clear, but the presence of different domesticated crops in different regions suggests that there were independent centers of domestication in China, Southeast Asia (what is now Malaysia, Thailand, Cambodia, and Vietnam), New Guinea, and Africa some time around or after 6000 B.C. In the New World, there appear to have been several early areas of cultivation and domestication: the highlands of Mesoamerica (about 7000 B.C.), the central Andes around Peru (about the same time, but perhaps even earlier), and the Eastern Woodlands of North America (about 2000 B.C.).

4. Theories about why food production originated remain controversial, but most archaeologists think that certain conditions must have pushed people to switch from collecting to producing food. Some possible causal factors include (1) population growth in regions of bountiful wild resources (which may have pushed people to move to marginal areas where they tried to reproduce their former abundance); (2) global population growth (which filled most of the world's habitable regions and may have forced people to utilize a broader spectrum of wild resources and to domesticate plants and animals); and (3) the emergence of hotter and drier summers and colder winters (which may have favored sedentarism near seasonal stands of wild grain; population growth in such areas

may have forced people to plant crops and raise animals to support themselves).

5. Regardless of why food production originated, it seems to have had important consequences for human life. Populations generally increased substantially after plant and animal domestication. Even though not all early cultivators were sedentary, sedentarism did increase with greater reliance on agriculture. Somewhat surprisingly, some prehistoric populations that relied heavily on agriculture seem to have been less healthy than earlier populations that relied on foraging. In the more permanent villages that were established after the rise of food production, houses and furnishings became more elaborate, and people began to make textiles and to paint pottery. These villages have also yielded evidence of increased long-distance trade.

GLOSSARY TERMS ○ ● ○

agriculture **184**	Mesolithic **184**
Archaic **184**	Neolithic **192**
domestication **192**	obsidian **194**
Epipaleolithic **184**	rachis **192**
food production **184**	sedentarism **184**

CRITICAL QUESTIONS ○ ○ ●

1. What factors might cause people to work harder to get food? Explain your answer.

2. How might people have domesticated sheep, goats, and cattle?

3. Do the various theories of the rise of food production explain why domestication occurred in many areas of the world within a few thousand years?

PEARSON
myanthrolab

Read the chapter by Mark Nathan Cohen titled "Were Early Agriculturalists Less Healthy than Food Collectors?" on MyAnthroLab. Answer the following questions:

1. Describe the basic arguments behind Cohen's question. What benefits did agriculture provide to human groups? What problems may have resulted from agriculture?

2. What does Cohen suggest his comparative data from modern foragers and modern agriculturalists demonstrate about the relative health of the two groups? Do data from ancient skeletons demonstrate a similar or a different pattern?

Origins of Cities and States

From the time agriculture first developed until about 6000 B.C., people in the Near East lived in fairly small villages. There were few differences in wealth and status from household to household, and apparently there was no governmental authority beyond the village. There is also no evidence that these villages had any public buildings or craft specialists or that one community was very different in size from its neighbors. In short, these settlements had none of the characteristics we commonly associate with "civilization."

But sometime around 6000 B.C., in parts of the Near East—and at later times in other places—a great transformation in the quality and scale of human life seems to have begun. For the first time, we can see evidence of differences in status among households. For example, some are much bigger than others. Communities begin to differ in size and to specialize in certain crafts. And there are signs that some political officials had acquired authority over several communities, that what anthropologists call "chiefdoms" had emerged.

Somewhat later, by about 3500 B.C., we can see many, if not all, of the conventional characteristics of **civilization:** the first inscriptions, or writing; cities; many kinds of full-time craft specialists; monumental architecture; great differences in wealth and status; and the kind of strong, hierarchical, centralized political system we call the **state** (see Figure 13–1).

This type of transformation has occurred many times and in many places in human history. The color map titled "The First Civilizations" shows the locations where early civilizations arose. The most ancient civilizations arose in the Near East around 3500 B.C., in northwestern India and in Peru about 2500 B.C., in northern China around 1750 B.C., in Mexico a few hundred years before the time of Christ, and in tropical Africa somewhat later.[1] At least some of these civilizations evolved independently of the others—for example, those in the New World and those in the Old World. Why did they do so? What conditions favored the emergence of centralized, statelike political systems? What conditions favored the establishment of cities? We ask this last question separately, because archaeologists are not yet certain that all the ancient state societies had cities when they first developed centralized government. In this chapter, we discuss some of the things archaeologists have learned or suspect about the growth of ancient civilizations. Our discussion focuses primarily on the Near East and Mexico because archaeologists know the most about the sequences of cultural development in those two areas.

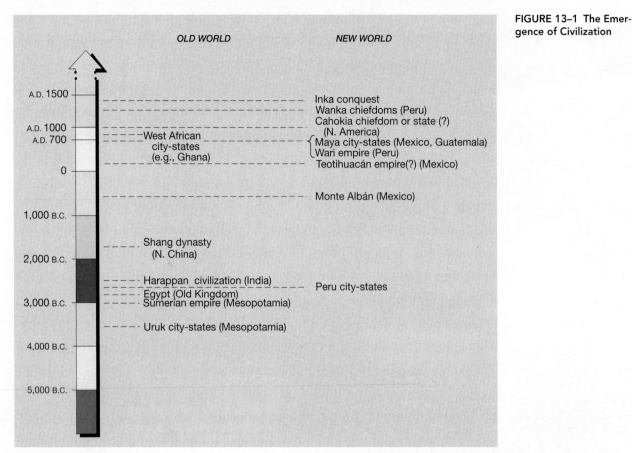

FIGURE 13–1 The Emergence of Civilization

ARCHAEOLOGICAL INFERENCES ABOUT CIVILIZATION

Archaeologists rather than historians have studied the most ancient civilizations because those civilizations evolved before the advent of writing. How do archaeologists infer that a particular people in the preliterate past had social classes, cities, or a centralized government?

As we have noted, it appears that the earliest Neolithic societies were *egalitarian;* that is, people did not differ much in wealth, prestige, or power. Some later societies show signs of social inequality, indicated by burial finds. Archaeologists generally assume that inequality in death reflects inequality in life, at least in status and perhaps also in wealth and power. Thus, we can be fairly sure that a society had differences in status if only some people were buried with special objects, such as jewelry or pots filled with food. And we can be fairly sure that high status was assigned at birth rather than achieved in later life if we find noticeable differences in children's tombs. For example, some (but not all) child burials from as early as 5500 B.C. to 5000 B.C. at Tell es-Sawwan in Iraq, and from about 800 B.C. at La Venta in Mexico, are filled with statues and ornaments, suggesting that some children had high status from birth.[2] But burials indicating differences in status do not necessarily mean a society had significant differences in wealth. Only when archaeologists find other substantial differences, as in house size and furnishings, can we be sure the society had different socioeconomic classes of people.

Reconstruction of the burial of a prehistoric Peruvian king, known as the "Lord of Sipan." Note the carefully laid-out wood tomb and the ornate cloth and gold items buried with the individual. Archaeologists assume that such special treatment indicates elite status.

new perspectives on gender

Effects of Imperialism on Women's Status

Archaeologists, and particularly women archaeologists, have begun to pay attention to the gender implications of archaeological materials. Do the findings from excavated houses imply anything about what women and men did where they lived? What do the findings in houses and other places suggest about the division of labor by gender? Can archaeology tell us about women's status in the culture and how it may have changed over time? Recent research suggests that if you look for gender-related results, you can often find some. As the title of a recent book indicated, new kinds of archaeology can be "engendered." For example, archaeologist Cathy Costin has studied the effects of Inka (Inca) imperialism on women's status in a conquered area.

Costin participated in a research project that studied culture change in the Yanamarca Valley of highland Peru. The project focused on the development of chiefdoms among the indigenous Wanka ethnic group between A.D. 1300 and A.D. 1470 and on the effects of the Inka conquest at the end of that period. According to the archaeology, most people before the Inka conquest were farmers, but some households specialized part-time in the production of pottery, stone tools, and perhaps textiles. Documents written after the arrival of the Spanish suggest that the Wanka had developed chiefdoms about A.D. 1300, possibly as a result of intensified warfare among the various communities. A high level of conflict is inferred from the locations and configurations of the settlements: Most people lived in fortified (walled) communities located on hills above the valley floor. According to the documentary sources, the Wanka chiefs had achieved their positions because of success as war leaders.

We know from documents that the Inka conquered the Wanka during the reign of the emperor Pachakuti (about A.D. 1470). The Wanka region became a province within the Inka Empire, and bureaucrats from the capital at Cuzco came to govern the Wanka. The Inka conquerors, including military personnel, formed the highest class in the valley. The Wanka chiefs became vassals of the Inka state and imitators of Inka ways, using Inka-like pottery and building Inka-style additions to their homes. The economy of the valley became more specialized, apparently to meet the needs of the Inka. People in some villages still mostly farmed, but most households in other villages specialized in the production of pottery, stone tools, and other crafts. Skeletal remains indicate that the commoners became healthier and lived longer after the Inka conquest.

How did the Inka conquest affect the status of women? One key to an answer was suggested by the presence in the excavations of several thousand perforated, round ceramic objects. They were spindle whorls, weights used in spinning to keep the thread tight and even. The thread (from llama and alpaca wool) was made into cloth, which became the major form of tax payment after the Inka took over. Each village had to produce a certain amount of cloth for the state tax collectors. The cloth collected was used to clothe men serving in the army and to "pay" other government personnel. The burden of producing the cloth fell on the traditional spinners and weavers, who we know from the post-Spanish documents were females of all ages.

Just before the Inka conquest, all households excavated had spindle whorls, indicating that the female occupants in all households spun and made cloth. More whorls were found the farther up the mountain the house was located, indicating that women who lived closer to the high grasslands, where the flocks of llamas and alpacas were kept, spun more thread than did women who lived farther down from the pastures. We might expect that elite women would do less work. But, to the contrary, the women in elite households seem to have produced more cloth than the women in commoner households, judging by the number of whorls in the households.

After the Inka conquest, households appear to have produced twice the amount of thread they did before, because there are twice the number of recovered spindle whorls. There is no indication, archaeological or documentary, that the women were freed from other tasks to make more time for spinning, so it would appear that women had to work harder under Inka domination to produce thread and cloth. But the producers do not appear to have benefited from the increased cloth production. Much if not most of the cloth produced was removed from the villages and taken to Inka storage facilities in the capital and redistributed from there.

In addition to working harder for the Inka, women seem to have fared worse than the men when it came to nutrition. Christine Hastorf's chemical analysis of bones from graves of the Inka period suggests that women ate less maize (corn) than did men. It seems that the men were "eating out" more than women. Maize was often consumed as chicha beer, a key component of state-sponsored feasts, which more men than women probably attended. Men also worked more in state-organized agricultural and production projects, where they probably were rewarded with meat, maize, and chicha for their service to the state.

So, under Inka domination, Wanka women had to produce more and received less. Is this a general effect of imperialism? And, if so, why?

Sources: Brumfiel 1992; Costin 2009; Gero and Conkey 1991.

The history of Ephesus, a former city lying in ruins in what is now western Turkey, illustrates the waxing and waning of states and empires. From about 1000 B.C. to 100 B.C., it was controlled by the Greeks, Lydians, Persians, Macedonians, and Romans, among others.

wholesale invasions that were exacerbated by famines, plagues, and poor leadership. By the time the last Roman emperor of the West was deposed in A.D. 476, the empire had withered to virtually nothing.[64]

Finally, internal conflict because of leaders' mismanagement or exploitation has been put forward to explain the collapse of states. For example, Peter Charanis has argued that the Byzantine Empire (the eastern half of the Roman Empire) collapsed because large, powerful landholders had been allowed to take over the land of too many small holders, creating a group of overtaxed, exploited peasants with no interest in maintaining the empire. When the landholders began vying with the emperor for power, civil wars erupted, leading to disunity that left the empire vulnerable to conquest.[65]

Many other ideas have been put forward to explain collapse, ranging from catastrophes to almost mystical factors such as "social decadence," but, as with theories for the origin of states, no single explanation seems to fit all or even most of the situations. Although it is still not clear what specific conditions led to the emergence, or collapse, of the state in each of the early centers of civilization, the question of why states form and decline is a lively focus of research today. More satisfactory answers may come out of ongoing and future investigations.

SUMMARY ● ○ ○

1. Archaeologists do not always agree on how a state should be defined, but most seem to agree that hierarchical and centralized decision making affecting a substantial population is the key criterion. Most states have cities with public buildings, full-time craft and religious specialists, an official art style, and a hierarchical social structure topped by an elite class from which the leaders are drawn. Most states maintain power with a monopoly on the use of force. The state uses force or the threat of force to tax its population and to draft people for work or war.

2. Early state societies arose within the Near East in what is now southern Iraq and southwestern Iran. Southern Iraq, or Sumer, was unified under a single government just after 3000 B.C. It had writing, large urban centers, imposing temples, codified laws, a standing army, wide trade networks, a complex irrigation system, and a high degree of craft specialization.

3. Probably the earliest city-state in Mesoamerica developed around 500 B.C. in the Valley of Oaxaca, with a capital at Monte Albán. Somewhat later, in the northeastern section of the Valley of Mexico, Teotihuacán developed. At the height of its power, A.D. 200 to A.D. 500, the city-state of Teotihuacán appears to have influenced much of Mesoamerica.

4. City-states arose early in other parts of the New World: in Guatemala, the Yucatán Peninsula of Mexico, Peru, and possibly near St. Louis, Missouri. In the Old World, early states developed in Africa, the Indus Valley of India, and northern China.

5. There are several theories of why states arose. The irrigation theory suggests that the administrative needs of maintaining extensive irrigation systems may have been the impetus for state formation. The circumscription theory suggests that states emerge when competition and warfare in circumscribed areas lead to the subordination of defeated groups, which are obliged to submit to the control of the most powerful

group. Theories involving trade suggest that the organizational requirements of producing exportable items, redistributing imported items, and defending trading parties would foster state formation. Which is correct? At this point, no one theory is able to explain the formation of every state. Perhaps different organizational requirements in different areas all favored centralized government.

6. When states arise, they have a dramatic impact. Populations grow and become concentrated in cities. Agriculture becomes more efficient, allowing many people to be removed from food production. States provide a context in which what we commonly call civilization—art, music, literature, and organized religion—can develop and flourish. But states also provide a context in which warfare and political terror can flourish. The social differentiation found in states produces an underclass of poor and often unhealthy people. States are prone to epidemic disease and periodic famine.

7. All ancient states collapsed eventually. Although we have no good answers to the question of why states collapse, research into this question may have implications for prolonging the lives of our modern state systems.

GLOSSARY TERMS ○ ● ○

civilization **206**	hieroglyphics **211**
cuneiform **211**	state **206**

CRITICAL QUESTIONS ○ ○ ●

1. Cities and states did not appear until after the emergence of food production. Why might food production be necessary, but not sufficient, for cities and states to develop?

2. Like the emergence of food production, the earliest cities and states developed within a few thousand years of each other. What might be the reasons?

3. Can you imagine a future world without states? What conditions might lead to that "state" of the world?

PEARSON
myanthrolab

Read the chapter by Joyce Marcus titled "Maya Hieroglyphs: History or Propaganda?" on MyAnthroLab. Answer the following questions:

1. Marcus describes a series of "pendulum swings" in the study of Mayan writing. What does she mean by a "pendulum swing"? Give an example.

2. How has the decipherment of Mayan writing led scholars to question the histories it apparently was used to convey?

3. What does Marcus mean by Maya "propaganda"? How might Mayan kings have used "propaganda"?

chapter 14

Culture and Culture Change

W e all consider ourselves to be unique individuals with our own set of personal opinions, preferences, habits, and quirks. Indeed, all of us are unique; and yet most of us also share many feelings, beliefs, and habits with most of the people who live in our society. If we live in North America, we are likely to have the feeling that eating dogs is wrong, have the belief that bacteria or viruses cause illness, and have the habit of sleeping on a bed. Most people hardly ever think about the ideas and customs they share with other people in their society, assuming them to be "natural." These ideas and behaviors are part of what we mean by *culture*. We only begin to become aware that our culture is different when we become aware that other peoples have different feelings, different beliefs, and different habits from ours. So most North Americans would never even think of the possibility of eating dog meat if they did not know that people in some other societies commonly do so. They would not realize that their belief in germs was cultural if they were not aware that people in some societies think that witchcraft or evil spirits causes illness. They might not become aware that it is their custom to sleep on beds if they were not aware that people in many societies sleep on the floor or on the ground. Only when we compare ourselves with people in other societies may we become aware of cultural differences and similarities. This is, in fact, the way that anthropology as a profession began. When Europeans began to explore and move to faraway places, they were forced to confront the sometimes striking facts of cultural variation.

Most of us are aware that "times have changed," especially when we compare our lives with those of our parents. Some of the most dramatic changes have occurred in attitudes about sex and marriage, changes in women's roles, and changes in technology. But such culture change is not unusual. Throughout history, humans have replaced or altered customary behaviors and attitudes as their needs have changed. Just as no individual is immortal, no particular cultural pattern is impervious to change. Anthropologists want to understand how and why such change occurs. Culture change may be gradual or rapid. Although there has always been contact between different societies, contact between faraway cultures through exploration, colonization, trade, and more recently multinational business has accelerated the pace of change within the last 600 years or so. Globalization has made the world more and more interconnected. We conclude this chapter with a discussion of the future of cultural diversity.

● ○ ●

CHAPTER OUTLINE

DEFINING CULTURE

In everyday usage, the word *culture* refers to a desirable quality we can acquire by attending a sufficient number of plays and concerts and visiting art museums and galleries. Anthropologists, however, have a different definition, as Ralph Linton explained:

Culture refers to the total way of life of any society, not simply to those parts of this way which the society regards as higher or more desirable. Thus culture, when applied to our own way of life, has nothing to do with playing the piano or reading Browning. For the social scientist such activities are simply elements within the totality of our culture. This totality also includes such mundane activities as washing dishes or driving an automobile, and for the purposes of cultural studies these stand quite on a par with "the finer things of life." It follows that for the social scientist there are no uncultured societies or even individuals. Every society has a culture, no matter how simple this culture may be, and every human being is cultured, in the sense of participating in some culture or other.[1]

Culture, then, refers to innumerable aspects of life, including many things we consider ordinary. Linton emphasized common habits and behaviors in what he considered culture, but the totality of life also includes not just what people do, but also how they commonly think and feel. As we define it here, **culture** is the set of learned behaviors and ideas (including beliefs, attitudes, values, and ideals) that are characteristic of a particular society or other social group. Behaviors can also produce products or *material culture*—things like houses, musical instruments, and tools that are the products of customary behavior.

Different kinds of groups can have cultures. People come to share behaviors and ideas because they communicate with and observe each other. Although groups from families to societies share cultural traits, anthropologists have traditionally been concerned with the cultural characteristics of *societies*. Many anthropologists define **society** as a group of people who occupy a particular territory and speak a common language not generally understood by neighboring peoples. By this definition, societies may or may not correspond to countries. There are many countries, particularly newer ones, that have within their boundaries different peoples speaking mutually unintelligible languages. By our definition of society, such countries are composed of many different societies and therefore many cultures. Also, by our definition of society, some societies may even include more than one country. For example, we would have to say that Canada and the United States form a single society because the two groups generally speak English, live next to each other, and share many common ideas and behaviors. That is why we refer to "North American culture" in this chapter. The terms *society* and *culture* are not synonymous. Society refers to a group of people; culture refers to the learned and shared behaviors, ideas, and characteristic of those people. As we will discuss shortly, we also have to be careful to describe culture as of particular time period; what is characteristic of one time may not be characteristic of another.

Culture Is Commonly Shared

If only one person thinks or does a certain thing, that thought or action represents a personal habit, not a pattern of culture. For a thought or action to be considered cultural, some social group must commonly share it. We usually share many behaviors and ideas with our families and friends. We commonly share cultural characteristics with those whose ethnic or regional origins, religious affiliations, and occupations are the same as or similar to our own. We share certain practices and ideas with most people in our society. We also share some cultural traits with people beyond our society who have similar interests (such as rules for international sporting events) or similar roots (as do the various English-speaking nations).

When we talk about the commonly shared customs of *a* society, which constitute the traditional and central concern of cultural anthropology, we are referring to *a* culture. When we talk about the commonly shared customs of a group within a society, which are a central concern of sociologists and increasingly of concern to anthropologists, we are referring to a **subculture.** (A subculture is not necessarily the same as an ethnic group; we discuss the concept of ethnicity further in the chapter on social stratification, ethnicity, and racism.) When we study the commonly shared customs of some group that includes different societies, we are talking about a phenomenon for which we do not have a single word—for example, as when we refer to *Western culture* (the cultural characteristics of societies in or derived from Europe) or the *culture of poverty* (the presumed cultural characteristics of poor people the world over).

We must remember that, even when anthropologists refer to something as cultural, there is always individual variation, which means that not everyone in a society shares a particular cultural characteristic of that society. For example, it is cultural in North American society for adults to live apart from their parents. But not all adults in our society do so, nor do all adults wish to do so. The custom of living apart from parents is considered cultural because

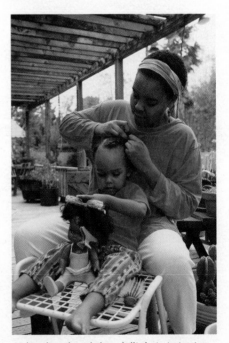

A daughter braids her doll's hair, imitating what her mother is doing.

most adults practice that custom. In every society studied by anthropologists—in the simplest as well as the most complex—individuals do not all think and act the same.[2] Indeed, individual variation is a major source of new culture.[3]

Culture Is Learned

Not all things shared generally by a group are cultural. Typical hair color is not cultural, nor is eating. For something to be considered cultural, it must be learned as well as shared. A typical hair color (unless dyed) is not cultural because it is genetically determined. Humans eat because they must; but what and when and how they eat are learned and vary from culture to culture. Most North Americans do not consider dog meat edible, and indeed the idea of eating dogs horrifies them. But in China, as in some other societies, dog meat is considered delicious. In North American culture, many people consider a baked ham to be a holiday dish. In several societies of the Middle East, however, including those of Egypt and Israel, eating the meat of a pig is forbidden by sacred writings.

To some extent, all animals exhibit learned behaviors, some of which most individuals in a population may share and may therefore consider cultural. But different animal species vary in the degree to which their shared behaviors are learned or are instinctive. The sociable ants, for instance, despite all their patterned social behavior, do not appear to have much, if any, culture. They divide their labor, construct their nests, form their raiding columns, and carry off their dead—all without having been taught to do so and without imitating the behavior of other ants. Our closest biological relatives, the monkeys and the apes, not only learn a wide variety of behaviors on their own, they also learn from each other. Some of their learned responses are as basic as those involved in maternal care; others are as frivolous as the taste for candy. Frans de Waal reviewed seven long-term studies of chimpanzees and identified at least 39 behaviors that were clearly learned from others.[4] If shared and socially learned, these behaviors could be described as cultural.

The proportion of an animal's life span occupied by childhood roughly reflects the degree to which the animal depends on learned behavior for survival. Monkeys and apes have relatively long childhoods compared to other animals. Humans have by far the longest childhood of any animal, reflecting our great dependence on learned behavior. Although humans may acquire much learned behavior by trial and error and imitation, as do monkeys and apes, most human ideas and behaviors are learned from others. Much of it is probably acquired with the aid of spoken, symbolic language. We will have much more to say about language in a later chapter. Using language, a human parent can describe a snake and tell a child that a snake is dangerous and should be avoided. If symbolic language did not exist, the parent would have to wait until the child actually saw a snake and then, through example, show the child that such a creature is to be avoided. Without language, we probably could not transmit or receive information so efficiently and rapidly, and thus would not be heir to so rich and varied a culture.

To sum up, we may say that something is cultural if it is a learned behavior or idea (belief, attitude, value, ideal) that the members of a society or other social group generally share.

Controversies About the Concept of Culture

Although we have explained what we mean by culture and we have tried to give the definition most anthropologists use, some would disagree with the definition. One of the disagreements is whether the concept of culture should refer just to the rules or ideas behind behavior,[5] or should also include the behaviors or the products of behavior, as is our choice here.

Cognitive anthropologists are most likely to say that culture refers to rules and ideas behind behavior, and therefore that culture resides in people's heads.[6]

Every individual will have slightly different constructs that are based in part on their own unique experiences. Because many people in a society share many of the same experiences, they will share many ideas—those shared ideas anthropologists describe as culture. This view allows for individual differences within a society, and also suggests that individual variation is the source of new culture.

Observers of human life often point to the seeming force of "culture," the profound effect on individuals of living in social groups. As we will see shortly in the section on cultural constraints, these social constraints suggest that culture exists outside of individuals. In the strongest view, one that was more acceptable in the past, culture is thought of as having a "life" of its own that could be studied without much regard for individuals at all.[7] According to this view, people are born blank slates, which culture can put its stamp on in each generation. Individuals may acquire their culture in the course of growing up, but understanding culture does not require understanding psychological processes.

There are a number of problems if we view culture as having a "life" of its own. First, where does it reside exactly? Second, if individuals do not matter, what are the mechanisms of culture change? And lastly, if psychological processes are irrelevant, how is it that there is considerable similarity across cultures?

As we will see in the next section, people do behave differently in social groups in ways that they might not even imagine ahead of time. Mob behavior is an extreme, but telling example. Therefore, we think we should look at behavior as well as rules or ideas in people's heads in describing a culture. It is not necessary to postulate that culture has a "life" of its own to explain why people sometimes behave differently in social groups. Humans are social beings and respond to others. So, in contrast to many cognitive anthropologists, we include behavior and the products of behavior in describing culture. But like cognitive anthropologists, we believe that one must consider individual variation in describing culture to sort out what is individual and what is shared. Those commonly shared and learned behaviors as well as ideas are the stuff of culture.

CULTURAL CONSTRAINTS

The noted French sociologist Émile Durkheim stressed that culture is something *outside* us, exerting a strong coercive power on us. We do not always feel the constraints of our culture because we generally conform to the types of conduct and thought it requires. Social scientists refer to standards or rules about what is acceptable behavior as **norms.** The importance of a norm usually can be judged by how members of a society respond when the norm is violated.

Cultural constraints are of two basic types, *direct* and *indirect.* Naturally, the direct constraints are the more obvious. For example, if you choose to wear a casual shorts outfit to a wedding, you will probably be subject to some ridicule and a certain amount of social isolation. But if you choose to wear nothing, you may be exposed to a stronger, more direct cultural constraint—arrest for indecent exposure.

Although indirect forms of cultural constraint are less obvious than direct ones, they are no less effective. Durkheim illustrated this point when he wrote, "I am not obliged to speak French with my fellow-countrymen, nor to use the legal currency, but I cannot possibly do otherwise. If I tried to escape this necessity, my attempt would fail miserably."[8] In other words, if Durkheim had decided he would rather speak Icelandic than French, nobody would have tried to stop him. But hardly anyone would have understood him either. And although he would not have been put into prison for trying to buy groceries with Icelandic money, he would have had difficulty convincing the local merchants to sell him food.

In a series of classic experiments on conformity, Solomon Asch revealed how strong social pressure can be. Asch coached the majority of a group of college students to give deliberately incorrect answers to questions involving visual stimuli. A "critical subject," the one student in the room who was not so coached, had no idea that the other participants would purposely misinterpret the evidence presented to them. Asch found that, in one-third of the experiments, the critical subjects consistently gave incorrect answers, seemingly allowing their own correct perceptions to be distorted by the obviously incorrect statements of the others. And in another 40 percent of the experiments, the critical subject yielded to the opinion of the group some of the time.[9] These studies have been replicated in the United States and elsewhere. Although the degree of conformity appears to vary in different societies, most studies still show conformity effects.[10] Many individuals still do not give in to the wishes of the majority, but a recent study using MRIs has shown that perceptions can actually be altered if participants consciously alter their answers to conform to others.[11]

ATTITUDES THAT HINDER THE STUDY OF CULTURES

Many of the Europeans who first traveled to faraway places were revolted or shocked by customs they observed. Such reactions are not surprising. People commonly feel that their own behaviors and attitudes are the correct ones and that people who do not share those patterns are immoral or inferior.[12] People who judge other cultures solely in terms of their own culture are **ethnocentric**—that is, they hold an attitude called **ethnocentrism.** Most North Americans would think that eating dogs or insects is disgusting, but most do not feel the same way about eating beef. Similarly, they would react negatively to child betrothal or digging up the bones of the dead.

Our own customs and ideas may appear bizarre or barbaric to an observer from another society. Hindus in

Because we are ethnocentric about many things, it is often difficult to criticize our own customs, some of which might seem shocking to a member of another society. The elderly in America often spend their days alone. In contrast, the elderly in Japan often live in a three-generational family.

India, for example, would consider our custom of eating beef disgusting. In their culture, the cow is a sacred animal and may not be slaughtered for food. In many societies, a baby is almost constantly carried by someone, in someone's lap, or asleep next to others.[13] People in such societies may think it is cruel of us to leave babies alone for long periods of time, often in devices that resemble cages (cribs and playpens). Even our most ordinary customs— the daily rituals we take for granted—might seem thoroughly absurd when viewed from an outside perspective. An observer of our society might justifiably take notes on certain strange behaviors that seem quite ordinary to us, as the following description shows:

> The daily body ritual performed by everyone includes a mouth-rite. Despite the fact that these people are so punctilious about the care of the mouth, this rite involves a practice which strikes the uninitiated stranger as revolting. It was reported to me that the ritual consists of inserting a small bundle of hog hairs into the mouth, along with certain magical powders, and then moving the bundle in a highly formalized series of gestures. In addition to the private mouth-rite, the people seek out a holy-mouth man once or twice a year. These practitioners have an impressive set of paraphernalia, consisting of a variety of augers, awls, probes, and prods. The use of these objects in the exorcism of the evils of the mouth involves almost unbelievable ritual torture of the client. The holy-mouth man opens the client's mouth and, using the above-mentioned tools, enlarges any holes which decay may have created in teeth. Magical materials are put into these holes. If there are no naturally occurring holes in the teeth, large sections of one or more teeth are gouged out so that the supernatural substance can be applied. In the client's view, the purpose of these ministrations is to arrest decay and to draw friends. The extremely sacred and traditional character of the rite is evident in the fact that the natives return to the holy-mouth man year after year, despite the fact that their teeth continue to decay.[14]

We are likely to protest that to understand the behaviors of a particular society—in this case, our own—the observer must try to find out what the people in that society say about why they do things. For example, the observer might find out that periodic visits to the "holy-mouth man" are for medical, not magical, purposes. Indeed, the observer, after some questioning, might discover that the "mouth-rite" has no sacred or religious connotations whatsoever. Actually, Horace Miner, the author of the passage on the "daily rite ritual," was not a foreigner. An American, he described the "ritual" the way he did to show how the behaviors involved might be interpreted by an outside observer.

Ethnocentrism hinders our understanding of the customs of other people and, at the same time, keeps us from understanding our own customs. If we think that everything we do is best, we are not likely to ask why we do what we do or why "they" do what "they" do.

We may not always glorify our own culture. Other ways of life may sometimes seem more appealing. Whenever we are weary of the complexities of civilization, we may long for a way of life that is "closer to nature" or "simpler" than our own. For instance, a young North American whose parent is holding two or three jobs just to provide the family with bare necessities might briefly be attracted to the lifestyle of the !Kung of the Kalahari Desert in the 1950s. The !Kung shared their food and therefore were often free to engage in leisure activities during the greater part of the day. They obtained all their food by men hunting animals and women gathering wild plants. They had no facilities for refrigeration, so sharing a large freshly killed animal was clearly more sensible than hoarding meat that would soon rot. Moreover, the sharing provided a kind of social security system for the !Kung. If a hunter was unable to catch an animal on a certain day, he could obtain food for himself and his family from someone else in his band. Then, at some later date, the game he caught would provide food for the family of another, unsuccessful hunter. This system of sharing also ensured that people too young or too old to help with collecting food would still be fed.

Could we learn from the !Kung? Perhaps we could in some respects, but we must not glorify their way of life either or think that their way of life might be easily imported into our own society. Other aspects of !Kung life would not appeal to many North Americans. For example, when the nomadic !Kung decided to move their camps, they had to carry all the family possessions, substantial amounts of food and water, and all young children below age 4 or 5. This is a sizable burden to carry for any distance. The nomadic !Kung traveled about 1,500 miles in a single year and families had few possessions.[15] It is unlikely that most North Americans would find the !Kung way of life enviable in all respects.

Both ethnocentrism and its opposite, the glorification of other cultures, hinder effective anthropological study.

CULTURAL RELATIVISM

As we discussed in the chapter on the history of theory in anthropology, the early evolutionists tended to think of Western cultures as being at the highest or most progressive stage of evolution. Not only were these early ideas based on very poor evidence of the details of world ethnography, they could also be ethnocentric glorifications of Western culture.

But Franz Boas and many of his students—like Ruth Benedict, Melville Herskovits, and Margaret Mead—felt otherwise.[16] They stressed that the early evolutionists did not sufficiently understand the details of the cultures they theorized about, nor did they understand the context in which these customs appeared. Challenging the attitude that Western cultures were obviously superior, the Boasians insisted that a society's customs and ideas should be described objectively and understood in the context of that society's problems and opportunities. This attitude is known as **cultural relativism.** Does cultural relativism mean that the actions of another society, or of our own, should not be judged? Does our insistence on objectivity mean that anthropologists should not make moral judgments about the cultural phenomena they observe and try to explain? Does it mean that anthropologists should not try to bring about change? Not necessarily. Although the concept of cultural relativism remains an important anthropological tenet, anthropologists differ in their interpretation of the principle of cultural relativism.

Many anthropologists are uncomfortable with the strong form of cultural relativism that suggests that all patterns of culture are equally valid. What if the people practice slavery, violence against women, torture, or genocide? If the strong doctrine of relativism is adhered to, then these cultural practices are not to be judged, and we should not try to eliminate them. A weaker form of cultural relativism asserts that anthropologists should strive for objectivity in describing a people and should be wary of superficial or quick judgment in their attempts to understand the reasons for cultural behavior. Tolerance should be the basic mode unless there is strong reason to behave otherwise.[17] The weak version of cultural relativity does not preclude anthropologists from making judgments or from trying to change behavior they think is harmful. But judgments need not, and should not, preclude accurate description and explanation.

Human Rights and Relativism

The news increasingly reports behaviors that Western countries consider to be violations of human rights. Examples range from jailing people for expressing certain political ideas to ethnic massacre. But faced with criticism from the West, people in other parts of the world are saying that the West should not dictate its ideas about human rights to other countries. Indeed, many countries say they have different codes of ethics. Are the Western countries being ethnocentric by taking their own cultural ideas and applying them to the rest of the world? Should we instead rely on the strong version of the concept of cultural relativism, considering each culture on its own terms? If we do that, it may not be possible to create a universal standard of human rights.

What we do know is that all cultures have ethical standards, but they do not emphasize the same things. For example, some cultures emphasize individual political rights; others emphasize political order. Some cultures emphasize protection of individual property; others emphasize the sharing or equitable distribution of resources. People in the United States may have freedom to dissent, but they can be deprived of health insurance or of food if they lack the money to buy them. Cultures also vary markedly in the degree to which they have equal rights for minorities and women. In some societies, women are killed when a husband dies or when they disobey a father or brother.

Some anthropologists argue strongly against cultural relativism. For example, Elizabeth Zechenter says that cultural relativists claim there are no universal principles of morality, but insist on tolerance for all cultures. If

tolerance is one universal principle, why shouldn't there be others? In addition, she points out that the concept of cultural relativism is often used to justify traditions desired by the dominant and powerful in a society. She points to a case in 1996, in Algeria, where two teenage girls were raped and murdered because they violated the fundamentalist edict against attending school. Are those girls any less a part of the culture than the fundamentalists? Would it make any difference if most Algerian women supported the murders? Would that make it right? Zechenter does not believe that international treaties such as the Universal Declaration of Human Rights impose uniformity among diverse cultures. Rather, they seek to create a floor below which no society is supposed to fall.[18]

Can the concept of cultural relativism be reconciled with the concept of an international code of human rights? Probably not completely. Paul Rosenblatt recognizes the dilemma but nonetheless thinks that something has to be done to stop torture and "ethnic cleansing," among other practices. He makes the case that "to the extent that it is easier to persuade people whose viewpoints and values one understands, relativism can be a tool for change . . . a relativist's awareness of the values and understanding of the elite makes it easier to know what arguments would be persuasive. For example, in a society in which the group rather than the individual has great primacy, it might be persuasive to show how respect for individual rights benefits the group."[19]

DESCRIBING A CULTURE

Earlier we discussed *participant-observation* and some other methods of research that cultural anthropologists use in doing fieldwork. But here we focus on another question: If all individuals are unique and all cultures have some internal variation, how do anthropologists discover what may be cultural? Understanding what is cultural involves two parts—separating what is shared from what is very individually variable, and understanding whether common behaviors and ideas are learned.

To understand better how an anthropologist might make sense of diverse behaviors, let us examine the diversity at a professional football game in the United States. When people attend a football game, various members of the crowd behave differently while "The Star-Spangled Banner" is being played. As they stand and listen, some people remove their hats; a child munches popcorn; a veteran of the armed forces stands at attention; a teenager searches the crowd for a friend; and the coaches take a final opportunity to intone secret chants and spells designed to sap the strength of the opposing team. Yet, despite these individual variations, most of the people at the game respond in a basically similar manner: Nearly everyone stands silently, facing the flag. Moreover, if you go to several football games, you will observe that many aspects of the event are notably similar. Although the plays will vary from game to game, the rules of the game are never different, and although the colors of the uniforms of the

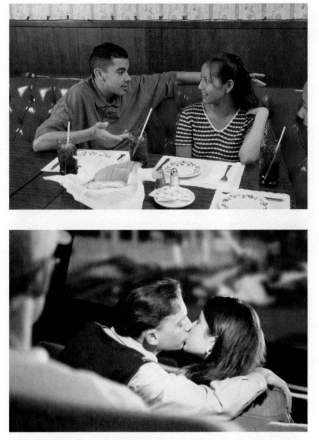

In deciding what is cultural behavior, anthropologists look for commonalities, understanding that there is always considerable variation. In North American culture, unmarried couples are allowed and even encouraged to spend time with each other, but how they spend their time varies.

teams are different, the players never appear on the field dressed in swimsuits.

Although the variations in individual reactions to a given stimulus are theoretically limitless, in fact they tend to fall within easily recognizable limits. A child listening to the anthem may continue to eat popcorn but will probably not do a rain dance. Similarly, the coaches will unlikely react to that same stimulus by running onto the field and embracing the singer. Variations in behavior, then, are confined within socially acceptable limits, and part of the anthropologists' goals is to find out what those limits are. They may note, for example, that some limitations on behavior have a practical purpose: A spectator who disrupts the game by wandering onto the field would be required to leave. Other limitations are purely traditional. In our society, it is considered proper for a man to remove his overcoat if he becomes overheated, but others would undoubtedly frown upon his removing his trousers even if the weather were quite warm. Using observation and interviewing, anthropologists discover the customs and the ranges of acceptable behavior that characterize the society under study.

Similarly, anthropologists interested in describing courtship and marriage in our society would encounter a variety of behaviors. Dating couples vary in where they go (coffee shops, movies, restaurants, bowling alleys), what behaviors they engage in on dates, how long they date before they split up or move on to more serious relationships. If they decide to marry, ceremonies may be simple or elaborate and involve either religious or secular rituals. Despite this variability, the anthropologists would begin to detect certain regularities in courting practices. Although couples may do many different things on their first and subsequent dates, they nearly always arrange the dates by themselves; they try to avoid their parents when on dates; they often manage to find themselves alone at the end of a date; they put their lips together frequently; and so forth. After a series of more and more closely spaced encounters, a man and woman may decide to declare themselves publicly as a couple, either by announcing that they are engaged or by revealing that they are living together or intend to do so. Finally, if the two of them decide to marry, they must in some way have their union recorded by the civil authorities.

In our society, a person who wishes to marry cannot completely disregard the customary patterns of courtship. If a man saw a woman on the street and decided he wanted to marry her, he could conceivably choose a quicker and more direct form of action than the usual dating procedure. He could get on a horse, ride to the woman's home, snatch her up in his arms, and gallop away with her. In Sicily, until the last few decades, such a couple would have been considered legally married, even if the woman had never met the man before or had no intention of marrying. But in North American society, any man who acted in such a fashion would be arrested and jailed for kidnapping and would probably have his sanity challenged. Although individual behaviors may vary, most social behavior falls within culturally acceptable limits.

In the course of observing and interviewing, anthropologists also try to distinguish actual behavior from the ideas about how people in particular situations ought to feel and behave. In everyday terms, we speak of these ideas as *ideals;* in anthropology, we refer to them as *ideal cultural traits.* Ideal cultural traits may differ from actual behavior because the ideal is based on the way society used to be. (Consider the ideal of "free enterprise," that industry should be totally free of governmental regulation.) Other ideals may never have been actual patterns and may represent merely what people would like to see as correct behavior. Consider the idealized belief, long cherished in North America, that everybody is "equal before the law," that everybody should be treated in the same way by the police and courts. Of course, we know that this is not always true. The rich, for example, may receive less jail time and be sent to nicer prisons. Nevertheless, the ideal is still part of our culture; most of us continue to believe that the law should be applied equally to all.

When dealing with customs that are overt or highly visible within a society—for example, the custom of sending children to school—an investigator can determine the existence of such practices by direct observation and by interviewing a few knowledgeable people. But when

Distance between people conversing varies cross-culturally. The faces of the Rajput Indian men on the left are much closer than the faces of the American women on the right.

the frequency distribution takes the form of a *bell-shaped curve,* as shown in Figure 14–1.

There, the characteristic being measured is plotted on the horizontal axis (in this case, the distance between conversational pairs), and the number of times each distance is observed (its frequency) is plotted on the vertical axis. If we were to plot how a sample of North American casual conversational pairs is distributed, we would probably get a bell-shaped curve that peaks at around 3 feet.[21] Is it any wonder, then, that we sometimes speak of keeping others "at arm's length"?

Although we may be able to discover by interviews and observation that a behavior, thought, or feeling is widely shared within a society, how do we establish that something commonly shared is learned, so that we can call it cultural? Establishing that something is or is not learned may be difficult. Because children are not reared apart from adult caretakers, the behaviors they exhibit as part of their genetic inheritance are not clearly separated from those they learn from others around them. We suspect that particular behaviors and ideas are largely learned if they vary from society to society. We also suspect genetic influences when particular behaviors or ideas are found in all societies. For example, as we will see in the chapter on language, children the world over seem to acquire language at about the same age, and the structure of their early utterances seems to be similar. These facts suggest that human children are born with an innate grammar. However, although early childhood language seems similar the world over, the particular languages spoken by adults in different societies show considerable variability. This variability suggests that particular

dealing with a domain of behavior that may include many individual variations, or when the people studied are unaware of their pattern of behavior and cannot answer questions about it, the anthropologist may need to collect information from a larger sample of individuals to establish what the cultural trait is.

One example of a cultural trait that most people in a society are not aware of is how far apart people stand when they are having a conversation. Yet there is considerable reason to believe that unconscious cultural rules govern such behavior. These rules become obvious when we interact with people who have different rules. We may experience considerable discomfort when another person stands too close (indicating too much intimacy) or too far (indicating unfriendliness). Edward Hall reported that Arabs customarily stand quite close to others, close enough, as we have noted, to be able to smell the other person. In interactions between Arabs and North Americans, then, the Arabs will move closer at the same time that the North Americans back away.[20]

If we wanted to arrive at the cultural rule for conversational distance between casual acquaintances, we could study a sample of individuals from a society and determine the *modal response,* or *mode.* The mode is a statistical term that refers to the most frequently encountered response in a given series of responses. So, for the North American pattern of casual conversational distance, we would plot the actual distance for many observed pairs of people. Some pairs may be 2 feet apart, some 2.5, and some 4 feet apart. If we count the number of times every particular distance is observed, these counts provide what we call a *frequency distribution.* The distance with the highest frequency is the *modal pattern.* Very often

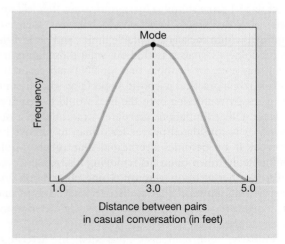

FIGURE 14–1 Frequency Distribution Curve

languages have to be learned. Similarly, if the courtship patterns of one society differ markedly from those of another, we can be fairly certain that those courtship patterns are learned and therefore cultural.

CULTURE IS PATTERNED

Anthropologists have always known that culture is not a hodgepodge of unrelated behaviors and ideas—that a culture is mostly integrated. In saying that a culture is mostly *integrated,* we mean that the elements or traits that make up that culture are not just a random assortment of customs but are mostly adjusted to or consistent with one another.

A culture may also tend to be integrated for psychological reasons. The ideas of a culture are stored in the brains of individuals. Research in social psychology has suggested that people tend to modify beliefs or behaviors that are not cognitively or conceptually consistent with other information.[22] We do not expect cultures to be completely integrated, just as we do not expect individuals to be completely consistent. But if a tendency toward cognitive consistency is found in humans, we might expect that at least some aspects of a culture would tend to be integrated for that reason alone. How this pressure for consistency works is not hard to imagine. Children, for example, seem to be very good at remembering *all* the things their parents say. If they ask for something and the parents say no, they may say, "But you said I could yesterday." This pressure for consistency may even make parents change their minds! Of course, not everything one wants to do is consistent with the rest of one's desires, but there surely is pressure from within and without to make it so.

Humans are also capable of rational decision making; they can usually figure out that certain things are not easy to do because of other things they do. For example, if a society has a long postpartum sex (a custom in which couples abstain from sex for a year or more after the birth of a baby), we might expect that most people in the society could figure out that it would be easier to observe the taboo if husband and wife did not sleep in the same bed. Or if people drive on the left side of the road, as in England, it is easier and less dangerous to drive a car with a steering wheel on the right because that placement allows you to judge more accurately how close you are to cars coming at you from the opposite direction.

Consistency or integration of culture traits may also be produced by less conscious psychological processes. As we discuss in the chapters on culture and the individual, religion and magic, and the arts, people may generalize (transfer) their experiences from one area of life to another. For example, where children are taught that it is wrong to express anger toward family and friends, it turns out that folktales parallel the childrearing; anger and aggression in the folktales tend to be directed only toward strangers, not toward family and friends. It seems as if the expression of anger is too frightening to be expressed close to home, even in folktales.

Adaptation to the environment is another major reason for traits to be patterned. Customs that diminish the survival chances of a society are not likely to persist. Either the people clinging to those customs will become extinct, taking the customs with them, or the customs will be replaced, thereby possibly helping the people to survive. By either process, **maladaptive customs**—those that diminish the chances of survival and reproduction—are likely to disappear. The customs of a society that enhance survival and reproductive success are **adaptive customs** and are likely to persist. Hence, we assume that if a society has survived long enough to be described in the annals of anthropology (the "ethnographic record"), much, if not most, of its cultural repertoire is adaptive, or was at one time.

When we say that a custom is adaptive, however, we mean it is adaptive only with respect to a specific physical and social environment. What may be adaptive in one environment may not be adaptive in another. Therefore, when we ask why a society may have a particular custom, we really are asking if that custom makes sense as an adaptation to that society's particular environmental conditions. If certain customs are more adaptive in particular settings, then those "bundles" of traits will generally be found together under similar conditions. For example, the !Kung, as we have mentioned, subsisted by hunting wild animals and gathering wild plants. Because wild game is mobile and different plants mature at different times, a nomadic way of life may be an adaptive strategy. That food-getting strategy cannot support that many people in one area, so small social groups make more sense than large communities. Because people move frequently, it is probably more adaptive to have few material possessions. As we will see, these cultural traits usually occur together when people depend on hunting and gathering for their food.

We must remember that not all aspects of culture are consistent, nor is a society forced to adapt its culture to changing environmental circumstances. Even in the face of changed circumstances, people may choose not to change their customs. For example, the Tapirapé of central Brazil did not alter their custom of limiting the number of births, even though they suffered severe population losses after contact with Europeans and their diseases. The Tapirapé population fell to fewer than 100 people from over 1,000. Clearly, they were on the way to extinction, yet they continued to value small families. Not only did they believe that a woman should have no more than three children, but they took specific steps to achieve this limitation. They practiced infanticide if twins were born, if the third child was of the same sex as the first two children, and if the possible fathers broke certain taboos during pregnancy or in the child's infancy.[23]

Of course, it is also possible that a people will behave maladaptively, even if they try to alter their behavior. After all, although people may alter their behavior according to what they perceive will be helpful to them, what they perceive to be helpful may not prove to be adaptive. The tendency for a culture to be integrated or patterned, then, may be cognitively and emotionally, as well as adaptively, induced.

HOW AND WHY CULTURES CHANGE

When you examine the history of a society, it is obvious that its culture has changed over time. Some of the shared behaviors and ideas that were common at one time are modified or replaced at another time. That is why, in describing a culture, it is important to understand that a description pertains to a particular time period. (Moreover, in many large societies, the description may only be appropriate for a particular subgroup.) For example, the !Kung of the 1950s were mostly dependent on the collection of wild plants and animals and moved their campsites frequently, but later they became more sedentary to engage in wage labor. Whether we focus on some aspect of past behavior or on contemporary behavior depends on what question we want to answer. If we want to maximize our understanding of cultural variation, such as variation in religious belief and practice, it may be important to focus on the earliest descriptions of a group before they were converted to a major world religion. On the other hand, if we want to understand why a people adopted a new religion or how they altered their religion or resisted change in the face of pressure, we need to examine the changes that occurred over time.

In the remainder of this chapter, we will discuss how and why cultures change and briefly review some of the widespread changes that have occurred in recent times. In general, the impetus for change may come from within the society or from without. From within, the unconscious or conscious pressure for consistency will produce culture change if enough people adjust old behavior and thinking to new. And change can also occur if people try to invent better ways of doing things. Michael Chibnik suggests that people who confront a new problem conduct mental or small "experiments" to decide how to behave. These experiments may give rise to new cultural traits.[24] A good deal of culture change may be stimulated by changes in the external environment. For example, if people move into an arid area, they will either have to give up farming or develop a system of irrigation. In the modern world, changes in the social environment are probably more frequent stimuli for culture change than changes in the physical environment. Many North Americans, for example, started to think seriously about conserving energy and about using sources of energy other than oil only after oil supplies from the Middle East were curtailed in 1973 and 1974. As we noted earlier, a significant amount of the radical and rapid culture change that has occurred in the last few hundred years has been due to the imperial expansion of Western societies into other areas of the world. Native Americans, for instance, were forced to alter their lifestyles drastically when they were driven off their lands and confined to reservations.

Discovery and Invention

Discoveries and inventions, which may originate inside or outside a society, are ultimately the sources of all culture change. But they do not necessarily lead to change. If an invention or discovery is ignored, no change in culture results. Only when society accepts an invention or discovery and uses it regularly can we begin to speak of culture change.

The new thing discovered or invented, the innovation, may be an object—the wheel, the plow, the computer—or it may involve behavior and ideas—buying and selling, democracy, monogamy. According to Ralph Linton, a discovery is any addition to knowledge, and an invention is a new application of knowledge.[25] Thus, a person might discover that children can be persuaded to eat nourishing food if the food is associated with an imaginary character that appeals to them. And then someone might exploit that discovery by inventing a character named Popeye who appears in a series of animated cartoons, acquiring miraculous strength by devouring cans of spinach.

Unconscious Invention In discussing the process of invention, we should differentiate between various types of inventions. One type is the consequence of a society's setting itself a specific goal, such as eliminating tuberculosis or placing a person on the moon. Another type emerges less intentionally. This second process of invention is often referred to as *accidental juxtaposition* or *unconscious invention*. Linton suggested that some inventions, especially those of prehistoric days, were probably the consequences of literally dozens of tiny initiatives by "unconscious" inventors. These inventors made their small contributions, perhaps over many hundreds of years, without being aware of the part they were playing in bringing one invention, such as the wheel or a better form of hand ax, to completion.[26] Consider the example of children playing on a fallen log, which rolls as they walk and balance on it, coupled with the need at a given moment to move a slab of granite from a cave face. The children's play may have suggested the use of logs as rollers and thereby set in motion a series of developments that culminated in the wheel.

In reconstructing the process of invention in prehistoric times, however, we should be careful not to look back on our ancestors with a smugness generated by our more highly developed technology. We have become accustomed to turning to the science sections of our magazines and newspapers and finding, almost daily, reports of miraculous new discoveries and inventions. From our point of view, it is difficult to imagine such a simple invention as the wheel taking so many centuries to come into being. We are tempted to surmise that early humans were less intelligent than we are. But the capacity of the human brain has been the same for perhaps 100,000 years; there is no evidence that the inventors of the wheel were any less intelligent than we are.

Intentional Innovation Some discoveries and inventions arise out of deliberate attempts to produce a new idea or object. It may seem that such innovations are obvious responses to perceived needs. For example, during the Industrial Revolution, there was a great demand for inventions that would increase productivity. James Hargreaves, in 18th-century England, is an example of an inventor

current research and issues

Culture Change and Persistence in China

In the years since the 1949 Communist takeover in China, the central government has initiated a variety of changes in family life. Many of these changes were literally forced; people who resisted them were often resettled or jailed. Ancestor worship and lineage organization were attacked or declared illegal. Most private property was abolished, undermining family loyalties. Why participate in family activities if there could be no economic reward? Still, the actions of the central government did not completely change family life. Even coercion has its limits.

The government may have wanted to restrict the family and kinship, but its investments in public health and famine relief reduced mortality, thereby strengthening family ties. Fewer infants died, more children lived long enough to marry, old age became more common—all of these developments allowed people in all social classes to have larger and more complex networks of kin than were possible before 1949. To be sure, government policies undercut the power and authority of extended family patriarchs. But the new healthier conditions were conducive to large, multigenerational households with economic as well as social ties to other kin.

As China became more accessible to anthropologists and other researchers from abroad, many investigators came to study the variability and similarity in Chinese family life. Most of these studies focused on the dominant Han Chinese (the Han constitute about 95 percent of the total population of China); investigators have also studied many of the 55 "recognized" minority cultures in China. Burton Pasternak, a U.S. anthropologist, Janet Salaff, a Canadian sociologist, and Chinese sociologists studied four communities of Han who had moved outside the Great Wall to colonize the Inner Mongolian frontier (Inner Mongolia is part of China). The results of their study suggest that, despite strong pressures from the government, what changes or persists in a culture mainly reflects what is possible ecologically and economically. A tradition of intensive agriculture cannot persist in the absence of sufficient watering. The government's insistence on one child per family cannot withstand a family's need for more children.

Han farmers who crossed the Great Wall were searching for a better life. They found difficulties in climate and soil that forced many to return home. But many adjusted to the grasslands and remained. Some continued to depend on farming on the fringes of the grasslands. Others farther out on the grasslands became herders. The Han who switched to herding are now in many respects more like the native Mongol herders than like Han or Mongol farmers. The gender division of labor among the Han pastoralists became much sharper than among the Han farmers because men are often far away with the herds. Pastoralist children, not that useful in herding because mistakes can be very costly, are more likely than farm children to stay in school for a long time. Perhaps because of the greater usefulness of children on the farm, Han farm families have more children than Han pastoralists. But both groups have more than one child per family. Herdsmen are less likely than farmers to need cooperative labor, so Han pastoralists are more likely to live as an independent family living apart from kin than as an extended family (which was traditional). In short, the adjustment of the Han to the grasslands seems to be explained more by ecological requirements than by ethnic traditions.

Although an increasing number of Han have become more like Mongols in their pastoral adaptations, many Mongols have adopted an urban way of life and moved away from their pastoral life. The Chinese government was initially responsible for encouraging non-Mongols to move into Inner Mongolia, particularly into its new capital, Hohhot. At the same time, many Mongols moved from the grasslands and into the capital city. Chinese government policy was intended to make each non-Han ethnic group a minority in its traditional land, but the government paradoxically also tried to encourage minority ethnic pride in their traditional culture. So the city of Hohhot is filled with images of the traditional herding culture in its buildings and monuments.

As described by anthropologist William Jankowiak, who studied the Mongols in the capital city of Hohhot, the results were not what the Chinese government intended. In many ways, to be sure, the urban Mongols had abandoned their traditional culture and assimilated to the dominant Han culture. But we see the force of ecology more than the hand of tradition in the outcome. Many Mongols in the city no longer speak the Mongol language. Parents find it difficult to get children to speak Mongol when they live among Han. The scarcity of housing makes it difficult for the Mongols to form an ethnic enclave, or even live near kin as they did in the past. In contrast to life in the rural areas, which revolves around kinship, city life requires interacting with strangers as well as relatives. Indeed, nonkin are often more important to you than kin. As one person said to Jankowiak, "We hide from our cousins but not our friends."

Sources: Davis and Harrell 1993; Pasternak 2009; Jankowiak 2004.

who responded to an existing demand. Textile manufacturers were clamoring for such large quantities of spun yarn that cottage laborers, working with foot-operated spinning wheels, could not meet the demand. Hargreaves, realizing that prestige and financial rewards would come to the person who invented a method of spinning large quantities of yarn in a short time, set about the task and developed the spinning jenny.

But perceived needs and the economic rewards that may be given to the innovator do not explain why only some people innovate. We know relatively little about why some people are more innovative than others. The ability to innovate may depend in part on individual characteristics such as high intelligence and creativity. And creativity may be influenced by social conditions.

A study of innovation among Ashanti artist carvers in Ghana suggests that creativity is more likely in some socioeconomic groups than in others.[27] Some carvers produced only traditional designs; others departed from tradition and produced "new" styles of carving. Two groups were found to innovate the most—the wealthiest and the poorest carvers. These two groups of carvers may tolerate risk more than the middle socioeconomic group. Innovative carving entails some risk because it may take more time and it may not sell. Wealthy carvers can afford the risk, and they may gain some prestige as well as income if their innovation is appreciated. The poor are not doing well anyway, and they have little to lose by trying something new.

Some societies encourage innovativeness more than others, and this can vary substantially over time. Patricia Greenfield and her colleagues describe the changes in weaving in a Mayan community in the Zinacantán region of Chiapas, Mexico.[28] In 1969 and 1970, innovation was not valued. Rather, tradition was; there was the old "true way" to do everything, including how one dressed. There were only four simple weaving patterns, and virtually all males wore ponchos with the same pattern. By 1991, virtually no poncho was the same and the villagers had developed elaborate brocaded and embroidered designs. In a period of 20 years, innovation had increased dramatically.

Two other things had also changed. The economy was more commercialized; textiles as well as other items were now bought and sold. The other change was a shift to a much less directed teaching style. Earlier, mothers would give highly structured instruction to their daughters, often with "four hands" on the loom. Later, girls were allowed to learn more by themselves, by trial and error, and they produced more abstract and varied designs.

Who Adopts Innovations? Once someone discovers or invents something, there is still the question of whether others will adopt the innovation. Many researchers have studied the characteristics of "early adopters." Such individuals tend to be educated, high in social status, upwardly mobile, and, if they are property owners, have large farms and businesses. The individuals who most need technological improvements—those who are less well off—are generally the last to adopt innovations. The theory is that only the wealthy can afford to take the substantial risks associated with new ways of doing things. In periods of rapid technological change, therefore, the gap between rich and poor is likely to widen because the rich adopt innovations sooner, and benefit more from them, than the poor.[29]

Does this imply that the likelihood of adopting innovations is a simple function of how much wealth a possible adopter possesses? Not necessarily. Frank Cancian reviewed several studies and found that upper-middle-class individuals show more conservatism than lower-middle-class individuals. Cancian suggested that, when the risks are unknown, the lower-middle-class individuals are more receptive to innovation because they have less to lose. Later on, when the risks are better known—that is, as more people adopt the innovation—the upper-middle class catches up to the lower-middle class.[30] So the readiness to accept innovation, like the likelihood of creativity among Ashanti carvers, may not be related to socioeconomic position in a linear way.

The speed of accepting an innovation may depend partly on how new behaviors and ideas are typically

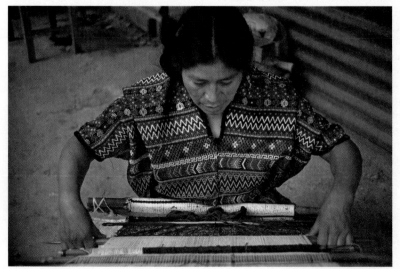

Mayan woman from San Martin Jilotepeque working on a hip-strap loom. Designs became more individual and complex by the 1990s.

transmitted in a society. In particular, is a person exposed to many versus few "teachers"? If children learn most of what they know from their parents or from a relatively small number of elders, then innovation will be slow to spread throughout the society, and culture change is likely to be slow. Innovations may catch on more rapidly if individuals are exposed to various teachers and other "leaders" who can influence many in a relatively short time. And the more peers we have, the more we might learn from them.[31] Perhaps this is why the pace of change appears to be so quick today. In societies like our own, and increasingly in the industrializing world, it is likely that people learn in schools from teachers, from leaders in their specialties, and from peers.

Costs and Benefits

An innovation that is technologically superior is not necessarily going to be adopted. There are costs as well as benefits for both individuals and large-scale industries. Take the computer keyboard. The keyboard used most often on computers today is called the QWERTY keyboard (named after the letters on the left side of the line of keys below the row of number keys). This keyboard was actually invented to slow typing speed down! Early typewriters had mechanical keys that jammed if the typist went too fast.[32] Computer keyboards don't have that problem, so an arrangement of keys that allowed faster typing would probably be better. Different keyboard configurations have been invented, but they haven't caught on. Most people probably would find it too hard or too time-consuming to learn a new style of typing, so the original style of keyboard persists.

In large-scale industries, technological innovations may be very costly to implement. A new product or process may require revamping a manufacturing or service facility and retraining workers. Before a decision is made to change, the costs of doing so are weighed against the potential benefits. If the market is expected to be large for a new product, the product is more likely to be produced. If the market is judged small, the benefits may not be sufficient inducement to change. Companies may also

judge the value of an innovation by whether competitors could copy it. If the new innovation can be easily copied, the inventing company may not find the investment worthwhile. Although the market may be large, the inventing company may not be able to hold onto market share if other companies could produce the product quickly without having to invest in research and development.[33]

Diffusion

The source of new cultural elements in a society may also be another society. The process by which cultural elements are borrowed from another society and incorporated into the culture of the recipient group is called **diffusion.** Borrowing sometimes enables a group to bypass stages or mistakes in the development of a process or institution. For example, Germany was able to accelerate its program of industrialization in the 19th century because it was able to avoid some of the errors its English and Belgian competitors made by taking advantage of technological borrowing. Japan did the same somewhat later. Indeed, in recent years, some of the earliest industrialized countries have fallen behind their imitators in certain areas of production, such as automobiles, televisions, cameras, and computers.

In a well-known passage, Linton conveyed the far-reaching effects of diffusion by considering the first few hours in the day of an American man in the 1930s. This man

> . . . awakens in a bed built on a pattern which originated in the Near East but which was modified in northern Europe before it was transmitted to America. He throws back covers made from cotton, domesticated in India, or linen, domesticated in the Near East, or silk, the use of which was discovered in China. All of these materials have been spun and woven by processes invented in the Near East. . . . He takes off his pajamas, a garment invented in India, and washes with soap invented by the ancient

A Masai man in Kenya can call home or around the world from the plains of Kenya.

Gauls. He then shaves, a masochistic rite which seems to have derived from either Sumer or ancient Egypt.

Before going out for breakfast he glances through the window, made of glass invented in Egypt, and if it is raining puts on overshoes made of rubber discovered by the Central American Indians and takes an umbrella, invented in southeastern Asia. . . .

On his way to breakfast he stops to buy a paper paying for it with coins, an ancient Lydian invention. . . . His plate is made of a form of pottery invented in China. His knife is of steel, an alloy first made in southern India, his fork a medieval Italian invention, and his spoon a derivative of a Roman original. . . . After his fruit (African watermelon) and first coffee (an Abyssinian plant), . . . he may have the egg of a species of bird domesticated in Indo-China, or thin strips of the flesh of an animal domesticated in eastern Asia which have been salted and smoked by a process developed in northern Europe. . . .

While smoking (an American Indian habit), he reads the news of the day, imprinted in characters invented by the ancient Semites upon a material invented in China by a process invented in Germany. As he absorbs the accounts of foreign troubles he will, if he is a good conservative citizen, thank a Hebrew deity in an Indo-European language that he is 100 percent American.[34]

Patterns of Diffusion   The following are the three basic patterns of diffusion: direct contact, intermediate contact, and stimulus diffusion.

1. **Direct contact.** Elements of a society's culture may first be taken up by neighboring societies and then gradually spread farther and farther afield. The spread of the use of paper (a sheet of interlaced fibers) is a good example of extensive diffusion by direct contact. The invention of paper is attributed to the Chinese Ts'ai Lun in A.D. 105. Within 50 years, paper was being made in many places in central China. Although the art of papermaking was kept secret for about 500 years, paper was distributed as a commodity to much of the Arab world through the markets at Samarkand. But when Samarkand was attacked by the Chinese in A.D. 751, a Chinese prisoner was forced to set up a paper mill. Paper manufacture then spread to the rest of the Arab world; it was first manufactured in Baghdad in A.D. 793, Egypt about A.D. 900, and Morocco about A.D. 1100. Papermaking was introduced as a commodity in Europe by Arab trade through Italian ports in the 12th century. The Moors built the first European paper mill in Spain about 1150. The technical knowledge then spread throughout Europe, with paper mills built in Italy in 1276, France in 1348, Germany in 1390, and England in 1494.[35] In general, the pattern of accepting the borrowed invention was the same in all cases: Paper was first imported as a luxury, then in ever-expanding quantities as a staple product. Finally, and usually within one to three centuries, local manufacture began.

2. **Intermediate contact.** Diffusion by intermediate contact occurs through the agency of third parties. Frequently, traders carry a cultural trait from the society that originated it to another group. As an example of diffusion through intermediaries, Phoenician traders spread the alphabet—which may have been invented by another Semitic group—to Greece. At times, soldiers serve as intermediaries in spreading a culture trait. European crusaders, such as the Knights Templar and the Knights of St. John, acted as intermediaries in two ways: They carried Christian culture to Muslim societies of North Africa and brought Arab culture back to Europe. In the 19th century, Western missionaries in all parts of the world encouraged natives to wear Western clothing. Hence, in Africa, the Pacific Islands, and elsewhere, native peoples can be found wearing shorts, suit jackets, shirts, ties, and other typically Western articles of clothing.

3. **Stimulus diffusion.** In stimulus diffusion, knowledge of a trait belonging to another culture stimulates the invention or development of a local equivalent. A classic example of stimulus diffusion is the Cherokee syllabic writing system created by a Native American named Sequoya so that his people could write down their language. Sequoya got the idea from his contact with Europeans. Yet, he did not adopt the English writing system; indeed, he did not even learn to write English. What he did was utilize some English alphabetic symbols, alter others, and invent new ones. All the symbols he used represented Cherokee syllables and in no way echoed English alphabetic usage. In other words, Sequoya took English alphabetic ideas and gave them a new, Cherokee form. The stimulus originated with Europeans; the result was peculiarly Cherokee.

The Selective Nature of Diffusion   Although there is a temptation to view the dynamics of diffusion as similar to a stone sending concentric ripples over still water, this would be an oversimplification of the way diffusion actually occurs. Not all cultural traits are borrowed as readily as the ones we have mentioned, nor do they usually expand in neat, ever-widening circles. Rather, diffusion is a selective process. The Japanese, for instance, accepted much from Chinese culture, but they also rejected many traits. Rhymed tonal poetry, civil service examinations, and foot binding, which the Chinese favored, were never adopted in Japan. The poetry form was unsuited to the structure of the Japanese language; the examinations were unnecessary in view of the entrenched power of the Japanese aristocracy; and foot binding was repugnant to a people who abhorred body mutilation of any sort.

Not only would we expect societies to reject items from other societies that are repugnant, we would also expect them to reject ideas and technology that do not satisfy some psychological, social, or cultural need. After all, people are not sponges; they don't automatically soak up the things around them. If they did, the amount of cultural variation in the world would be extremely small, which is clearly not the case. Diffusion is also selective because cultural traits differ in the extent to which they can be communicated. Elements of material culture, such as mechanical processes and techniques, and other traits, such as physical sports and the like, are not especially difficult to demonstrate. Consequently, they are accepted or rejected on their merits. But the moment we move out of the material context, we encounter real difficulties. Linton identified the problem in these words:

> Although it is quite possible to describe such an element of culture as the ideal pattern for marriage . . . it is much less complete than a description of basketmaking. . . . The most thorough verbalization has difficulty in conveying the series of associations and conditioned emotional responses which are attached to this pattern [marriage] and which gave it meaning and vitality within our own society. . . . This is even more true of those concepts which . . . find no direct expression in behavior aside from verbalization. There is a story of an educated Japanese who after a long discussion on the nature of the Trinity with a European friend . . . burst out with: "Oh, I see now, it is a committee."[36]

Finally, diffusion is selective because the overt form of a particular trait, rather than its function or meaning, frequently seems to determine how the trait will be received. For example, the enthusiasm in women for bobbed hair (short haircuts) that swept through much of North America in the 1920s never caught on among the Native Americans of northwestern California. To many women of European ancestry, short hair was a symbolic statement of their freedom. To Native American women, who traditionally cut their hair short when in mourning, it was a reminder of death.[37]

In the process of diffusion, then, we can identify a number of different patterns. We know that cultural borrowing is selective rather than automatic, and we can describe how a particular borrowed trait has been modified by the recipient culture. But our current knowledge does not allow us to specify when one or another of these outcomes will occur, under what conditions diffusion will occur, and why it occurs the way it does.

Acculturation

On the surface, the process of change called **acculturation** seems to include much of what we have discussed under the label of diffusion, because acculturation refers to the changes that occur when different cultural groups come into intensive contact. As in diffusion, the source of new cultural items is the other society. But more often than not, anthropologists use the term *acculturation* to describe a situation in which one of the societies in contact is much more powerful than the other. Thus, acculturation can be seen as a process of extensive cultural borrowing in the context of superordinate-subordinate relations between societies.[38] There is probably always some borrowing both ways, but generally the subordinate or less powerful society borrows the most.

External pressure for culture change can take various forms. In its most direct form—conquest or colonialization—the dominant group uses force or the threat of force to try to bring about culture change in the other group. For example, in the Spanish conquest of Mexico, the conquerors forced many of the native groups to accept Catholicism. Although such direct force is not always exerted in conquest situations, dominated peoples often have little choice but to change. Examples of such indirectly forced change abound in the history of Native Americans in the United States. Although the federal government made few direct attempts to force people to adopt American culture, it did drive many native groups from their lands, thereby obliging them to give up many aspects of their traditional ways of life. To survive, they had no choice but to adopt many of the dominant society's traits. When Native American children were required to go to schools, which taught the dominant society's values, the process was accelerated.

A subordinate society may acculturate to a dominant society even in the absence of direct or indirect force. Perceiving that members of the dominant society enjoy more secure living conditions, the dominated people may identify with the dominant culture in the hope that they will be able to share some of its benefits by doing so. Or, they may elect to adopt cultural elements from the dominant society because they perceive that the new element has advantages. For example, in Arctic areas, many Inuit and Lapp groups seemed eager to replace dog sleds with snowmobiles without any coercion.[39] There is evidence that the Inuit weighed the advantages and disadvantages of the snowmobile versus the dog sled and that its adoption was gradual. Similarly, rifles were seen as a major technological improvement, increasing the success rate in hunting, but the Inuit did not completely abandon their former ways of hunting. More recently the Inuit are trying out GPS devices for navigating.[40]

Acculturation processes vary considerably depending upon the wishes of the more powerful society, the attitudes of the less powerful, and whether there is any choice. More powerful societies do not always want individuals from another culture to assimilate or "melt into" the dominant culture completely; instead, they may prefer and even actively promote a *multicultural* society. Multiculturalism can be voluntary or it may arise out of deliberate segregation. Then too, even though the less powerful group may be pressured by the dominant group to acquire some of their culture traits, they may resist or even reject those cultural elements, at least for a considerable length of time.

Many millions of people, however, never had a chance to acculturate after contact with Europeans. They simply died, sometimes directly at the hands of the conquerors, but probably more often as a result of the new diseases the Europeans inadvertently brought with them. Depopulation because of measles, smallpox, and tuberculosis was particularly common in North and South America and on the islands of the Pacific. Those areas had previously been isolated from contact with Europeans and from the diseases of that continuous landmass we call the Old World—Europe, Asia, and Africa.[41] (See the DK Map

applied anthropology

Why the Bedouin Do Not Readily Settle Down

Most countries of the world today want to "develop." They want to increase their crop yields and their exports, build major roads and irrigation projects, and industrialize. Anthropologists interested in development have pointed out that many development schemes have failed in part because they do not adequately consider the culture of the people whose lives they affect. Thus, the international agencies that lend money have increasingly turned for advice to anthropologists to help plan and evaluate development projects.

Governments often view traditional ways of life negatively and fail to recognize that the old ways of life may be adaptive. Because culture is integrated, people cannot be expected to change an aspect of culture that is central to their lives. It is not that people do not want to change, but change is unlikely if it doesn't integrate well with other aspects of their lifestyle.

In many countries of the Middle East, governments want the Bedouin—people who herd animals over vast stretches of semiarid grassland—to settle down. Governments have tried to settle them by force or by enticements, but settlement schemes have failed time after time. In retrospect, such failures are not surprising. The Bedouin continue to try to herd animals near newly constructed settlements, but such grazing often results in human-made deserts near the settlements, so the settlements are abandoned. The traditional Bedouin pattern of herding animals depends on mobility. When the animals eat the tops of the grasses in a particular place, the people need to move on. When water starts drying up in one location, the herds need to be moved. Overgrazing near a settlement and plowing land in a semiarid environment can lead to quick erosion of the soil and the loss of plant cover. After the failure of many settlement schemes, governments may try to encourage a return to more traditional methods of grazing.

It is not that the Bedouin are reluctant to change in all respects. Many Bedouin readily gave up relying on camels for transport in favor of trucks. Trucks are a modern adaptation, yet they still allow mobility. Now the Bedouin are able to get water from wells and transport water to their animals by truck. The adoption of trucks led to other changes in Bedouin life. Small animals can be more readily transported to new pastures by truck, so many Bedouin have given up their dependence on camels and shifted to sheep and goat herding. Money is required to buy trucks and pay for gasoline and repairs, so more time is spent working for wages in temporary jobs.

In the 1980s, Dawn Chatty was asked by the government of the Middle Eastern country of Oman to help design a project to extend basic social services to the Bedouin without coercing them to alter their way of life. It isn't often that governments fund in-depth studies to understand the needs of the people being affected, but Chatty was able to persuade the Oman government that such a study was necessary as a first step. With United Nations funding, she began a study of the Harasiis pastoralists of southern Oman to evaluate their needs. The government wanted some action right away, so the project soon incorporated a mobile health unit that could begin a program of primary care as well as immunization against measles, whooping cough, and polio. After a period of evaluation, the project team also recommended an annual distribution of tents, the establishment of dormitories so children could live at schools, a new system of water delivery, and veterinary and marketing assistance.

Unfortunately, a development project often ends without any guarantee that health and other services will continue to be provided. As Chatty found out, long-term change is not as easy to achieve as short-term change. Along with other applied anthropologists, she continues to push for what Michael Cernea called "putting people first."

Sources: Chatty 1996; Cernea 1991, 7.

"Biological Exchanges" in the back of the book.) The story of Ishi, the last surviving member of a group of Native Americans in California called the Yahi, is a moving testimonial to the frequently tragic effect of contact with Europeans. In the space of 22 years, the Yahi population was reduced from several hundred to near zero. The historical record on this episode of depopulation suggests that European Americans murdered 30 to 50 Yahi for every European American murdered, but perhaps 60 percent of the Yahi died in the 10 years following their initial exposure to European diseases.[42]

Nowadays, many powerful nations—and not just Western ones—may seem to be acting in more humanitarian ways to improve the life of previously subjugated as well as other "developing" peoples. For better or worse, these programs, however, are still forms of external pressure. The tactic used may be persuasion rather than force, but most of the programs are nonetheless designed to bring about acculturation in the direction of the dominant societies' cultures. For example, the introduction of formal schooling cannot help but instill new values that may contradict traditional cultural patterns. Even health care programs may alter traditional ways of life by undermining the authority of shamans and other leaders and by increasing population beyond the number that can be supported in traditional ways. Confinement to "reservations" or other kinds of direct force are not the only ways a dominant society can bring about acculturation.

The process of acculturation also applies to immigrants, most of whom, at least nowadays, choose to leave one country for another. Immigrants are almost always a minority in the new country and therefore are in a subordinate position. If the immigrant's culture changes, it is almost always in the direction of the dominant culture. Immigrant groups vary considerably in the degree and speed with which they adopt the new culture and the social roles of the new society in which they live. An important area of research is explaining the variation in acculturation and assimilation. (*Assimilation* is a concept very similar to acculturation, but *assimilation* is a term more often used by sociologists to describe the process by which individuals acquire the social roles and culture of the dominant group.) Why do some immigrant groups acculturate or assimilate faster than others? As we will see in the chapter on language, a comparative study by Robert Schrauf assessed the degree to which immigrant groups coming to North America retained their native language over time. He looked at whether they lived in tightly knit communities, retained religious rituals, had separate schools and special festivals, visited their homeland, did not intermarry, or worked with others of their ethnic group. All of these factors might be expected to lead to retention of the native language (and presumably other cultural patterns), but only living in tightly knit communities and retaining religious rituals strongly predicted retaining the native language over a long period of time.[43]

CULTURE CHANGE AND ADAPTATION

Earlier in this chapter when we discussed the fact that culture is patterned, we indicated that adaptation to the environment is one reason why certain culture traits will cluster, because more than one trait is likely to be *adaptive* in a particular environment. We make the assumption that most of the customary behaviors of a culture are probably *adaptive*, or at least not maladaptive, in that environment. Even though customs are learned and not genetically inherited, cultural adaptation may resemble biological adaptation in one major respect. The frequency of certain genetic alternatives is likely to increase over time if those genetic traits increase their carriers' chances of survival and reproduction. Similarly, the frequency of a new learned behavior will increase over time and become customary in a population if the people with that behavior are most likely to survive and reproduce.

One of the most important differences between cultural evolution and genetic evolution is that individuals often can decide whether or not to accept and follow the way their parents behave or think, whereas they cannot decide whether or not to inherit certain genes. When enough individuals change their behavior and beliefs, we say that the culture has changed. Therefore, it is possible for culture change to occur much more rapidly than genetic change.

A dramatic example of intentional cultural change was the adoption and later elimination of the custom of *sepaade* among the Rendille, a pastoral population that herds camels, goats, and sheep in the desert in northern Kenya. According to the *sepaade* tradition, some women had to wait to marry until all their brothers were married. These women could well have been over 40 by the time they married. The Rendille say that this tradition was a result of intense warfare between the Rendille and the Borana during the mid-19th century. Attacked by Borana on horseback, the male warriors had to leave their camels unattended and the frightened camels fled. The daughters of one male age-set were appointed to look after the camels, and the *sepaade* tradition developed. In 1998, long after warfare with the Borana ceased, the elders decided to free the *sepaade* from their obligation to postpone their own marriages. Interviews with the Rendille in the 1990s revealed that many individuals were fully aware of the reason for the tradition in the first place. Now, they said, there was peace, so there was no longer any reason for the *sepaade* tradition to continue.[44]

The adoption of the *sepaade* is an example of culture change in a changing environment. But what if the environment is stable? Is culture change more or less likely? Robert Boyd and Peter Richerson have shown mathematically that, when the environment is relatively stable and individual mistakes are costly, staying with customary modes of behavior (usually transmitted by parents) is probably more adaptive than changing.[45] But what happens when the environment, particularly the social environment, is changing? There are plenty of examples in the modern world: People have to migrate to new places for work; medical care leads to increased population so that land is scarcer; people have had land taken away from them and are forced to make do with less land; and so on.

It is particularly when circumstances change that individuals are likely to try ideas or behaviors that are different from those of their parents. Most people would want to adopt behaviors that are more suited to their present circumstances, but how do they know which behaviors are better? There are various ways to find out. One way is by experimenting, trying out various new behaviors. Another way is to evaluate the experiments of others. If a person who tries a new technique seems successful, we would expect that person to be imitated, just as we would expect people to stick with new behaviors they have personally tried and found successful. Finally, one might choose to do what most people in the new situation decide to do.[46]

Why one choice rather than another? In part, the choice may be a function of the cost or risk of the innovation. It is relatively easy, for example, to find out how long it takes to cut down a tree with an introduced steel ax, as compared with a stone ax. Not surprisingly, innovations such as a steel ax catch on relatively quickly because comparison is easy and the results clear-cut. But what if the risk is very great? Suppose the innovation involves adopting a whole new way of farming that you have never practiced before. You can try it, but you might not have any food if you fail. As we discussed earlier, risky innovations are likely to be tried only by those individuals who can afford the risk. Other people may then evaluate their success and adopt the new strategy if it looks promising. Similarly, if you migrate building blocks such as prepositions (*to, on,* and so forth) and auxiliary verbs (designating future and other tenses). If a pidgin language is used merely as system of communicating in a limited setting, it may not develop into a fully developed language. However, children may begin to use pidgin as their first language. The pidgin language may expand and become more complex grammatically.[21] Many pidgin languages developed into and were replaced by so-called *creole languages,* which incorporate much of the vocabulary of another language (often the masters' language) but also have a grammar that differs from it and from the grammars of the laborers' native languages.[22]

Derek Bickerton argues that there are striking grammatical similarities in creole languages throughout the world. This similarity, he thinks, is consistent with the idea that some grammar is inherited by all humans. Creole languages, therefore, may resemble early human languages. All creoles use intonation instead of a change in word order to ask a question. The creole equivalent of the question "Can you fix this?" would be "You can fix this?" The creole version puts a rising inflection at the end; in contrast, the English version reverses the subject and verb without much inflection at the end. All creoles express the future and the past in the same grammatical way, by the use of particles (such as the English *shall*) between subject and verb, and they all employ double negatives, as in the Guyana English Creole "Nobody no like me."[23]

It is possible that many other things about language are universal, that all languages are similar in many respects, because of the way humans are "wired" or because people in all societies have similar experiences. For example, names for frogs may usually contain *r* sounds because frogs make them.[24]

Children's Acquisition of Language

Apparently a child is equipped from birth with the capacity to reproduce all the sounds used by the world's languages and to learn any system of grammar. Research on 6-month-old infants finds that they can distinguish sounds of approximately 600 consonants and 200 vowels—all the sounds of all the languages of the world. But, by about the time of their first birthdays, babies become better at recognizing the salient sounds and sound clusters of their parents or caretakers and become less adept at distinguishing those of other languages.[25]

Children's acquisition of the structure and meaning of language has been called the most difficult intellectual achievement in life. If that is so, it is pleasing to note that they accomplish it with relative ease and vast enjoyment. As we have noted, many believe that this "difficult intellectual achievement" may in reality be a natural response to the capacity for language that is one of humans' genetic characteristics. All over the world, children begin to learn language at about the same age, and in no culture do children wait until they are 7 or 10 years old. By 12 or 13 months of age, children are able to name a few objects and actions, and by 18 to 20 months, they can make one key word stand for a whole sentence: "Out!" for "Take me out for a walk right now"; "Juice!" for "I want some juice

now." Evidence suggests that children acquire the concept of a word as a whole, learning sequences of sounds that are stressed or at the ends of words (e.g., "raffe" for giraffe). Even children with hearing impairments who are learning signs in ASL tend to acquire and use signs in a similar fashion.[26]

Children the world over tend to progress to two-word sentences at about 18 to 24 months of age. In their sentences, they express themselves in "telegraph" form—using nounlike words and verblike words but leaving out the seemingly less important words. So a two-word sentence such as "Shoes off" may stand for "Take my shoes off," or "More milk" may stand for "Give me more milk, please."[27] They do not utter their two words in random order, sometimes saying "off" first, other times saying "shoes" first. If children say, "Shoes off," then they will also say, "Clothes off" and "Hat off." They seem to select an order that fits the conventions of adult language, so they are likely to say, "Daddy eat," not "Eat Daddy." In other words, they tend to put the subject first, as adults do. And they tend to say "Mommy coat" rather than "Coat Mommy" to indicate "Mommy's coat."[28] Adults do not utter sentences such as "Daddy eat," so children seem to know a lot about how to put words together with little or no direct teaching from their caretakers. Consider the 5-year-old who, confronted with the unfamiliar "Gloria in Excelsis," sings quite happily, "Gloria eats eggshells." To make the words fit the structure of English grammar is more important than to make the words fit the meaning of the Christmas pageant.

If there is a basic grammar imprinted in the human mind, we should not be surprised that children's early and later speech patterns seem to be similar in different languages. We might also expect children's later speech to be similar to the structure of creole languages. And it is, according to Derek Bickerton.[29] The "errors" children make in speaking are consistent with the grammar of creoles. For example, English-speaking children 3 to 4 years old tend to ask questions by intonation alone, and they tend to use double negatives, such as "I don't see no dog," even though the adults around them do not speak that way and consider the children's speech "wrong."

But some linguists argue that the evidence for an innate grammar is weak because children the world over do not develop the same grammatical features at similar ages. For example, word order is a more important determinant of meaning in English than in Turkish; the endings of words are more important in Turkish. The word at the beginning of the sentence in English is likely to be the subject. The word with a certain ending in Turkish is the likely subject. Consistent with this difference, English-speaking children learn word order earlier than Turkish children do.[30]

Future research on children's acquisition of language and on the structure of creole languages may bring us closer to an understanding of the origins of human language. But, even if much of grammar is universal, we still need to understand how and why the thousands of languages in the world vary, which brings us to the conceptual tools linguists have had to invent to study languages.

migrants and immigrants

Why Are "Mother Tongues" Retained, and for How Long?

The longer an immigrant group lives in another country, the more they incorporate the culture of their new home. At some point, the original language is no longer even partially understood. Consider people who originally came from Wales, the region west of England in Great Britain. In that region, until about 100 years ago, most people spoke the Welsh language, which belongs to the Celtic subfamily of Indo-European along with Irish and Scottish Gaelic and Breton. (Celtic is a different subfamily from the one English belongs to, which is Germanic.) In 1729, the Welsh in Philadelphia established the Welsh Society, the oldest ethnic organization in the United States. Many of the members, if not all, spoke Welsh in addition to English at that time. But, by the 20th century, hardly any of their descendants did.

If immigrant groups eventually lose their "mother tongues" in many if not most countries, this doesn't mean that the process occurs at the same speed in every group. Why is that? Why do some immigrant groups lose their language faster than others? Is it because they do not live in tightly knit ethnic enclaves? Or because they marry outside their ethnic group? Or because they do not have traditional festivals or celebrations marking their separate identity? A comparative study by Robert Schrauf discovered the most likely reasons. First, Schrauf assessed the degree to which immigrant groups coming to North America retained their native language over time. The greatest retention was defined as when the third generation (the grandchildren of immigrants) continued to use the native language. Examples were Chicanos, Puerto Ricans, Cubans, and Haitians. On the other hand, the third generation in some groups had no comprehension of the native language except for isolated words. Even the second generation (the children of immigrants) mostly spoke and understood only English. Examples were Italians, Armenians, and Basques. Chinese and Koreans were in the middle, with some evidence that the third generation understands a little of the native language. Schrauf then measured seven social factors that might explain longer versus shorter retention of the mother tongue. He looked at whether the group lived in tightly knit communities, retained religious rituals from the old country, had separate schools and special festivals, visited their homeland, did not intermarry, or worked with others of their ethnic group.

Schrauf used data on 11 North American ethnic groups drawn from the HRAF Collection of Ethnography. The major advantage of the HRAF materials is that ethnographies written for more general purposes, or for purposes other than linguistic ones, contain a wealth of information concerning sociocultural features of ethnic groups that may be tested for their possible effects on language retention and loss.

We might suspect that all of the factors Schrauf measured would lead people to retain their native language (and presumably other native cultural patterns). But not all do, apparently. Only living in tightly knit communities and retaining religious rituals strongly predict retention of the mother tongue in the home into the third generation. Why? Possibly because living in an ethnic community and religious rituals are experienced early in life: Conditions associated with early socialization might have more lasting effects than conditions experienced later in life, such as schooling, visits to the homeland, marriage, and work. Participation in celebrations and festi-

Living in an ethnic neighborhood as in San Francisco's Chinatown encourages retention of the mother tongue.

vals is probably important too, but it does not have quite as strong an effect, perhaps because celebrations and festivals are not everyday experiences.

As always, in the case of research, this study raises questions for future research. Would the same effects be found outside of North America? Would the results be the same if we looked also at other immigrant groups in North America? Does frequent travel back to the homeland help language retention? Do some immigrant groups live in close-knit communities because of discrimination or choice? If choice, are some groups more interested in assimilating than others? And if so, why?

Sources: Caulkins 1997; Schrauf 1999.

Getting Food

or most people in our society, getting food consists of a trip to the supermarket. Within an hour, we can gather enough food from the shelves to last us a week. Seasons don't daunt us. Week after week, we know food will be there. But we do not think of what would happen if the food were not delivered to the supermarket. We wouldn't be able to eat, and without eating for a while, we would die. Despite the old adage "Man [or woman] does not live by bread alone," we could not live at all without bread or the equivalent. Food-getting activities, then, take precedence over other activities important to survival. Reproduction, social control (the maintenance of peace and order within a group), defense against external threat, and the transmission of knowledge and skills to future generations—none could take place without energy derived from food. But it is not merely energy that is required for survival and long-term reproduction. Food-getting strategies need to provide the appropriate combination of nutrients throughout varying seasons and changing environmental conditions. Food-getting activities are also important because the way a society gets its food strongly predicts other aspects of a culture, from community size and permanence of settlement to type of economy and degree of inequality and type of political system, and even art styles and religious beliefs and practices.

In contrast with our own and similar societies, most societies have not had food-getting specialists. Rather, almost all able-bodied adults were largely engaged in getting food for themselves and their families. Such economies are described as **subsistence economies**. For millions of years, humans obtained their food by gathering wild plants, hunting or scavenging wild animals, and fishing. Agriculture is a relatively recent phenomenon, dating back only about 10,000 years. And industrial or mechanized agriculture is hardly more than a century old. Harvesting machines have been used a little bit longer, but self-propelled machines had to wait for the internal combustion engine and the rise of the oil industry.

In this chapter, we look at the ways different societies get food and discuss some of the features associated with the different patterns. We ask why societies vary in their food-getting strategies. We shall see that the physical environment by itself has only a limited or restraining effect on how a society gets most of its food. To explain the variation more fully, we discuss at the end of the chapter why societies in the prehistoric past switched from collecting wild food resources to cultivating plants and raising animals.

● ○ ●

FORAGING

Foraging or *food collection* may be generally defined as a food-getting strategy that obtains wild plant and animal resources through gathering, hunting, scavenging, or fishing. Although this was the way humans got their food for most of human history, foragers in

unable to finance the investment and borrowing of capital that they need to continue. So technological, social, and political factors rather than environmental factors mostly determine what kind of food-getting can be practiced in a given environment.

THE ORIGIN, SPREAD, AND INTENSIFICATION OF FOOD PRODUCTION

To understand why most people today are food producers rather than food collectors, we need to consider why plant and animal domestication may have emerged in the first place. In the chapter on the origins of food production and settled life, we examined some theories that suggested why people started to produce food. Most of the theories currently considered that people made the changeover because they were pushed into it. The possible reasons include:

1. Population growth in regions of bountiful wild resources pushed people to move to marginal areas, where they tried to reproduce their former abundance.

2. Global population growth filled up most of the world's habitable regions and forced people to utilize a broader spectrum of wild resources and to domesticate plants and animals.

3. Climatic change—hotter, drier summers and colder winters—favored settling near seasonal stands of wild grain; population growth in such areas would force people to plant crops and raise animals.

Whatever the reasons for the switch to food production, we still need to explain why food production has supplanted foraging as the primary mode of subsistence. We cannot assume that collectors would automatically adopt production as a superior way of life once they understood the process of domestication. After all, as we have noted, domestication may entail more work and provide less security than the food-collecting way of life.

The spread of agriculture may be linked to the need for territorial expansion. As a sedentary, food-producing population grew, it may have been forced to expand into new territory. Some of this territory may have been vacant, but much of it was probably already occupied by foragers. Although food production is not necessarily easier than collection, it is generally more productive per unit of land. Greater productivity enables more people to be supported in a given territory. In the competition for land between the faster-expanding food producers and the foragers, the food producers may have had a significant advantage: They had more people in a given area. Thus, the foraging groups may have been more likely to lose out in the competition for land. Some groups may have adopted cultivation, abandoning the foraging way of life to survive. Other groups, continuing as foragers, may have been forced to retreat into areas the cultivators did not desire. Today, as we have seen, the small number of remaining foragers inhabit areas not particularly suitable for cultivation—dry lands, dense tropical forests, and polar regions.

Just as prior population growth might account for the origins of domestication, further population growth and ensuing pressure on resources at later periods might also at least partly explain the transformation of horticultural systems into intensive agricultural systems. Ester Boserup suggested that intensification of agriculture, with a consequent increase in yield per acre, is not likely to develop naturally out of horticulture, because intensification requires much more work.[47] She argued that people will be willing to intensify their labor only if they have to. Where emigration is not feasible, the prime mover behind intensification may be prior population growth. The need to pay taxes or tribute to a political authority may also stimulate intensification.

Boserup's argument about intensification is widely accepted. However, her assumption that more work is required with intensive agriculture has recently been questioned. Comparing horticultural (swidden or shifting) rice production with rice produced on permanent fields using irrigation, Robert Hunt found that *less,* not more, labor is required with irrigation.[48] Still, population increase may generally provide the impetus to intensify production to increase yields to support the additional people.

Intensive agriculture has not yet spread to every part of the world. Horticulture continues to be practiced in certain tropical regions, and there are still some pastoralists and foragers. Some environments may make it somewhat more difficult to adopt certain subsistence practices. For example, intensive agriculture cannot supplant horticulture in some tropical environments without tremendous investments in chemical fertilizers and pesticides, not to mention the additional labor required.[49] And enormous amounts of water may be required to make agriculturalists out of foragers and pastoralists who now exploit semiarid environments. However, difficulty is not impossibility. Anna Roosevelt points out that, although horticulture was a common food-getting strategy in Amazonia in recent times, archaeological evidence indicates that there were complex societies practicing intensive agriculture on raised, drained fields in the past.[50] The physical environment does not completely control what can be done with it.

SUMMARY ● ○ ○

1. Foraging—hunting, gathering, and fishing—depends on wild plants and animals and is the oldest human food-getting technology. There is a lot of variation with regard to which food-getting activity is most important to a society. Recent foragers depended most on fishing, followed by gathering and hunting. Today, only a small number of societies depend largely on foraging, and they tend to inhabit marginal environments.

2. Foragers can be found in various physical habitats. Most foragers are nomadic, and population density is low. Usually, the small bands consist of related families, with the division of labor along age and

gender lines only. Personal possessions are limited, individuals' land rights are seldom recognized, and people are not differentiated by class.

3. Beginning about 10,000 years ago, certain peoples in widely separated geographic locations began to make the revolutionary changeover to food production—the cultivation and raising of plants and animals. Over the centuries, food production began to supplant food collection as the predominant mode of subsistence.

4. Horticulturalists farm with relatively simple tools and methods and do not cultivate fields permanently. Their food supply is sufficient to support larger, more densely populated communities than can be fed by foraging. Their way of life is sedentary, although communities may move after some years to farm a new series of plots.

5. Intensive agriculture is characterized by techniques such as fertilization and irrigation that allow fields to be cultivated permanently. In contrast with horticultural societies, intensive agriculturalists are more likely to have towns and cities, a high degree of craft specialization, large differences in wealth and power, and more complex political organization. They are also more likely to face food shortages. In the modern world, intensive agriculture is increasingly mechanized and geared to production for a market.

6. Pastoralism is a subsistence technology involving principally the raising of large herds of animals. It is generally found in low-rainfall areas. Pastoralists tend to be nomadic, to have small communities consisting of related families, and to depend significantly on trade because they do not produce items (including certain types of food) they need.

7. Anthropologists generally agree that the physical environment normally exercises a restraining rather than a determining influence on how people in an area get their food; technology as well as social and political factors may be more important.

8. We see the first evidence of a changeover to food production in the Near East about 10,000 years ago (8000 B.C.). Theories about why food production originated remain controversial, but most archaeologists think that certain conditions must have pushed people to switch from collecting to producing food. Some possible causal factors include (1) population growth in regions of bountiful wild resources, which may have pushed people to move to marginal areas where they tried to reproduce their former abundance; (2) global population growth, which filled most of the world's habitable regions and may have forced people

to utilize a broader spectrum of wild resources and to domesticate plants and animals; and (3) the emergence of hotter and drier summers and colder winters, which may have favored sedentarization near seasonal stands of wild grain; population growth in such areas may have forced people to plant crops and raise animals to support themselves.

9. Because food producers can support more people in a given territory than foragers can, they may have had a competitive advantage in confrontations with foragers.

GLOSSARY TERMS ○ ● ○

cash crops **277**
commercialization **279**
extensive or shifting
    cultivation **275**
foraging **270**
horticulture **275**
hunter-gatherers **272**

intensive agriculture **277**
pastoralism **279**
prairie **283**
slash-and-burn **275**
steppe **283**
subsistence economies **270**

CRITICAL QUESTIONS ○ ○ ●

1. Why might meat be valued more than plant foods in many societies?

2. Why might foragers be less likely than intensive agriculturalists to suffer from food shortages?

3. Why do certain foods in a society come to be preferred?

PEARSON
myanthrolab

Read the chapter by Burton Pasternak, "Han: Pastoralists and Farmers on a Chinese Frontier," on MyAnthroLab and answer the following questions.

1. The Han Chinese traditionally depended on intensive agriculture. The Mongols traditionally depended on pastoralism. What happened to the Han when they moved beyond the Great Wall to a grassland environment?

2. How has the change to more pastoralism affected marriage and family among the Han?

3. How have the Mongols changed?

Economic Systems

hen we think of economics, we think of things and activities involving money. We think of the costs of goods and services, such as food, rent, haircuts, and movie tickets. We may also think of factories, farms, and other enterprises that produce the goods and services we need, or think we need. In industrial societies, workers may stand before a moving belt for eight hours, tightening identical bolts that glide by. For this task, they are given bits of paper that may be exchanged for food, shelter, and other goods or services. But many societies—indeed, most that are known to anthropology—did not have money or the equivalent of the factory worker until relatively recently. Still, all societies have economic systems, whether or not they involve money. All societies have customs specifying how people gain access to natural resources; customary ways of transforming or converting those resources, through labor, into necessities and other desired goods and services; and customs for distributing and perhaps exchanging goods and services.

In the earlier days of anthropology, it was easier to study the economic system of a people in relative isolation from other societies. But now, almost every area of the earth has been affected by global political and economic forces—colonialism, imperialism, the spread of capitalism, and involvement in a world market system. Most people had no choice about becoming part of that system, but there is considerable variation in how and to what degree change was accepted or resisted. Even for people who resisted, many aspects of traditional economic systems have altered over the last few centuries. In the sections that follow, we describe the traditional economic system first and then turn to some of the more recent changes.

As we shall see in this chapter, a great deal of the cross-cultural variation in economic systems is related to how a society primarily gets its food. However, other aspects of the culture also affect the economies. These other influences, which we cover in subsequent chapters, include the presence or absence of social (class and gender) inequality, family and kinship groups, and the political system.

● ○ ●

THE ALLOCATION OF RESOURCES

Natural Resources: Land

Every society has access to natural resources—land, water, plants, animals, minerals—and every society has cultural rules for determining who has access to particular resources and what can be done with them. In societies like the United States, where land and many other things may be bought and sold, land is divided into precisely measurable units, the borders of which may be visible or invisible. Individuals usually own relatively small plots of land and the resources on them. Large plots of land are generally owned collectively. The owner may be a government agency, such as the National Park Service, which owns land on behalf of the entire population of the United States (referred to as public ownership). Or the owner may be a corporation—a private collective of shareholders. In the United States, property ownership entails a more or less exclusive right to use land or other resources (called *usufruct*) in whatever ways the owner wishes, including the right to withhold or

prevent use by others. In the United States and many other societies, property ownership also includes the right to "alienate" property—that is, to sell, give away, bequeath, or destroy the resources owned. This type of property ownership by individuals, families, or private corporations is often referred to as a *private property* system.

Society specifies what is considered property and the rights and duties associated with that property.[1] These specifications are social in nature, for they may be changed over time. For example, France declared all its beaches to be public, thereby stating, in effect, that the ocean shore is not a resource that an individual can own. As a result, all the hotels and individuals that had fenced-off portions of the best beaches for their exclusive use had to remove the barriers. Even in countries with private property, such as the United States, people cannot do anything that they want with their property. Federal, state, and local governments have adopted legislation to prevent the pollution of the air and the water supply. Such regulation may be new, but the rights of ownership in the United States have been limited for some time. For example, government may take land for use in the construction of a highway; compensation is paid, but the individual cannot prevent confiscation. Similarly, people are not allowed to burn their houses or to use them as brothels or munitions arsenals. In short, even with an individualistic system of ownership, property is not entirely private.

How societies differ in their rules for access to land and other natural resources seems to be related in part to how they differ in food-getting. Let us now examine how foragers, horticulturalists, pastoralists, and intensive agriculturalists structure rights to land in different ways. We look at traditional patterns first. As we shall see later, traditional rights to land have been considerably affected by state societies that have spread to and colonized native societies in the New World, Africa, and Asia.

Foragers Members of food-collecting societies generally do not have private ownership of land. If there is collective ownership, it is always by groups of related people (kinship groups) or by territorial groups (bands or villages). Land is not bought and sold.

The reason is probably that land itself generally has no intrinsic value for foragers; what is of value is the presence of game and wild plant life on the land. If game moves away or food resources become less plentiful, the land is less valuable. Therefore, the greater the possibility that the wild food supply in a particular locale will fluctuate, the less desirable it is to parcel out small areas of land to individuals and the more advantageous it is to make land ownership communal. The Hadza of Tanzania, for example, do not believe that they have exclusive rights over the land on which they hunt. Members of the group can hunt, gather, or draw water wherever they like.[2] This is not to say that private ownership of land does not exist among foragers. Among foragers heavily dependent on fishing in rivers, individual or family ownership is more common,[3] perhaps because the fishing in rivers is more predictable than other kinds of foraging. And, in some foraging societies, individuals and families have private rights to trees.[4] Although foragers generally do not have private ownership of important land resources, there is considerable

variation in the extent of communal ownership. In some societies, such as the Hadza, groups do not claim or defend particular territories. In fact, the Hadza do not even restrict use of their land to members of their own language group. But the Hadza are somewhat unusual. It is more common in food-collecting societies for a group of individuals, usually kin, to "own" land. To be sure, such ownership is not usually exclusive; typically some degree of access is provided to members of neighboring bands.[5]

At the other extreme, local groups try to maintain exclusive rights to particular territories. Why have some foragers been more territorial than others? One suggestion is that, when the plants and animals collected are predictably located and abundant, groups are more likely to be sedentary and to try to maintain exclusive control over territories. In contrast, when plant and animal resources are unpredictable in location or amount, territoriality will tend to be minimal.[6] Territorial foragers appear to have predictably located resources *and* more permanent villages, so it is hard to know which factor is more important in determining whether territory will be defended.

Horticulturalists Like foragers, most horticulturalists do not have individual or family ownership of land. This may be because rapid depletion of the soil necessitates letting some of the land lie fallow for a period of years or abandoning an area after a few years and moving to a new location. There is no reason for individuals or families to claim permanent access to land that, given available technology, is not usable permanently. But, in contrast to foragers, horticulturalists are more likely to allocate particular plots of land to individuals or families for their use, although these individuals or families do not commonly own the land in our sense of potentially permanent ownership.

Among the Mundurucú of Brazil, the village controls the rights to use land. People in the community can hunt and fish where they like, and they have the right to clear a garden plot wherever land belonging to the community is not being used. Gardens can be cultivated for only two years before the soil is exhausted; then the land reverts to the community. The Mundurucú distinguish between the land and the produce on the land, so that a person who cultivates the land owns the produce. Similarly, the person who kills an animal or catches a fish owns it, no matter where it was obtained. But because all food is shared with others, it does not really matter who owns it. Rights to land became more individualized when Mundurucú men began to tap rubber trees for sale. Rights to a particular path in the forest where trees were tapped could not be bought and sold, but the rights could be inherited by a son or son-in-law.[7]

Pastoralists The territory of pastoral nomads usually far exceeds that of most horticultural societies. Because their wealth ultimately depends on mobile herds, uncultivated pasture for grazing, and water for drinking, pastoralists often combine the adaptive potential of both foragers and horticulturalists. Like foragers, they generally need to know the potential of a large area of land. The Basseri, described in the last chapter, moved over an area of 15,000 square miles to obtain supplies of grass and water. And, like horticulturalists, pastoralists must move on when a resource

current research and issues

Does Communal Ownership Lead to Economic Disaster?

In a paper called "The Tragedy of the Commons," Garrett Hardin suggested that, if animals are grazed on common land, it is economically rational for individual animal owners to graze as many animals as possible, because they do not incur the pasture costs. According to Hardin, tragedy results because pasture is degraded by overgrazing, and productivity falls. Similarly, why shouldn't a fisher take as much fish as possible from the ocean, a kind of commons, and not worry about the consequences? On the other hand, if the resource is privately owned, individuals might try to conserve their resources because degrading those resources will cost them in the long run by decreasing their yields. The theory, then, is that private owners will find it rational to conserve their resources to minimize costs and maximize yields.

Is it really true that communal ownership tends to result in overexploitation of resources and lower yields, and private ownership tends to result in conservation of resources and higher yields? This is an active area of research in economic anthropology. We do know about instances where communal grazing lands have been more productive than private grazing lands in comparable climates. For example, the Borana of Ethiopia, who have communal grazing, produce more animal protein per acre at lower cost than Australian cattle ranches, although their climates are similar. And there are instances, such as the overgrazing in the Great American Desert (described in the box "The Effect of Food-Getting on the Environment" in the preceding chapter), where private ownership did lead to degradation of the environment.

Commercialization may be more important than private versus communal ownership in explaining overgrazing or overfishing, at least initially. In the Micronesian islands of Palau, which had traditional conservation practices, serious overfishing became a problem apparently only when

Fishing people often have communal rights to places to fish as in this area of Zaire.

people started to sell fish to Japanese colonists for imported trade goods. Some of those goods (nets and motors) helped to make fishing easier. Eventually, overfishing resulted in reduced catches and increased costs of fishing, and the Palauans had to buy much of their fish in imported cans.

It may also be that sustainability requires some regulation by political authorities. Before 1995, the halibut fishery in Alaska was facing collapse. Competing fishers rushed to fill their holds, no matter how dangerous the weather. Because the fishers often overshot the industry quota, regulators shortened the fishing season to just a few days. And when the boats returned after a few days with a year's worth of fish, the market was flooded and prices fell. In 1995, business became better and safer after a system of "catch shares" was adopted. The fishers were each allocated a transferable quota that they could use to catch fish or sell to others. The quotas are a percentage of the total allowable catch, which regulators set each year. The results: Captains could plan when to fish without worrying about weather or being beaten to the schools of fish by other fishers, regulators

could extend the fishing season, and prices for halibut climbed. The new regulatory system was a success. The halibut fishery was sustained and the fishers were better off. But regulation does not always work, judging by the "groundfishing" (fishing for fish, like cod, that feed off the ocean bottom) industry off the New England coast. In contrast to lobster fisherman who have accepted regulation, groundfishers have not. Perhaps this is because the groundfishing industry did not play a role in creating the regulations, nor do they have a cohesive community that can police itself.

Is there a lesson here for sustaining and even enhancing resources in general? So, which is more likely to lead to conservation, communal ownership or private ownership? We cannot say yet with any confidence. We need more comparisons of cases to tell us. It may be that conservation can be fostered in either type of system, if the people involved are so motivated.

Sources: Hardin 1968; Johannes 1981; Dirks 2009; Stokstad 2008; Acheson 2006.

A Surui village in the Amazon with cleared land for horticulture in the foreground and the surrounding rain forest in the background.

is exhausted (in this case, until grass renews itself). Also like horticulturalists, they depend for subsistence on human manipulation of a natural resource—animals—as opposed to the horticulturalists' land.

Because land is only good if there is sufficient pasture and water, there would be considerable risk to individuals or families to own land that did not predictably have grass and water. So, like most foragers and horticulturalists, community members generally have free access to pasture land.[8] Although grazing land tends to be communally held, it is customary for pastoralist individuals to own animals.[9] Fredrik Barth argued that, if animals were not so owned, the whole group might be in trouble because the members might be tempted to eat up their productive capital—their animals—in bad times. When animals are owned individually, a family whose herd drops below the minimum number of animals necessary for survival can drop out of nomadic life, at least temporarily, and work for wages in sedentary agricultural communities. But, in so doing, such a family does not jeopardize other pastoral families. On the other hand, if the fortunate were to share their herds with the unfortunate, all might approach bankruptcy. Thus, Barth argued, individual ownership is adaptive for a pastoral way of life.[10]

John Dowling questioned that interpretation. As he pointed out, pastoral nomads are not the only ones who have to save some of their "crop" for future production. Horticulturalists also must save some of their crop, in the form of seeds or tubers, for future planting. But horticulturalists generally lack private ownership of productive resources, so the necessity to save for future production cannot explain private ownership of animals in pastoral societies. Dowling suggested that private ownership will develop only in pastoral societies that depend on selling their products to nonpastoralists.[11] Thus, it may be the opportunity to sell their products as well as their labor that explains both the possibility of dropping out of nomadic life and the private ownership of animals among most pastoralists.

As among hunter-gatherers, pastoralists vary in how much a group actually has ownership rights to the territories through which they move their animals. The Basseri have

rights to pass through certain areas, including agricultural areas and even cities, but they do not own the entire territory. The Baluch, another pastoralist group in the border region between Iran, Pakistan, and Afghanistan, claim a "tribal" territory, which they defend by force, if necessary.[12]

Intensive Agriculturalists   Individual ownership of land resources—including the right to use the resources and the right to sell or otherwise dispose of them—is common among intensive agriculturalists. The development of such ownership is partly a result of the possibility of using land season after season, which gives the land more or less permanent value. But the concept of individual ownership is also partly a political and social matter. So, for example, the occupation and cultivation of frontier land in the United States was transformed by law into individual ownership. Under the Homestead Act of 1862, if a person cleared a 160-acre piece of land and farmed it for five years, the federal government would consider that person the owner of the land. This practice is similar to the custom in some societies by which a kin group, a chief, or a community is obligated to assign a parcel of land to anyone who wishes to farm it. The difference is that, once the American homesteader had become the owner of the land, the laws of the country gave the homesteader the right to dispose of it at will by selling or giving it away. Once individual ownership of land has become established, property owners may use their economic, and hence political, power to pass laws that favor themselves. In the early years of the United States, only property owners could vote.

Private individual ownership is usually associated with intensive agriculture, but not always. As we mentioned in the preceding chapter, intensive agriculture is usually associated with more complex political systems and with differences in wealth and power, so we need to understand the larger political and social context to understand particular systems of land allocation. Some communist and socialist nations with intensive agriculture formed agricultural collectives. For example, after World War II, the small farm holdings in a village in Bulgaria named Zamfirovo were incorporated into a village cooperative.

Most of the villagers worked as laborers on the new cooperative, but the cooperative allocated to every household a small plot on which to grow its own grain, vegetables, and grapes. These plots were fairly productive, and Westerners often attributed their productivity to private enterprise. But the cooperative provided much of the labor needed to plant and plow these plots, so they could hardly be considered private property. In 1989, after the overthrow of the communist regime, the cooperative was dissolved, and the land was divided and sold to private owners.[13]

Colonialism, the State, and Land Rights Almost universally around the world, colonial conquerors and settlers have taken land away from the natives or aborigines. Even if the natives were given other land in exchange, as in Brazil and the United States, these reservations were often, if not always, poorer in potential than the original land. (If the reservation land hadn't been poorer in quality, the settlers would have taken it for themselves.) For example, in the 19th century, the land of the pastoral Maasai stretched from the Lake Turkana area of northern Kenya down to northern Tanzania. The British pushed the Maasai onto a reserve in the southern part of Kenya, south of the Mombasa-Uganda railway, and gave some of their prime grazing lands and water resources to Europeans for farming and ranching near Nairobi as well as near the Naivasha and Nakuru lakes. The Maasai grazing land was reduced by about 60 percent and the Maasai were also forbidden to graze in the areas where game parks were established by the British for tourism.[14] Europeans, who constituted less than 1 percent of the population in Kenya, acquired access to or control of 20 percent of the land, mostly in the highlands, where there was the greatest potential for commercial production of tea and coffee.[15]

In addition, the new centralized governments often tried to change how the natives owned the land, almost always in the direction of individual or private ownership. If kin groups or larger social entities owned the land, it would be more difficult for the settlers to get the natives to give it up, either by sale or threat. Individual owners could be dispossessed more easily.[16]

The newcomers who benefited from these forced changes were not always people of European background,

but they were commonly people from expanding state societies. Beginning in the late 15th century, the expanding groups came mostly from western Europe. But in recent times, as well as in the millennia before and after the time of Christ, conquerors and settlers have come from India, China, Japan, Arabia, Scandinavia, Russia, and other countries. This is not to say that native peoples in Africa, Asia, and the New World were never guilty of conquering and exploiting others on their continents or elsewhere. They were. The Aztecs in Mexico and Central America, the native kingdoms in West Africa after about 800 years ago, and the Arabs after the rise of Islam were just some of the expanding state societies of the past, before the rise of the West. Wherever there have been "civilized" (urban) societies, there have been imperialism and colonialism. In North America, the British recognized the principle that lands not ceded to the crown would be native hunting grounds, but such recognition of rights by the British and then by the United States remained in force only as long as the various native groups remained numerous enough to constitute a threat to the settlers. President Andrew Jackson, for example, called for removal of all eastern Native American groups to "permanent" settlements west of the Mississippi. Some 90,000 people were removed. But, as settlers moved west, the reservations were often reduced in size.[17] In much of colonial Africa, governments ceded land to European-owned companies for development. Reserves were established for large native populations, who then were invariably forced to work as laborers on European-owned plantations and in European-owned mines.[18]

The taking of land by state authorities does not just happen with colonialism and imperialism. Indigenous revolutionary movements have collectivized land, as in Russia, or broken up large private landholdings, as in Mexico. Typically, state authorities do not like communal land-use systems. State authorities particularly view mobile pastoralists unfavorably, because their mobility makes them difficult to control. Governments usually try to settle pastoralists or break up communally held pasture into small units.[19] In Kenya, after independence from the British, the pastoral Maasai continued to lose grazing territory. The national government strongly promotes tourism, for which game parks are vital, and development, such as the construction of greenhouses growing flowers for the European market. With the advice of international development agencies, the Kenyan government pushed for privatization of grazing land. But grazing on individual-owned plots requires capital to grow or buy food for cattle, pay for medicines, and to get cattle to market.[20]

Technology

To convert resources to food and other goods, every society makes use of a technology, which includes tools, constructions (such as fish traps), and required skills (such as how and where to set up a fish trap). Societies vary considerably in their technologies and in the way access to technology is allocated. For example, foragers and pastoralists typically have fairly small tool kits. They must limit their tools, and their material possessions in general, to what they can comfortably carry with them. As for access to

Colonial governments have often taken land away from the natives to establish plantations. A family in Guatemala works on a coffee plantation.

technology, foragers and horticulturalists generally allow equal opportunity. In the absence of specialization, most individuals have the skills to make what they need. But in an industrial society like our own, the opportunity to acquire or use a particular technology (which may be enormously expensive as well as complex) is hardly available to all. Most of us may be able to buy a drill or a hammer, but few of us can buy the factory that makes it.

The tools foragers most need are weapons for the hunt, digging sticks, and receptacles for gathering and carrying. Of all foragers, the Inuit probably had the most sophisticated weapons, including harpoons, compound bows, and ivory fishhooks. Yet the Inuit also had relatively fixed settlements with available storage space and dog teams and sleds for transportation.[21]

Among foragers, tools are considered to belong to the person who made them. There is no way of gaining superiority over others through possession of tools, because whatever resources for toolmaking are available to one are available to all. In addition, the custom of sharing applies to tools as well as to food. For example, Elizabeth Thomas, speaking of the !Kung, said, "The few possessions that Bushmen have are constantly circulating among the members of their groups."[22]

Pastoralists, like foragers, are somewhat limited in their possessions, for they too are nomadic. But pastoralists can use their animals to carry some possessions. Each family owns its own tools, clothes, and perhaps a tent, as well as its own livestock. The livestock are the sources of other needed articles, for the pastoralists often trade their herd products for the products of the townspeople. Horticulturalists, on the other hand, are more self-sufficient than pastoralists. Their principal farming tools are the knife for slashing and the hoe or stick for digging. What a person makes is considered his or her own, yet everyone is often obligated to lend tools to others. In Chuuk society, the owner of a canoe has first use of it; the same is true for farming implements. Yet, if a close relative needs the canoe and finds it unused, the canoe may be taken without permission. A distant relative or neighbor must ask permission to borrow any tools, but the owner may not refuse. If owners were to refuse, they would risk being scorned and refused if they were to need tools later.

Societies with intensive agriculture and industrialized societies are likely to have tools made by specialists, which means that tools must be acquired by trade or purchase. Probably because complex tools cost a considerable amount of money, they are less likely than simple tools to be shared except by those who contributed to the purchase price. For example, a diesel-powered combine requires a large amount of capital for its purchase and upkeep. The person who has supplied the capital is likely to regard the machine as individual private property and to regulate its use and disposal. The owner must then use the machine to produce enough surplus to pay for its cost and upkeep as well as for its replacement. The owner may rent the machine to neighboring farmers during slack periods to obtain a maximum return on the investment.

Expensive equipment, however, is not always individually owned in societies with intensive agriculture or industrialized economies. Even in capitalist countries, there may be collective ownership of machines by cooperatives or co-ownership with neighbors.[23] Governments often own very expensive equipment or facilities such as airports, highways, and dams. Such resources are owned collectively by the whole society. Rights of use depend on the facility. Anyone can use a highway, but only contributing municipalities can draw upon the water in a dam. Other productive resources in industrial societies, such as factories or service companies, may be owned jointly by shareholders, who purchase a portion of a corporation's assets in return for a proportionate share of its earnings. The proportion of technology and facilities owned by various levels of government also reflects the type of political-economic system—socialist and communist countries have more public ownership than do capitalist countries.

THE CONVERSION OF RESOURCES

In all societies, resources have to be transformed or converted through labor into food, tools, and other goods. These activities constitute what economists call *production*. In this section, after briefly reviewing different types of production, we examine what motivates people to work, how societies divide up the work to be done, and how they organize work. As we shall see, some aspects of the conversion of natural resources are culturally universal, but there is also an enormous amount of cultural variation.

Types of Economic Production

At the times they were first described, most of the societies known to anthropology had a *domestic*—family or kinship—mode of production. People labored to get food and to produce shelter and implements for themselves and their kin. Usually families had the right to exploit productive resources and control the products of their labor. Even part-time specialists, such as potters, could still support themselves without that craft if they needed to. At the other extreme are *industrial* societies, where much of the work is based on mechanized production, as in factories but also in mechanized agriculture. Because machines and materials are costly, only some individuals (capitalists), corporations, or governments can afford the expenses of production. Therefore, most people in industrial societies labor for others as wage earners. Although wages can buy food, people out of work lose their ability to support themselves, unless they are protected by welfare payments or unemployment insurance. Then there is the *tributary* type of production system, found in nonindustrial societies in which most people still produce their own food but an elite or aristocracy controls a portion of production (including the products of specialized crafts). The feudal societies of medieval western Europe were examples of tributary production, as was czarist Russia under serfdom.[24]

Many people have suggested that our own and other developed economies are now moving from *industrialism* to *postindustrialism*. In many areas of commerce, computers have radically transformed the workplace. Computers "drive" machines and robots, and much of the manual work required in industry is disappearing. Businesses are

In postindustrial economies, computers and robots rather than people do much of the work in factories. There are few people in this Bavarian brewery.

now more knowledge- and service-oriented. Information is more accessible with telecommunication, so much so that *telecommuting* has entered our vocabulary to describe how people can now work (for wages) at home. This economic transformation has important implications for both home life and the workplace. With inexpensive home computers and speedy data transmission by telephone and other means, more people are able to work at home. In addition, when information and knowledge become more important than capital equipment, more people can own and have access to the productive resources of society.[25] If "who owns what" partly determines who has political and other influence, the wider ownership of resources that is possible in postindustrial society may eventually translate into new, more democratic political forms and processes.

Incentives for Labor

Why do people work? Probably all of us have asked ourselves this question. Our concern may not be why other people are working, but why we have to work. Clearly, part of the answer is that work is necessary for survival. Although there are always some able-bodied adults who do not work as much as they should and rely on the labor of others, no society would survive if most able-bodied adults were like that. In fact, most societies probably succeed in motivating most people to want to do (and even enjoy) what they have to do. But are the incentives for labor the same in all societies? Anthropologists think the answer is both yes and no. One reason people may work is because they must. But why do people in some societies apparently work *more* than they must?

We can be fairly certain that a particular and often-cited motive—the profit motive, or the desire to exchange something for more than it costs—is not universal or always the dominant motive. There can be no profit motive among people who produce food and other goods primarily for their own consumption, as do most foragers, most horticulturalists, and even some intensive agriculturalists. Such societies have what we call a *subsistence economy*, not a money or commercial economy. Anthropologists have noticed that people in subsistence economies (with a domestic mode of production) often work less than people in

commercial economies (with tributary or industrial modes of production). Indeed, foragers appear to have a considerable amount of leisure time, as do many horticulturalists. It has been estimated, for example, that the men of the horticultural Kuikuru tribe in central Brazil spent about three and a half hours a day on subsistence. It appears that the Kuikuru could have produced a substantial surplus of manioc, their staple food, by working 30 minutes more a day.[26] Yet, they and many other peoples do not produce more than they need. Why should they? They cannot store a surplus for long because it would rot; they cannot sell it because there is no market nearby; and they do not have a political authority that might collect it for some purpose. Although we often think "more is better," a food-getting strategy with such a goal might even be disastrous, especially for foragers. The killing of more animals than a group could eat might seriously jeopardize the food supply in the future, because overhunting could reduce reproduction among the hunted animals.[27] Horticulturalists might do well to plant a little extra, just in case part of the crop failed, but a great deal extra would be a tremendous waste of time and effort.

It has been suggested that, when resources are converted primarily for household consumption, people will work harder if they have more consumers in the household. That is, when there are few able-bodied workers and a proportionately large number of consumers (perhaps because there are many young children and elderly people), the workers have to work harder. But when there are proportionately more workers, they can work less. This idea is called *Chayanov's rule*.[28] Alexander Chayanov found this relationship in data on rural Russians before the Russian Revolution.[29] But it appears to work in other places too. Paul Durrenberger and Nicola Tannenbaum collected data in Thailand in several villages and found general support for Chayanov's rule.[30] And Michael Chibnik found support for Chayanov's rule when he compared data from 12 communities in five areas of the world. The communities ranged in complexity from New Guinea horticulturalists to commercial Swiss farmers. Although Chayanov restricted his theory to farmers who mostly produced food for their own consumption and did not hire labor, Chibnik's analysis suggests that Chayanov's rule applies even for hired labor.[31] However, Durrenberger and Tannenbaum found that political and social factors explained some of the variability in household production. For example, in the villages that lacked social classes, families with a high ratio of workers to consumers produced less, apparently to avoid doing much better than other families. In contrast, in the villages that had social classes, households with a high ratio of workers to consumers produced more, and gained prestige from their efforts.[32]

There appear to be many societies in which some people work harder than they need to just for their own families' subsistence. What motivates them to work harder? Sharing and other transfers of food and goods often go well beyond the household, sometimes including the whole community or even groups of communities, as we will see later in this chapter. In such societies, social rewards come to those who are generous, who give things away. Thus, people who work harder than they have to for subsistence may be motivated to do so because they thereby gain respect or esteem.[33] In many societies too, as we shall see in subsequent chapters, extra food and goods may be needed at times for special purposes and occasions; goods and services may be needed to arrange and celebrate marriages, to form alliances, and to perform rituals and ceremonies (including what we would call sporting events). Thus, how the culture defines what one works for and what is needed may go beyond what is necessary.

In commercial economies such as our own—where foods, other goods, and services are sold and bought—people seem to be motivated to keep any extra income for themselves and their families. Extra income is converted into bigger dwellings, more expensive furnishings and food, and other elements of a "higher" standard of living. But the desire to improve one's standard of living is probably not the only motive operating. Some people may work partly to satisfy a need for achievement,[34] or because they find their work enjoyable. In addition, just as in precommercial societies, some people may work partly to gain respect or influence by giving some of their income away. Not only do we respect philanthropists and movie stars for giving to charities; our society encourages such giving by making it an allowable tax deduction. Still, the emphasis on giving in commercial societies is clearly less developed than in subsistence economies. We consider charity by the religious or rich appropriate and even admirable, but we would think it foolish or crazy for people to give so much away that they become poverty-stricken.

Forced and Required Labor

Thus far, we have mostly discussed *voluntary labor*—voluntary in the sense that no formal organization within the society compels people to work and punishes them for not working. Social training and social pressure are powerful enough to persuade an individual to perform some useful task. In both food-collecting and horticultural societies, individuals who can stand being the butt of jokes about laziness will still be fed. At most, the other members of the group will ignore them. There is no reason to punish them and no way to coerce them to do the work expected of them.

More complex societies have ways of forcing people to work for the authorities, whether those authorities are kings or presidents. An indirect form of forced labor is taxation. The average tax in the United States (local, state, and federal) is about 33 percent of income, which means that the average person works four months out of the year for the various levels of government. If a person decides not to pay the tax, the money will be taken forcibly or the person may be put in prison.

Money is the customary form of tax payment in a commercial society. In a politically complex but nonmonetary society, people may pay their taxes in other ways—by performing a certain number of hours of labor or by giving up a certain percentage of what they produce. The **corvée**, a system of required labor, existed in the Inca Empire in the central Andes before the Spanish conquest. Each male commoner was assigned three plots of land to work: a temple plot, a state plot, and his own plot. The enormous stores of food that went into state warehouses were used to

The Great Wall of China, like many monumental works in ancient societies, was built with forced labor.

supply the nobles, the army, the artisans, and all other state employees. If labor became overabundant, the people were still kept occupied; it is said that one ruler had a hill moved to keep some laborers busy. In addition to subsistence work for the state, Inca commoners were subject to military service, to duty as personal servants for the nobility, and to other "public" service.[35] Elderly villagers in the Chiang Mai area of Thailand describe corvée this way: "Villagers had to work one *rai* [*rai myong* or 0.1 acre] per person for them for nothing. And one had to do it properly. The lord's underlings would take a banana tree trunk and stick it upright in the field after it was plowed. If it fell over, that meant it was well plowed. Otherwise, one would have to keep on plowing until the ground was soft."[36]

Conscription or the draft, or compulsory military service, is also a form of corvée, in that a certain period of service is required, and failure to serve can be punished by a prison term or involuntary exile. Emperors of China had soldiers drafted to defend their territory and to build the Great Wall along the northern borders of the empire. The wall extends over 1,500 miles, and thousands were drafted to work on it. Slavery is the most extreme form of forced work, in that slaves have little control over their labor. Because slaves constitute a category or class of people in many societies, we discuss slavery more fully in the chapter on social stratification.

Division of Labor

All societies have some division of labor, some customary assignment of different kinds of work to different kinds of people. Universally, males and females and adults and children do not do the same kinds of work. In a sense, then, division of labor by gender and age is a kind of universal specialization of labor. Many societies known to anthropology divide labor only by gender and age; other societies have more complex specialization.

By Gender and Age All societies make use of gender differences to some extent in their customary assignment

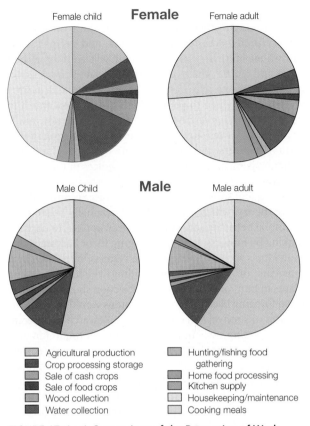

Female

Female child   Female adult

Male

Male Child   Male adult

☐ Agricultural production
☐ Crop processing storage
☐ Sale of cash crops
☐ Sale of food crops
☐ Wood collection
☐ Water collection

☐ Hunting/fishing food
    gathering
☐ Home food processing
☐ Kitchen supply
☐ Housekeeping/maintenance
☐ Cooking meals

FIGURE 17–1   A Comparison of the Proportion of Work Tasks Done by Adults and Children

Source: From J. Levine et al. 2002.

of labor. In the chapter on sex, gender, and culture, we discuss the division of labor by gender in detail.

Age is also a universal basis for division of labor. Clearly, children cannot do work that requires a great deal of strength. But, in many societies, girls and boys contribute much more in labor than do children in our own society. For example, they help in animal tending, weeding, and harvesting and do a variety of domestic chores such as child care, fetching water and firewood, and cooking and cleaning. In agricultural communities in the Ivory Coast, children's tasks mirror the tasks of same-sex adults (see Figure 17–1). In some societies, a child that is 6 years old is considered old enough to be responsible for a younger sibling for a good part of the day.[37] Animal tending is often important work for children. Children in some societies spend more time at this task than adults.[38]

Why do children do so much work in some societies? If adults, particularly mothers, have heavy workloads, and children are physically and mentally able to do the work, a good part of the work is likely to be assigned to children.[39] As we have seen, food producers probably have more work than foragers, so we would expect that children would be likely to work more where there is herding and farming. Consistent

with this expectation, Patricia Draper and Elizabeth Cashdan found differences in children's work between nomadic and settled !Kung. Even though recently settled !Kung have not switched completely from foraging to food production, children's as well as adults' activities have changed considerably. The children living in nomadic camps had virtually no work at all; adults did all the gathering and hunting. But the settled children were given lots of chores, ranging from helping with animals to helping with the harvest and food processing.[40]

What we have said about the !Kung should not imply that children in foraging societies always do little work. For example, among the Hadza of Tanzania, children between the ages of 5 and 10 are able to get one-third to one-half of their calories as they forage with their mothers. The Hadza also have more children than the !Kung.[41] Is there a relationship between children's work and fertility? When children in a society do a great deal of work, parents may value them more and may consciously want to have more children.[42] This may be one of the reasons why birth rates are especially high in intensive agricultural societies where workloads are very high.[43]

Beyond Gender and Age   In societies with relatively simple technologies, there is little specialization of labor beyond that of gender and age. But as a society's technology becomes more complex and it is able to produce large quantities of food, more of its people are freed from subsistence work to become specialists in some other tasks.

In contrast with foragers, horticultural societies may have some part-time specialists. Some people may devote special effort to perfecting a particular skill or craft—pottery making, weaving, house building, doctoring—and in return for their products or services be given food or other gifts. Among some horticultural groups, the entire village may specialize part-time in making a particular product, which can then be traded to neighboring people.

With the development of intensive agriculture, full-time specialists—potters, weavers, blacksmiths—begin to appear. The trend toward greater specialization reaches its

These Haitian women specialize in making and selling baskets for sale.

peak in industrialized societies, where workers develop skills in one small area of the economic system. Full-time specialization makes people dependent on the necessity to sell their labor or products to make a living. In societies with full-time occupational specialization, different jobs are usually associated with differences in prestige, wealth, and power, as we shall see in the chapter on social stratification.

The Organization of Labor

The degree to which labor has to be organized reaches its peak in industrial societies, which have great occupational specialization and complex political organization. The co-ordination required to produce an automobile on an assembly line is obvious; so is the coordination required to collect taxes from every wage earner.

In many food-collecting and horticultural societies, there is little formal organization of work. Work groups tend to be organized only when productive work requires it and to dissolve when they are no longer needed. Furthermore, the groups so organized often have changing composition and leadership; participation tends to be individualistic and voluntary.[44] Perhaps this flexibility is possible because, when virtually everyone has the same work to do, little instruction is needed, and almost anyone can assume leadership. Still, some types of work require more organization than others. Hunting big game usually requires coordinated efforts by a large number of hunters; so might catching fish in large nets. For example, on Moala, a Fijian island in the Pacific, net fishing is a group affair. A party of 20 to 30 women wades out on the reef and makes a semicircle of nets. At a signal from an experienced woman, usually the chief's wife, the women move together at the ends, forming a circle. After the fish are caught in the nets, the women bite them on the backs of their heads to kill them and put them in baskets that they carry ashore. Around Christmas, the village, or several villages, undertakes a larger fish drive. The day before, more than 100 people make a "sweep," some 1,600 yards long, from coconut fronds. The next day, the men, women, and children all participate in the surround, catching thousands of fish.[45]

Kinship ties are an important basis for work organization, particularly in nonindustrial societies. For example, among the horticultural Kapauku of western New Guinea, the male members of a village are a kin group, and all work together to build drainage ditches, large fences, and bridges.[46] With increasing technological complexity, the basis of work organization begins to shift to more formally organized groups.[47] In modern industrial societies, the predominant basis of organization is the *contract*—the agreement between employers and employees whereby the latter perform a specified amount of work for a specified amount of wages. Although the arrangement may be entered into voluntarily, laws and the power of the state enforce the obligation of the parties to abide by the contract.

Making Decisions About Work

Foragers ignore many of the plant and animal species in their environment, choosing to go after only some. Why? The people may say that some animals are taboo whereas others are delicious. But where do such customary beliefs come from? Are they adaptive? And if there are no customary preferences for certain plants and animals, how can we explain why a food collector will go after certain foods and ignore others on a particular day? Food producers also make choices constantly. For example, a farmer has to decide when to plant, what to plant, how much to plant, when to harvest, how much to store, and how much to give away or sell. Researchers have tried to explain why certain economic decisions become customary and why individuals make certain economic choices in their everyday lives.

A frequent source of ideas about choices is **optimal foraging theory,** which was developed originally by students of animal behavior and which has been applied to decision making by foragers. Optimal foraging theory assumes that individuals seek to maximize the returns, in calories and nutrients, on their labor in deciding which animals and plants to hunt or collect. Natural selection should favor optimal foraging because "good" decisions would increase the chances of survival and reproduction. Research in different food-collecting societies supports the optimal foraging model.[48] For example, the Aché of eastern Paraguay consistently prefer to hunt peccaries (wild piglike mammals) rather than armadillos. Although peccaries take much longer to find and are harder to kill than armadillos, a day spent hunting peccaries yields more than 4,600 calories per hour of work, whereas hunting armadillos yields only about 1,800 calories an hour.[49] Other factors in addition to calorie yield, such as predictability of resources, may also influence which foods are collected. For example, the !Kung of the Kalahari Desert depend largely on mongongo nuts, even though these nuts yield fewer calories per hour of work than does meat. But mongongo nuts in season are more dependable than game is. Once a group of !Kung hikes to a grove of ripe mongongo nuts, they know they can obtain food there until the supply is exhausted; they are not as certain of getting game when they seek it.[50] Similarly on Ifaluk, an atoll in the Federated States of Micronesia where fishing is the main source of animal protein, men most often choose to fish in the place where there is the highest return on average. But they do not always fish there; if the return on a previous day was lower than average, they tend to choose other spots.[51]

How does a farmer decide whether to plant a particular crop and how much land and labor to devote to it? Christina Gladwin and others suggested that farmers make decisions in steps, with each choice point involving a yes or no answer. For example, in the high-altitude region of Guatemala, farmers could choose to plant about eight crops, or combinations of them, such as corn and beans, which grow together well. A farmer will quickly exclude some choices because of the answers to certain questions: Can I afford the seed and fertilizer? Can this crop be watered adequately? Is the altitude appropriate? And so on. If any of the answers is no, the crop is not planted. By a further series of yes-or-no decisions, farmers presumably decide which of the remaining possibilities will be planted.[52]

Individuals may not always be able to state clearly their rules for making decisions, nor do they always have complete knowledge about the various possibilities, particularly when some of the possibilities are new. That does not mean, however, that researchers cannot predict or explain economic choices. For example, Michael Chibnik found that men in two villages in Belize and in Central America were not able to say why they devoted more or less time to working for wages versus growing crops. But their behavior was still predictable. Older men grew crops because wage labor was more physically demanding; and in the village with a higher cost of living, men were more likely to work for wages.[53]

THE DISTRIBUTION OF GOODS AND SERVICES

Goods and services are distributed in all societies by systems that, however varied, can be classified under three general types: reciprocity, redistribution, and market or commercial exchange.[54] The three systems often coexist in a society, but one system usually predominates. The predominant system seems to be associated with the society's food-getting technology and, more specifically, its level of economic development.

Reciprocity

Reciprocity consists of giving and taking without the use of money; it mainly takes the form of gift giving or generalized reciprocity. There may also be exchanges of equal value (barter or nonmonetary trade) or balanced reciprocity, without the use of money.[55]

Generalized Reciprocity When goods or services are given to another, without any apparent expectation of a return gift, we call it **generalized reciprocity.** Generalized reciprocity sustains the family in all societies. Parents give food, clothing, and labor to children because they want to or perhaps feel obliged to, but they do not usually calculate exactly how their children will reciprocate years later. These gifts are one-way transfers. In this sense, all societies have some kind of generalized reciprocity. But some societies depend on it almost entirely to distribute goods and services.

Lorna Marshall recounted how the !Kung divided an eland brought to a site where five bands and several visitors were camping—more than 100 people in all. The owner of the arrow that had first penetrated the eland was, by custom, the owner of the meat. He first distributed the forequarters to the two hunters who had aided him in the kill. After that, the distribution depended on kinship: Each hunter shared with his wives' parents, wives, children, parents, and siblings, and they in turn shared with their kin. Sixty-three gifts of raw meat were recorded, after which further sharing of raw and cooked meat was begun. The !Kung distribution of large game—clearly, generalized reciprocity—is common among foragers. But giving away is not limited to game. For example, when Marshall left the band that had sponsored her in 1951, she gave each woman in the band a present of enough cowrie shells to make a necklace—one large shell and 20 small ones. When

Sharing can occur even in a socially stratified society. Here we see men in a village in Yunnan, China, cutting the meat from a steer into 72 portions for the families of the village.

she returned in 1952, she found no cowrie shell necklaces and hardly a single shell among the people in the band. Instead, the shells appeared by ones and twos in the ornaments of the people of neighboring bands.[56]

Although generalized reciprocity may seem altruistic or unselfish, researchers have suggested that giving may in fact benefit the givers in various ways. For example, parents who help their children may not only perpetuate their genes (the ultimate biological benefit) but may also be likely to receive care and affection from their grown-up children when the parents are old. And giving parents may be happier and enjoy life more than nongiving parents. So, in the shorter as well as the longer run, givers may derive economic and psychological benefits, in addition to reproductive benefits.

Parent-child giving may seem easy to understand, but why do some societies rely more on generalized reciprocity than others, particularly beyond the family? Sharing may be most likely if resources are unpredictable. So a !Kung band may share its water with other bands because they may have water now but not in the future. A related group in the Kalahari, the G//ana,[57] has been observed to share less than other groups. It turns out that the resources available to the G//ana are more predictable, because the G//ana supplement their hunting and gathering with plant cultivation and goat herding. Cultivated melons (which store water) appear to buffer the G//ana against water shortages, and goats buffer them against shortages of game. Thus, whereas the !Kung distribute the meat right after a kill, the G//ana dry it and then store it in their houses.[58]

The idea that unpredictability favors sharing may also explain why some foods are more often shared than others. Wild game, for example, is usually unpredictable; when hunters go out to hunt, they cannot be sure that they will come back with meat. Wild plants, on the other hand, are more predictable; gatherers can be sure when they go out that they will come back with at least some plant foods. In any case, it does appear that foragers tend to share game much more than wild plant foods.[59] Even among people who depend largely on horticulture, such as the Yanomamö of Venezuela and Brazil, food items that are less predictably obtained (hunted game and fish) are shared more often than the more predictably obtained garden produce.[60] But, although meat is shared more than plant food, horticulturalists often share foraged or cultivated plants. Why? Sharing plant food may be advantageous to horticulturalists who are some distance from their gardens because they may not have to go as often. And sharing may solidify a social relationship so that other families will help in times of need, such as sickness or accident, when it may be hard to work.[61] Does food sharing increase the food supply for an individual? Calculations for the Aché of eastern Paraguay, who get most of their food from hunting when they go on food-collecting trips, suggest that the average individual gets more food when food is shared. Even the males who actually do the hunting get more, although the benefits are greater for the females and children on the trip.[62] Mathematically, the risk that an individual food collector will not find enough food on a particular day will be appreciably reduced if at least six to eight adult collectors share the food they collect. Food-collecting bands may often contain only 25 to 30 people, which is about the size that is needed to ensure that there are six to eight adult collectors.[63]

Although giving things to others may be expected in some societies, this does not necessarily mean that everyone does so willingly or without some social pressure. For example, the !Kung call "far-hearted" anyone who does not give gifts, and they express their disapproval openly.

Day-to-day unpredictability is one thing; more prolonged scarcity is another. What happens to a system of generalized reciprocity when resources are scarce because of a drought or other disaster? Does the ethic of giving break down? Evidence from a few societies suggests that the degree of sharing may actually *increase* during the period of food shortage.[64] For example, in describing the Netsilik Inuit, Asen Balikci said, "Whenever game was abundant, sharing among non-relatives was avoided, since every family was supposedly capable of obtaining the necessary catch. In situations of scarcity, however, caribou meat was more evenly distributed throughout camp."[65] Sharing may increase during mild scarcity because people can minimize their deprivation, but generalized reciprocity may be strained by extreme scarcity such as famine.[66]

Researchers generally have difficulty explaining sharing because they assume that, other things being equal, individuals would tend to be selfish. But experimental evidence suggests that sharing is likely even with people who do not know each other or who have no expectation of any return in the future from that person. Experimenters set up "games" in which they can control for or eliminate certain responses. For example, in one game, a particular player is given a certain amount of money and the player decides how much of the money to offer to the second player in the game. The second player can accept or reject the offer. If the division is rejected, no one gets any money. If the division is accepted, both players receive the proposed division. If selfishness were normal, one would expect that the proposer of the division would try to give away as little as possible and the second player should always accept whatever is offered because otherwise nothing is gained.

Surprisingly, equal divisions are commonly proposed and low offers are commonly rejected because they are viewed as unfair. If a person views the offer as unfair and forfeits any money, that player seems willing to "punish" the greedy individual. Although such experiments were mostly done at first in Western societies, we now have results from over 15 other societies that largely confirm the earlier results.[67] And there is now evidence suggesting that cooperation may even evoke pleasure. Researchers studying brain activity in women, who are playing a game allowing either cooperative or greedy strategies, found to their surprise that cooperation made certain areas of the brain light up. These areas are normally associated with pleasure, such as when eating desserts. So cooperation may be more "natural" than some people think.[68]

Balanced Reciprocity **Balanced reciprocity** is explicit and short term in its expectations of return. In contrast to generalized reciprocity or a one-way transfer, which has no expectation of a return, balanced reciprocity involves either an immediate exchange of goods or services or an agreed-upon exchange over a limited period of time. *Barter* is the term used most often for this type of nonmonetary exchange of goods and services. The !Kung, for instance, trade with the Tswana Bantu: a gemsbok hide for a pile of tobacco, five strings of beads made from ostrich eggshells for a spear, or three small skins for a good-sized knife.[69] In the 1600s, the Iroquois of the North American Northeast traded deerskin to Europeans for brass kettles, iron hinges, steel axes, woven textiles, and guns.[70] The !Kung and Iroquois acquired trade goods by balanced reciprocity, but such exchanges were not crucial to their economies.

In contrast, some societies depend much more heavily on balanced reciprocity. For example, the Efe, who hunt and gather in the Ituri forest of central Africa, get most of their calories from manioc, peanuts, rice, and plaintains grown by another group—the agricultural Lese. Efe men and women provide labor to the Lese, and in exchange, receive a portion of the harvest as well as goods such as metal pots and spears.[71] Pastoralists, too, are rarely self-sufficient, as we mentioned in the preceding chapter. They have to trade their pastoral products to agriculturalists to get the grain and other things they need.

Balanced reciprocity may mostly involve labor. Cooperative work parties usually exchange or balance gifts of labor. A cooperative work party, or *kuu*, among the Kpelle of Liberia may number from 6 to 40 people, all of whom are generally relatives or friends. In addition to promising return work on a particular date, each farmer rewards the work party's hard day's labor by providing a feast and sometimes rhythmic music to work by.[72] When we say that an exchange is balanced, we do not mean to imply that the things exchanged are exactly equivalent in value or that the exchange is purely economic. In the absence of a money economy, where there is no explicit standard by which value can be judged, there is no way to assess value objectively. The point is that the parties in balanced reciprocity are freely giving each other the respective goods and services they each want; they are not coerced into doing so, so presumably they are not conceiving of the exchange as unbalanced.[73] And when something is valued, it may be valued for other than economic reasons. The exchange itself may also be fun, adventuresome, or aesthetically pleasing, or it may enhance social relationships.

Because exchanges can have different motivations, they can have different meanings. Consequently, some economic anthropologists now want to distinguish between gift and commodity exchanges. *Gift exchanges* are personal and involve the creation or perpetuation of some kind of enduring relationship between people and groups. In our society, the exchange of dinner invitations or Christmas gifts is motivated by social considerations; we are not interested only in the actual food or objects received. In contrast, *commodity exchanges,* which can occur even in the absence of money, focus on the objects or services received—the transaction itself is the motive. When the transaction is completed, the relationship between the parties involved usually ends.[74]

The* Kula *Ring The horticultural Trobriand Islanders, who live off the eastern coast of New Guinea, worked out an elaborate scheme for trading ornaments, food, and other necessities with the people of neighboring islands. The exchange of goods between far-flung islands is essential, for some of the islands are small and rocky and cannot produce enough food to sustain their inhabitants, who specialize instead in canoe building, pottery making, and other crafts. Other islanders produce far more yams, taro, and pigs than they need. However, the practical side of the trade is hidden beneath a complex ceremonial exchange, called the *kula* ring, an exchange of valued shell ornaments across a set of far-flung islands.[75]

Two kinds of ornaments are involved in the ceremonial exchanges—white shell armbands (*mwali*), which are given only in a counterclockwise direction, and red shell necklaces (*soulava*), which are given only in a clockwise direction. The possession of one or more of these ornaments allows a man to organize an expedition to the home of one of his trading partners on another island. The high point of an expedition is the ceremonial giving of the valued *kula* ornaments. During the two- to three-day visit, the trading of necessities goes on. Some of the exchange takes the form of gift giving between trading partners. By the time the visitors leave, they have accomplished a year's trading, without seeming to do so.

But the practical advantages of the *kula* ring are not the only gains. There may be purely social ones, for goods are traded with ease and enjoyment. A trading expedition takes on the flavor of adventure rather than of business. Many of the traditions of the islands are kept alive: Myth, romance, ritual, and history are linked to the circulating ornaments, especially the larger, finer pieces, which are well known and recognized as heirlooms. A man is able to possess many valued things within his lifetime, each for a year or so. Each object, when it is received, arouses enthusiasm in a way that one lifelong possession could not.[76] The *kula* ring continued to be an important institution after Papua New Guinea became an independent country. For example, active participation in the *kula* ring helped candidates in the 1960s and the 1970s to be elected to the national parliament.[77]

The *kula* is not the only form of exchange in Trobriand life. For example, on the two days following a burial, the kin of the deceased give yams, taro, and valuables to those who helped care for the deceased before death, to those who participated in the burial ceremonies, and to those who came to mourn the deceased. After these initial exchanges, the hamlet settles into mourning. Women from other hamlets bring food to the people in mourning, and the mourning women prepare bundles of banana leaves and weave skirts of banana fiber for later distribution. Husbands help their wives accumulate valuables to "buy" extra bundles of banana leaves. Then the women's mortuary ceremony is held. It is very competitive—each of the mourning women tries to distribute the most bundles and skirts. As many as 5,000 bundles and 30 skirts might be distributed by one mourning woman in a single day. Each of these giveaways completes a balanced reciprocity: The giver is reciprocating for gifts of goods and services received in the past. A woman's brothers gave her yams and taro during the year. She gives her brothers' wives bundles or skirts, which are also given to those who helped make the special mourning skirts and to those who brought or cooked food during the mourning period.[78]

Sometimes the line between generalized and balanced reciprocity is not so clear. Consider our gift giving at Christmas. Although such gift giving may appear to be generalized reciprocity, and it often is in the case of gift giving from parents to children, there may be strong expectations of balance. Two friends or relatives may try to exchange presents of fairly equal value, based on calculations of what last year's gift cost. If a

Men perform the *kula* dance at an interisland exchange celebration in the Trobriand Islands, Papua New Guinea.

person receives a $5 present when he or she gave a $25 present, that person may be hurt and perhaps angry. On the other hand, a person who receives a $500 present when he or she gave a $25 present may well also be dismayed. But Christmas giving, like the Trobriand *kula* ring, also illustrates that exchanges are not simply economic, but serve many other purposes, including fun.

Kinship Distance and Type of Reciprocity   Most food-collecting and horticultural societies depend on some form of reciprocity for the distribution of goods and labor. Marshall Sahlins suggested that the form of the reciprocity depends largely on the kinship distance between people. Generalized reciprocity may be the rule for family members and close kinsmen. Balanced reciprocity may be practiced among equals who are not closely related. People who would consider it inappropriate to trade with their own families will trade with neighboring groups.[79] In general, the importance of reciprocity declines with economic development.[80] In societies with intensive agriculture, and even more so in industrialized societies, reciprocity distributes only a small proportion of goods and services.

Reciprocity as a Leveling Device   Reciprocal gift giving may do more than equalize the distribution of goods within a community, as in the !Kung's sharing. It may also tend to equalize the distribution of goods between communities.

Many Melanesian societies in and near New Guinea have the custom of holding pig feasts in which 50, 100, or even 2,000 pigs are slaughtered. Andrew Vayda, Anthony Leeds, and David Smith suggested that these enormous feasts, though apparently wasteful, are just one of the outcomes of a complex of cultural practices that are highly advantageous. The people of these societies cannot accurately predict how much food they will produce during the year. Some years they will have bumper crops and other years, very poor crops because of fluctuations in the weather. So it might be wise to overplant just in case the yield is poor. Yet overplanting results in overproduction during average and exceptionally good years. What can be done with this extra food? Root crops such as yams and taro do not keep well over long periods, so any surplus is fed to pigs, which become, in effect, food-storing repositories. Pigs are then available for needed food during lean times. But if there are several years of surpluses, pigs can become too much of a good thing. Pigs wanting food can destroy yam and taro patches. When the pig population grows to menacing proportions, a village may invite other villages to a gigantic feast that results in a sharp reduction of the pig population and keeps the fields from being overrun. Over the years, the pig feasts serve to equalize the food consumption, and especially the protein consumption, of all the villages that participate in the feasts.[81] Thus, the custom of pig feasts may be a way for villages to "bank" surplus food by storing up "social credit" with other villages, which will return that credit in subsequent feasts.

In some Melanesian societies, the pig feasts foster an element of competition among the men who give them. "Big men" may try to bolster their status and prestige by the size of their feasts. A reputation is enhanced not by keeping wealth but by giving it away. A similar situation existed among many Native American groups of the Pacific Northwest, where a chief might attempt to enhance his status by holding a **potlatch.** At a potlatch, a chief and his group would give away blankets, pieces of copper, canoes, large quantities of food, and other items to their guests. The host chief and his group would later be invited to other potlatches.

The competitive element in the potlatch appears to have intensified after contact with Europeans. Because of the fur trade, the number of trade goods increased, and so more items could be given away. Possibly more important was the population decline among the Indians, caused by diseases such as smallpox that European traders introduced. Distant relatives of chiefs who had no direct heirs might compete for the right to the title, each attempting to give away more than the others.[82] Chiefs may also have attempted to attract men to their half-empty villages by spectacular giveaways.[83] Decimated groups might have coalesced to maintain the potlatching. For example, when the Tlingit population declined to a low in the 1910s, kin groups coalesced to assemble enough resources for a potlatch.[84] Although the potlatch system seems wasteful in that goods were often destroyed in the competition, the system probably also served to equalize the distribution of goods among competing groups.

On one level of analysis, the Melanesian pig feasts, and the Pacific Northwest potlatches were all reciprocal exchanges between communities or villages. But these exchanges were not just intercommunity versions of reciprocal gift giving between individuals. Because these feasts were organized by people who collected goods, they also involved another mode of distribution, which anthropologists call *redistribution*.

Redistribution

Redistribution is the accumulation of goods or labor by a particular person, or in a particular place, for the purpose of subsequent distribution. Although redistribution is found in all societies, it becomes an important mechanism only in societies that have political hierarchies—that is, chiefs or other specialized officials and agencies. In all societies, there is some redistribution, at least within the family. Members of the family pool their labor, products, or income for the common good. But in many societies, there is little or no redistribution beyond the family. It seems that redistribution on a territorial basis emerges when there is a political apparatus to coordinate centralized collection and distribution of goods or to mobilize labor for some public purpose.

In the African state of Bunyoro, in western Uganda, for example, the king (called the *mukama*) retained much of the wealth for himself and his close kin. The *mukama* had the authority to grant the use of land and all other natural resources to his subordinate chiefs, and they in turn granted it to the common people. In return, everyone was required to give the *mukama* large quantities of food, crafts, and even labor services. The *mukama* then redistributed these goods and services, in theory at least, to all the people. The *mukama* was praised with names that emphasized his generosity: *Agutamba* ("he who relieves distress") and *Mwebingwa* ("he to whom the people run for help"). But it is clear that much of what the king redistributed did not find its way back to the common people, who produced the bulk of the goods. Instead, the wealth was distributed largely according to rank within the state.[85]

Other redistribution systems are more equal. For example, among the Buin of Melanesia, "the chief is housed, dressed, and fed exactly like his bondsman."[86] Even though the chief owns most of the pigs, everyone shares equally in the consumption of the wealth. In general, where redistribution is important, as in societies with higher levels of productivity, the wealthy are more likely than the poor to benefit from the redistributions.[87]

Why do redistribution systems develop? Elman Service suggested that they develop in agricultural societies that contain subregions suited to different kinds of crops or natural resources. Foragers can take advantage of environmental variation by moving to different areas. With agriculture, the task is more difficult; it might be easier to move different products across different regions.[88] If the demand for different resources or products becomes too great, reciprocity between individuals might become awkward. So it might be more efficient to have someone—a chief, perhaps—coordinate the exchanges.

Marvin Harris agreed that redistribution becomes more likely with agriculture, but for a somewhat different reason. He argued that competitive feasting, as in New Guinea, is adaptive because it encourages people to work harder to produce somewhat more than they need. Why would this feature be adaptive? Harris argued that, with agriculture, people really have to produce more than they need so that they can protect themselves against crises such as crop failure. The groups that make feasts may be indirectly ensuring themselves against crises by storing up social credit with other villages, who will reciprocate by making feasts for them in the future. On the other hand, inducements to collect more than they need may not be advantageous to food-collecting groups, who might lose in the long run by overcollecting.[89]

Market or Commercial Exchange

When we think of markets, we usually think of bustling, colorful places where goods are bought and sold. The exchanges usually involve money. In our own society, we have supermarkets and the stock market and other places for buying and selling that we call shops, stores, and malls. In referring to **market** or **commercial exchange,** economists and economic anthropologists are referring to exchanges or transactions in which the "prices" are subject to supply and demand, whether or not the transactions actually occur in a marketplace.[90] Market exchange involves not only the exchange (buying and selling) of goods but also transactions of labor, land, rentals, and credit.

On the surface, many market exchanges resemble balanced reciprocity. One person gives something and receives something in return. How, then, does market exchange differ from balanced reciprocity? It is easy to distinguish market exchange from balanced reciprocity when money is directly involved, because reciprocity is defined as not involving money. But market exchange need not always involve money directly.[91] For example, a landowner grants a tenant farmer the right to use the land in exchange for a portion of the crop. So, to call a transaction market exchange, we have to ask whether supply and demand determine the price. If a tenant farmer gave only a token gift to the landowner, we would not call it market exchange, just as a Christmas gift to a teacher is not payment for teaching. If tenants, however, are charged a large portion of their crops when the supply of land is short, or if landowners lower their demands when few people want to tenant-farm, then we would call the transactions market or commercial exchange. The forces of supply and demand create considerable risk for those dependent on monetary exchange for life's necessities. A wage earner who loses a job may not be able to afford food or shelter; a farmer relying on a cash crop may not get a price sufficient to support the family. Societies with monetary exchange usually have considerable inequities in wealth and power.

Kinds of Money Although market exchange need not involve money, most commercial transactions, particularly nowadays, do involve what we call money. Some anthropologists define money according to the functions and characteristics of the **general-purpose money** used in our own and other complex societies, for which nearly all goods, resources, and services can be exchanged. According to this definition, money performs the basic functions of serving as an accepted medium of exchange, a standard of value, and a store of wealth. As a medium of exchange, it allows all goods and services to be valued in the same objective way; we say that an object or service is worth so much money. Also, money is nonperishable, and therefore savable or storable, and almost always transportable and divisible, so transactions can involve the buying and selling of goods and services that differ in value.

Although money can technically be anything, the first money systems used rare metals such as gold and silver. These metals are relatively soft and therefore can be melted and shaped into standard sizes and weights. The earliest standardized coins we know of are said to have been made by the Lydians in Asia Minor and the Chinese, in the 7th century A.D. It is important to realize that money has little or no intrinsic value; rather, it is society that determines its value. In the United States today, paper bills, bank checks, and credit and debit cards are fully accepted as money, and money is increasingly transferred electronically.

General-purpose money is used both for commercial transactions (buying and selling) and for noncommercial transactions (payment of taxes or fines, personal gifts, contributions to religious and other charities). General-purpose money provides a way of condensing wealth: Gold dust or nuggets are easier to carry around than bushels of wheat; paper bills, a checkbook, and plastic cards are handier than a herd of sheep or goats.

In many societies, money is not an all-purpose medium of exchange. Many peoples whose food production per capita is not sufficient to support a large population of nonproducers of food have **special-purpose money.** This consists of objects of value for which only some goods and services can be exchanged on the spot or through balanced reciprocity. In some parts of Melanesia, pigs are assigned value in terms of shell money—lengths of shells strung together in units each roughly as long as the distance covered by a man's outstretched arms. According to its size, a pig will be assigned a value in tens of such units up to 100.[92] But shell money cannot be exchanged for all the goods or services a person might need. Similarly, a Pacific Northwest native could exchange food, but not most other goods and services, for a "gift of wealth," such as blankets. The gift was a "receipt" that entitled the person to receive an equal amount of food, but little else, later.

Degrees of Commercialization Most societies were not commercialized at all, or only barely so, when first described in the ethnographic record by explorers, missionaries, and anthropologists. That is, most societies as first described did not rely on market or commercial exchange to distribute goods and services. But commercial exchange has become the dominant form of distribution in the modern world. Most societies of the ethnographic past are now incorporated into larger nation-states; for example, the Trobriand Islanders and other societies in Melanesia are now districts in the nation of Papua New Guinea. Selling today goes far beyond the nation-state. The world is now a multinational market.[93]

But there is considerable variation in the degree to which societies today depend on market or commercial exchange. Many societies still allocate land without purchase and distribute food and other goods primarily by reciprocity and redistribution, participating only peripherally in market exchange. These are societies in transition; their traditional subsistence economies are becoming commercialized. Among the Luo of western Kenya, for example, most rural families still have land that their kin groups allocated to them. The food they eat they mostly produce themselves. But many men also work for wages—some nearby, others far away in towns and cities, where they spend a year or two. These wages are used to pay government taxes, to pay for children's schooling, and to buy commercially produced items, such as clothes, kerosene lamps, radios, fish from Lake Nyanza, tea, sugar, and coffee. Occasionally, families sell agricultural surpluses or craft items such as reed mats. Economies such as that of the rural Luo are not fully commercialized, but they may become so in the future.

What anthropologists call *peasant economies* are somewhat more commercialized than transitional subsistence economies such as that of the Luo. Although **peasants** also produce food largely for their own consumption, they regularly sell part of their surplus (food, other goods, or labor) to others, and land is one of the commodities they buy, rent, and sell. But, although their production is somewhat commercialized, peasants are still not like the fully commercialized farmers in industrialized societies, who rely on the market to exchange all or almost all of their crops for all or almost all of the goods and services they need.

In fully commercialized societies such as our own, market or commercial exchange dominates the economy; prices and wages are regulated, or at least significantly affected, by the forces of supply and demand. A modern industrial or postindustrial economy may involve international as well as national markets in which everything—natural resources, labor, goods, services, prestige items, religious and ceremonial items—has a price, stated in the same money terms. Reciprocity is reserved for family members and friends or remains behind the scenes in business transactions. Redistribution, however, is an important mechanism. It is practiced in the form of taxation and the use of public revenue for transfer payments and other benefits to low-income families—welfare, Social Security, health care, and so on. But commercial exchange is the major way goods and services are distributed.

Why Do Money and Market Exchange Develop?

Most economists think that money is invented in a society, or copied from another society, when trade increases and barter becomes increasingly inefficient. The more important or frequent trade is, the more difficult it is to find a person who can give something you want and wants something you have to give. Money makes it easy to trade. It is a valuable that may be exchanged for *anything,* and so it is an efficient medium of exchange when trade becomes important. In contrast, many anthropologists do not link the origins of money or market exchange to the necessities of trade. Instead, they link the origins of money to various noncommercial "payments," such as the *kula* valuables and the taxes that have to be paid to a political authority. All of the available explanations of money suggest that money will be found mostly in societies at higher levels of economic development; and indeed it is. When simpler societies have money, dominant and more complex societies have usually introduced it.[94] In the next major section, we discuss more fully the impact of colonialism and global markets on societies that were not so long ago subsistence economies.

Most theories about the development of money and market exchange assume that producers have regular surpluses they want to exchange. But why do people produce surpluses in the first place? Perhaps they are motivated to produce extra only when they want to obtain goods from a distance and the suppliers of such goods are not well known to them, making reciprocity less likely as a way to obtain those goods. So some theorists suggest that market exchange begins with external, or intersocietal, trade; kin would not likely be involved, so transactions would involve bargaining, and therefore are market exchange, by definition. Finally, some argue that, as societies become more complex and more densely populated, social bonds between individuals become less kinlike and friendly, and therefore reciprocity becomes less likely.[95] Perhaps this is why traders in developing areas are often foreigners or recent immigrants.[96]

In any case, Frederic Pryor's cross-cultural research supports the notion that all types of market exchange—goods, labor, land, and credit—are more likely with higher levels of economic productivity. Pryor also found that

Fiesta sponsors spend a great deal of money for food and drink as well as for musicians and dancers. Here we see a fiesta in Oaxaca, Mexico.

market exchange of goods appears at lower levels of economic development than market exchange of labor and credit; market exchange of land, probably because it is associated with private property (individual ownership), appears mostly at the highest levels of productivity. Perhaps surprisingly, smaller societies tend to have more market exchange or trade with other societies. Larger societies can presumably get more of what they need from inside the society; for example, until recently, China had relatively little foreign trade throughout much of its history.[97]

Possible Leveling Devices in Commercial Economies As we will see in the next chapter, societies that depend substantially on market or commercial exchange tend to have marked differences in wealth among the people. Nonetheless, there may be mechanisms that lessen the inequality, that act at least partially as leveling devices. Some anthropologists have suggested that the fiesta complex in highland Indian communities of Latin America may be a mechanism that tends to equalize income.[98] In these peasant villages, fiestas are held each year to celebrate important village saints. The outstanding feature of this system is the extraordinary amount of money and labor a sponsoring family must contribute. Sponsors must hire ritual specialists, pay for church services, musicians, and costumes for dancers, and cover the complete cost of food and drink for the entire community. The costs incurred can very easily amount to a year's wages.[99]

Some anthropologists have suggested that, although the richer Indians who sponsor fiestas are clearly distributing a good deal of wealth to the poorer members of their own and other communities, the fiestas do not really level

wealth at all. First, true economic leveling would entail the redistribution of important productive resources such as land or animals; the fiesta only temporarily increases the general level of consumption. Second, the resources the sponsors expend are usually extra resources that have been accumulated specifically for the fiesta, which is why the sponsors are always appointed in advance. Third, and perhaps most important, the fiestas do not seem to have reduced long-term wealth distinctions within the villages.[100]

In nations such as ours, can the income tax and the social-assistance programs it pays for, such as welfare and disaster relief, be thought of as leveling devices? Theoretically, our tax system is supposed to work that way, by taxing higher incomes at higher rates. But we know that, in fact, it doesn't. Those in higher income brackets can often deduct an appreciable amount from their taxable incomes and therefore pay taxes at a relatively low rate. Our tax system may help some to escape extreme poverty, but, like the fiesta system, it has not eliminated marked distinctions in wealth.

THE WORLDWIDE TREND TOWARD COMMERCIALIZATION

One of the most important changes resulting from the expansion of Western societies and the capitalist system is the increasingly worldwide dependence on commercial exchange. The borrowed customs of buying and selling may at first be supplementary to traditional means of distributing goods in a society. But, as the new commercial customs take hold, the economic base of the receiving

E. J. Hobsbawm noted some of the developments that accompanied the introduction of commercial agriculture in 18th-century England and in continental Europe somewhat later.[111] The close, near-familial relationship between farmer and farm laborer disappeared, as did the once-personal connection between landlord and tenant. Land came to be regarded as a source of profit rather than a way of life. Fields were merged into single units and enclosed, and local grazing and similar privileges were reduced. Labor was hired at market rates and paid in wages. Eventually, as the emphasis on large-scale production for a mass market increased, machines began to replace farmers.

The introduction of commercial agriculture brings several important social consequences. Gradually, a class polarization develops. Farmers and landlords become increasingly separated from laborers and tenants, just as the employer in town becomes socially separated from the employees. Gradually, too, manufactured items of all sorts are introduced into rural areas. Laborers migrate to urban centers in search of employment, often meeting even less sympathetic conditions there than exist in the country.

The changeover to commercial agriculture may result in an improved standard of living in the short and long run. But sometimes the switch is followed by a decline in the standard of living if the market price for the commercial crop declines. For example, the changeover of the farmer-herders of the arid *sertão* region of northeastern Brazil after 1940 to the production of sisal (a plant whose fibers can be made into twine and rope) seemed to be a move that could provide a more secure living in their arid environment. But when the world price for sisal dropped and the wages of sisal workers declined, many workers were forced to curtail the caloric intake of their children. The poorer people were obliged to save their now more limited food supplies for the money earners, at the expense of the children.[112]

Commercialization can start in various ways: People can begin to sell and buy because they begin to work near home or away for wages, or because they begin to sell nonagricultural products, surplus food, or cash crops (crops grown deliberately for sale). One type of commercialization does not exclude another; all types can occur in any society. However commercialization begins, it seems to have predictable effects on traditional economics. The ethic of generalized reciprocity declines, particularly with respect to giving away money. (Perhaps because it is nonperishable and hideable, money seems more likely than other goods to be kept for one's immediate family rather than shared with others.) Property rights become individualized rather than collective when people begin to buy and sell. Even in societies that were previously egalitarian, commercialization usually results in more unequal access to resources and hence a greater degree of social stratification.

SUMMARY ● ○ ○

1. All societies have economic systems, whether or not these involve the use of money. All societies have customs specifying access to natural resources; customary ways of transforming or converting those resources, through labor, into necessities and other desired goods and services; and customs for distributing and perhaps exchanging goods and services.

2. Regulation of access to natural resources is a basic factor in all economic systems. The concept of individual or private ownership of land—including the right to use its resources and the right to sell or otherwise dispose of them—is common among intensive agriculturalists. In contrast, foragers, horticulturalists, and pastoralists generally lack individual ownership of land. Among pastoral nomads, however, animals are considered family property and are not usually shared.

3. Every society makes use of a technology, which includes tools, constructions, and required skills. Even though foragers and horticulturalists tend to think of tools as "owned" by the individuals who made them, the sharing of tools is so extensive that individual ownership does not have much meaning. Among intensive agriculturalists, toolmaking tends to be a specialized activity. Tools tend not to be shared, except mainly by those who have purchased them together.

4. Incentives for labor vary cross-culturally. Many societies produce just for household consumption; if there are more consumers, producers work harder. In some subsistence economies, people may work harder to obtain the social rewards that come from giving to others. Forced labor generally occurs only in complex societies.

5. Division of labor by gender is universal. In many nonindustrial societies, large tasks are often accomplished through the cooperative efforts of a kinship group. Such cooperation is not as prevalent in industrialized societies. In general, the more technically advanced a society is, the more surplus food it produces and the more some of its members engage in specialized work.

6. The organization of labor reaches its peak in complex societies; work groups tend to be formally organized, and sometimes there is an enforced obligation to participate. In food-collecting and horticultural societies, in contrast, there is little formal organization of work.

7. Goods and services are distributed in all societies by systems that can be classified under three types: reciprocity, redistribution, and market or commercial exchange. Reciprocity is giving and taking without the use of money and generally assumes two forms: generalized reciprocity and balanced reciprocity. Generalized reciprocity is gift giving without any immediate or planned return. In balanced reciprocity, individuals exchange goods and services immediately or in the short term.

8. Redistribution is the accumulation of goods or labor by a particular person, or in a particular place, for the purpose of subsequent distribution. It becomes an important mechanism of distribution only in societies with political hierarchies.

9. Market or commercial exchange, where "prices" depend on supply and demand, tends to occur with increasing levels of economic productivity. Especially nowadays, market exchange usually involves an all-purpose medium of exchange—money. Most societies today

are at least partly commercialized; the world is becoming a single market system.

10. Many of the cultural changes observed in the modern world have been generated, directly or indirectly, by the dominance and expansion of Western societies. One of the principal changes resulting from the expansion of Western culture is the increasing dependence of much of the world on commercial exchange—that is, the proliferation of buying and selling in markets, usually accompanied by the use of money as the medium of exchange. The borrowed custom of buying and selling may at first be supplementary to traditional means of distributing goods, but as the new commercial customs take hold, the economic base of the receiving society alters. Inevitably, this alteration is accompanied by other changes, which have broad social, political, and even biological and psychological ramifications.

11. One way commercialization can occur is for members of a community to become migratory workers, traveling to a place nearby that offers the possibility of working for wages. Commercialization can also occur when a simple, self-sufficient hunting or agricultural society comes to depend more on trading for its livelihood. A third way commercialization occurs is when those cultivating the soil produce more than they require for subsistence. The surplus is then sold for cash. In many instances, this cash income must be used to pay rent or taxes; under such circumstances, commercialization may be said to be associated with the formation of a peasantry. A fourth way in which commercialization can come about is through the introduction of commercial agriculture, in which all the cultivated commodities are produced for sale rather than for personal consumption. Along with this change, the system of agriculture may be industrialized, with some of the production processes being done by machine.

GLOSSARY TERMS ○ ● ○

balanced reciprocity **298**
corvée **294**
generalized
   reciprocity **297**
general-purpose
   money **301**
market or commercial
   exchange **301**

optimal foraging
   theory **296**
peasants **302**
potlatch **300**
reciprocity **297**
redistribution **300**
special-purpose
   money **302**

CRITICAL QUESTIONS ○ ○ ●

1. What conditions might enable us to achieve a world of sustainable resources?

2. What are the possible effects of a postindustrial economy in which a large proportion of the population has inexpensive access to computers and information?

3. Do you expect any appreciable change in the amount of resources privately owned in the future? State your reasons.

4. We tend to emphasize the negative consequences of the worldwide trend toward commercialization. Have there been any beneficial consequences?

5. Why might an increasing understanding of cultural variation also provide an increasing understanding of culture change?

PEARSON
myanthrolab

Read "Yanomamö: Varying Adaptations of Foraging Agriculturalists" by Raymond B. Hames on MyAnthroLab and answer these case study questions:

1. Why does Hames refer to the Yanomamö as "foraging horticulturalists"?

2. Customary behavior in all societies varies somewhat over time as well as over space. What kinds of differences did Hames find in food-getting and economy between lowland and highland groups?

3. Hames measured how people spend their time during the day. What differences did he find between women and men's work? Which gender generally worked more? Does the conclusion change depending on how work is defined?

chapter 18

Social Stratification: Class, Ethnicity, and Racism

long-enduring value in the United States is the belief that "all men are created equal." These famous words from the American Declaration of Independence do not mean that all people are equal in wealth or status but rather that all (including women nowadays) are supposed to be equal before the law. Equality before the law is the ideal. But the ideal is not always the actuality. Some people have advantages in legal treatment, and they generally also tend to have advantages of other kinds, including economic advantages. Without exception, recent and modern industrial and postindustrial societies such as our own are *socially stratified*—that is, they contain social groups such as families, classes, or ethnic groups that have unequal access to important advantages such as economic resources, power, and prestige.

Hasn't such inequality always existed? Anthropologists, based on first-hand observations of recent societies, would say not. To be sure, even the simplest societies (in the technological sense) have some differences in advantages based on age, ability, or gender—adults have higher status than children, the skilled more than the unskilled, men more than women (we discuss this topic in the chapter on sex, gender, and culture). But anthropologists would argue that *egalitarian* societies exist where *social groups* (e.g., families) have more or less the same access to rights or advantages. As we noted in the last chapter, the economic systems of many food collectors and horticulturalists promote equal access to economic resources for all families in the community. Moreover, such societies also tend to emphasize the sharing of food and other goods, which tends to equalize any small inequalities in resources between families. Until about 10,000 years ago, all human societies depended on food they hunted, gathered, and/or fished. And so we might expect that egalitarianism characterized most of human history. That is indeed what archaeologists suggest. Substantial inequality generally appears only with permanent communities, centralized political systems, and intensive agriculture, which are cultural features that began to appear in the world only in the last 10,000 years. Before that time, then, most societies were probably egalitarian. In the world today, egalitarian societies have all but disappeared because of two processes—the global spread of commercial or market exchange and the voluntary or involuntary incorporation of many diverse people into large, centralized political systems. In modern societies, some groups have more advantages than others. These groups may include *ethnic* groups. That is, ethnic diversity is almost always associated with differential access to advantages. When ethnic diversity is also associated with differences in physical features such as skin color, the social stratification may involve *racism*, the belief that some "racial" groups are inferior.

Systems of social stratification are strongly linked to the customary ways in which economic resources are allocated, distributed, and converted through labor into goods and services. So we would not expect much inequality if all people had relatively equal access to economic resources. But stratification cannot be understood solely in terms of economic resources; there are other benefits such as prestige and power that may be unequally distributed. We first examine how societies vary in their systems of stratification. Then we turn to possible explanations of why they vary.

● ○ ●

VARIATION IN DEGREE OF SOCIAL INEQUALITY

Societies vary in the extent to which social groups, as well as individuals, have unequal access to advantages. In this chapter, we are concerned with differential or unequal access to three types of advantages: (1) wealth or economic resources, (2) power, and (3) prestige. **Economic resources** are things that have value in a culture; they include land, tools and other technology, goods, and money. **Power,** a second but related advantage, is the ability to make others do what they do not want to do; power is influence based on the threat of force. When groups in a society have rules or customs that give them unequal access to wealth or resources, they generally also have unequal access to power. So, for example, when we speak of a "company town" in the United States, we are referring to the fact that the company that employs most of the residents of the town usually has considerable control over them. Finally, there is the advantage of **prestige.** When we speak of prestige, we mean that someone or some group is accorded particular respect or honor. Even if it is true that there is always unequal access by individuals to prestige (because of differences in age, gender, or ability), some societies in the ethnographic record have no social groups with unequal access to prestige.

Thus, anthropologists conventionally distinguish three types of society in terms of the degree to which different social groups have unequal access to advantages: *egalitarian, rank,* and *class societies* (see Table 18–1). Some societies in the ethnographic record do not fit easily into any of these three types; as with any classification scheme,

some cases seem to straddle the line between types.[1] **Egalitarian societies** contain no social groups with greater or lesser access to economic resources, power, or prestige. **Rank societies** do not have very unequal access to economic resources or to power, but they do contain social groups with unequal access to prestige. Rank societies, then, are partly stratified. **Class societies** have unequal access to all three advantages—economic resources, power, and prestige.

EGALITARIAN SOCIETIES

Egalitarian societies can be found not only among foragers such as the !Kung, Mbuti, Australian aborigines, Inuit, and Aché, but also among horticulturalists such as the Yanomamö and pastoralists such as the Lapps. An important point to keep in mind is that egalitarian does not mean that all people within such societies are the same. There will always be differences among individuals in age and gender and in such abilities or traits as hunting skill, perception, health, creativity, physical prowess, attractiveness, and intelligence. According to Morton Fried, egalitarian means that, within a given society, "there are as many positions of prestige in any given age/sex grade as there are persons capable of filling them."[2] For instance, if a person can achieve high status by fashioning fine spears, and if many people in the society fashion such spears, then many acquire high status as spear makers. If high status is also acquired by carving bones into artifacts, and if only three people are considered expert carvers of bones, then only those three achieve high status as carvers. But the next generation might produce eight spear makers and 20 carvers. In an egalitarian society, the number of prestigious positions is adjusted to fit the number of qualified candidates. We would say, therefore, that such a society is not socially stratified.

There are, of course, differences in position and prestige arising out of differences in ability. Even in an egalitarian society, differential prestige exists. But, although some people may be better hunters or more skilled artists than others, there is still *equal access* to status positions for people of the same ability. Any prestige gained by achieving high status as a great hunter, for instance, is neither transferable nor inheritable. Because a man is a great hunter, it is not assumed that his sons are also great hunters. There also may be individuals with more influence, but it cannot be inherited, and there are no groups with appreciably more influence over time. An egalitarian society keeps inequality at a minimal level.

TABLE 18–1 Stratification in Three Types of Societies				
	SOME SOCIAL GROUPS HAVE GREATER ACCESS TO:			
Type of Society	**Economic Resources**	**Power**	**Prestige**	**Examples**
Egalitarian	No	No	No	!Kung, Mbuti, Australian aborigines, Inuit, Aché, Yanomamö
Rank	No	No	Yes	Samoans, Tahiti, Trobriand Islands, Ifaluk
Class/caste	Yes	Yes	Yes	United States, Canada, Greece, India, Inca

Any differences in prestige that do exist are not related to economic differences. Egalitarian groups depend heavily on *sharing*, which ensures equal access to economic resources despite differences in acquired prestige. For instance, in some egalitarian communities, some members achieve higher status through hunting. But even before the hunt begins, how the animal will be divided and distributed among the members of the band has already been decided according to custom. The culture works to separate the status that members achieve—recognition as great hunters—from actual possession of the wealth, which in this case would be the slain animal.

Just as egalitarian societies do not have social groups with unequal access to economic resources, they also do not have social groups with unequal access to power. As we will see later in the chapter on political life, unequal access to power by social groups seems to occur only in state societies, which have full-time political officials and marked differences in wealth. Egalitarian societies use a number of customs to keep leaders from dominating others. Criticism and ridicule can be very effective. The Mbuti of central Africa shout down an overassertive leader. When a Hadza man (in Tanzania) tried to get people to work for him, other Hadza made fun of him. Disobedience is another strategy. If a leader tries to command, people just ignore the command. In extreme cases, a particularly domineering leader may be killed by community agreement; this behavior was reported among the !Kung and the Hadza. Finally, particularly among more nomadic groups, people may just move away from a leader they don't like. The active attempts to put down upstarts in many egalitarian societies prompts Christopher Boehm to suggest that dominance comes naturally to humans. Egalitarian societies work hard to reverse that tendency.[3] The Mbuti provide an example of a society almost totally equal: "Neither in ritual, hunting, kinship nor band relations do they exhibit any discernible inequalities of rank or advantage."[4] Their hunting bands have no leaders, and recognition of the achievement of one person is not accompanied by privilege of any sort. Economic resources such as food are communally shared, and even tools and weapons are frequently passed from person to person. Only within the family are rights and privileges differentiated.

Foraging societies with extensive sharing of resources are more readily labeled egalitarian as compared with some pastoral societies where households may vary considerably in the number of animals they own. Should we consider a pastoral society with unequal distribution of animals egalitarian? Here there is controversy. One important issue is whether unequal ownership persists through time—that is, inherited. If vagaries of weather, theft, and gifts of livestock to relatives make livestock ownership fluctuate over time, wealth differences may mostly be temporary. A second important issue is whether the inequalities in livestock ownership make any difference in the ease of acquiring other "goods," such as prestige and political power. If wealth in livestock is ephemeral and is not associated with differential access to prestige and power, then some anthropologists would characterize such pastoral societies as egalitarian.[5] It is easy to imagine how an egalitarian society with some wealth differences, as opposed to one with no wealth differences, could become a rank or a class society. All you would need is a mechanism for retaining more wealth in some families over time.

RANK SOCIETIES

Most societies with social *ranking* practice agriculture or herding, but not all agricultural or pastoral societies are ranked. Ranking is characterized by social groups with unequal access to prestige or status but *not* significantly unequal access to economic resources or power. Unequal

In egalitarian societies, such as among the Mbuti hunter-gatherers, houses tend to look the same.

access to prestige is often reflected in the position of chief, a rank which only some members of a specified group in the society can achieve.

Unusual among rank societies were the 19-century Native Americans who lived along the northwestern coast of the United States and the southwestern coast of Canada. An example were the Nimpkish, a Kwakiutl group.[6] These societies were unusual because their economy was based on food collecting. But huge catches of salmon—which were preserved for year-round consumption—enabled them to support fairly large and permanent villages. These societies were similar to food-producing societies in many ways, not just in their development of social ranking. Still, the principal means of proving one's high status was to give away wealth. The tribal chiefs celebrated solemn rites by grand feasts called *potlatches,* at which they gave gifts to every guest.[7]

In rank societies, the position of chief is at least partly hereditary. The criterion of superior rank in some Polynesian societies, for example, was genealogical. Usually the eldest son succeeded to the position of chief, and different kinship groups were differentially ranked according to their genealogical distance from the chiefly line. In rank societies, chiefs are often treated with deference by people of lower rank. For example, among the Trobriand Islanders of Melanesia, people of lower rank must keep their heads lower than a person of higher rank. So, when a chief is standing, commoners must bend low. When commoners have to walk past a chief who happens to be sitting, he may rise and they will bend. If the chief chooses to remain seated, they must crawl.[8]

Although there is no question that chiefs in a rank society enjoy special prestige, there is some controversy over whether they really do not also have material advantages. Chiefs may sometimes look as if they are substantially richer than commoners, for they may receive many gifts and have larger storehouses. In some instances, the chief may even be called the "owner" of the land. However, Marshall Sahlins maintains that the chief's storehouses only house temporary accumulations for feasts or other redistributions. And although the chief may be designated the "owner" of the land, others have the right to use the land. Furthermore, Sahlins suggests that the chief in a rank society lacks power because he usually cannot make people give him gifts or force them to work on communal projects. Often the chief can encourage production only by working furiously on his own cultivation.[9]

This picture of economic equality in rank societies is beginning to be questioned. Laura Betzig studied patterns of food sharing and labor on Ifaluk, a small atoll in the Western Carolines.[10] Chiefly status is inherited geneaologically in the female line, although most chiefs are male. (In the chapter on sex, gender, and culture, we discuss why political leaders are usually male, even in societies structured

In societies with rank and class, deference is usually shown to political leaders, as in the case of this Fon chief in the lowlands of Cameroon, Africa.

around women.) As in other chiefly societies, Ifaluk chiefs are accorded deference. For example, during collective meals prepared by all the island women, chiefs were served first and were bowed to. The Ifaluk chiefs are said to control the fishing areas. Were the catches equitably distributed? Betzig measured the amount of fish each household got. All the commoners received an equal share, but the chiefs got extra fish; their households got twice as much per person as other households. Did the chiefs give away more later?

Theoretically, generosity is supposed to even things out, but Betzig found that the gifts from chiefs to other households did not equal the amount the chiefs received from others. Furthermore, although everyone gave to the chiefs, the chiefs gave mostly to their close relatives. On Ifaluk, the chiefs did not work harder than others; in fact, they worked less. Is this true in other societies conventionally considered to be rank societies? We do not know. However, we need to keep in mind that the chiefs in Ifaluk were not noticeably better off either. If they lived in palaces with servants, had elaborate meals, or were dressed in fine clothes and jewelry, we would not need measures of food received or a special study to see if the chiefs had greater access to economic resources, because their wealth would be obvious. But rank societies may not have had as much economic equality as we used to think.

CLASS SOCIETIES

In class societies, as in rank societies, there is unequal access to prestige. But, unlike rank societies, class societies are characterized by groups of people that have substantially greater or lesser access to economic resources and power. That is, not every social group has the same opportunity to obtain land, animals, money, or other economic benefits or the same opportunity to exercise power that other groups have. Fully stratified or class societies range from somewhat open to virtually closed class, or *caste,* systems.

Open Class Systems

A **class** is a category of people who all have about the same opportunity to obtain economic resources, power, and prestige. Different classes have differing opportunities. We call class systems *open* if there is some possibility of moving from one class to another. Since the 1920s, there have been many studies of classes in towns and cities in the United States. Researchers have produced profiles of these different communities—known variously as Yankee City, Middletown, Jonesville, and Old City—all of which support the premise that the United States has distinguishable, though somewhat open, social classes. Both W. Lloyd Warner and Paul Lunt's Yankee City study[11] and Robert and Helen Lynd's Middletown study[12] concluded that the social status or prestige of a family is generally correlated with the occupation and wealth of the head of the family. Class systems are by no means confined to the United States. They are found in all nations of the modern world.

Although class status is not fully determined at birth in open class societies, there is a high probability that most people will stay close to the class into which they were born and will marry within that class. Classes tend to perpetuate themselves through the inheritance of wealth. John Brittain suggested that, in the United States, the transfer of money through bequests accounts for much of the wealth of the next generation. As we might expect, the importance of inheritance seems to increase at higher levels of wealth. That is, the wealth of richer people comes more from inheritance than does the wealth of not-so-rich people.[13]

Other mechanisms of class perpetuation may be more subtle, but they are still powerful. In the United States, many institutions make it possible for an upper-class person to have little contact with other classes. Private day and boarding schools put upper-class children in close contact mostly with others of their class. Attending these schools makes it more likely they will get into universities with higher prestige. Debutante balls and exclusive private parties ensure that young people meet the "right people." Country clubs, exclusive city clubs, and service in particular charities continue the process of limited association. People of the same class also tend to live in the same neighborhoods. Before 1948, explicit restrictions kept certain groups out of particular neighborhoods, but after the U.S. Supreme Court ruled such discrimination unconstitutional, more subtle methods were developed. For instance, zoning restrictions may prohibit multiple-family dwellings in a town or neighborhood and lots below a certain acreage.[14]

Identification with a social class begins early in life. In addition to differences in occupation, wealth, and prestige, social classes vary in many other ways, including religious

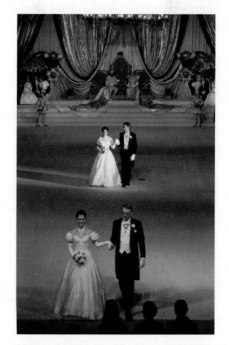

People of the same social class tend to socialize together, where they live, where they vacation, or through shared activities. Debutantes and their escorts are presented at the Krewe of Rex ball during Mardi Gras in New Orleans.

affiliation, closeness to kin, ideas about childrearing, job satisfaction, leisure-time activities, style of clothes and furniture, and (as noted in the chapter on communication and language) even in styles of speech.[15] People from each class tend to be more comfortable with those from the same class; they talk similarly and are more likely to have similar interests and tastes.

Class boundaries, though vague, have been established by custom and tradition; sometimes they have been reinforced by the enactment of laws. Many of our laws serve to protect property and thus tend to favor the upper and upper-middle classes. The poor, in contrast, seem to be disadvantaged in our legal system. The crimes the poor are most likely to commit are dealt with harshly by the courts, and poor people rarely have the money to secure effective legal counsel.

In open class systems, it is not always clear how many classes there are. In Stanley Barrett's study of "Paradise," Ontario, some people thought that there were only two classes in the past. One person said, "There was the hierarchy, and the rest of us." Another said that there were three classes: "The people with money, the in-between, and the ones who didn't have anything." Many said there were four: "The wealthy businessmen, the middle class, blue collar workers, and the guys that were just existing."[16] A few insisted that there were five classes. With the breakdown of the old rigid class structure, there are more people in the middle.[17]

Degree of Openness   Some class systems are more open than others; that is, it is easier in some societies to move from one class position to another. Social scientists typically compare the class of people with the class of their parent or parents to measure the degree of mobility. Although most people aspire to move up, mobility also includes moving down. Obtaining more education, particularly a university education, is one of the most effective ways to move upward in contemporary societies. For example, in the United States, individuals with a college bachelor's degree average 75 percent more income than those with only a high school diploma. And individuals with professional degrees earn on average 119 percent more than those with a bachelor's degree.[18] In many countries, educational attainment predicts one's social class better than parents' occupation does.[19]

How do the United States and Canada compare with other countries in degree of class mobility? Canada, Finland, and Sweden have more mobility than the United States and Britain. Mexico and Peru have less mobility than the United States and Brazil, and Colombia considerably less.[20]

Class openness also varies over time. In "Paradise," Ontario, Barrett found that the rigid stratification system of the 1950s opened up considerably as new people moved into the community. No one disputed who belonged to the elite in the past. They were of British background, lived in the largest houses, had new cars, and vacationed in Florida. Moreover, they controlled all the leadership positions in the town. By the 1980s, though, the leaders came mostly from the middle and working classes.[21]

Degree of Inequality   Degree of class mobility, however, is not the same as degree of economic inequality. For example, Japan, Italy, and Germany have less mobility than the United States, but less inequality (see later). Degree of inequality can vary considerably over time. In the United States, inequality has fluctuated considerably from the 1900s to the present. The greatest inequality was just before the 1929 stock market crash, when the top 1 percent had 42.6 percent of all the wealth. The least inequality was in the mid-1970s, after the stock market declined by 42 percent. Then the top 1 percent controlled 17.6 percent of the wealth.

Change over time in the degree of inequality sometimes appears to have economic causes; for example, the 1929 crash made the wealthy less wealthy. But some of the change over time is due to shifts in public policy. During the New Deal of the 1930s, tax changes and work programs shifted more income to ordinary people; in the 1980s, tax cuts for the wealthy helped the rich get richer. In the 1990s, the rich continued to get richer and the poor got poorer.[22] By 2006, inequality was more concentrated at the top than since the 1929 crash. Only since the severe recession between 2007 and 2009 have the rich gotten somewhat poorer.[23] One way of calculating the disparity between rich and poor is to use the ratio of income held by the top fifth of the households divided by the income held by the bottom fifth. Comparatively speaking, the United States presently has more inequality than any of the countries in western Europe, with a ratio of 8.5 to 1 (see Figure 18–1). That is, the top 20 percent of U.S. households controls 8.5 times the wealth controlled by the bottom 20 percent. Norway, on the other hand, has a ratio of about 4 to 1. And Germany has a ratio of about 4.3 to 1. The degree of inequality in the United States exceeds that of India, with a ratio of about 4.7 to 1. Brazil is one of the most unequal countries, with ratios of 32 to 1.

Recognition of Class

Societies that have open class systems vary in the degree to which members of the society recognize that there are classes, albeit somewhat open classes. The United States is unusual in that, despite objective evidence of multiple social classes, many people deny their existence. The ideology that hard work and strong character can transform anyone into a success appears to be so powerful that it masks the realities of social inequality.[24] A recent poll found that more people in the United States now believe that the chance of moving up has improved in the last few decades, when in reality mobility has declined.[25] When we were growing up, we were told that "Anyone can be President of the United States." As "proof," people pointed to a few individuals who rose from humble beginnings. But consider the odds. How many presidents have come from poor families? How many were not European in background? How many were not Protestant? (And, as we discuss in the chapter on sex, gender, and culture, how many were not male?) So far, almost all of the presidents of the United States have been mainly

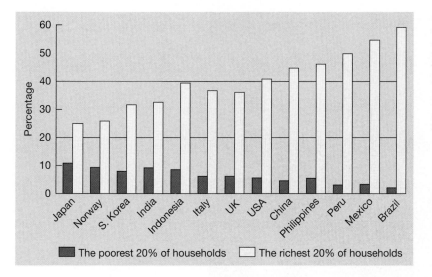

FIGURE 18–1 Proportion of National Income Earned by the Richest 20 Percent of Households Compared with the Poorest 20 Percent: Selected Country Comparisons. The countries are ordered by their Gini coefficients, a widely used measure of degree of income inequality.

Source: These data are abstracted from World Bank 2004, 60–62.

European in ancestry, all but one have been Protestant, and all have been male. And only a handful came from humble beginnings. The paradox of an open class system is that, to move up in the social ladder, people seem to have to believe that it is possible to do so. However, it is one thing to believe in mobility; it is another thing to deny the existence of classes. Why might people need to deny that classes exist?

Caste Systems

Some societies have classes (called castes) that are virtually closed. A **caste** is a ranked group in which membership is determined at birth, and marriage is restricted to members of one's own caste. The only way you can belong is by being born into the group; and because you cannot marry outside the group, your children cannot acquire another caste status either. In India, for example, there are several thousand hereditary castes. Although the precise ranking of these thousands of groups is not clear, there appear to be four main levels of hierarchy. The castes in India are often thought to be associated with different occupations, but that is not quite true. Most Indians live in rural areas and have agricultural occupations, but their castes vary widely.[26]

Castes may exist in conjunction with a more open class system. Indeed, in India today, members of a low caste who can get wage-paying jobs, chiefly those in urban areas, may improve their social standing in the same ways available to people in other class societies. In general, however, they still cannot marry someone in a higher caste, so the caste system is perpetuated.

Questions basic to all stratified societies, and particularly to a caste society, were posed by John Ruskin, a 19th-century British essayist: "Which of us . . . is to do the hard and dirty work for the rest—and for what pay? Who is to do the pleasant and clean work, and for what pay?"[27] In India, those questions have been answered by the caste system, which mainly dictates how goods and services are exchanged, particularly in rural areas.[28] Who is to do the hard and dirty work for the rest of society is clearly established: A large group of Untouchables forms the bottom of

the hierarchy. Among the Untouchables are subcastes such as the Camars, or leatherworkers, and the Bhangis, who traditionally are sweepers. At the top of the hierarchy, performing the pleasant and clean work of priests, are the Brahmans. Between the two extremes are thousands of castes and subcastes.[29] In a typical village, a potter makes clay drinking cups and large water vessels for the entire village population. In return, the principal landowner gives him a house site and supplies him twice yearly with grain. Some other castes owe the potter their services: The barber cuts his hair; the sweeper carries away his rubbish; the washer washes his clothes; the Brahman performs his children's weddings. The barber serves every caste in the village except the Untouchables; he, in turn, is served by half of the others. He has inherited the families he works for, along with his father's occupation. All castes help at harvest and at weddings for additional payment, which sometimes includes a money payment.

This description is, in fact, an idealized picture of the caste system of India. In reality, the system operates to the advantage of the principal landowning caste—sometimes the Brahmans and sometimes other castes. Also, it is not carried on without some resentment; signs of hostility are shown toward the ruling caste by the Untouchables and other lower castes. The resentment does not appear to be against the caste system as such. Instead, the lower castes exhibit bitterness at their own low status and strive for greater equality. For instance, one of the Camars' traditional services is to remove dead cattle; in return, they can have the meat to eat and the hide to tan for their leatherworking. Because handling dead animals and eating beef are regarded as unclean acts, the Camars of one village refused to continue this service. Thus, they lost a source of free hides and food in a vain attempt to escape unclean status.

Since World War II, the economic basis of the caste system in India has been undermined somewhat by the growing practice of giving cash payment for services. For instance, the son of a barber may be a teacher during the week, earning a cash salary, and confine his haircutting to weekends. But he still remains in the barber caste (Nai) and must marry within that caste.

Caste is somewhat less important in India, but has not disappeared. In Mumbai, the washers of the Dhobi caste process laundry.

Perpetuation of the caste system is ensured by the power of those in the upper castes, who derive three main advantages from their position: economic, prestige, and sexual gains. The economic gain is the most immediately apparent. An ample supply of cheap labor and free services is maintained by the threat of sanctions. Lower-caste members may have their use of a house site withdrawn; they may be refused access to the village well or to common grazing land for animals; or they may be expelled from the village. Prestige is also maintained by the threat of sanctions; people in the higher castes expect deference and servility from those in the lower castes. The sexual gain is less apparent but equally real. The high-caste male has access to two groups of females, those of his own caste and those of lower castes. High-caste females are kept free of the "contaminating" touch of low-caste males because low-caste males are allowed access only to low-caste women. Moreover, the constant reminders of ritual uncleanness serve to keep those of the lower castes "in their place." People in higher castes do not accept water from Untouchables, sit next to them, or eat at the same table with them.

Japan also had a caste group within a class society. Now called *burakumin* (instead of the pejorative *eta*), this group traditionally had occupations that were considered unclean.[30] Comparable to India's Untouchables, they were a hereditary, endogamous (in-marrying) group. Their occupations were traditionally those of farm laborer, leatherworker, and basket weaver; their standard of living was very low. The burakumin are physically indistinguishable from other Japanese.[31] Despite that, the burakumin were considered a separate "race" by some for centuries.[32] The Japanese government officially abolished discrimination against the burakumin in 1871, but the burakumin did not begin organizing to bring about change until the 20th century. As of 1995, 73 percent of burakumin marriages were with non-burakumin. In public opinion polls, two-thirds of burakumin now said

that they had not encountered discrimination. However, most burakumin still live in segregated neighborhoods where unemployment, crime, and alcoholism rates are high.[33]

In a considerable number of sub-Saharan African societies, some occupational specialties are only performed by certain castes. The specialties usually involve metalworking, pottery, woodworking, leatherworking, playing musical instruments, and praise-singing. There may be different castes for different specialties or one caste for many specialties. In some cases, the caste consists of people who traditionally hunted and gathered. In almost all cases, the specialists had to marry within their own group and their social position was inherited. These castes usually constituted only a small minority of the society's population and were not the lowest ranking groups in society. Only slaves had a lower rank. Some of the castes took on additional tasks, such as go-betweens for arranging marriages, messengers, and circumcisers. The caste vocational distinctions have weakened in recent times as people have become more educated.[34]

In Rwanda, long before the ethnic division arose between the Hutu and Tutsi (see discussion later in the ethnicity section), the Twa, who comprised less than 1 percent of the population, were subject to serious discrimination. Their bodies were viewed as dangerous and polluting and they were avoided whenever possible. For example, if a Twa were present while others were eating or drinking, separate utensils were reserved only for Twa. The Twa traditional occupations were foraging, making pottery, entertaining, and serving as torturers or executioners for the Rwandan king. Mutton was considered a Twa food and other Rwandans would not eat mutton.[35]

In the United States, African Americans used to have more of a castelike status determined partly by the inherited characteristic of skin color. Until recently, some states had laws prohibiting an African American from marrying a European American. When interethnic marriage did

current research and issues

The Gap Between Poor and Rich Countries

When people support themselves by what they collect and produce themselves, as most people did until a few thousand years ago, it is difficult to compare the standards of living of different societies because we cannot translate what people have into market or monetary value. Only where people are at least partly involved in the world market economy can we measure the standard of living in monetary terms. Today, this comparison is possible for most of the world. Many people in most societies depend on buying and selling for a living; and the more people who depend on international exchange, the more possible it is to compare them in terms of standard economic indicators. We do not have such indicators for all the different societies, but we do have them for many countries. Those indicators suggest that the gap between the rich and poor countries in the world is not only very substantial but has generally increased in the last couple of decades.

To convey just how economically unequal the world has become, let us compare economic data for the years 1960, 1978, and 2000. In 1960, about a third of 126 countries (41) were classified as rich, and 17 percent were in the next lower rank—contenders to be rich. By 1978, about one-quarter (or 11) of the rich countries slipped down into the ranks of the contenders and about 7 percent (three) moved into the Third World category. By 2000, an additional five rich countries

slipped down. During the same time frame, only four countries moved up to join the rich—Singapore, Hong Kong, Taiwan, and South Korea. During the same time periods, almost all of the poorest countries stayed at the bottom, and if there was movement among the non-rich countries, it was mostly downward. Western countries increased their hold on the world's wealth during this period. Of the 41 originally rich countries in 1960, almost half (19) were non-Western. In 2000, there were fewer rich countries—only 31—but only 30 percent (nine) were non-Western.

If the world as a whole is seeing improvements in technology and economic development, why is the gap between the rich and poor countries increasing? As we saw in the chapter on culture and culture change, often the rich within a society benefit most from new technology, at least initially. They are not only the most likely to be able to afford it, they also are the only ones who can afford to take the risks that it involves. The same may be true for nations. Those that already have capital are more likely than the poorer nations to take advantage of improvements in technology. In addition, the poorer countries generally have the highest rates of population growth, so income per capita can fall if population increases faster than the rate of economic development. Economists tell us that a developing country may, at least initially, experience

an increase in inequality, but the inequality often decreases over time. Will the inequalities among countries also decrease as the world economy develops further?

If it is true that the disparity between rich and poor countries has increased in recent years, it is also true that the world has seen improvement in some respects. The United Nations has computed a "human development index" for 177 countries, combining measures of life expectancy, literacy, and a measure of per capita purchasing power. According to this index, most countries, including developing countries, have improved substantially between 1990 and 2005. For example, Bangladesh, China, and Uganda have increased their ranking by about 20 percent between 1990 and 2005. Some countries are doing worse—most of these are in sub-Saharan Africa or had been parts of the former Soviet Union. World leaders at the United Nations Millennium Declaration have committed themselves to a number of goals by the year 2015, including halving the proportion of people living in extreme poverty and halving the proportion of people suffering from hunger. Even if those goals are achieved, much more will remain to be done if we are to achieve a more equal world.

Sources: United Nations Development Programme 2007; UN News Centre 2005; Milanovic 2005.

occur, children of the union were often regarded as having lower status than European American children, even though they may have had blond hair and light skin. In the South, where treatment of African Americans as a caste was most apparent, European Americans refused to eat with African Americans or sit next to them at lunch counters, on buses, and in schools. Separate drinking fountains and toilets reinforced the idea of ritual uncleanness. The economic advantages and gains in prestige that European Americans enjoyed are well documented.[36]

In the following sections on slavery, racism, and inequality, we discuss the social status of African Americans in more detail.

Slavery

Slaves are people who do not own their own labor, and as such they represent a class. We may associate slavery with a few well-known examples, such as ancient Egypt, Greece, and Rome or the southern United States, but slavery has existed in some form in almost every part of the world at one time or another, in simpler as well as in more complex societies. Slaves are often obtained from other cultures directly: kidnapped, captured in war, or given as tribute. Or they may be obtained indirectly as payment in barter or trade. Slaves sometimes come from the same culture; one became a slave as payment of a debt, as a punishment for a crime, or even as a chosen alternative to poverty. Slave societies vary in the degree to which it is possible to become freed from slavery.[37] Sometimes the slavery system has been a closed class, or caste, system, sometimes a relatively open class system. In different slave-owning societies, slaves have had different, but always some, legal rights.[38]

In ancient Greece, slaves often were conquered enemies. Because city-states were constantly conquering one another or rebelling against former conquerors, slavery was a threat to everyone. After the Trojan War, the transition of Hecuba from queen to slave was marked by her cry, "Count no one happy, however fortunate, before he dies."[39] Nevertheless, Greek slaves were considered human beings, and they could even acquire some higher-class status along with freedom. Andromache, Hecuba's daughter-in-law, was taken as a slave and concubine by one of the Greek heroes. When his legal wife produced no children, Andromache's slave son became heir to his father's throne. Although slaves had no rights under law, once they were freed, either by the will of their master or by purchase, they and their descendants could become assimilated into the dominant group. In other words, slavery in Greece was not seen as the justified position of inferior people. It was regarded, rather, as an act of fate—"the luck of the draw"—that relegated one to the lowest class in society.

Among the Nupe, a society in central Nigeria, slavery was of quite another type.[40] The methods of obtaining slaves—as part of the booty of warfare and, later, by purchase—were similar to those of Europeans, but the position of the slaves was very different. Mistreatment was rare. Male slaves were given the same opportunities to earn money as other dependent males in the household—younger brothers, sons, or other relatives. A slave might be given a garden plot of his own to cultivate, or he might be given a commission if his master was a craftsman or a tradesman. Slaves could acquire property, wealth, and even slaves of their own. But all of a slave's belongings went to the master at the slave's death.

Manumission—the granting of freedom to slaves—was built into the Nupe system. If a male slave could afford the marriage payment for a free woman, the children of the resulting marriage were free; the man himself, however, remained a slave. Marriage and concubinage were the easiest ways out of bondage for a slave woman. Once she had produced a child by her master, both she and the child had free status. The woman, however, was only figuratively free; if a concubine, she had to remain in that role. As might be expected, the family trees of the nobility and the wealthy were liberally grafted with branches descended from slave concubines.

The most fortunate slaves among the Nupe were the house slaves. They could rise to positions of power in the household as overseers and bailiffs, charged with law enforcement and judicial duties. (Recall the Old Testament story of Joseph, who was sold into slavery by his brothers. Joseph became a household slave of the pharaoh and rose to the position of second in the kingdom because he devised an ingenious system of taxation.) There was even a titled group of Nupe slaves, the Order of Court Slaves, who were trusted officers of the king and members of an elite. Slave status in general, though, placed one at the bottom of the social ladder. In the Nupe system, few slaves, mainly princes from their own societies, ever achieved membership in the titled group. Nupe slavery was abolished at the beginning of the 20th century.

In the United States, slavery originated as a means of obtaining cheap labor, but the slaves soon came to be regarded as deserving of their low status because of their alleged inherent inferiority. Because the slaves were from Africa and were dark-skinned (see the DK map "Trading in Human Lives" at the back of the book), some European Americans justified slavery and the belief in "black" people's inferiority by quoting scripture out of context ("They shall be hewers of wood and drawers of water"). Slaves could not marry or make any other contracts, nor could they own property. In addition, their children were also slaves, and the master had sexual rights over the female slaves. Because the status of slavery was determined by birth in the United States, slaves constituted a caste. During the days of slavery, therefore, the United States had both a caste and a class system. It is widely assumed that slavery occurred only in the southern United States, but although not on as large a scale, slavery existed in the northern states as well. New Jersey was the last northern state to legally give up slavery around the time of the U.S. Civil War.[41]

Even after the abolition of slavery, as we have noted, some castelike elements remained. It is important to note that these castelike elements were not limited to the American South where slavery had been practiced. For example, although Indiana was established as a "free" state in 1816, in its first constitution, "negros" did not have the right to vote nor could they intermarry with "whites." In the constitution of 1851, Indiana did not allow "negros" to come into the state, nor did it allow the existing African American residents to attend public schools even though they had to pay school taxes.[42] In Muncie, Indiana, in the first half of the 20th century, there was customary segregation in shows, restaurants, and parks. Not until the 1950s was the public swimming pool desegregated.[43]

As for why slavery may have developed in the first place, cross-cultural research is as yet inconclusive. We do know, however, that slavery is not an inevitable stage in economic development, contrary to what some have assumed. In other words, slavery is not found mainly in certain economies, such as those dependent on intensive agriculture. Unlike the United States until the Civil War, many societies with intensive agriculture did not develop any variety of slavery. Also, the hypothesis that slavery develops where available resources are plentiful but labor is scarce is not supported by the cross-cultural evidence. All we can say definitely is that slavery does not occur in developed or industrial economies; either it disappears or it was never present in them.[44]

RACISM AND INEQUALITY

Racism is the belief that some "races" are inferior to others. In a society composed of people with noticeably different physical features, such as differences in skin color, racism is almost invariably associated with social stratification. Those "races" considered inferior make up a larger proportion of the lower social classes or castes. Even in more open class systems, where individuals from all backgrounds can achieve higher status positions, individuals from groups deemed inferior may be subject to discrimination in housing or may be more likely to be searched or stopped by the police.

In some societies, such as the United States, the idea that humans are divided into "races" is taken so much for granted that people are asked for their "race" on the census. Most Americans probably assume that the classification of people into categories such as "white" or "black" reflects important biological categories. But that is not so. We now know from genetic research that there is enormous genetic diversity within the African continent, in fact, more than between Africa and any other continent.[45] There is no clear boundary where one trait is present or absent. For example, in the area around Egypt, there is a gradient of skin color as you move from north to south in the Nile Valley. Nose shape varies with humidity, but its gradient is not the same as the gradient for skin color, so the two distributions are quite different. Both of these characteristics make it impossible to draw discrete boundaries between groups on the basis of external traits such as skin color and nose shape. (We discussed the inapplicability of the "race" concept to humans more thoroughly in the human variation chapter.) The genetic diversity within Africa is consistent with the fossil evidence that the African continent is where both early humans and modern humans emerged. This is as you may remember, parallel to linguistic diversity—English developed in England, and

there we find the most dialect diversity. Modern humans emerged first in Africa, so it is accurate to say that we are all African, and members of the "human race."

You may have noticed that we put "race" in quotes to reflect the fact that most anthropologists are now persuaded that the biological concept of "race" is not scientifically useful when applied to humans. However, "race" is a social concept that is important as a classifier in some societies.

Race as a Social Category

Racial classifications are social categories to which individuals are assigned, by themselves and others, to separate "our" group from others. We have seen that people tend to be *ethnocentric,* to view their culture as better than other cultures. Racial classifications may reflect the same tendency to divide "us" from "them," except that the divisions are supposedly based on biological differences.[46] The "them" are almost always viewed as inferior to "us."

We know that racial classifications have often been, and still are, used by certain groups to justify discrimination, exploitation, or genocide. The "Aryan race" was supposed to be the group of blond-haired, blue-eyed, white-skinned people whom Adolf Hitler wanted to dominate the world, to which end he and others attempted to destroy as many members of the Jewish "race" as they could. (An estimated 6 million Jews and others were murdered in what is now called the Holocaust.[47]) But who were the Aryans? Technically, Aryans are any people, including the German-speaking Jews in Hitler's Germany, who speak one of the Indo-European languages. The Indo-European languages include such disparate modern tongues as Greek, Spanish, Hindi, Polish, French, Icelandic, German, Gaelic, and English. And many Aryans speaking these languages have neither blond hair nor blue eyes. Similarly, all kinds of people may be Jews, whether or not they descend from the

It is an illusion that there are races. The diversity of human beings is so great and so complicated that it is impossible to classify the 5.8 billions of individuals into discrete "races."

Some of our physical differences give the impression that it is possible to divide us into races. But when these physical characteristics are subjected to detailed study, that cannot be concluded at all. Instead it becomes obvious that our physical diversity reflects continuous changes from one extreme to the other. To place any boundaries within this continuous diversity would be, therefore, completely arbitrary. Human diversity is in fact infinitely more complicated than the idea we have constructed of it. This is why attempts to make racial classifications that are typically made don't yield any coherent results; there is nothing scientific about "race".

applied anthropology

Unequal in Death: African Americans Compared with European Americans

Everyone dies of something. Yet, if you consider cardiovascular disease, the leading cause of death in the United States, it turns out that after controlling for the effects of age and gender, African Americans die more often from that disease than European Americans. The same kind of disparity occurs also with almost every other major cause of death—cancer, cirrhosis of the liver, kidney disease, diabetes, injuries, infant mortality, and homicide. Medical anthropologists and health policy researchers want to know why. Without such understanding, it is hard to know how to reduce the disparity.

One reason may be subtle discrimination by the medical profession itself. For example, a European American with chest pain in the United States is more likely than an African American to be given an angiogram, a medical procedure that injects radioactive dye into the heart to look for deficits in blood flow through the coronary arteries that supply blood to the heart. And even if coronary heart disease is detected by an angiogram, an African American is less likely to receive bypass surgery. Thus, the death rate from cardiovascular disease may be higher for African Americans than for European Americans because of unequal medical care. Seeing a patient physically appears to make a difference. When heart specialists reviewed cases to make decisions about subsequent treatment after catheterization, recommendations did not differ by "race" when the doctors did not know the "race" of the patient.

Yet, although some difference in mortality may be due to disparity in medical treatment, this could only be part of the picture. African Americans may be more prone to cardiovascular disease because they are about twice as likely as European Americans to have high rates of hypertension (high blood pressure). But, why the disparity in hypertension? Three possible explanations, not mutually exclusive, are discussed in the research literature. The first is a possible difference in genetics. The second is a difference in lifestyle. The third is class difference.

Most of the Africans that came to the Americas were forcibly taken as slaves between the 16th and 19th centuries, largely from West Africa. In one comparative study of hypertension, African Americans had much higher blood pressure than Africans in Nigeria and Cameroon, even in urban areas. People with African ancestry in the Caribbean were in the middle of the range. Lifestyle differences were also vast—the West Africans had plenty of exercise, were lean, and ate low-fat and low-salt diets. Any possible difference in genes would seem to be insignificant. Jared Diamond has suggested that individuals who could retain salt would have been most likely to survive the terrible conditions of the sailing ships that brought slaves to the New World. Many died from diarrhea and dehydration (salt-depleting conditions) on those voyages. Retention of salt would have been a genetic advantage then, but disadvantageous in places such as the United States with high-salt, high-fat diets. Critics of this theory suggest that salt-depleting diseases were not the leading causes of death in the slave voyages; tuberculosis and violence were more frequent causes of death. Furthermore, critics say that the slave ship theory would predict little genetic diversity in African American populations with respect to hypertension, but in fact there is great diversity.

Hypertension could be related also to differences in lifestyle and wealth. As we noted in the section on racism and inequality, African Americans in the United States are disproportionately poorer. Study after study has noted that healthier lifestyle habits are generally correlated with higher positions on the socioeconomic ladder. Moreover, individuals from higher social positions are more likely to have health insurance and access to care in superior hospitals. But even after correcting for factors such as obesity, physical activity, and social class, the health differential persists—African Americans still have a much higher incidence of hypertension than European Americans.

William Dressler suggests that stress is another possible cause of higher rates of hypertension. Despite increased economic mobility in recent years, African Americans are still subject to prejudice and may consequently have more stress even if they have higher income. Stress is related to higher blood pressure. In a color-conscious society, a very dark-skinned individual walking in a wealthy neighborhood at night may be thought not to live there and may be stopped by the police. If Dressler is correct, darker-skinned African Americans who have objective indicators of higher status should have much higher blood pressure than would be expected from their relative education, age, body mass, or social class alone. And that seems to be true. Racism may affect health.

Sources: Smedley et al. 2003, 3; Geiger 2003; Dressler 1993; Cooper et al. 1999, 56–63; Diamond 1991.

ancient Near Eastern population that spoke the Hebrew language. There are light-skinned Danish Jews and darker Jewish Arabs. One of the most orthodox Jewish groups in the United States is based in New York City and is composed entirely of African Americans.

The arbitrary and social basis of most racial classifications becomes apparent when you compare how they differ from one place to another. Consider, for example, what used to be thought about the "races" in South Africa. Under apartheid, which was a system of racial segregation and discrimination, someone with mixed "white" and "black" ancestry was considered "colored." However, when important people of African ancestry (from other countries) would visit South Africa, they were often considered "white." Chinese were considered "Asian"; but the Japanese, who were important economically to South Africa, were considered "white."[48] In some parts of the United States, laws against interracial marriage continued in force through the 1960s. You would be considered a "negro" if you had an eighth or more "negro" ancestry (if one or more of your eight grandparents were "negro").[49] In some states, an even smaller proportion made you "negro." Some refer to this concept as the "one-drop" rule—just a tiny bit of "negro" (now called "black") ancestry was sufficient to determine your "racial" classification.[50] So only a small amount of "negro" ancestry made a person "negro." But a small amount of "white" ancestry did not make a person "white." Biologically speaking, this makes no sense, but socially it was another story.[51]

In much of Latin America and the Caribbean, the reverse rule is the case. A small amount of European blood can make you "white." When people from Dominica, Haiti, or Cuba come to the United States, they often find that their "race" has changed. They might have been considered "white" at home, but they are considered "black" in the United States. In contrast to the United States with a two-part division of "white" and "black," concepts of race in Latin America are on more of a continuum from light to dark, with important middle positions (such as "mestizo"). Wealth makes a difference too—if you are dark-skinned, but wealthy, you will tend to be considered "whiter."[52]

If people of different "races" are viewed as inferior, they are more likely going to end up on the lower rungs of the social ladder in a socially stratified society. Discrimination will keep them out of the better-paying or higher-status jobs and in neighborhoods that are poorer. As the box "Unequal in Death" shows, people of different "races" also suffer from differential access to health care and have more health problems.

ETHNICITY AND INEQUALITY

If "race" is not a scientifically useful category because people cannot be clearly divided into different "racial" categories based on sets of physical traits, then racial classifications such as "black" and "white" in the United States might better be described as *ethnic* classifications. How else can we account for the following facts? Groups that are thought of as "white" now in the United States were earlier thought of as belonging to inferior "races." For example, in the latter half of the 19th century, newspapers would often talk about the new immigrants from Ireland as belonging to the Irish "race." Similarly, before World War II, Jews were thought of as a separate "racial" group, and only became "white" afterward.[53] It is hard to escape the idea that changes in "racial" classification occurred as the Irish, Jews, and other immigrant groups became more accepted by the majority in the United States.[54]

It is apparent that *ethnic groups* and *ethnic identities* emerge as part of a social and political process. The process of defining **ethnicity** usually involves a group of people emphasizing common origins and language,

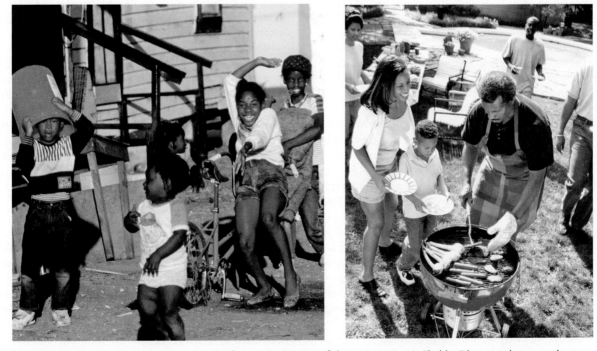

Members of minority ethnic groups are more often at the bottom of the socioeconomic "ladder," but not always, as these pictures from the United States illustrate.

shared history, and selected cultural differences such as a difference in religion. Those doing the defining can be outside or inside the ethnic group. Outsiders and insiders often perceive ethnic groups differently. In a country with one large core majority group, often the majority group doesn't think of itself as an ethnic group. Rather, they consider only the minority groups to have ethnic identities. For example, in the United States, it is not common for the majority to call themselves European Americans, but other groups may be called African Americans, Asian Americans, or Native Americans. The minority groups, on the other hand, may also have different named identities.[55] Asian Americans may identify themselves more specifically as Japanese Americans, Korean Americans, Chinese Americans, or Hmong. The majority population often uses derogatory names to identify people who are different. The majority may also tend to lump people of diverse ethnicities together. Naming a group establishes a boundary between it and other ethnic groups.[56]

Ethnic differences can sometimes arise from class differences. Rwanda is a good case in point. By the end of the 19th century, Rwandans were part of a kingdom with significant class distinctions, but the distinctions between Hutu and Tutsi, so important in recent times, were not very important or clear.[57] Cattle were an important form of wealth and, although many people known as Tutsi were cattle herders and many known as Hutu were agriculturalists, many Tutsi and Hutu were both. If Hutu acquired wealth and intermarried with Tutsi, they could move up in rank. A Tutsi could lose cattle and turn to cultivation.[58] Colonialism did not create differentiation between Tutsi and Hutu, but it did accentuate it. For example, the Belgian administration tried to reinforce the power of the "natural rulers" (the Tutsi), and they issued identity cards in the 1930s to distinguish Tutsi, Hutu, and Twa (the Twa were discussed earlier in the caste section). During the colonial period, the idea developed that the three groups were biologically different from each other. It was commonly thought that the taller Tutsi were different people who originally conquered the others.[59]

When the Hutu united to demand more of the rewards of their labor in 1959, the king and many of the Tutsi ruling elite were driven out of the country. The Hutu then established a republican form of government and declared independence from Belgium in 1962. In 1990, Tutsi rebels invaded from Uganda, and attempts were made to negotiate a multiparty government. However, civil war continued, and in 1994 alone, over a million people, mostly Tutsi, were killed. Almost 2 million refugees, mostly Hutu, fled to Zaire as the Tutsi-led rebels established a new government.[60] In the intervening years, the Rwandan government has made progress in bringing home the refugees, bringing those who committed genocide to trial, and integrating different groups into the government.[61]

Ethnic identity may be manipulated, by insiders and by outsiders, in different situations. A particularly repressive regime that emphasizes nationalism and loyalty to the state may not only suppress the assertiveness of ethnic claims; it may also act to minimize communication among people who might otherwise embrace the same ethnic identity.[62] More democratic regimes may allow more expression of difference and celebrate ethnic difference. However, manipulation of ethnicity does not come just from the top. It may be to the advantage of minority groups to lobby for more equal treatment as a larger entity, such as Asian American, rather than as Japanese, Chinese, Hmong, Filipino, or Korean American. Similarly, even though there are hundreds of Native American groups, originally speaking different languages, there may be political advantages for all if they are treated as Native Americans.

In many multiethnic societies, ethnicity and diversity are things to be proud of and celebrated. Shared ethnic identity often makes people feel comfortable with similar people and gives them a strong sense of belonging. Still, ethnic differences in multiethnic societies are usually associated with inequities in wealth, power, and prestige. In other words, ethnicity is part of the system of *stratification*.

Although some people believe that inequities are deserved, the origins of ethnic stereotypes, prejudice, and discrimination usually follow from historical and political events that give some groups dominance over others. For example, even though there were many early stories of help given by native peoples to the English settlers in the 17th century in the land now known as North America, the English were the invaders, and negative stereotypes about native peoples developed to justify taking their land and their lives. Referring to the negative stereotypes of Native Americans that developed, J. Milton Yinger said, "One would almost think that it had been the Indian who had invaded Europe, driven back the inhabitants, cut their population to one-third of its original size, unilaterally changed treaties, and brought the dubious glories of firewater and firearms."[63]

Similarly, as we noted in the section on slavery, African slaves were initially acquired as cheap labor, but inhumane treatment of slaves was justified by beliefs about their inferiority. Unfortunately, stereotypes can become self-fulfilling prophesies, especially if those discriminated against come to believe the stereotypes. It is easy to see how this can happen. If there is a widespread belief that a group is inferior, and that group is given inferior schools and little chance for improvement or little chance for a good job, the members of that group may acquire few skills and not try hard. The result is often a vicious cycle.[64]

And yet, the picture is not all bleak. Change has occurred. The ethnic identity a minority group forges can help promote political activism, such as the nonviolent civil rights movement in the United States in the 1960s. That activism, helped by some people in the more advantaged groups, helped break down many of the legal barriers and segregationist practices that reinforced inequality.

The traditional barriers in the United States have mostly been lifted in recent years, but the "color line" has not disappeared. African Americans are found in all social classes, but they remain underrepresented in the wealthiest group and overrepresented at the bottom. Discrimination may be lessened, but it is still not gone. In research done with matched pairs of "whites" and "blacks" applying for jobs or for housing, discrimination is still evident.[65] Thus, African Americans may have to be better than others to get promoted, or it may be assumed that they got ahead just because they were African American and were hired because of affirmative action programs. European Americans often expect African Americans to be "ambassadors," to be called on mainly for knowledge about how to handle situations involving other African Americans. African Americans may work with others, but they usually go home to African American neighborhoods. Or they may live in mixed neighborhoods and experience considerable isolation. Few African Americans can completely avoid the anguish of racism.[66]

THE EMERGENCE OF STRATIFICATION

Anthropologists are not certain why social stratification developed. Nevertheless, they are reasonably sure that higher levels of stratification emerged relatively recently in human history. Archaeological sites dating before about 8,000 years ago do not show extensive evidence of inequality. Houses do not appear to vary much in size or content, and different communities of the same culture are similar in size and otherwise. Signs of inequality appear first in the Near East, about 2,000 years after agriculture emerged in that region. Inequality in burial suggests inequality in life. Particularly telling are unequal child burials. It is unlikely that children could achieve high status by their own achievements. So, when archaeologists find statues and ornaments only in some children's tombs, as at the 7,500-year-old site of Tell es-Sawwan in Iraq,[67] the grave goods suggest that those children belonged to a higher-ranking family or a higher class.

Another indication that stratification is a relatively recent development in human history is the fact that certain cultural features associated with stratification also developed relatively recently. For example, most societies that depend primarily on agriculture or herding have social classes.[68] Agriculture and herding developed within the past 10,000 years, so we may assume that most food collectors in the distant past lacked social classes. Other recently developed cultural features associated with class stratification include fixed settlements, political integration beyond the community level, the use of money as a medium of exchange, and the presence of at least some full-time specialization.[69]

In 1966, the comparative sociologist Gerhard Lenski suggested that the trend toward increasing inequality since 8,000 years ago was reversing. He argued that inequalities of power and privilege in industrial societies—measured in terms of the concentration of political power and the distribution of income—are less pronounced than inequalities in complex preindustrial societies. Technology in industrialized societies is so complex, he suggested, that

those in power are compelled to delegate some authority to subordinates if the system is to work. In addition, a decline in the birth rate in industrialized societies, coupled with the need for skilled labor, has pushed the average wage of workers far above the subsistence level, resulting in greater equality in the distribution of income. Finally, Lenski also suggested that the spread of the democratic ideology, and particularly its acceptance by elites, has significantly broadened the political power of the lower classes.[70] A few studies have tested and supported Lenski's hypothesis that inequality has decreased with industrialization. In general, nations that are highly industrialized exhibit a lower level of inequality than nations that are only somewhat industrialized.[71] But, as we have seen, even the most industrialized societies may still have an enormous degree of inequality.

Why did social stratification develop in the first place? On the basis of his study of Polynesian societies, Marshall Sahlins suggested that an increase in agricultural productivity results in social stratification.[72] According to Sahlins, the degree of stratification is directly related to the production of a surplus, which is made possible by greater technological efficiency. The higher the level of productivity and the larger the agricultural surplus, the greater the scope and complexity of the distribution system. The status of the chief, who serves as redistributing agent, is enhanced. Sahlins argued that the differentiation between distributor and producer inevitably gives rise to differentiation in other aspects of life:

> First, there would be a tendency for the regulator of distribution to exert some authority over production itself—especially over productive activities which necessitate subsidization, such as communal labor or specialist labor. A degree of control of production implies a degree of control over the utilization of resources, or, in other words, some preeminent property rights. In turn, regulation of these economic processes necessitates the exercise of authority in interpersonal affairs; differences in social power emerge.[73]

Sahlins later rejected the idea that a surplus leads to chiefships, postulating instead that the relationship may be the other way around—that is, leaders encourage the development of a surplus so as to enhance their prestige through feasts, potlatches, and other redistributive events.[74] Of course, both trajectories are possible—surpluses may generate stratification, and stratification may generate surpluses; they are not mutually exclusive.

Lenski's theory of the causes of stratification is similar to Sahlins's original idea. Lenski, too, argued that production of a surplus is the stimulus in the development of stratification, but he focused primarily on the conflict that arises over control of that surplus. Lenski concluded that the distribution of the surplus will be determined on the basis of power. Thus, inequalities in power promote unequal access to economic resources and simultaneously give rise to inequalities in privilege and prestige.[75]

The "surplus" theories of Sahlins and Lenski do not really address the question of why the redistributors or leaders will want, or be able, to acquire greater control over resources. After all, the redistributors or leaders in many rank societies do not have greater wealth than others, and custom seems to keep things that way. One suggestion is that, as long as followers have mobility, they can vote with their feet by moving away from leaders they do not like. But when people start to make more permanent "investments" in land or technology (e.g., irrigation systems or weirs for fishing), they are more likely to put up with a leader's aggrandizement in exchange for protection.[76] Another suggestion is that access to economic resources becomes unequal only when there is population pressure on resources in rank or chiefdom societies.[77] Such pressure may be what induces redistributors to try to keep more land and other resources for themselves and their families.

C. K. Meek offered an example of how population pressure in northern Nigeria may have led to economic stratification. At one time, a tribal member could obtain the right to use land by asking permission of the chief and presenting him with a token gift in recognition of his higher status. But, by 1921, the reduction in the amount of available land had led to a system under which applicants offered the chief large payments for scarce land. As a result of these payments, farms came to be regarded as private property, and differential access to such property became institutionalized.[78]

Future research by archaeologists, sociologists, historians, and anthropologists should provide more understanding of the emergence of social stratification in human societies and how and why it may vary in degree.

SUMMARY ● ○ ○

1. Without exception, recent and modern industrial and postindustrial societies such as our own are socially stratified—that is, they contain social groups such as families, classes, or ethnic groups that have unequal access to important advantages, such as economic resources, power, and prestige. Anthropologists, based on firsthand observations, would say that such inequality has not always existed among the societies they have studied. Although even the simplest societies (in the technological sense) have some differences in advantages based on age, ability, or gender—adults have higher status than children, the skilled more than the unskilled, men more than women (we discuss gender stratification in the chapter on sex, gender, and culture)—anthropologists would argue that egalitarian societies exist where social groups (e.g., families) have more or less the same access to rights or advantages.

2. The presence or absence of customs or rules that give certain groups unequal access to economic resources, power, and prestige can be used to distinguish three types of societies. In egalitarian societies, social groups do not have unequal access to economic resources, power, or prestige; they are unstratified. In rank societies, social groups do not have very unequal access to economic resources or power, but they do have unequal access to prestige. Rank societies, then, are partially stratified. In class societies, social groups have unequal access to economic resources, power, and prestige. They are more completely stratified than are rank societies.

3. Stratified societies range from somewhat open class systems to caste systems, which are extremely rigid, because caste membership is fixed permanently at birth.

4. Slaves are people who do not own their own labor; as such, they represent a class and sometimes even a caste. Slavery has existed in various forms in many times and places, regardless of "race" and culture. Sometimes slavery is a rigid and closed, or caste, system; sometimes it is a relatively open class system.

5. Within a society composed of people from widely divergent backgrounds and different physical features, such as skin color, racism is almost invariably associated with social stratification. Those "races" considered inferior make up a larger proportion of the lower social classes or castes. In the opinion of many biological anthropologists, "race" is not a scientifically useful device for classifying humans. "Racial" classifications should be recognized for what they mostly are—social categories to which individuals are assigned, by themselves and others, on the basis of supposedly shared biological traits.

6. In multiethnic societies, ethnic differences are usually associated with inequities in wealth, power, and prestige. In other words, ethnicity is part of the system of stratification.

7. Social stratification appears to have emerged relatively recently in human history, about 8,000 years ago. This conclusion is based on archaeological evidence and on the fact that certain cultural features associated with stratification developed relatively recently.

8. One theory suggests that social stratification developed as productivity increased and surpluses were produced. Another suggestion is that stratification can develop only when people have "investments" in land or technology and therefore cannot move away from leaders they do not like. A third theory suggests that stratification emerges only when there is population pressure on resources in rank societies.

GLOSSARY TERMS ○ ● ○

CRITICAL QUESTIONS ○ ○ ●

1. What might be some of the social consequences of large differences in wealth? Explain your reasoning.

2. Is an industrial or a developed economy incompatible with a more egalitarian distribution of resources? Why or why not?

3. In a multiethnic society, does ethnic identity help or hinder social equality? Explain your answer.

4. Why do you suppose the degree of inequality has decreased in some countries in recent years?

PEARSON myanthrolab

Read "Haitians: From Political Repression to Chaos" by Robert Lawless on MyAnthroLab. Answer the questions below.

1. In what ways does Lawless suggest that the elite in Haiti maintain their power?

2. Why does Lawless say that "Voodoo" is an egalitarian religion?

3. Explain what role slavery played in Haitian history.

chapter 19

Culture and the Individual

nthropology, with its focus on culture, may seem to ignore the individual. To be sure, individuals provide information about culture, but their psychological characteristics, a central concern of psychology, are often considered irrelevant. However, there are anthropologists who think that understanding individuals and psychological processes is vital to anthropological understanding. Take culture change as an example. As we discussed in the chapter on the concept of culture and culture change, *individuals* are ultimately the source of culture change. They discover and invent, they adopt new behaviors or ideas from others, or they resist or accommodate to changes other societies try to impose. Culture changes only when enough individuals alter their ideas or their patterns of behavior. Individuals are the *agents* of change.

Anthropologists who are interested in the relationships between culture and the individual and the importance of understanding psychological processes call themselves *psychological anthropologists.* Psychologists who study people in two or more societies call themselves *cross-cultural psychologists.* Four main questions seem to characterize psychological anthropology: (1) To what extent do all human beings develop psychologically in the same ways? (2) If there are differences, what are they and what may account for them? (3) How do people in different societies conceive of individuals and their psychological development? and (4) How can understanding individuals or psychological processes help us understand culture and culture change? This chapter discusses some of the attempts of researchers to answer some of these questions.

● ○ ●

THE UNIVERSALITY OF PSYCHOLOGICAL DEVELOPMENT

Anthropologists became interested in psychology in the early years of the 20th century partly because they did not believe that human nature was completely revealed in Western societies, as psychologists then generally assumed. Only recently have many psychologists joined anthropologists in questioning the assumption that humans are exactly the same psychologically in all societies. Psychologist Otto Klineberg, for example, scolded his psychologist colleagues in 1974: "My contact with anthropology affected me somewhat like a religious conversion. How could psychologists speak of *human* attributes and *human* behavior when they knew only one kind of human being?"[1]

How can we know what is universal about human behavior and what is variable until we study all kinds of humans? Because humans the world over are the same species and share a very large proportion of their genes, we might assume that there is a good deal of similarity across societies in the way people develop psychologically from birth to maturity or in the ways they think, feel, and behave. We have already discussed many universals—culture, language, marriage, the incest taboo—but here we discuss some that are related more to psychology. Donald Brown compiled a list of probable human universals in the psychological

329

realm.[2] They include the ability to create taxonomies, make binary contrasts, order phenomena, use logical operators (e.g., *and, not, equals*), plan for the future, and have an understanding of the world and what it is about.

With regard to ideas about people, it seems universal to have a concept of the self or person, to recognize individual faces, to try to discern other peoples' intentions from observable clues in their faces, utterances, and actions, and to imagine what others are thinking. With regard to emotions, people seem universally to be able to empathize with the feelings of others; facially communicate and recognize, as well as hide or mimic, the emotions of happiness, sadness, anger, fear, surprise, disgust, and contempt (see the box "Do Masks Show Emotion in Universal Ways?" in the chapter on the arts); smile when friendly; cry when in pain or unhappy; play for fun; show and feel affection for others; feel sexual attraction, envy, and jealousy; and have similar childhood fears (e.g., fear of strangers). Indeed, it seems that people in different cultures even conceive of love in much the same ways, despite love's reputation as something mysterious and culturally variable.[3]

What about psychological development? We saw in the chapter on communication and language that certain aspects of language acquisition appear to be universal across cultures. In what respects is psychological development the same the world over? In what respects is it different?

Early Research on Emotional Development

When Margaret Mead went to American Samoa in the mid-1920s, psychologists believed that adolescence was universally a period of "storm and stress" because of the physiological changes that occur at puberty. Mead's observations of, and interviews with, Samoan adolescent girls led her to doubt the idea that adolescence was necessarily a time of turmoil. Samoan girls apparently showed little evidence of emotional upheaval and rebelliousness, and therefore it was questionable whether psychological development in adolescence was the same in all societies.[4]

Bronislaw Malinowski, another early anthropologist, questioned the universality of an assumption about emotional development, in this case Freud's assumption that young boys universally see themselves, unconsciously, as sexual rivals of their fathers for possession of their mothers. Freud called these feelings the *Oedipus complex,* after the character in Greek mythology who killed his father and married his mother without knowing that they were his parents. Freud thought that all boys before the age of 7 or so would show hostility toward their fathers, but Malinowski disagreed on the basis of his fieldwork in the Trobriand Islands.[5]

Malinowski suggested that young boys in male-oriented societies may feel hostility toward the father not as a sexual rival but as the disciplinarian. Malinowski proposed this theory because he thought that the Oedipus complex works differently in societies organized around the female line, such as the matrilineal Trobriands. In matrilineal

societies, the mother's brother is the main authority figure in the matrilineal kin group—than toward their father.

Derek Freeman criticized Mead's conclusions about Samoa,[6] and Melford Spiro challenged Malinowski's conclusions about the Trobriand Islanders.[7] Mead and Malinowski may or may not have been correct about the societies they studied, but the issues they raised remain crucial to the question of whether psychological development is similar across societies. To find out, we need research in many societies, not just a few. Only on the basis of extensive cross-cultural research will we be able to decide whether stages of emotional development can be affected by cultural differences.

For example, only recently has adolescence been systematically studied cross-culturally. Alice Schlegel and Herbert Barry reported that adolescence is generally not a period of overt rebelliousness. The reason, they suggested, is related to the fact that most people in most societies live with or near (and depend on) close kin before and after they grow up. Only in societies like our own, where children leave home when they grow up, might adolescents be rebellious, possibly to prepare emotionally for going out on their own.[8] (See the box "Neolocality and Adolescent Rebellion: Are They Related?" in the chapter on marital residence and kinship.)

Adolescence in many societies is a time for developing work skills. An Asmat boy in Indonesian New Guinea is learning to carve, and an adult is supervising.

Research on Cognitive Development

One day the Embers went out for pizza. The pizza maker was laughing hilariously, and we asked what was so funny. He told us: "I just asked the guy ahead of you, 'How many slices do you want me to cut the pizza into, six or eight?' 'Six,' he said, 'I'm not very hungry.'" According to a theory of cognitive (intellectual) development suggested by Jean Piaget, the renowned Swiss psychologist, the "not very hungry" guy may not have acquired the concept of *conservation,* which characterizes a stage of thinking normally acquired by children between the ages of 7 and 11 in Western societies.[9] The pizza customer ahead of us, like many very young children, seemed not to understand that certain properties of an object, such as quantity, weight, and volume, remain constant even if the object is divided into small pieces or removed to a container of a different shape. They have not acquired the mental image of *reversibility,* the ability to imagine that if you put the pizza back together again it would be the same size whether you had cut it into eight or six slices. To the child or adult who has not acquired the ability to reverse actions mentally, eight slices may seem like more pizza than six slices, because eight is more than six.

Piaget's theory says that the development of thinking in humans involves a series of stages, each of which is characterized by different mental skills. To get to a higher stage of thinking, one has to pass through a lower stage. So Piaget's theory would predict that the pizza customer would not be able to think systematically about the possible outcomes of hypothetical situations, a defining feature of Piaget's *formal-operational* stage, because he had not acquired the notion of conservation and the other mental skills that characterize the previous, *concrete-operational* stage of cognitive development.

What does the evidence suggest about the universality of Piaget's supposed stages? And do people the world over get to each stage at the same age? The first stage of development, *sensorimotor,* has not been investigated in many societies, but the results of studies conducted so far are remarkably consistent. They support Piaget's notion that there is a predictable order in the sequence of stages.[10] And, on the basis of their reactions to the same conditions, babies in different places seem to think similarly. For example, a comparison of French babies and Baoulé babies in the Ivory Coast showed that the Baoulé babies, who had never seen objects such as red plastic tubes and paper clips, nevertheless tried to pass the clips through the tubes in the same way the French babies did. The two sets of babies even made the same kinds of errors.[11] And even though they had few toys, the Baoulé babies showed advances over French babies on such tasks as using instruments to increase the reach of the arm. But Baoulé babies are allowed to touch all kinds of objects, even things that Europeans consider dangerous.[12]

Most of the cross-cultural studies of Piaget's stages have focused on the transition between the second, *preoperational,* and third, *concrete-operational,* stages, particularly the attainment of the concept of conservation. The results of many of these studies are somewhat puzzling. Although older children are generally more likely to show conservation than younger children, it is not clear what to make of the apparent finding that the attainment of conservation is much delayed in many non-Western populations. Indeed, in some places, most of the adults tested do not appear to understand one or more of the conservation properties.

Can this be true? Do people in different cultures differ that much in intellectual functioning, or is there some problem with the way conservation is measured? Is it possible that an adult who just brought water from the river in a large jug and poured it into five smaller containers does not know that the quantity of water is still the same? We may also be skeptical about the findings on the formal-operational stage. Most of the studies of formal-operational thinking have found little evidence of such thinking in non-Western populations. But people in nonliterate societies surely have formal-operational thinking if they can navigate using the stars, remember how to return to camp after a 15-mile trek, or identify how people are related to each other three and more generations back.

One reason to be skeptical about the apparent findings regarding delay of conservation and formal-operational thinking is that most of the cross-cultural psychologists have taken tests developed in our own and other Western countries to measure cognitive development elsewhere.[13] This procedure puts non-Westerners at a considerable disadvantage, because they are not as familiar as Westerners with the test materials and the whole testing situation. In tests of conservation, for example, researchers have often used strange-looking glass cylinders and beakers. Some researchers who have used natively familiar materials, however, have gotten different results. Douglass Price-Williams found no difference between Tiv, in West Africa, and European children in understanding the conservation of earth, nuts, and number.[14] Also, some researchers have retested children after brief training sessions and found that they improved substantially. It would seem, then, that children anywhere can acquire the concept of conservation if they have had preparatory life experiences or appropriate training.[15]

The results of tests elsewhere on formal-operational thinking may also be questionable. Such tests ask questions dealing with content that is taught in science and mathematics classes. It should not be surprising, then, that schooled individuals usually do better than the unschooled on tests of formal-operational thinking. Where compulsory schooling is lacking, we should not expect people to do well on tests of such thinking.[16]

In trying to find out what may be universal in emotional and cognitive development, researchers have discovered some apparent differences between societies. These differences, to which we now turn, need to be explored and explained.

THE ANTHROPOLOGY OF CHILDHOOD

One thing is common in all human societies—a long period in which the young are dependent on parents and other caretakers. This is one of the most notable human characteristics that differentiates us from our closest biological relatives. Also unusual is the parental role fathers play and the long stage of life following reproduction.[17] In many animals, life ends shortly after reproduction ends. Human females typically stop being able to reproduce much earlier than males, but this gives them a long period of time to be grandmothers and help their children with their reproduction. Exactly why the long period of dependency evolved is a matter of some debate,[18] but this period of time, which we are loosely calling childhood (including here infancy and adolescence), is critical for understanding what kind of people we become. It provides a long period of time to acquire much of the complexity of human social and cultural life. Childhood is also a time when learning from nonparental figures can lead to rapid changes in ideas and behavior. Consider the changes in technology in the world today. Children are much more comfortable, as well as much more adept, with technological innovations than their parents. Children often become the teachers of their parents, showing the parents how to use the new technology.

Anthropologists interested in childhood are increasingly looking at children as agents and actors, not just as recipients of socialization. Children not only have their own culture they can tell us about, but they also have opinions, anxieties, and fears that only they can express. But their voices are often ignored, just as women's voices were often ignored in the past.[19]

It is generally agreed that our personalities are the result of an interaction between genetic inheritance and life experiences. But a considerable portion of one's life experiences, as well as one's genes, is shared with others. Parents undoubtedly exert a major influence on the way we grow up. Because family members share similar life experiences and genes, they may be somewhat similar in personality. But we have to consider why a particular family raises children the way it does. Much of the way parents rear children is influenced by their culture—by typical

patterns of family life and by shared conceptions of the way to bring up children.

Socialization is a term both anthropologists and psychologists use to describe the development, through the influence of parents and other people, of patterns of behavior, and attitudes and values, in children that conform to cultural expectations. (The term **enculturation** has a similar meaning.) But, although these terms imply a mechanism to replicate culture (the "cookie-cutter" view of culture), we know that parents don't always follow societal dictates. Moreover, most parents consciously or unconsciously change with changing times, particularly as their family circumstances change. If a family no longer relies on agriculture because they now rely on wage labor, their expectations and their treatment of children will probably change.

It is not easy to determine the extent to which members of a society share conceptions about childrearing. As we look at families in our own society, we see differences in upbringing that reflect different ideas about the "right" way to raise children. Some parents seem to go along with "conventional" ideas about childrearing; others seem determined to bring up their children in ways that buck the conventional. Still, in a study of California families headed by single mothers, unmarried couples, or living in communes, researchers found that these so-called "unconventional parents" actually did not differ that much from "conventional" parents (married, living in nuclear families) compared with parents in other societies.[20] For example, even though unconventional California mothers breast-fed their children for a significantly longer period than conventional mothers did, both groups usually stopped breast-feeding after about a year, which is far below the worldwide average. In 70 percent of the world's societies, mothers typically breast-feed children for at least two years; last-born children may be weaned even later. In a few societies, such as the Chenchu of India, children typically were not weaned until they were 5 or 6 years old.[21] In the California study, no parent, conventional or unconventional, was observed to carry a baby more than 25 percent of the time, but it is common in many preindustrial societies for babies to be held more than half the day.[22] The point here is that, although some parents tried to be different, and indeed were different, they were in many respects not that different from each other when compared on a worldwide scale. But did the unconventional parents bring about culture change? The parental style of holding babies may not be that common in American culture, but it is much more common than it used to be. So although the new behaviors are not yet customary, cultural patterns have shifted.

Explaining Variation in Childhood and Beyond

When we discuss variation in how children are brought up in the following sections, there are two common types of explanation. The first has to do with general belief systems about children. Societies do not just have ideas about individual aspects of childrearing, such as how often to nurse

Children are adept at using new technology, as this young monk in Burma (Myanmar) demonstrates as he plays a video game.

and for how long, and where to put children to sleep, but societies also have their own theories about childhood. These theories suggest why societies do what they do. In heterogenous societies, different ethnic groups and different classes of people often have different theories. But what might explain these different belief systems? Some belief systems and consequently some childrearing systems may have consequences for survival. Adaptational explanations may suggest why different childrearing customs are adapted to different environments. Finally, there is the possibility that some aspects of personality have genetic or physiological explanations.

Parents' Belief Systems In most of the world, parents do not read books about how to bring up children. Indeed, they may not consciously think at all about their behavior toward children. But parents in all cultures do have ideas about what kinds of children they want to raise and how children should be treated. Many of these ideas are culturally patterned; they have been called "ethnotheories."[23] For example, Sara Harkness and Charles Super, who studied Dutch parents and infants, found that Dutch parents believe in what they term the "three Rs"—*rust* (rest), *regelmaat* (regularity), and *reinheid* (cleanliness). Parents follow a calm and regular routine for babies, try not to overstimulate their children by giving them too many things to look at, and surprisingly, for Americans, have babies who sleep a great deal more. (At six months of age, Dutch babies slept an average of 15 hours a day compared with 13 hours for American babies.) When an American mother will think a baby is bored and give her another toy, a Dutch mother will think the baby is tired and put her to sleep.[24]

Although it is important to understand parental ethnotheories, it is also important to evaluate whether parents behave in accordance with their theories, and whether parental behaviors produce the effects that parents want. Researchers need to observe parent-child behavior, not just understand what parents say they want to do, and they need to observe outcomes in children. Some behaviors by parents and other caretakers do not have the intended effects. American parents, particularly middle-class parents, stress independence and self-reliance, but behavior observations suggest that children frequently seek attention from parents and parents reward this kind of dependency. Even countercultural parents who reject many middle-class values behave in the same ways with their children.[25]

Adaptational Explanations Cultural anthropologists seek not only to establish connections between childrearing customs and personality traits but also to learn why those customs differ in the first place. Some anthropologists believe that childrearing practices are largely adaptive—that a society produces the kinds of personalities best suited to performance of the activities necessary for the survival of the society. As John Whiting and Irvin Child expressed it, "The economic, political and social organs of a society—the basic customs surrounding the nourishment, sheltering, and protection of its members . . . seem a likely source of influence on child training practices."[26]

The belief that childrearing practices are adaptive does not mean that societies always produce the kinds of people they need. Just as in the biological realm, where we see poor adaptations and extinctions of species and subspecies, so we may expect that societies sometimes produce personality traits that are maladapted to the requirements of living in that society. So we cannot assume that a trait must be adaptive just because it is present. We cannot come to that conclusion unless we carefully investigate whether the trait is beneficial or harmful.[27] But we do expect that most societies that have survived to be recorded have produced personality traits that are mostly adaptive.

The anthropology of childrearing involves comparison. Our own cultural conceptions begin to become apparent only when we examine other societies and their patterns of childrearing.

Possible Genetic and Physiological Influences Some researchers have suggested that genetic or physiological differences between populations predispose them to have different personality characteristics. Daniel Freedman found differences in "temperament" in newborn babies of different ethnic groups; because he observed newborns, the differences between them were presumed to be genetic. Comparing Chinese and European American newborns with the families matched on income, number of previous children, and so on, Freedman found that European American babies cried more easily, were harder to console, and fought experimental procedures more. Chinese babies, on the other hand, seemed calmer and more adaptable. Navajo babies were similar to the Chinese, showing even more calmness.[28] Freedman also suggested that an infant's behavior can influence how the parents respond. A calm baby may encourage a calm parental response; a more active baby may encourage a more active response.[29] So, in Freedman's view, babies' genetically determined behavior can lead to ethnic differences in adult personality and caretaking styles. But we cannot rule out nongenetic explanations of babies' behavior. For example, the mother's diet or her blood pressure could affect the baby's behavior. And it may be that the baby can learn even in the womb. After all, babies in the womb apparently can hear and respond to sounds and other stimuli. Therefore, it is possible that in societies in which pregnant women are calm, their babies may have learned calmness even before they were born. Last, we still do not know if the initial differences observed in newborn babies persist to become personality differences in adulthood.

Just as the diet of the mother, including the intake of alcohol and drugs, may affect the developing fetus, the diet of infants and children may also affect their intellectual development and their behavior. Studies have shown that malnutrition is associated with lower levels of activity, less attentiveness, lack of initiative, and low tolerance of frustration. Behavior of children can change with short-term nutrition supplements. For example, Guatemalan children who were given nutritional supplements were observed to have less anxiety, more exploratoriness, and greater involvement in games than children who were not given supplements.[30] The problem of malnutrition is not just a matter

One major difference in childrearing between the West and other places is the degree to which caretakers hold infants during the day. In the United States and other Western countries, infants spend much of the day in a crib, playpen, or stroller. The Dao babies from Yunnan Province in China (on the right) spend a good deal of time in physical contact with their mother or other caretaker.

of nutrition. Other kinds of care may also be reduced. For example, caretakers of malnourished children may interact with them less than do caretakers of healthy children. As a malnourished child shows reduced activity, caretakers tend to respond to the child with lower frequency and less enthusiasm. Then the child withdraws from interaction, creating a potentially serious vicious cycle.[31] Another possible influence, which we discuss later, is how hypoglycemia may affect adult expressions of aggression.

CROSS-CULTURAL VARIATION IN CHILDREARING

In what follows, we examine some aspects of childhood that appear to vary cross-culturally.[32] When we can, we discuss possible explanations for these patterns.

Parental Responsiveness to Infants and Baby-Holding

Consider how societies vary in how quickly parents respond to an infant's needs, in other words, the degree of "indulgence." In many aspects of indulgence—amount of time holding, feeding on demand, responding to crying—industrialized societies such as the United States tend to indulge babies less than do preindustrialized societies. In contrast to those preindustrial societies in which babies are held more than half the day, sometimes almost all day, consider the United States, England, and the Netherlands, where babies may spend most of the day in devices such as playpens, rockers, swings, or cribs. It is estimated that babies are held or touched only 12 percent to 20 percent of their daytime hours in these countries and in Japan. The same pattern continues at nighttime. In most preindustrial societies, babies are much more apt to be close to another person, usually sleeping with the mother in the same bed or, if not in the same bed, in the same room. During the

day, babies are breast-fed in all preindustrial societies, usually on demand. In industrialized societies, bottle-feeding is common, and feeding is usually spaced out every few hours; in some preindustrial societies, babies are breast-fed 20 to 40 times a day. And in many preindustrial societies, people respond very quickly to an infant's crying. For example, among the Efe of the Ituri Forest in central Africa, a 3-month-old infant who cries gets a response within 10 seconds 75 percent of the time. In the United States, a caregiver deliberately *does not* respond at all about 45 percent of the time.[33]

The cross-cultural variation just described seems to reflect cultural attitudes toward childrearing. Parents in the United States say that they do not want their babies to be dependent and clingy; they want to produce independent and self-reliant children. Whether children become self-reliant because of our kind of childrearing is debatable,[34] but our attitudes about childrearing are certainly consistent with our practices.

We think of a quick response of parents to infants as "indulgence," but although many mothers respond quickly to the baby's physical needs, this does not mean that mothers interact with them when they respond, by looking at the baby in the eye, responding to babbling, or kissing and hugging them. Often the mother is doing something else while she nurses the baby.[35]

Ruth and Robert Munroe studied the effects of more versus less holding by the mother in infancy on Logoli children.[36] The Munroes had observational information on how often infants were held, and they were able to interview many of these individuals as children five years later. They were interested in seeing whether children who had been held more often by their mothers were more secure, trusting, and optimistic. So they designed a series of personality measures appropriate for young children. As a measure of optimism, they showed children smiling faces and nonsmiling faces and asked which they preferred. As measures of trust, they looked to see how long a child was willing to stay in a room with a stranger or play with new toys.

The results of the study suggest that children who were often held or carried by their mothers as infants are significantly more trusting and optimistic at age 5 than are other children. Somewhat to their surprise, the Munroes found that, although time held by other caregivers did not predict more trust and optimism, the sheer number of different people who had held the infant did predict more trust and optimism. Holding by the mother was important, but trust was even greater if a large number of other people had held the baby. One possible explanation is that a highly trusting mother is likely to allow many others to hold the baby; by doing so, she conveys trust to the baby.

Robert LeVine suggested an adaptational explanation for the frequent holding and feeding of infants and quick response of caretakers in preindustrial societies.[37] Only 1 percent of infants die in industrial societies in the first year of life, but typically more than 20 percent die in preindustrial societies. What can parents do? Parents often do not have access to modern medical care, but they can respond to a baby's fussing immediately if the baby is with them. Also, babies may be safer off the ground if there are cooking fires, dangerous insects, and snakes in the vicinity. When survival is not so much at issue, LeVine suggests, parents can safely leave babies more on their own.

High mortality of infants may also explain why mothers in many of these same societies rarely interact with their infants in more emotional ways—it may help protect them emotionally in case of the infant's early death.

We really don't know much about the long-range effects of short or long response times on the infant. As long as a baby is fed fairly regularly and held some of the time, it might make little difference to the ultimate outcome. We can be more sure that, if a baby's needs are seriously ignored, there will be negative physical and social consequences.

Parent-Child Play

In Western societies, it is commonly thought that "good" parents should provide their children with toys and play with them frequently, starting from birth and continuing through adolescence. Parents who do not do this are viewed as deficient. Yet, cross-culturally. parent-child play is exceedingly rare except perhaps in foraging groups. It is not that play is rare. Children the world over play by themselves or with peers. Often, they make their own toys or pretend objects. Adults play too, usually games, but they don't play as often as children. And when children and adults play, they generally do so separately.[38]

Inuit mothers and babies are together for long periods in their houses when the weather is harsh. Under traditional conditions, there are often no playmates or other caretakers nearby, so perhaps it is not surprising that mothers play with their infants and young children, and make toys for them. Play with infants also occurs in many small foraging bands, but it is typically play with others beside their mothers.[39]

Lack of play with parents may be related to the same factor that probably explains high responsiveness to infant physical needs—high mortality of infants and the psychological need of parents to create emotional distance. But some societal ethnotheories suggest to parents that not playing may be better than play. The Yucatec Maya believe that "a quiet baby is a healthy baby" and, rather than stimulate babies, they are lulled to sleep whenever possible.[40] Babies are commonly thought to be "brainless" and so there is no point to interaction. On Ifaluk, in the Caroline Islands, parents say that "Infants younger than two years of age do not have any thoughts/feelings—*nunuwan*. Without nunuwan, . . . it's useless . . . talking to babies younger than two."[41]

We turn now to the period of time after infancy.

Parental Acceptance and Rejection of Children

What about the overall quality of parenting? Are there positive effects on personality when parents show love, warmth, and affection to their children and negative effects when parents are indifferent or hostile to their children?

Children the world over play, sometimes with toys they make themselves.

These questions are difficult to investigate cross-culturally because cultures vary in the ways feeling is expressed. If love and affection are not expressed in the same ways, outsiders may misinterpret parental behavior. Nevertheless, Ronald Rohner and his colleagues did extensive work on the effects of parental acceptance and rejection on children after infancy. In a cross-cultural comparison of 101 societies, using measures based on ethnographic materials, Rohner found that children tend to be hostile and aggressive when they are neglected and not treated affectionately by their parents. In societies in which children tend to be rejected, adults seem to view life and the world as unfriendly, uncertain, and hostile.[42] A large number of other studies have compared individuals in different cultures to see if the cross-cultural findings were supported. In general, they were. In addition to finding the world more unfriendly and hostile, individuals who think they were rejected are likely to be hostile and aggressive, emotionally unresponsive or unstable, and have negative evaluations of themselves.[43]

Under what conditions is parental rejection likely in childhood? The Rohner study suggests that rejection is likely where mothers get no relief from child care; when fathers and grandparents play a role in child care, rejection is less likely. Foraging societies (those dependent on wild food resources) tend to show warmth and affection to their children. More complex societies are less likely to be affectionate to their children.[44] It is not clear why this should be, but perhaps parental rejection is more likely where parents have less leisure time. Less leisure time may make parents more tired and irritable and therefore have less patience with their children. As we noted in the chapter on economic systems, leisure time probably decreases as cultural complexity increases. More complex societies, which rely on intensive agriculture, also tend to have more economic uncertainty, as we noted in the chapter on getting food. Not only do they tend to have more risk of famines and food shortages, but they also tend to have social inequality. In societies with social classes, many families may not have enough food and money to satisfy their needs, and this factor can also produce frustration in the parents. Whatever the reasons for parental rejection, it seems to perpetuate itself: Children who were rejected tend to reject their own children.

Compliance or Assertiveness

Herbert Barry, Irvin Child, and Margaret Bacon cross-culturally investigated the possibility that child-training practices are adapted to the economic requirements of a society. Such requirements, they theorized, might explain why some societies strive to develop "compliant" (responsible, obedient, nurturant) children, whereas others aim more for "assertiveness" (independence, self-reliance, and achievement).[45] The cross-cultural results indicated that agricultural and herding societies are likely to stress responsibility and obedience, whereas hunting and gathering societies tend to stress self-reliance and individual assertiveness. The investigators suggested that agricultural and herding societies cannot afford departures from established routine, because departures might jeopardize the food supply for long periods. Such societies, therefore, are

Children in many societies learn a lot by imitation as well as by instruction.

likely to emphasize compliance with tradition. Departures from routine in a hunter-gatherer society cannot cause much damage to a food supply that has to be collected anew almost every day. So hunter-gatherers can afford to emphasize individual initiative.

Although our own society relies on food production and has large stores of accumulated food, we seem more like hunter-gatherers in emphasizing individual initiative. Are we, then, exceptions to the Barry et al. findings? Not really. Hardly any of us are farmers (in the United States, less than 2 percent of the total population is still on the farm), and most of us expect that we can "forage" in the supermarket or "store" just about anytime. Perhaps more important is the fact that our highly commercial economy, with most people dwelling in or near cities, requires us to compete to get jobs to make a living. In our kind of economy, then, individual initiative is important too. Consider the results of a cross-national comparison of eight countries in which the researchers asked parents what quality they most wanted their school-age children to have. Parents in the more rural countries (Indonesia, Philippines, and Thailand) seldom mentioned independence and self-reliance but those in the more urban countries (Korea, Singapore, and the United States) did.[46]

Attitudes Towards Aggression

Societies also differ considerably in their attitudes toward aggression in children. Some societies actively encourage children to be aggressive, not only to each other but even to the parents. Among the Xhosa of southern Africa, 2- or 3-year-old boys will be prodded to hit each other in the face and women look on laughing. Similar behavior is described for the Gapun of Papua New Guinea; even raising a knife to an older sibling is rewarded.[47] Yanomamö boys of the Venezuelan-Brazilian Amazon are encouraged to be aggressive and are rarely punished for hitting either their parents or the girls in the village. One father, for example, lets his son Ariwari

> beat him on the face and head to express his anger and temper, laughing and commenting on his ferocity. Although Ariwari is only about 4 years old, he has already learned that the appropriate response to a flash of anger is to strike someone with his hand or with an object, and it is not uncommon for him to give his father a healthy smack in the face whenever something displeases him. He is frequently goaded into hitting his father by teasing, being rewarded by gleeful cheers of assent from his mother and from the other adults in the household.[48]

In contrast, the Semai of central Malaya are famous for their timidity. Robert Dentan reports that they say that they do not get angry.[49] Whereas other societies clearly and actively encourage aggression, the Semai communicate nonviolence in more subtle ways. They say, in fact, that they do not teach children. The Semai expect children to be nonviolent and are shocked when they are not. When a child loses his or her temper, an adult will simply cart the child off. The Semai do not physically punish a child's

aggression, and this approach may be one of the most important teaching devices of all. With such teaching—by example—a child rarely sees an aggressive model and thus has no aggression to imitate.[50] In comparison, hardly any North American parents would encourage children to hit them in the face or encourage them to hit other children. Yet many probably use physical punishment sometimes, and many feel that boys especially should "stand up for themselves" if another child provokes a fight.

With regard to aggression, research has shown that children who are physically punished when they are aggressive (the parents trying to minimize aggression) actually exhibit more aggression than children who are not physically punished. Children who are hit may learn not to hit their parents and other caretakers, but the aggression caretakers exhibit seems to be a model for children's aggressive behavior. If children see a parent or other caretaker acting aggressively, they may conclude that it is okay for them to act aggressively.[51]

As we discuss later in the global problems chapter, a society's involvement in war cross-culturally predicts parental encouragement of aggression, particularly in boys. Socialization for aggression appears to decrease after a society is pacified or forced to stop fighting.[52]

Task Assignment

In our society, young children are not expected to help much with chores. If they do have chores, such as tidying up their rooms, they are not likely to affect the welfare of the family or its ability to survive. In contrast, in some societies known to anthropology, young children, even 3- and 4-year-olds, are expected to help prepare food, care for animals, and carry water and firewood, as well as clean. A child between 5 years and 8 years of age may even be given the responsibility of caring for an infant or toddler for much of the day while the mother works in the fields.[53] What are the effects of such task assignment on personality development?

We now have evidence from more than 10 cultures that children who regularly babysit are more nurturant—that is, offer more help and support to others—than are other children, even when the children who babysit are not babysitting. Some of this evidence comes from a project known as the Six Cultures study, in which different research teams observed children's behavior in Kenya (Nyansongo), Mexico, India, the Philippines, Okinawa, and the United States (New England).[54] Ruth and Robert Munroe collected data on children's behavior in four other cultures that show the same relationship between babysitting and nurturant behavior; the Munroes' data come from Kenya (Logoli), Nepal, Belize, and American Samoa.[55] Clearly, children who babysit infrequently are less attuned to others' needs than are children who babysit often.

Why might task assignment affect the behaviors of children? One possibility is that children learn certain behaviors during performance of the task, and these behaviors become habitual. For example, a responsible babysitter is supposed to offer help. Mothers might directly instruct the babysitter to make sure that happens. But there is probably also an intrinsic satisfaction in doing a job

applied anthropology

Schools: Values and Expectations

Most people think of schools as teaching skills such as reading and writing and subjects such as history, math, biology, or social science. But schools also convey much more about the society and individuals' places in it. They do not just teach content. We focus here on cultural values and expectations.

Joseph Tobin, David Wu, and Dana Davidson videotaped preschool classroom scenes in Japan, China, and the United States. In each country, they asked children, teachers, parents, and school administrators to comment on the scenes in all three countries. We can get a feel for how different values are implicitly taught in each country by reviewing the comments.

When individuals in the United States viewed the Japanese tape, two things generally bothered them. One was the fact that children in Japan often did the same things simultaneously as a group. For example, the teacher showed what to fold first and subsequently to make an origami bird figure, and the children followed along. Parents and teachers in the United States said that children should have more choice in what to do and how to do it. The second

thing that bothered people in the United States, as well as in China, was that the teacher in Japan appeared to ignore what we might consider "unruly" behavior by the children. For example, when children got restless during a group workbook activity, they would leave their seats, joke with friends, or go to the bathroom. In the tape, a particularly troublesome boy talked loudly, sometimes purposely hurt other children, and threw things around, but the teacher seemed to ignore these behaviors. People in the United States and China thought that the teacher should try to do something in such situations. In Japan, however, most of the teachers preferred not to call attention to, or single out, a troublesome child. Japanese teachers expect such a child eventually to behave more appropriately, and they encourage the other children to exert social pressure in that direction. In Lois Peak's words: "Learning to go to school in Japan is primarily defined as training in group life."

Most of the activities in the Chinese preschool were highly structured. For example, the first task of the day was building with blocks, but in contrast to the style at the

Japanese preschool, the children in China were expected to complete the task on their own and to do so in silence. If they spoke, the teacher reprimanded them. They used a picture as a guide for what to do. When they were done, the teachers checked their work. If they got it right, they took it apart and rebuilt it; if they got it wrong, they were asked to correct it. An arithmetic lesson followed. Children then ate the lunch that was brought for them into the classroom. Teachers monitored the lunch to make sure that the children ate all their food and ate in silence. After an afternoon nap, the children listened to a patriotic story and then had relay races, which were followed by 15 minutes of free play. Supper was served at 5:00 P.M. and parents came at 6:00. In seeing the videotapes, Americans and Japanese were bothered by the rigidity and "overcontrol" of the children and by the lack of privacy in their communal bathroom.

In the U.S. preschool, in Honolulu, as in Japan, parents brought their children at different times, but some parents stayed with the child for as long as a half hour. Compared with the other preschools, the U.S.

performance raises the serious issue of how much of what we observe about child development in our society and in other Western societies is simply a function of what children are taught in school. After all, children who grow up in this society not only get older each year, they also go one year further in school. Schools are not just places to learn a particular curriculum. Children learn to interact with one another and with adults who are not parents and family. Therefore, we might expect that schools not only shape cognition but also convey important cultural attitudes, values, and appropriate ways of behaving toward others (see the box "Schools: Values and Expectations").

Schooling does seem to predict having a personality trait we call "patience." The more schooling you have, the more patience you have. In a study conducted among the Tsimane, a horticultural people living in the Bolivian Amazon, patience or a tolerance for delayed gratification is associated with a wide range of advantages, including higher income, more wealth, and better health. These positive

outcomes may be partly the result of respect for authority, obedience, and conformity, which schooling may instill.[65]

PSYCHOLOGICAL VARIATION IN ADULTHOOD

So far, we have focused on the anthropology of childhood. But there are characteristics of adults (as well as children) that appear to vary as well. Some of these concepts, such as ideas about the self, may shape childrearing as well.

Concepts of the Self   Anthropologists have begun to study different cultural ideas of personhood or concept of the "self." Many have concluded that the concept of self in many non-Western societies is quite different from the Western conception. Clifford Geertz described the Western conception of the person as "bounded, unique, . . . a dynamic center of awareness, emotion, judgment, and action organized into a distinctive whole."[66] He claimed, preschool emphasized individual participation and individualized activity. For example, "show and tell" was voluntary; sometimes only three kids decided to get up and talk. In an activity involving a felt board, each child was asked to add something to the board. Much of the rest of the day was spent in "learning centers"; the teachers helped the children decide which center they would like to go to. Children started at one activity but could change if they wished. Even lunch was more individual. All children took their lunch boxes to a big table where they all ate and talked animatedly. The U.S. teacher, in contrast to the Japanese teacher, intervened when a child misbehaved, such as when one boy grabbed a block from another. Without raising her voice, the teacher asked the two children to talk to each other about the disagreement. She resorted to a "time-out" (a period of isolation) when the dispute was not settled by talking.

Even though they do not teach values explicitly, these preschools clearly convey values. The value of the individual appears to be stressed most in the U.S. preschool, where most of the daily activities allowed individual choice of some kind. In both Japan and China, group activities predominated, although the Japanese preschool allowed flexible arrival times, more free play, and more freedom to talk or move about than the Chinese preschool. Second

is the source of control. The Japanese teachers relied informally on the group to control the children's behavior. For example, after nine months, the unruly boy sat by himself at lunch; the other children did not want to sit with him. In contrast, the Chinese teachers saw to it that the children behaved like others in the group by exerting strong control over the children's behavior. The U.S. teachers also intervened in response to unruly behavior.

Cultural values are not unchanging. For example, although many Japanese educational administrators thought that the Japanese preschool was quite "Japanese" in style, and therefore satisfactory, a considerable number of Japanese parents and teachers were critical of the school and said there were "better" schools in Japan that were more like the U.S. preschool. And some Japanese thought that more attention should be paid to the individual needs of troubled children. When some Chinese saw the tapes of the Chinese school, they complained that it was too "old-fashioned."

Recent research also shows how much cultural expectations shape school performance. Most of this research has focused on minority students. Most of them are not often expected to do well by their teachers and others because of cultural stereotypes. Indeed, in most tests in school, these students do less well. The important

question is whether stereotyped expectations hamper performance, or whether performance has to do with factors having nothing to do with school. Many experiments have confirmed that, even after controlling for factors like family wealth, even subtle reminders of cultural stereotypes cause performance to suffer. The cues can be as simple as saying that the test measures intelligence (in contrast to the control group told that they will not be evaluated on their performance) or asking the person for their "race" (in contrast to not asking) as one of a number of background questions.

What can be done to improve performance? Some suggestions are to tell students that human abilities and skills are changeable, not fixed; another is to give them challenging work that conveys that they are capable. One of the most fascinating studies was a comparison of African American and European American students before and after Barack Obama was elected President of the United States. Before the election, the African Americans, even though matched on ability, did worse than the European Americans. After the election, the differences practically disappeared. This study strongly suggests that conditions in the larger society affect performance.

Sources: Tobin et al. 1989; Peak 1991; Lock 2009; Aronson 2002; Nisbett 2009.

---

on the basis of his fieldwork in Java, Bali, and Morocco, that those societies have very different conceptions of a person, not only different from each other but quite different from the Western conception. For example, Geertz said that the Balinese describe a person as having many different roles, like an actor who plays different characters. The unique characteristics of a person are not emphasized; what is emphasized are the "masks" people wear and the "parts" they play.

Geertz focused on the variation and uniquenesses in different cultures' conceptions of the self. But other scholars think that there are recognizable and predictable patterns in this variation. One of the most talked-about patterns is the Western emphasis on the self as an autonomous individual and the non-Western emphasis on the relations a person has with others.[67] Labels used to describe such Western and non-Western cultural differences are "individualism" versus "holism" or "collectivism," "egocentric" versus "sociocentric," and the like.[68] For example,

the Japanese concept of self is often described as "relational" or "situational"; people exist in networks of relationships and the ideal person has the ability to shift easily from one social situation to another.[69]

There are two major objections to the idea that the Western sense of self should be contrasted with the non-Western. The first is that studies of other cultures have suggested other dimensions of variation besides "individualism" versus "collectivism." For example, the traditional Inuit concept *inummarik*, "a genuine person," seems to include a lifelong process of ecological involvement—interacting with animals and the environment as well as people.[70] A culture's concept of self, then, may include other dimensions besides individual versus collective. A second objection to the Western/non-Western contrast is that it may not be based on adequate evidence. As Melford Spiro pointed out, it is necessary to find out how a sample of individuals in a society actually view themselves. The ideal in the culture might be different from the actual.[71]

individual child's potential, and in recent times with the introduction of schools, they value education for their children. School is not free, so parents have to sacrifice to send their children to school. Schoolgirls stress that schooling gives them more options, not only to get better paying jobs in the future, but also to have more freedom and less dependency on a husband. Schoolgirls emphasize that schooling allows them to be honorable. Honor brings privilege and prestige, but the concept also involves becoming more rational and controlling choices, including being more choosy about men with whom to be involved, and controlling the conditions under which they become mothers. It is not that young women believe in abstaining from sex—sex is viewed as natural and important, but young women employ strategies to delay motherhood. These include periodic abstinence, aborting pregnancies, and giving up children to fosterage if they are not ready to be mothers. Rationality also entails knowing that you cannot have a lot of children if there are not enough resources.[90]

In Senegal, after independence, development programs favored men by promoting plow agriculture and distributing seed to heads of households. But judging by the Wolof peanut farmers that Donna Perry studied, men's advantages were short-lived. In the mid-1980s, agricultural cooperatives were dissolved and economic supports were eliminated. Cash-cropping by small farm households has diminished, and men appear to be suffering a crisis of masculinity as their wives trade more in the weekly markets (*loumas*). Men express their frustration: "You wake up in the morning now and don't even know who the head of the household is!"[91] It is hard to know in advance where this anxiety will lead. It could be that, as males' authority diminishes, they will become more conservative in an attempt to recapture the old ways. Or, males and females could move toward more shared authority. Conflict may play out at the individual level, which may lead to culture change.

SUMMARY ● ○ ○

1. Anthropologists who are interested in the relationships between culture and the individual and the importance of understanding psychological processes call themselves psychological anthropologists. Four main questions characterize psychological anthropology: (1) To what extent do all human beings develop psychologically in the same ways? (2) If there are differences, what are they and what may account for them? (3) How do people in different societies conceive of individuals and their psychological development? and (4) How can understanding individuals or psychological processes help us understand culture and culture change?

2. Early research in psychological anthropology was concerned mainly with how cultural differences seem to affect supposedly universal stages of emotional development. Some doubt has been cast on the idea that adolescence is necessarily a time of "storm and stress" and that the Oedipus complex, at least in the form stated by Freud, is universal. But there appear to be some universals in the psychological realm, including creating taxonomies, plans for the future, a concept of the self or person, trying to discern the intention of others, the ability to recognize emotions and to play, and to feel affection, sexual attraction, envy, and jealousy.

3. Recent research on universals in psychological development has been concerned more with cognitive, or intellectual, development. In looking for universals, many researchers have discovered some apparent differences. Most of the tests used in research may favor people in Western cultures and those who attend formal schools.

4. To understand cross-cultural variation in psychological characteristics, many researchers have tried to discover if variation in childrearing customs can account for the observed psychological differences.

5. Humans have a long period in which the young are dependent on caretakers. *Socialization* is a term anthropologists and psychologists use to describe the development, through the influence of parents and others, of patterns of behavior in children that conform to cultural expectations. But children are also agents and actors, not just recipients of socialization. They can learn from others, such as peers, in ways that may lead to rapid changes in behavior.

6. Many of the ideas parents have about childrearing come from societal belief systems or "ethnotheories" about children and how they should be treated. Some anthropologists believe societies produce the kinds of personality best suited to performance of the activities necessary for the survival of the society.

7. Societies vary considerably in how quickly they respond to an infant's needs, how much infants are held, how much parents play with infants and young children, how much warmth and affection they show children, how much they expect children to comply with adults or assert themselves, and how aggressive they want children to be. There is also considerable variation in how much children are assigned chores and responsibilities and go to school.

8. One of the most profound effects on cognitive thinking appears to be how much schooling a person has.

9. Some adult differences in psychological traits have been documented in different societies. These include a difference in perceptual style known as field independence versus field dependence (that may be related to economic differences) and difference in display of aggression (that may be also related to economic differences as well as to involvement in war).

10. Psychological anthropologists are interested not only in the possible causes of psychological differences between societies but also in the possible consequences of psychological variation, particularly how psychological

characteristics may help us understand statistical associations between various aspects of culture.

11. Recently, anthropologists have explored how individuals can be agents of culture change.

GLOSSARY TERMS ○ ● ○

enculturation **332**

personality integration
   of culture **344**

primary institutions **344**

projective tests **345**

secondary
   institutions **344**

socialization **332**

CRITICAL QUESTIONS ○ ○ ●

1. Do you think indulging children makes them more or less self-reliant as adults? Why do you think so?
2. What may explain adolescent rebelliousness?

3. Agriculturalists and foragers seem to have somewhat different personalities, so the method of food-getting may be related to personality. Do you think there is a similar relationship between occupation and personality? If so, why?

PEARSON
myanthrolab

Read the chapter by Susan Schaefer Davis titled "Morocco: Adolescents in a Small Town" on MyAnthroLab, and answer the following questions:

1. Why do many (but not all) cultures have a stage of life called "adolescence"?
2. Do you think that rebelliousness is inevitable in adolescence?
3. Describe some of the aspects of adolescence that are different in Morocco from your own culture.

The division into just two genders—male/female—is very common cross-culturally. But a strict dichotomy is far from universal. Some societies, like the Cheyenne Native Americans of the Great Plains, recognized male, female, and a third gender, referred to by the Cheyennes as "two-spirits." "Two-spirit" people were usually biological males. The gender status of "two-spirit" was often recognized after a boy finished his vision quest, usually in his preadolescent years. A two-spirit person would wear women's dress and take on many of the activities of women. A two-spirit might even be taken as a second wife by a man, but whether the man and the two-spirit person engaged in sex is unknown. The role of a "two-spirit" person was not equivalent to becoming a woman, because two-spirits played special roles at weddings and childbirth. Europeans referred to a two-spirit individual as a *berdache*.[4] Accounts of "two-spirit" biological females who take on the role of men are relatively rare, but they do occur in a number of native North American societies, such as the Kaska of Yukon Territory, the Klamath of southern Oregon, and the Mohave of the Colorado River area in the southwestern United States. These biological female "two-spirits" could marry women, and such relationships were known to be lesbian relationships [5]

In Oman, there is a third gender role called *xanith*. Anatomically male, *xaniths* speak of themselves as "women." However, *xaniths* have their own distinctive dress—they wear clothes that are neither male nor female. In fact, their clothes and dress seem in-between. Men wear white clothes, women bright patterns, and *xaniths* wear unpatterned pastels. Men have short hair, women long, and *xaniths* are medium-length. Women are generally secluded in their houses and can only go out with permission from their husbands, but the *xanith* is free to come and go and works as a servant and/or a homosexual prostitute. But the *xanith* gender role is not necessarily forever. A *xanith* may decide to marry, and if he is able to have intercourse with his bride, he becomes a "man." An older *xanith* who is no longer attractive may decide to become an "old man."[6]

PHYSIQUE AND PHYSIOLOGY

As we noted earlier, males and females cannot readily be distinguished in some animal species. Although they differ in chromosome makeup and in their external and internal organs of reproduction, they do not differ otherwise. In contrast, humans are *sexually dimorphic*—that is, the two sexes of our species are generally different in size and appearance. Females have proportionately wider pelvises. Males typically are taller and have heavier skeletons. Females have a larger proportion of their body weight in fat; males have a larger proportion of body weight in muscle. Males typically have greater grip strength, proportionately larger hearts and lungs, and greater aerobic capacity (greater intake of oxygen during strenuous activity).

North American culture tends to view "taller" and "more muscled" as better, which may reflect a bias toward males. But how did these differences come about? Natural selection may have favored these traits in males but selected against them in females. Because females bear children, selection may have favored earlier cessation of growth, and therefore less ultimate height so that the nutritional needs of a fetus would not compete with a growing mother's needs.[7] (Females achieve their ultimate height shortly after puberty, but boys continue to grow for years after puberty.) Similarly, there is some evidence that females are less affected than males by nutritional shortages, presumably because they tend to be shorter and have proportionately more fat.[8] Natural selection may have favored more proportionate "fatness" in females because that resulted in greater reproductive success.

Athletes can build up their muscle strength and increase their aerobic work capacity through training. Given that fact, cultural factors, such as how much a society expects and allows males and females to engage in muscular activity, could influence the degree to which females and males differ muscularly and in aerobic capacity. Similar training may account for the recent trend toward decreasing differences between females and males in certain athletic events, such as marathons and swim meets. Even

Hmong women carry large loads of firewood to market.

when it comes to female and male physique and physiology, then, what we see may be the result of both culture and genes.[9]

GENDER ROLES

Productive and Domestic Activities

In the chapter on economic systems, we noted that all societies assign or divide labor somewhat differently between females and males. Because role assignments have a clear cultural component, we speak of them as **gender roles**. What is of particular interest here about the gender division of labor is not so much that every society has different work for males and females but rather that so many societies divide up work in similar ways. The question, then, is: Why are there universal or near-universal patterns in such assignments?

Table 20–1 summarizes the worldwide patterns indicating which activities are performed by which gender in all or almost all societies, which activities are usually performed by one gender, and which activities are commonly assigned to either gender or both. If every culture assigned work arbitrarily to the genders, there wouldn't be any patterns in the table. Although many tasks are assigned to both genders (the middle column), clearly some patterns are worldwide. One of the most striking is in primary subsistence activities; males almost always hunt and trap animals and females usually gather wild plants. Does this and the other distributions of activities in the table suggest

why females and males generally do different things? Scholars have suggested four explanations or theories that we label: *strength theory, compatibility-with-child-care theory, economy-of-effort theory,* and *expendability theory.*

The *strength theory* focuses on the generally greater strength of males and their superior capacity to mobilize their strength in quick bursts of energy (because of greater aerobic work capacity). Certainly, males may generally best perform activities that require lifting heavy objects (hunting large animals, butchering, clearing land, or working with stone, metal, or lumber), throwing weapons, and running with great speed (as in hunting). And none of the activities females usually perform, with the possible exception of collecting firewood, seem to require the same degree of physical strength or quick bursts of energy. But the strength theory is not completely convincing, if only because it cannot readily explain all the observed patterns. For example, it is not clear that the male activities of trapping small animals, collecting wild honey, or making musical instruments require much physical strength. Moreover, as we will see shortly, women do hunt in some societies, suggesting that differences in strength cannot play a very important role.

The *compatibility-with-child-care theory* emphasizes that women's tasks need to be compatible with child care. Although males can take care of infants, most traditional societies rely on breast-feeding of infants, which men cannot do. (In most societies, women breast-feed their children for two years on the average.) Women's tasks may be those that do not take them far from home for long

TABLE 20–1	Worldwide Patterns in the Division of Labor by Gender				
Type of Activity	Males Almost Always	Males Usually	Either Gender or Both	Females Usually	Females Almost Always
Primary subsistence activities	Hunt and trap animals, large and small	Fish Herd large animals Collect wild honey Clear land and prepare soil for planting	Collect shellfish Care for small animals Plant crops Tend crops Harvest crops Milk animals	Gather wild plants	
Secondary subsistence and household activities		Butcher animals	Preserve meat and fish	Care for children Cook Prepare vegetable foods, drinks, and dairy products Launder Fetch water Collect fuel	Care for infants
Other	Lumber Mine and quarry Make boats, musical instruments, and bone, horn, and shell objects Engage in combat	Build houses Make nets and rope Exercise political leadership	Prepare skins Make leather products, baskets, mats, clothing, and pottery	Spin yarn	

Source: Mostly adapted from Murdock and Provost 1973, 203–25. The information on political leadership and warfare comes from Whyte 1978a, 217. The information on child care comes from Weisner and Gallimore 1977, 169–80.

periods, do not place children in potential danger if they are taken along, and that can be stopped and resumed if an infant needs care. [10]

The compatibility theory may explain why *no* activities other than infant care are listed in the right-hand column of Table 20–1. That is, it may be that there are practically no universal or near-universal women-only activities because until recently most women have had to devote much of their time to nursing and caring for infants, as well as caring for other children. This theory may also explain why men usually perform tasks such as hunting, trapping, fishing, collecting honey, lumbering, and mining. Those tasks are dangerous for infants to be around, and in any case, would be difficult to coordinate with infant care.[11]

Finally, the compatibility theory may also explain why men seem to take over certain crafts in societies with full-time specialization. Although the distinction is not shown in Table 20–1, crafts such as making baskets, mats, and pottery are women's activities in noncommercial societies but tend to be men's activities in societies with full-time craft specialists.[12] Similarly, weaving tends to be a female activity unless it is produced for trade.[13] Full-time specialization and production for trade may increase incompatibility with child care. Cooking is a good example in our own society. Many women are excellent cooks and traditionally did most of the cooking at home, but chefs and bakers tend to be men. Women might be more likely to work as chefs if they could leave their babies and young children in safe places to be cared for by other people or if the hours chefs and bakers work were not so long.

But the compatibility theory does not explain why men usually prepare soil for planting, make objects out of wood, or work bone, horn, and shell. All of those tasks could probably be stopped to tend to a child, and none of them is any more dangerous to children nearby than is cooking. Why, then, do males tend to do them? The *economy-of-effort theory* may help explain patterns that cannot readily be explained by the strength and compatibility theories. For example, it may be advantageous for men to make wooden musical instruments because men generally lumber.[14] Lumbering may give men more knowledge about the physical properties of various woods and make it more likely that they know how to work with different woods. The economy-of-effort interpretation also suggests that it would be advantageous for one gender to perform tasks that are physically located near each other. If women have to be near home to take care of nursing and young children, it would be economical for them to perform other chores in or near the home.

Expendability theory suggests that men, rather than women, will tend to do the dangerous work in a society because the loss of men is less disadvantageous reproductively than the loss of women. If some men lose their lives in hunting, deep-water fishing, mining, quarrying, lumbering, and the like, reproduction need not suffer as long as most fertile women have sexual access to men—for example, if the society permits two or more women to be married to the same man.[15] If something is dangerous, why would anybody, male or female, be willing to do it?

In many farming societies, women can do some agriculture and take care of their young children at the same time, as this mother in Zambia demonstrates.

Perhaps only when society glorifies those roles and endows them with high prestige and other rewards.

Although the various theories, singly or in combination, seem to explain much of the division of labor by gender, there are some unresolved problems. Critics of the strength theory have pointed out that women in some societies do engage in very heavy labor.[16] If women in some societies can develop the strength to do such work, perhaps strength is more a function of training than traditionally has been believed.

The compatibility theory also has some problems. It suggests that labor is divided to conform to the requirements of child care. But sometimes it seems the other way around. For example, women who spend a good deal of time in agricultural work outside the home often ask others to watch and feed their infants while they are unavailable to nurse.[17] Consider, too, the mountain areas of Nepal, where agricultural work is incompatible with child care; heavy loads must be carried up and down steep slopes, fields are far apart, and labor takes up most of the day. Yet women do this work anyway and leave their infants with others for long stretches of time.[18]

Furthermore, in some societies, women hunt—one of the activities most incompatible with child care and generally not done by women. Many Agta women of the Philippines regularly hunt wild pig and deer; women alone or in groups kill almost 30 percent of the large game.[19] The women's hunting does not seem to be incompatible with child care. Women take nursing babies on hunting trips, and the women who hunt do not have lower reproductive rates than the women who choose not to hunt. Agta women may find it possible to hunt because the hunting grounds are only about a half hour from camp, the dogs that accompany the women assist in the hunting and protect the women and babies, and the women generally hunt in groups, so others can help carry babies as well as carcasses. Hunting by women is also fairly common among the Aka, forest foragers in the Central African Republic. Aka women participate in and sometimes lead in organizing cooperative net-hunting, in which an area is circled and animals are flushed out and caught in nets. Women spend approximately 18 percent of their time net-hunting, which is more than men do.[20] In the Canadian subarctic, teams of Chipewyan women would hunt small animals such as muskrats or rabbits, and would commonly join their husbands to hunt large animals such as moose. However, women noted that they would avoid hunting moose after their fourth or fifth month of pregnancy, so they mainly were part of the team when they were newly married and later when they were older. Women did not participate in long-distance hunts,[21] which also suggests that compatibility with child care was a consideration.

As the cases just described suggest, we need to know a lot more about labor requirements. More precisely, we need to know exactly how much strength is required in particular tasks, how dangerous those tasks are, and whether a person could stop working at a task to care for a child. So far, we have mostly guesses. When there is more systematically collected evidence on aspects of particular tasks, we will be in a better position to evaluate the various theories. In any case, none of the available theories implies that the worldwide patterns of division of labor shown in Table 20–1 will persist. As we know from our own and other industrial societies, a strict gender division of labor begins to disappear when machines replace human strength, when women have fewer children, and when women can assign child care to others.

RELATIVE CONTRIBUTIONS TO WORK

In the United States, there is a tendency to equate "work" with a job earning income. Until relatively recently, being a "homemaker" was not counted as an occupation. Anthropologists also tended to ignore household work; indeed, most of the research on division of labor by gender focuses on **primary subsistence activities**—gathering, hunting, fishing, herding, and farming—and relatively less attention is paid to gender contributions to **secondary subsistence activities,** those that involve the processing and preparation of food for eating or storing. With a few exceptions, food almost never can be consumed without preparation of some kind. For example, hunting cannot contribute much to the diet unless the meat is brought back home (cut up or carried whole) and butchered. If the animal is large, the meat often has to be prepared for distribution and/or storage. And as skins and other parts are

often used for clothing or tools, someone has to prepare those. As Hetty Jo Brumbach and Robert Jarvenpa point out, the Western model of hunting focuses on the "kill" (perhaps derived from the notion of sport-hunting) and ignores the complexity of processes associated with it. This view may hide women's role in "hunting" and emphasizes the male role as the "hunter."[22]

Overall Work

We can also ask whether males or females generally do more work. We do not yet have that many studies of how females and males spend their time, but studies of horticultural and intensive agricultural societies so far suggest that, if we count all the kinds of economic activities shown in Table 20–1, women typically work more total hours per day than men.[23] We do not know if this is a truly cross-cultural universal. However, we do know that, in many societies where women earn wages, they are still responsible for the bulk of the household work as well as the child care at home.

Subsistence Work

If we focus on contribution to primary subsistence activities, which are generally located further from the home, female and male contributions are more variable cross-culturally. Estimates of time actually working are not generally available, so most comparisons estimate how much each gender contributes to the diet in terms of caloric intake from primary subsistence activities.

In some societies, women have traditionally contributed more to the economy than men by any measure. For example, among the Tchambuli of New Guinea in the 1930s, the women did all the fishing—going out early in the morning by canoe to their fish traps and returning when the sun was hot. Some of the catch was traded for sago (a starch) and sugarcane, and it was the women who went on the long canoe trips to do the trading.[24]

In contrast, men did almost all of the primary subsistence work among the Toda of India. As they were described early in the 20th century, they depended for subsistence almost entirely on the dairy products of their water buffalo, either by using the products directly or by selling them for grain. Women were not allowed to have anything to do with dairy work; only men tended the buffalo and prepared the dairy products. Women's work was largely household work. Women prepared the purchased grain for cooking, cleaned house, and decorated clothing.[25]

A survey of a wide variety of societies has revealed that these extremes are not common. Usually both women and men contribute a good deal to primary food-getting activities, but men usually contribute more in most societies.[26] Because women are almost always occupied with infant and child care responsibilities, it is not surprising that men usually do most of the primary subsistence work, which generally has to be done away from the home.

Why do women in some societies do as much or more than men in primary subsistence work? Some of the variation is explained by the type of food-getting activities in the society. In societies that depend on hunting, fishing,

new perspectives on gender

Why Do Some Societies Allow Women to Participate in Combat?

U.S. women can serve in the military but are not in units directly engaged in combat. Some women feel that such exclusion is unfair and decreases their chances of promotion in the military. Other people, including some women, insist that female participation in combat would be detrimental to military performance or is inappropriate for women. Women in the U.S. military have been attacked in the course of their duties in Iraq and some have died. Some countries currently allow women to engage in combat. And in the 18th and 19th centuries, women made up one wing of the standing army in the West African Kingdom of Dahomey and at one point constituted one-third of the armed forces. Most societies, however, have excluded women from combat, and some have excluded women from any involvement in military activities or planning.

Why, then, do some societies allow women to be warriors? Psychologist David Adams compared about 70 societies studied by anthropologists to try to answer that question. Although most societies exclude women from war, Adams found that women are active warriors, at least occasionally, in 13 percent of the sample societies. In native North America, such societies included the Comanche, Crow, Delaware, Fox, Gros Ventre, and Navajo. In the Pacific, there were active warrior women among the Maori of New Zealand, on Majuro Atoll in the Marshall Islands, and among the Orokaiva of New Guinea. In none of

these societies were the warriors usually women, but women were allowed to engage in combat if they wanted to.

How are the societies with women warriors different from those that exclude women from combat? They differ in one of two ways. Either they conduct war only against people in other societies (this is called "purely external" war) or they marry within their own community. Adams argues that these two conditions, which are not particularly common, preclude the possibility of conflicts of interest between wives and husbands, and therefore women can be permitted to engage in combat because their interests are the same as those of their husbands. Because marriages in most cases involve individuals from the same society, husbands and wives will have the same loyalties if the society has purely external war. And even if war occurs between communities and larger groups in the same society (what we call "internal" war), there will be no conflict of interest between husband and wife if they both grew up in the same community. In contrast, there is internal war at least occasionally in most societies, and wives usually marry in from other communities. In this situation, there may often be a conflict of interest between husband and wife; if women were to engage in combat, they might have to fight against their fathers, paternal uncles, and brothers. And wouldn't we expect the wives to try to warn kin in their home communities if the

husbands planned to attack them? Indeed, the men's likely fear of their wives' disloyalty would explain why women in these societies are forbidden to make or handle weapons or go near meetings in which war plans are discussed.

Many countries today engage in purely external war, so other things being equal, we would not expect conflicts of interest to impede women's participation in combat. Therefore, extrapolating from Adams's findings, we might expect that the barriers against female participation in combat will disappear completely. But other conditions may have to be present before women and men participate equally in combat. In Adams's study, not all societies with purely external war or intracommunity marriage had women warriors. So we may also have to consider the degree to which the society seeks to maximize reproduction (and therefore protect women from danger) and the degree to which the society depends on women for subsistence during wartime.

There are other related questions to explore: Does military participation by women increase women's participation in politics? Does the presence of war in a society decrease or increase women's political participation? Does women's participation in politics or in the military change the nature of war?

Source: From D. B. Adams 1983; J. S. Goldstein 2001; 2004.

---

dominate politics because they get around more in the outside world than do women. Men's activities typically take them farther from home; women tend to work more around the home. If societies choose leaders at least in part because of what they know about the larger world, then men will generally have some advantage. In support of this reasoning, Patricia Draper found that, in settled !Kung groups, women no longer engaged in long-distance gathering, and they seemed to have lost much of their former influence in decision making.[49] Involvement in child care may also detract from influence in decision making. In a study of village leadership among the Kayapo

of Brazil, Dennis Werner found that women with heavy child care burdens were less influential than women not as involved in child care; he suggests that they had fewer friends and missed many details of what was going on in the village.[50]

These various explanations suggest why men generally dominate politics, but we still need to explain why women participate in politics more in some societies than in others. Marc Ross investigated this question in a cross-cultural survey of 90 societies.[51] In that sample, the degree of female participation in politics varied considerably. For example, among the Mende of Sierra Leone, women regularly held high office, but among the Azande of Zaire, women took no part in public life. One factor that predicts the exclusion of women from politics is the organization of communities around male kin. As we will see later, when they marry, women usually have to leave their communities and move to their husband's place. If women are "strangers" in a community with many related males, then the males will have political advantages because of their knowledge of community members and past events.

THE RELATIVE STATUS OF WOMEN

There are probably as many definitions of status as there are researchers interested in the topic. To some, the relative status of the sexes means how much importance society confers on females versus males. To others, it means how much power and authority men and women have relative to each other. And to still others, it means what kinds of rights women and men possess to do what they want to do. In any case, many social scientists ask why the status of women appears to vary from one society to another. Why do women have few rights and little influence in some societies and more of each in other societies? In other words, why is there variation in degree of **gender stratification**?

In the small Iraqi town of Daghara, women and men live very separate lives.[52] In many respects, women appear to have very little status. Like women in some other parts of the Islamic world, women in Daghara live their lives mostly in seclusion, staying in their houses and interior courtyards. If women must go out, which they can do only with male approval, they must shroud their faces and bodies in long black cloaks. These cloaks must be worn in mixed company, even at home. Women are essentially excluded from political activities. Legally, they are considered to be under the authority of their fathers and husbands. Even the sexuality of women is controlled. There is strict emphasis on virginity before marriage. Because women are not permitted even casual conversations with strange men, the possibilities for extramarital or even premarital relationships are very slight. In contrast, hardly any sexual restrictions are imposed on men.

But some societies such as the Mbuti seem to approach equal status for males and females. Like most food collectors, the Mbuti have no formal political organization to make decisions or to settle disputes. Public disputes occur, and both women and men take part in the uproar that is part of such disputes. Not only do women make their positions known, but their opinions are often heeded. Even in domestic quarrels involving physical violence between husband and wife, others usually intervene to stop them, regardless of who hit whom first.[53] Women control the use of dwellings; they usually have equal say over the disposal of resources they or the men collect, over the upbringing of their children, and about whom their children should marry. One of the few signs of inequality is that women are somewhat more restricted than men with respect to extramarital sex.[54]

There are many theories about why women have relatively high or low status. One of the most common is that women's status will be high when they contribute substantially to primary subsistence activities. This theory would predict that women should have very little status when food-getting depends largely on hunting, herding, or intensive agriculture. A second theory suggests that men will be more valued and esteemed than women where warfare is particularly important. A third theory suggests that men will have higher status where there are centralized political hierarchies. The reasoning in this theory is essentially the same as the reasoning in the warfare theory: Men usually play the dominant role in political behavior, so men's status should be higher wherever political behavior is more important or frequent. Finally, there is the theory that women will have higher status where kin groups and couples' places of residence after marriage are organized around women.

One of the problems in evaluating these theories is that decisions have to be made about the meaning of *status*. Does it mean value? Rights? Influence? And do all these aspects of status vary together? Cross-cultural research by Martin Whyte suggests that they do not. For each sample society in his study, Whyte rated 52 items that might be used to define the relative status of the sexes. These items included such things as which sex can inherit property, who has final authority over disciplining unmarried children, and whether the gods in the society are male, female, or both. The results of the study indicate that very few of these items are related. Therefore, Whyte concluded, we cannot talk about status as a single concept. Rather, it seems more appropriate to talk about the relative status of women in different spheres of life.[55]

Even though Whyte found no necessary connection between one aspect of status and another, he decided to ask whether some of the theories correctly predict why some societies have many, as opposed to few, areas in which the status of women is high. Let us turn first to the ideas *not* supported by the available cross-cultural evidence. Contrary to popular belief, the idea that generally high status stems from a greater caloric contribution to primary subsistence activities is not supported.[56] For example, women seem to have higher status the more a society depends upon hunting, but women do little of the primary subsistence work in hunting societies. And it is commonly thought that warfare should bolster male status, but there is no consistent evidence that a high frequency of warfare generally lowers women's status in different spheres of life.[57]

What does predict higher status for women in many areas of life? Although the results are not strong, there is some support in Whyte's study for the theory that women have somewhat higher status where kin groups and marital residence are organized around women. (We discuss these features of society more fully in the chapter on marital residence and kinship.) The Iroquois are a good example. Even though Iroquois women could not hold formal political office, they had considerable authority within and beyond the household. Related women lived together in longhouses with husbands who belonged to other kin groups. In the

The bride's relatives arrive at the groom's home bearing gifts and Piki bread from the bride's family at a traditional Hopi engagement ceremony in Arizona.

"woman" or "man," even though "she" or "he" is not that sex biologically. As we noted in the previous chapter, the Cheyenne Indians allowed a married man to take as a second wife a biological man belonging to the third gender, "two-spirits."

Although it is not clear that the Cheyenne male-male marriages involved homosexual relationships, it is clear that temporary homosexual marriages did occur among the Azande of Africa. Before the British took control over what is now Sudan, Azande warriors who could not afford wives often married "boy-wives" to satisfy their sexual needs. As in normal marriages, gifts (although not as substantial) were given by the "husband" to the parents of his boy-wife. The husband performed services for the boy's parents and could sue any other lover of the boy in court for adultery. The boy-wives not only had sexual relations with their husbands but also performed many of the chores female wives traditionally performed for their husbands.[7]

Female-female marriages are reported to have occurred in many African societies, but there is no evidence of any sexual relationship between the partners. It seems, rather, that female-female marriages were a socially approved way for a woman to take on the legal and social roles of a father and husband.[8] For example, among the Nandi, a pastoral and agricultural society of Kenya, about 3 percent of the marriages are female-female marriages. Such marriages appear to be a Nandi solution to the problem of a regular marriage's failure to produce a male heir to property. The Nandi solution is to have the woman, even if her husband is still alive, become a "husband" to a younger female and "father" the younger woman's children. The female husband provides the marriage payments required for obtaining a wife, renounces female work, and takes on the obligations of the husband to that woman. Although no sexual relations are permitted between the female husband and the new wife (or between the female husband and her own husband), the female husband arranges a male consort so that the new wife can have children. Those children, however, consider the female husband to be their father because she (or more aptly the gender role "he") is the socially designated father. If asked who their

father is, a child of such a marriage will name the female who is the husband.[9]

WHY IS MARRIAGE NEARLY UNIVERSAL?

Because virtually all societies practice female-male marriage as we have defined it, we can assume that the custom is adaptive. But saying that does not specify exactly how it may be adaptive. Several interpretations have traditionally been offered to explain why all human societies have the custom of marriage. Each suggests that marriage solves problems found in all societies—how to share the products of a gender division of labor; how to care for infants, who are dependent for a long time; and how to minimize sexual competition. To evaluate the plausibility of these interpretations, we must ask whether marriage provides the best or the only reasonable solution to each problem. After all, we are trying to explain a custom that is virtually universal. The comparative study of other animals, some of which have something like marriage, may help us to evaluate these explanations.

Gender Division of Labor

We noted in the preceding chapter that every society known to anthropology has had a gender division of labor. Males and females in every society perform different economic activities. This gender division of labor has often been cited as a reason for marriage.[10] As long as there is a division of labor by gender, society has to have some mechanism by which women and men share the products of their labor. Marriage would be one way to solve that problem. But it seems unlikely that marriage is the only possible solution. The hunter-gatherer rule of sharing could be extended to include all the products brought in by both women and men. Or a small group of men and women, such as brothers and sisters, might be pledged to cooperate economically. Thus, although marriage may solve the problem of sharing the fruits of a division of labor, it clearly is not the only possible solution.

Prolonged Infant Dependency

Humans exhibit the longest period of infant dependency of any primate. The child's prolonged dependence places the greatest burden on the mother, who is the main child caregiver in most societies. The burden of prolonged child care by human females may limit the kinds of work they can do. They may need the help of a man to do certain types of work, such as hunting, that are incompatible with child care. Because of this prolonged dependency, it has been suggested, marriage is necessary.[11] But here the argument becomes essentially the same as the division-of-labor argument, and it has the same logical weakness. It is not clear why a group of women and men, such as a hunter-gatherer band, could not cooperate in providing for dependent children without marriage.

Sexual Competition

Unlike most other female primates, the human female may engage in intercourse at any time throughout the year. Some scholars have suggested that more or less continuous female sexuality may have created a serious problem—considerable sexual competition between males for females. It is argued that society had to prevent such competition to survive, that it had to develop some way of minimizing the rivalry among males for females to reduce the chance of lethal and destructive conflict.[12]

There are several problems with this argument. First, why should continuous female sexuality make for more sexual competition in the first place? One might argue the other way around. There might be more competition over the scarcer resources that would be available if females were less frequently interested in sex. Second, males of many animal species, even some that have relatively frequent female sexuality (as do many of our close primate relatives), do not show much aggression over females. Third, why couldn't sexual competition, even if it existed, be regulated by cultural rules other than marriage? For instance, society might have adopted a rule whereby men and women circulated among all the opposite-sex members

of the group, each person staying a specified length of time with each partner. Such a system presumably would solve the problem of sexual competition. On the other hand, such a system might not work particularly well if individuals came to prefer certain other individuals. Jealousies attending those attachments might give rise to even more competition.

Other Mammals and Birds: Postpartum Requirements

None of the theories we have discussed explains convincingly why marriage is the only or the best solution to a particular problem. Also, we now have some comparative evidence on mammals and birds that casts doubt on those theories.[13] How can evidence from other animals help us evaluate theories about human marriage? If we look at the animals that, like humans, have some sort of stable female-male mating, as compared with those that are completely promiscuous, we can perhaps see what sorts of factors may predict male-female bonding in the warm-blooded animal species. Most species of birds, and some mammals such as wolves and beavers, have "marriage." Among 40 mammal and bird species, none of the three factors discussed previously—division of labor, prolonged infant dependency, and greater female sexuality—predicts or is correlated strongly with male-female bonding. With respect to division of labor by sex, most other animals have nothing comparable to a humanlike division of labor, but many have stable female-male matings anyway. The two other supposed factors—prolonged infant dependency and female sexuality—predict just the opposite of what we might expect. Mammal and bird species that have longer dependency periods or more female sexuality are less likely to have stable matings.

Does anything predict male-female bonding? One factor does among mammals and birds, and it may also help explain human marriage. Animal species in which females can simultaneously feed themselves and their babies after birth (*postpartum*) tend not to have stable matings; species in which postpartum mothers cannot feed themselves and their babies at the same time tend to have stable matings. Among the typical bird species, a mother would have difficulty feeding herself and her babies simultaneously. Because the young cannot fly for a while and must be protected in a nest, the mother risks losing them to other animals if she goes off to obtain food. But if she has a male bonded to her (as most bird species do), he can bring back food or take a turn watching the nest. Among animal species that have no postpartum feeding problem, babies are able to travel with the mother almost immediately after birth as she moves about to eat (as do grazers such as horses), or the mother can transport the babies as she moves about to eat (as do baboons and kangaroos). We think the human female has a postpartum feeding problem. When humans lost most of their body hair, babies could not readily travel with the mother by clinging to her fur. And when humans began to depend on certain kinds of food-getting that could be dangerous (such as hunting), mothers could not engage in such work with their infants along.[14]

"I do love you. But, to be perfectly honest, I would have loved any other lovebird who happened to turn up."
(Rothco Cartoons)

Recent research on the Hadza foragers of Tanzania appears to support this view. Frank Marlowe found that the caloric contribution of mothers and fathers depends on whether or not they have a nursing infant. Women may generally contribute more calories than men to the diet, but married women who are nursing contribute substantially less than other married women. The lower contribution of nursing mothers appears to be made up by the father. Fathers with nursing children contribute significantly more food to the household than fathers with older children.[15]

Even if we assume that human mothers have a postpartum feeding problem, we still have to ask if marriage is the most likely solution to the problem. We think so, because other conceivable solutions probably would not work as well. For example, if a mother took turns babysitting with another mother, neither might be able to collect enough food for both mothers and the two sets of children dependent on them. But a mother and father share the same set of children, and therefore it would be easier for them to feed themselves and their children adequately. Another possible solution is no pair bonding at all, just a promiscuous group of males and females. But in that kind of arrangement, we think, a particular mother probably would not always be able to count on some male to watch her baby when she had to go out for food or to bring her food when she had to watch her baby. Thus, it seems to us that the problem of postpartum feeding by itself helps to explain why some animals, including humans, have relatively stable male-female bonds.[16] Of course, there is still the question of whether research on other animals can be applied to human beings. We think it can, but not everybody will agree.

HOW DOES ONE MARRY?

When we say that marriage is a socially approved sexual and economic union, we mean that all societies have some way of marking the onset of a marriage, but the ways of doing so vary considerably. For reasons that we don't fully understand, some cultures mark marriages by elaborate rites and celebrations; others mark marriages in much more informal ways. And most societies have economic transactions before, during, or even after the onset of the marriages.

Marking the Onset of Marriage

Many societies have ceremonies marking the beginning of marriage. But others, such as the Taramiut Inuit, the Trobriand Islanders of the South Pacific, and the Kwoma of New Guinea, use different social signals to indicate that a marriage has taken place. Among the Taramiut Inuit, the betrothal is considered extremely important and is arranged between the parents at or before the time their children reach puberty. Later, when the youth is ready, he moves in with his betrothed's family for a trial period. If all goes well—that is, if the girl gives birth to a baby within a year or so—the couple are considered married. At this time, the wife goes with her husband to his camp.[17]

In keeping with the general openness of their society's attitudes toward sexual matters, a Trobriand couple advertise their desire to marry "by sleeping together regularly, by showing themselves together in public, and by remaining with each other for long periods at a time."[18] When a girl accepts a small gift from a boy, she demonstrates that her parents favor the match. Before long, she moves to the boy's house, takes her meals there, and accompanies her husband all day. Then the word goes around that the two are married.[19]

The Kwoma of New Guinea practice a trial marriage followed by a ceremony that makes the couple husband and wife. The girl lives for a while in the boy's home. When the boy's mother is satisfied with the match and knows that her son is too, she waits for a day when he is away from the house. Until that time, the girl has been cooking only for herself, and the boy's food has been prepared by his womenfolk. Now the mother has the girl prepare his meal. The young man returns and begins to eat his soup. When the first bowl is nearly finished, his mother tells him that his betrothed cooked the meal, and his eating it means that he is now married. At this news, the boy customarily rushes out of the house, spits out the soup, and shouts, "Faugh! It tastes bad! It is cooked terribly!" A ceremony then makes the marriage official.[20]

Just in the last three decades, "living together" has become more of an option in the United States and other Western countries. For most, living together is a prelude to marriage or kind of a trial marriage. For some, living together has become an alternative to marriage. Statistics in the United States suggest that a third of married women under age 45 have lived together with a man for at least some time period.[21]

Among those societies that have ceremonies marking the onset of marriage, feasting is a common element. It expresses publicly the unification of the two families by marriage. The Reindeer Tungus of Siberia set a wedding date after protracted negotiations between the two families and their larger kin groups. Go-betweens assume most of the responsibility for the negotiating. The wedding day opens with the two kin groups, probably numbering as many as 150 people, pitching their lodges in separate areas and offering a great feast. After the groom's gifts have been presented, the bride's dowry is loaded onto reindeer and carried to the groom's lodge. There, the climax of the ceremony takes place. The bride takes the wife's place—that is, at the right side of the entrance of the lodge—and members of both families sit in a circle. The groom enters and follows the bride around the circle, greeting each guest, while the guests, in their turn, kiss the bride on the mouth and hands. Finally, the go-betweens spit three times on the bride's hands, and the couple are formally husband and wife. More feasting and revelry bring the day to a close.[22]

In many cultures, marriage includes ceremonial expressions of hostility. Mock fights are staged in many societies. On occasion, hostility can have genuinely aggressive overtones, as among the Gusii of Kenya:

> Five young clansmen of the groom come to take the bride and two immediately find the girl and post

A young Iraqi couple in 2008 look at gold jewelry that will be part of her dowry. It is considered to be hers no matter what happens to the marriage.

themselves at her side to prevent her escape, while the others receive the final permission of her parents. When it has been granted the bride holds onto the house posts and must be dragged outside by the young men. Finally she goes along with them, crying and with her hands on her head.[23]

But the battle is not yet over. Mutual antagonism continues right onto the marriage bed, even up to and beyond coitus. The groom is determined to display his virility; the bride is equally determined to test it. "Brides," Robert and Barbara LeVine remarked, "are said to take pride in the length of time they can hold off their mates." Men can also win acclaim. If the bride is unable to walk the following day, the groom is considered a "real man."[24] Such expressions of hostility usually occur in societies in which the two sets of kin are actual or potential rivals or enemies. In many societies, it is common to marry women from "enemy" villages.

As this example suggests, marriage ceremonies often symbolize important elements of the culture. Whereas the Gusii ceremony may symbolize hostility between the two families, the ceremony may promote harmony between the families in other societies. For example, on the Polynesian island of Rotuma, a female clown is an important part of the ceremony. She is responsible for creating an enjoyable, joking atmosphere that facilitates interaction between the two sides.[25]

Economic Aspects of Marriage

"It's not man that marries maid, but field marries field, vineyard marries vineyard, cattle marry cattle." In its down-to-earth way, this German peasant saying indicates that, in many societies, marriage involves economic considerations. In our culture, economic considerations may or may not be explicit. However, in about 75 percent of the societies known to anthropology,[26] one or more explicit economic transactions take place before or after the marriage. The economic transaction may take several forms: bride price, bride service, exchange of females, gift exchange, dowry, or indirect dowry. The distribution of those forms among societies that have economic marriage transactions is shown in Figure 21–1.

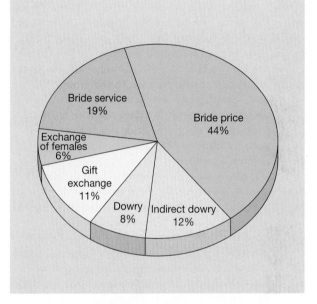

FIGURE 21–1   Distribution of Economic Marriage Transactions Among Societies That Have Them
Note that there are societies in the ethnographic record (25 percent) that lack any substantial economic transactions at marriage.

Source: Based on data from Schlegel and Eloul 1988, 291–309.

Bride Price   Bride price or **bride wealth** is a gift of money or goods from the groom or his kin to the bride's kin. The gift usually grants the groom the right to marry the bride and the right to her children. Of all the forms of economic transaction involved in marriage, bride price is the most common. In one cross-cultural sample, 44 percent of the societies with economic transactions at marriage practiced bride price; in almost all of those societies, the bride price was substantial.[27] Bride price occurs all over the world but is especially common in Africa and Oceania. Payment can be made in different currencies; livestock and food are two of the more common. With the increased importance of commercial exchange, money has increasingly become part of the bride price payments. Among the Nandi, the bride price consists of about five to seven cattle, one or two sheep and goats, cowrie shells, and money equivalent to the value of one cow. Even in unusual female-female marriages, the female "husband" must pay a bride price to arrange the marriage and be considered the "father."[28]

The Subanun of the Philippines have an expensive bride price—several times the annual income of the groom plus three to five years of bride service (described in the next section).[29] Among the Manus of the Admiralty Islands off New Guinea, a groom requires an economic backer, usually an older brother or an uncle, if he is to marry, but it will be years before he can pay off his debts. Depending on the final bride price, payments may be concluded at the time of the marriage, or they may continue for years afterward.[30]

Despite the connotations that bride price may have for us, the practice does not reduce a woman to the position of slave—although it is associated, as we shall see, with relatively low status for women. The bride price may be important to the woman and her family. Indeed, the fee they receive can serve as a security. If the marriage fails through no fault of hers and the wife returns to her kin, the family might not return the bride price to the groom. On the other hand, the wife's kin may pressure her to remain with her husband, even though she does not wish to, because they do not want to return the bride price or are unable to do so. A larger bride price is associated with more difficulty in obtaining a divorce.[31]

What kinds of societies are likely to have the custom of bride price? Cross-culturally, societies with bride price are likely to practice horticulture and lack social stratification. Bride price is also likely where women contribute a great deal to primary subsistence activities[32] and where they contribute more than men to all kinds of economic activities.[33] Although these findings might suggest that women are highly valued in such societies, recall that the status of women relative to men is not higher in societies in which women contribute a lot to primary subsistence activities. Indeed, bride price is likely to occur in societies in which men make most of the decisions in the household,[34] and decision making by men is one indicator of lower status for women.

Bride Service

Bride service, which is the next most common type of economic transaction at marriage—occurring in about 19 percent of the societies with economic transactions—requires the groom to work for the bride's family, sometimes before the marriage begins, sometimes after. Bride service varies in duration. In some societies, it lasts for only a few months; in others, as long as several years. Among the North Alaskan Eskimo, for example, the boy works for his in-laws after the marriage is arranged. To fulfill his obligation, he may simply catch a seal for them. The marriage may be consummated at any time while he is in service.[35] In some societies, bride service sometimes substitutes for bride price. An individual might give bride service to reduce the amount of bride price required. Native North and South American societies were likely to practice bride service, particularly if they were egalitarian food collectors.[36]

Exchange of Females

Of the societies that have economic transactions at marriage, 6 percent have the custom whereby a sister or female relative of the groom is exchanged for the bride. Among these societies are the Tiv of West Africa and the Yanomamö of Venezuela and Brazil. These societies tend to be horticultural, egalitarian, and to have a relatively high contribution of women to primary subsistence.[37]

Gift Exchange

Gift exchange, which involves the exchange of gifts of about equal value by the two kin groups about to be linked by marriage, occurs somewhat more often than the exchange of females (about 11 percent of those with economic transactions).[38] For example, among the Andaman Islanders, as soon as a boy and girl indicate their intention to marry, their respective sets of parents cease all communication and begin sending gifts of food and other objects to each other through a third party. This arrangement continues until the marriage is completed and the two kin groups are united.[39]

Dowry

A **dowry** is usually a substantial transfer of goods or money from the bride's family to the bride, the groom, or the couple.[40] Unlike the types of transactions we have discussed so far, the dowry, which occurs in about 8 percent of the societies with economic transactions, is usually not a transaction between the kin of the bride and the kin of the groom. A family has to have wealth to give a dowry, but because the goods go to the new household, no wealth comes back to the family that gave the dowry. Payment of dowries was common in medieval and Renaissance Europe, where the size of the dowry often determined the desirability of the daughter. The custom is still practiced in parts of eastern Europe and in sections of southern Italy and France, where land is often the major item the bride's family provides. Parts of India also practice the dowry.

In contrast to societies with bride price, societies with dowry tend to be those in which women contribute relatively little to primary subsistence activities, there is a high degree of social stratification, and a man is not allowed to be married to more than one woman simultaneously.[41] Why does dowry tend to occur in these types of societies? One theory suggests that the dowry is intended to guarantee future support for a woman and her children, even though she will not do much primary subsistence work. Another theory is that the dowry is intended to attract the best bridegroom for a daughter in monogamous societies with a high degree of social inequality. The dowry strategy is presumed to increase the likelihood that the daughter and her children will do well reproductively. Both theories are supported by recent cross-cultural research, with the second predicting dowry better.[42] But many stratified societies in which women and men have only one spouse at a time (including our own) do not practice dowry. Why this is so still needs to be explained.

Indirect Dowry

The dowry is provided by the bride's family to the bride, the groom, or the couple. But sometimes the payments to the bride originate from the groom's family. Because the goods are sometimes first given to the bride's father, who passes most if not all of them to her, this kind of transaction is called **indirect dowry.**[43] Indirect dowry occurs in about 12 percent of the societies in which marriage involves an economic transaction. For example, among the Basseri of southern Iran, the groom's father assumes the expense of setting up the couple's new household. He gives cash to the bride's father, who uses at least some of the money to buy his daughter household utensils, blankets, and rugs.[44]

RESTRICTIONS ON MARRIAGE: THE UNIVERSAL INCEST TABOO

Hollywood and its press agents notwithstanding, marriage is not always based solely on mutual love, independently discovered and expressed by the two life-partners-to-be. Nor is it based on sex or wealth alone. Even when love, sex, and economics are contributing factors, regulations specify whom one may or may not marry. Perhaps the most rigid regulation, found in *all* cultures, is the **incest taboo,** which prohibits sexual intercourse or marriage between some categories of kin.

The most universal aspect of the incest taboo is the prohibition of sexual intercourse or marriage between mother and son, father and daughter, and brother and sister. No society in recent times has permitted either sexual intercourse or marriage between those pairs. A few societies in the past, however, did permit incest, mostly within the royal and aristocratic families, though generally it was forbidden to the rest of the population. For example, the Incan and Hawaiian royal families allowed marriage within the family. Probably the best-known example of allowed incest involved Cleopatra of Egypt.

It seems clear that the Egyptian aristocracy and royalty indulged in father-daughter and brother-sister marriages. Cleopatra was married to two of her younger brothers at different times.[45] The reasons seem to have been partly religious—a member of the family of the pharaoh, who was considered a god, could not marry any "ordinary" human—and partly economic, for marriage within the family kept the royal property undivided. In Egypt, between 30 B.C. and A.D. 324, incest was allowed not just in the royal family; an estimated 8 percent of commoner marriages were brother-sister marriages.[46]

But, despite these exceptions, the fact remains that no culture we know of today permits or accepts incest within the nuclear family. Why is the familial incest taboo universal? Several explanations have been suggested.

Childhood-Familiarity Theory

The childhood-familiarity theory, suggested by Edward Westermarck, was given a wide hearing in the early 1920s. Westermarck argued that people who have been closely associated with each other since earliest childhood, such as siblings, are not sexually attracted to each other and therefore would avoid marriage with each other.[47] This theory was subsequently rejected because of evidence

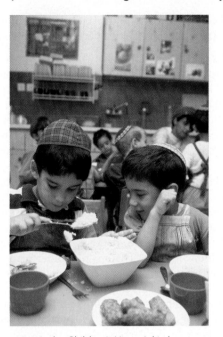

Children eating in the Children's House's kitchen on an Israeli kibbutz.

that some children were sexually interested in their parents and siblings. Studies have suggested, however, that there might be something to Westermarck's theory.

Yonina Talmon investigated marriage patterns among the second generation of three well-established collective communities (*kibbutzim*) in Israel. In these collectives, children live with many members of their peer group in quarters separate from their families. They are in constant interaction with their peers, from birth to maturity. The study revealed that, among 125 couples, there was "not one instance in which both mates were reared from birth in the same peer group,"[48] despite parental encouragement of marriage within the peer group. Children reared in common not only avoided marriage, they also avoided any sexual relations among themselves.

Talmon stated that the people reared together firmly believed that overfamiliarity breeds sexual disinterest. As one of them told her, "We are like an open book to each other. We have read the story in the book over and over again and know all about it."[49] Talmon's evidence reveals not only the onset of disinterest and even sexual antipathy among children reared together, but a correspondingly heightened fascination with newcomers or outsiders, particularly for their "mystery."

Arthur Wolf's study of the Chinese in northern Taiwan also supports the idea that something about being reared together produces sexual disinterest. Wolf focused on a community still practicing the Chinese custom of *t'ung-yang-hsi*, or "daughter-in-law raised from childhood":

> When a girl is born in a poor family . . . she is often given away or sold when but a few weeks or months old, or one or two years old, to be the future wife of a son in the family of a friend or relative which has a little son not betrothed in marriage. . . . The girl

is called a "little bride" and taken home and brought up in the family together with her future husband.[50]

Wolf's evidence indicates that this arrangement is associated with sexual difficulties when the childhood "couple" later marry. Informants implied that familiarity results in disinterest and lack of stimulation. As an indication of their disinterest, these couples produce fewer offspring than spouses not raised together, they are more likely to seek extramarital sexual relationships, and they are more likely to get divorced.[51]

The Talmon and Wolf studies suggest, then, that children raised together are not likely to be sexually interested in each other when they grow up. Such disinterest is consistent with Westermarck's notion that the incest taboo may be more an avoidance of certain matings than a prohibition of them. There is one other piece of evidence consistent with this explanation of the incest taboo. Hilda and Seymour Parker compared two samples of fathers: those who had sexually abused their daughters and those who supposedly had not.[52] To maximize their similarities otherwise, the Parkers selected the two samples of fathers from the same prisons and psychiatric facilities. The Parkers found that the fathers who had committed incest with their daughters were much more likely than the other sample of fathers to have had little to do with bringing up their daughters, because they were not at home or hardly at home during the daughters' first three years of life. In other words, the fathers who avoided incest had been more closely associated with their daughters in childhood. That finding is consistent with Westermarck's suggestion that the incest taboo is a result of familiarity in childhood.

Although Westermarck was talking about the development of sexual aversion during early childhood, some researchers have asked how the childhood familiarity theory could explain the extension of incest taboos to first cousins. The familiarity argument implies that first-cousin marriage should be prohibited in societies in which first cousins grow up together in the same community. But that is not the case. Such societies are not more likely to prohibit first-cousin marriage.[53]

Even if there is something about familiarity in childhood that normally leads to sexual disinterest,[54] we still are left with the question of why societies have to prohibit marriages that would voluntarily be avoided because of disinterest. And why do many couples remain actively interested in each other sexually after years of marriage?

Freud's Psychoanalytic Theory

Sigmund Freud proposed that the incest taboo is a reaction against unconscious, unacceptable desires.[55] He suggested that the son is attracted to his mother (as the daughter is to her father) and as a result feels jealousy and hostility toward his father. But the son knows that these feelings cannot continue, for they might lead the father to retaliate against him; therefore, they must be renounced or repressed. Usually the feelings are repressed and retreat into the unconscious. But the desire to possess the mother continues to exist in the unconscious, and, according to

Freud, the horror of incest is a reaction to, or a defense against, the forbidden unconscious impulse.

Although Freud's theory may account for the aversion felt toward incest, or at least the aversion toward parent-child incest, it does not explain why society needs an explicit taboo, particularly on brother-sister incest. Nor does it account for the findings of sexual disinterest we discussed in connection with the Westermarck hypothesis.

Family-Disruption Theory

The family-disruption theory, often associated with Bronislaw Malinowski,[56] can best be summed up as follows: Sexual competition among family members would create so much rivalry and tension that the family could not function as an effective unit. Because the family must function effectively for society to survive, society has to curtail competition within the family. The familial incest taboo is thus imposed to keep the family intact.

But there are inconsistencies in this approach. Society could have shaped other rules about the sexual access of one member of the family to another that would also eliminate potentially disruptive competition. Also, why would brother-sister incest be so disruptive? As we noted, such marriages did exist in ancient Egypt. Brother-sister incest would not disrupt the authority of the parents if the children were allowed to marry when mature. The family-disruption theory, then, does not explain the origin of the incest taboo.

Cooperation Theory

The cooperation theory was proposed by the early anthropologist Edward B. Tylor and was elaborated by Leslie A. White and Claude Lévi-Strauss. It emphasizes the value of the incest taboo in promoting cooperation among family groups and thus helping communities to survive. As Tylor saw it, certain operations necessary for the welfare of the community can be accomplished only by large numbers of people working together. To break down suspicion and hostility between family groups and make such cooperation possible, early humans developed the incest taboo to ensure that individuals would marry members of other families. The ties created by intermarriage would serve to hold the community together. Thus, Tylor explained the incest taboo as an answer to the choice "between marrying out and being killed out."[57]

The idea that marriage with other groups promotes cooperation sounds plausible, but is there evidence to support it? After all, there are societies such as the Gusii in which marriage is often between hostile groups. But is that society an exception? Does marriage promote cooperation? Because people in all recent societies marry outside the family, we cannot test the idea that such marriages promote cooperation more than marriages within the family. We can, however, ask whether other kinds of out-marriage, such as marriage with other communities, promote cooperation with those communities. The evidence on that question does not support the cooperation theory. There is no greater peacefulness between communities when marriages are forbidden within the community and always arranged with other communities than when they are not.[58]

But even if marriage outside the family promoted cooperation with other groups, why would it be necessary to prohibit all marriages within the family? Couldn't families have required some of their members to marry outside the family if they thought it necessary for survival but permitted incestuous marriages when such alliances were not needed? Although the incest taboo might enhance cooperation between families, the need for cooperation does not adequately explain the existence of the incest taboo in all societies; other customs might also promote alliances. Furthermore, the cooperation theory does not explain the sexual aspect of the incest taboo. Societies could conceivably allow incestuous sex and still insist that children marry outside the family.

Inbreeding Theory

One of the oldest explanations for the incest taboo is inbreeding theory. It focuses on the potentially damaging consequences of inbreeding or marrying within the family. People within the same family are likely to carry the same harmful recessive genes. Inbreeding, then, will tend to produce offspring who are more likely to die early of genetic disorders than are the offspring of unrelated spouses. Recent evidence also suggests that inbreeding tends to increase the likelihood of diseases that affect people later in life, such as heart disease and diabetes.[59] For many years, inbreeding theory was rejected because, on the basis of dog-breeding practices, it was thought that inbreeding need not be harmful. The inbreeding practiced to produce prize-winning dogs, however, is not a good guide to whether inbreeding is harmful; dog breeders don't count the runts they cull when they try to breed for success in dog shows. We now have a good deal of evidence, from humans as well as other animals, that the closer the degree of inbreeding, the more harmful the genetic effects.[60]

Genetic mutations occur frequently. Although many pose no harm to the individuals who carry a single recessive gene, matings between two people who carry the same gene often produce offspring with a harmful or lethal condition. Close blood relatives are much more likely than unrelated individuals to carry the same harmful recessive gene. So, if close relatives mate, their offspring have a higher probability than the offspring of nonrelatives of inheriting the harmful trait.

One study compared children produced by familial incest with children of the same mothers produced by nonincestuous unions. About 40 percent of the incestuously produced children had serious abnormalities, compared with about 5 percent of the other children.[61] Matings between other kinds of relatives not as closely related also show harmful, but not as harmful, effects of inbreeding. These results are consistent with inbreeding theory. The likelihood that a child will inherit a double dose of a harmful recessive gene is lower the more distantly the child's parents are related. Also consistent with inbreeding theory is the fact that rates of abnormality are consistently higher

in the offspring of uncle-niece marriages (which are allowed in some societies) than in the offspring of cousin marriages; for the offspring of uncle-niece marriages, the likelihood of inheriting a double dose of a harmful recessive is twice that for the offspring of first cousins.[62]

Although most scholars acknowledge the harmful effects of inbreeding, some question whether people in former days would have deliberately invented or borrowed the incest taboo because they knew that inbreeding was biologically harmful. William Durham's cross-cultural survey suggests that they did. Ethnographers do not always report the perceived consequences of incest, but in 50 percent of the reports Durham found, biological harm to the offspring was mentioned.[63] For example, Raymond Firth reported on the Tikopia, who live on an island in the South Pacific:

> The idea is firmly held that unions of close kin bear with them their own doom, their *mara*. . . . The idea [*mara*] essentially concerns barrenness. . . . The peculiar barrenness of an incestuous union consists not in the absence of children, but in their illness or death, or some other mishap. . . . The idea that the offspring of a marriage between near kin are weakly and likely to die young is stoutly held by these natives and examples are adduced to prove it.[64]

So, if the harm of inbreeding was widely recognized, people may have deliberately invented or borrowed the incest taboo.[65] But whether or not people actually recognized the harmfulness of inbreeding, the demographic consequences of the incest taboo would account for its universality, because reproductive and hence competitive advantages probably accrued to groups practicing the taboo. Thus, although cultural solutions other than the incest taboo might provide the desired effects assumed by the family-disruption theory and the cooperation theory, the incest taboo is the only possible solution to the problem of inbreeding.

As is discussed toward the end of the next section, a society may or may not extend the incest taboo to first cousins. That variation is also predictable from inbreeding theory, which provides additional support for the idea that the incest taboo was invented or borrowed to avoid the harmful consequences of inbreeding.

WHOM SHOULD ONE MARRY?

Probably every child in our society knows the story of Cinderella—the poor, downtrodden, but lovely girl who accidentally meets, falls in love with, and eventually marries a prince. It is a charming tale, but it is misleading as a guide to mate choice in our society. The majority of marriages simply do not occur in so free and coincidental a way in any society. In addition to the incest taboo, societies often have rules restricting marriage with other people, as well as preferences about which other people are the most desirable mates.

Tibetans, their practice of polyandry minimizes population growth. There are as many women as men of marriageable age. But about 30 percent of the women do not marry, and, although these women do have some children, they have far fewer than married women. Thus, the practice of polyandry minimizes the number of mouths to feed and therefore maximizes the standard of living of the polyandrous family. In contrast, if the Tibetans practiced monogamy and almost all women married, the birth rate would be much higher and there would be more mouths to feed with the severely limited resources.[101]

Polyandry is still customary in some Tibetan communities although monogamous marriages actually outnumber polyandrous marriages. This is because a set of brothers may start off being married to one woman, younger brothers may later opt to marry separately and form their own households. Also, some households have only one son or daughter and polyandrous marriages are not possible. Wealth increases the likelihood of a young brother leaving, but mostly when the polyandrous household lacks agricultural fields, herds, and opportunities for trade.[102] Actually, in polygynous societies, monogamous marriages also outnumber polygynous marriages at any given time. But the reasons are different. Most polygynous societies practice nonsororal marriages and, when a man first marries, he is married monogamously. It usually requires significant resources to marry again (a bride price is common) and so subsequent marriages occur later in life.

THE FAMILY

Although family form varies from one society to another and even within societies, all societies have families. A **family** is a social and economic unit consisting minimally of one or more parents (or parent substitute) and their children. Members of a family always have certain reciprocal rights and obligations, particularly economic ones. Family members usually live in one household, but common residence is not a defining feature of families. In our society, children may live away while they go to college. Some members of a family may deliberately set up separate households to manage multiple business enterprises while maintaining economic unity.[103] In simpler societies, the family and the household tend to be indistinguishable; only in more complex societies, and in societies becoming dependent on commercial exchange, may some members of a family live elsewhere.[104]

Adoption

In many societies, the family does not have enough kin in the nuclear or extended family. They need to add new members to perform all of the necessary chores or to inherit access to family property. They may have a shortage because introduced diseases or natural disasters such as hurricanes have killed members (particularly young children) or because the adults don't get along and can't cooperate in the traditional ways. Many societies adopt children to deal with one or another of these problems. Or

they adopt one or more related children to relieve the pressure on resources in the family that adopts the child "out." This last one was the motive in the family Melvin Ember lived with at the beginning of his fieldwork in the Pacific islands of American Samoa.

The family already had six children. The oldest (Tavita), 11 at the time, was in school most of the day, as were three of the other children. Tavita was adopted informally. His natural mother, who lived in the same village, was a sister of Tavita's adoptive mother. By adopting Tavita "out," his natural family was relieved of the responsibility to feed and care for him; they already had nine children. The need to reduce the number of mouths to feed was a common motive for adoption in Samoan villages then, as it was elsewhere in the far Pacific islands because of depopulation and hurricanes.[105] In American Samoa, the availability of more jobs (teaching in the village, working for the central government and the canneries on the main island), and improved medical care (there was a medical dispensary in every village and a hospital on the main island) had generated unusual population growth. Many had already moved to Hawaii and the mainland United States to seek jobs. American Samoans can move to the United States without difficulty; all you need is the money to pay for an airline ticket. Remittances from living and working abroad constitute a major source of income for the family members still in American Samoa.[106]

Adoption does not just occur in developing societies. It occurs in industrial societies too. As of the 1990s (the latest figures available), there were more than 100,000 formal (legally recognized) adoptions in the United States per year. About 50 percent of the adoptions are of children who are relatives, usually close relatives; a large number of these adoptions may be solutions to resource problems for the natural mothers. Then more than 10,000 children from abroad who are not usually relatives are adopted each year. Most of the known adoptions, foreign and domestic, are arranged by middle-class or wealthier people. A sizeable amount of money may have to be spent, particularly with the foreign adoptions. Most of the adopted children, domestic and foreign, turn out as well as natural children.[107]

Variation in Family Form

The minimal family has one parent (or parent substitute). Single-parent families, usually headed by the mother, are common in some societies, but most societies typically have larger families. These larger family units usually include at least one **nuclear family** (a married couple and their children), but there is often polygamy, so there may be more than one spouse with more than one set of children. If a single-parent family, nuclear family, polygynous, or polyandrous family lives alone, each is an **independent family.** However, the **extended family** is the prevailing form of family in more than half the societies known to anthropology.[108] It may consist of two or more single-parent, monogamous, polygynous, or polyandrous families linked by a blood tie. Most commonly, the extended family consists of a

current research and issues

One-Parent Families: Why the Recent Increase?

Not only is the custom of marriage almost universal, but in most societies known to anthropology, most people marry. And they usually remarry if they divorce. This means that, except for the death of a spouse or temporarily during times of divorce or separation, one-parent families are relatively uncommon in most societies.

In many Western countries, however, there has been a dramatic increase recently in the percentage of one-parent families, most of which (about 90 percent) are female-headed families. For example, in the 1960s, about 9 percent of families in the United States were one-parent families, but in the mid-1980s, the figure jumped to about 24 percent. In 2004, the figure was 28 percent. Whereas Sweden once led the Western countries in percentage of one-parent families—about 13 percent in the 1970s—the United States now has the highest percentage.

Before we examine the reasons for the increase, we need to consider that there are a variety of ways to become a one-parent family. First, many one-parent families result from the divorce or separation of two-parent families. Second, many one-parent families result from births out of wedlock. In addition, some result from the death of a spouse, and others from the decision by a single person to have a child.

Many researchers suggest that the ease of divorce is largely responsible for the increase in one-parent families. On the face of it, this explanation seems plausible. But it is flawed. In many countries during the late 1960s and early 1970s, changes in the law made getting a divorce much easier, and the percentage of one-parent families did rise after that. But why did so many countries ease divorce restrictions at the same time? Did attitudes about marriage change first? A high divorce rate by itself will make for a higher percentage of one-parent households only if individuals do not remarry quickly. In the United States, for example, remarriage rates did decline sharply in the mid-1960s, particularly among younger, better-educated women, and so the

percentage of one-parent households may have risen for that reason. In many other countries, divorce rates stabilized in the 1980s, but the percentage of one-parent families still increased. Thus, easier divorce does not fully explain the increase in number of one-parent families.

Although some parents are clearly choosing to stay single, many might prefer to marry if they could find an appropriate spouse. In some countries, and among some ethnic groups within some countries, there are many fewer males than females, and sometimes a high proportion of the males have poor economic prospects. In the former Soviet Union, there are many more women than men because males are more likely to have died from war, alcoholism, and accidents. The United States does not have such a skewed sex ratio, but in some neighborhoods, particularly poor neighborhoods, there are very high mortality rates for young males. And many males in such neighborhoods do not have work. One study by Daniel Lichter and his colleagues estimated that for every 100 African American women between the ages of 21 and 28, there were fewer than 80 available African American men. If we count only men who are employed full- or part-time, the number of available men per 100 women drops below 50. And a recent comparison of 85 countries finds that single parenthood is much more likely when there is higher male unemployment as well as when there are fewer men than women of a comparable age. So there may be considerable merit to the argument that one-parent families (usually headed by women) will be likely when a spouse (particularly an employed one) is hard to find.

Another popular explanation for the rise in number of one-parent families is that, in contrast to the past, women can manage without husbands because of support from the state. This scenario seems to fit Sweden, where unmarried and divorced mothers receive many social supports and allowances for maternity

and educational leave. But Iceland has few social supports from the government and yet has the highest rate of out-of-wedlock births of all the Scandinavian countries. In the United States, the welfare argument fails to predict changes over time. The program called Aid to Families with Dependent Children provided aid largely to single mothers. If the theory about government help was correct, increases in such aid would generally predict increases in the percentage of mother-headed households. But, in fact, during the 1970s, the percentage of families receiving aid and the value of aid decreased, whereas the percentage of mother-headed households increased. In the 1980s, it was more difficult to go "on welfare," but the percentage of mother-headed households increased anyway.

Women might be more able to manage alone if they have high-paying employment, and therefore we might expect more one-parent families by choice, as more women enter the job market. But, although this may explain the choices of some women, recent research finds that employed women generally are *more* rather than less likely to marry.

In any case, there seems to be a general association between commercial economies and the possibility of one-parent families. Is there something about subsistence economies that promotes marriage and something about commercial economies that detracts from it? Although marriage is not universally based on love or companionship, it entails a great deal of economic and other kinds of interdependence, particularly in not-so-commercial economies. Market economies allow other possibilities; goods and services can be bought and sold, and governments may take over functions that kin and family normally handle. So the one-parent family is likely to remain an option—either a choice or a necessity—for some people.

Sources: Burns and Scott 1994; Lichter et al. 1992; Whitehead and Popenoe 2005; Barber 2003.

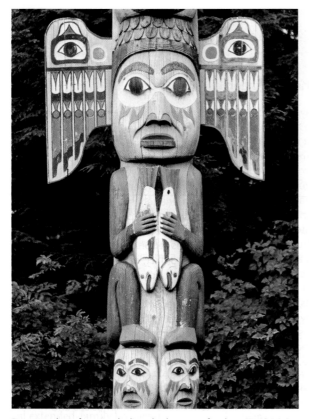

Totem poles often symbolize the history of a descent group. A totem pole in Ketchikan, Alaska.

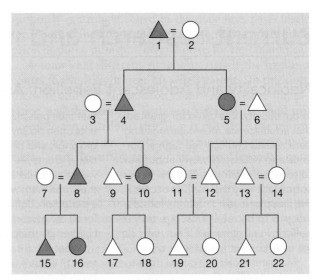

FIGURE 22–2 Patrilineal Descent
Individuals 4 and 5, who are the children of 1 and 2, affiliate with their father's patrilineal kin group, represented by the color red. In the next generation, the children of 3 and 4 also belong to the red kin group, because they take their descent from their father, who is a member of that group. However, the children of 5 and 6 do not belong to this patrilineal group, because they take their descent from their father, who is a member of a different group. That is, although the mother of 12 and 14 belongs to the red patrilineal group, she cannot pass on her descent affiliation to her children, and because her husband (6) does not belong to her patrilineage, her children (12 and 14) belong to their father's group. In the fourth generation, only 15 and 16 belong to the red patrilineal group, because their father is the only male member of the preceding generation who belongs to the red patrilineal group. In this diagram, then, 1, 4, 5, 8, 10, 15, and 16 are affiliated by the patrilineal descent; all the other individuals belong to other patrilineal groups.

Types of Affiliation with Kin

We distinguish three main types of affiliation with kin: *unilineal descent, ambilineal descent,* and *bilateral kinship.* The first two types (unilineal descent and ambilineal descent) are based on **rules of descent,** which are rules that connect individuals with particular sets of kin because of known or presumed common ancestry. By the particular rule of descent operating in their society, individuals can know more or less immediately which set of kin to turn to for support and help. As we shall see, bilateral kinship is not based on rules of descent or ancestry and does not create clear and unambigous groups.

Unilineal descent refers to the fact that a person is affiliated with a group of kin through descent links of one sex only—either males only or females only. Thus, unilineal descent can be either patrilineal or matrilineal.

1. **Patrilineal descent** affiliates individuals with kin of both sexes related to them *through men only.* As Figure 22–2 indicates, the children in patrilineal systems in each generation belong to the kin group of their father; their father, in turn, belongs to the group of his father; and so on. Although a man's sons and daughters are all members of the same descent group, affiliation with that group is transmitted only by the sons to their children. Just as patrilocal residence is much more common than matrilocal residence, patrilineal descent is more common than matrilineal descent.

2. **Matrilineal descent** affiliates individuals with kin of both sexes related to them *through women only.* In each generation, then, children belong to the kin group of their mother (see Figure 22–3). Although a woman's sons and daughters are all members of the same descent group, only her daughters can pass on their descent affiliation to their children.

Some have questioned the existence of unilineal descent and descent groups, suggesting that theorists have only imagined them. Reality could not possibly have been like that. But recent ethnohistorical analyses confirm that Native North American societies, like the Omaha, really did have patrilineal descent groups in the 19th century,[4] and the Chuuk (in the Pacific) still have functioning matrilineal groups, despite many years of Western contact.[5]

Unilineal rules of descent affiliate an individual with a line of kin extending back in time and into the future. By virtue of this line of descent, whether it extends through males or females, some very close relatives are excluded. For example, in a patrilineal system, your mother and your mother's parents do not belong to your patrilineal group, but your father and his father (and their sisters) do. In your own generation in a matrilineal or patrilineal system, some cousins are excluded, and in your children's generation, some of your nieces and nephews are excluded.

However, although unilineal rules of descent exclude certain relatives from membership in one's kin group, the excluded relatives are not necessarily ignored or forgotten, just as practical considerations restrict the effective size of

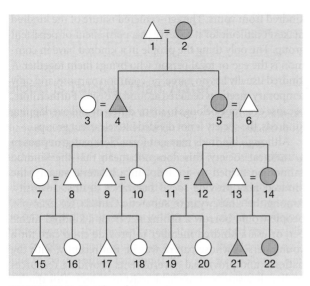

FIGURE 22–3 Matrilineal Descent
Individuals 4 and 5, who are the children of 1 and 2, affiliate with their mother's kin group, represented by the color green. In the next generation, the children of 5 and 6 also belong to the green kin group, because they take their descent from their mother, who is a member of that group. However, the children of 3 and 4 do not belong to this matrilineal group, because they take their descent from their mother, who is a member of a different group; their father, although a member of the green matrilineal group, cannot pass his affiliation on to them under the rule of matrilineal descent. In the fourth generation, only 21 and 22 belong to the green matrilineal group, because their mother is the only female member of the preceding generation who belongs. Thus, individuals 2, 4, 5, 12, 14, 21, and 22 belong to the same matrilineal group.

kinship networks in our own society. Indeed, in many unilineal societies, they may be entrusted with important responsibilities. For example, when a person dies in a patrilineal society, some members of the mother's patrilineal descent group may customarily be accorded the right to perform certain rituals at the funeral.

Unilineal rules of descent can form clear-cut, and hence unambiguous, groups of kin, which can act as separate units even after the death of individual members. Referring again to Figures 22–2 and 22–3, we can see that the individuals in the highlight color belong to the same patrilineal or matrilineal descent group without ambiguity; individuals in the fourth generation belong to the group just as much as those in the first generation. Say the patrilineal group has a name, the Hawks. Individuals know whether or not they are Hawks. If not, they belong to some other group, for each person belongs to only one line of descent. This fact is important if kin groups are to act as separate, nonoverlapping units. It is difficult for people to act together unless they know exactly who should get together. And it is easier for individuals to act together as a group if each one belongs to only one such group or line.

In contrast to unilineal descent, **ambilineal descent** affiliates individuals with kin related to them through men *or* women. In other words, some people in the society affiliate with a group of kin through their fathers; others affiliate through their mothers. Consequently, the descent groups show both female and male genealogical links, as illustrated in Figure 22–4.

These three rules of descent (patrilineal, matrilineal, and ambilineal) are usually, but not always, mutually exclusive. Most societies can be characterized as having only one rule of descent, but two principles are sometimes used to affiliate individuals with different sets of kin for different purposes. Some societies have, then, what is called **double descent or double unilineal descent,** whereby individuals affiliate for some purposes with a group of matrilineal kin and for other purposes with a group of patrilineal kin. Thus, two rules of descent, each traced through links of one sex only, are operative at the same time. For example, if there is a patrilineal system and a matrilineal one, individuals would belong to two groups at birth: the matrilineal group of the mother and the patrilineal group of the father. Imagine combining Figures 22–2 and 22–3. Individuals 4 and 5 would belong to both the patrilineal group (red in Figure 22–2) to which their father belongs and the matrilineal group (green in Figure 22–3) to which their mother belongs.

The way a society assigns names does not necessarily convey any information about a rule of descent. It is customary in North American society for children to have a last, or "family," name—usually their father's last name. All the people with the same last name do not conceive of themselves as descended from the same common ancestor; all Smiths do not consider themselves related. Nor do such people act together for any particular purpose. And many societies, even with rules of descent, do not give individuals the name of their kin group or of their father or mother. For example, among the patrilineal Luo of Kenya, babies were traditionally given names that described the circumstances of their birth (such as "born-in-the-morning"); their names did not include their father's or kin group's name. Only after the British established a colony in Kenya, and continuing after independence, did children get their father's personal name as a family name.

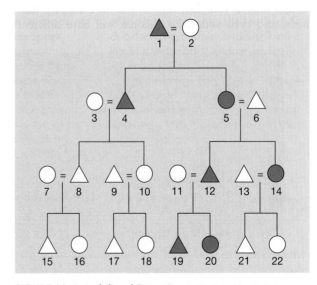

FIGURE 22–4 Ambilineal Descent
A hypothetical ambilineal group of kin is indicated by the color blue. Members 4 and 5 belong to this group because of a male link, their father (1); members 12 and 14 belong because of a female link, their mother (5); and members 19 and 20 belong because of a male link, their father (12). This is a hypothetical example because any combination of lineal links is possible in an ambilineal descent group.

Ojibwa Indian word *ototeman,* "a relative of mine." In some societies, people have to observe taboos relating to their clan totem animal. For example, clan members may be forbidden to kill or eat their totem.

Although it may seem strange that an animal or plant should be a symbol of a kin group, animals as symbols of groups are familiar in our own culture. Football and baseball teams, for example, are often named for animals (Detroit Tigers, Baltimore Ravens, Philadelphia Eagles, Chicago Bears). Voluntary associations, such as men's clubs, are sometimes called by the name of an animal (Elks, Moose, Lions). Entire nations may be represented by an animal; we speak, for instance, of the American eagle and the British lion.[8] Why humans so often choose animal names to represent groups is an intriguing question for which we have no tested answer as yet.

Phratries A **phratry** is a unilineal descent group composed of supposedly related clans or sibs. As with clans, the descent links in phratries are unspecified.

Moieties When a whole society is divided into two unilineal descent groups, we call each group a **moiety.** (The word *moiety* comes from a French word meaning "half.") The people in each moiety believe themselves to be descended from a common ancestor, although they cannot specify how. Societies with moiety systems usually have relatively small populations (fewer than 9,000 people). Societies with phratries and clans tend to be larger.[9]

Combinations Although we have distinguished several different types of unilineal descent groups, we do not wish to imply that all unilineal societies have only one type of descent group. Many societies have two or more types in various combinations. For example, some societies have lineages and clans; others may have clans and phratries but no lineages; and still others may have clans and moieties but neither phratries nor lineages. Aside from the fact that a society that has phratries must also have clans (because phratries are combinations of clans), all combinations of descent groups are possible. Even if societies have more than one type of unilineal kin group—for example, lineages and clans—there is no ambiguity about membership. Small groups are simply subsets of larger units; the larger units include people who say they are unilineally related further back in time.

Patrilineal Organization

Patrilineal organization is the most frequent type of descent system. The Kapauku Papuans, a people living in the central highlands of western New Guinea, are an example of a patrilineal society with various types of descent groups.[10] The hierarchy of groups to which the Kapauku are affiliated by virtue of the patrilineal descent system plays an extremely important part in their lives. All Kapauku belong to a patrilineage, to a patriclan that includes their lineage, and to a patriphratry that includes their clan.

The male members of a patrilineage—all the living males who can trace their actual relationship through males to a common ancestor—constitute the male population of a single village or, more likely, a series of adjoining villages. In other words, the lineage is a *territorial unit.* The male members of the lineage live together by virtue of a patrilocal rule of residence and a fairly stable settlement pattern. A son stays near his parents and brings his wife to live in or near his father's house; the daughters leave home and go to live with their husbands. If the group lives in one place over a long period, the male descendants of one man will live in the same territory. If the lineage is large, it may be divided into sublineages composed of people who trace their descent from one of the sons of the lineage ancestor. The male members of a sublineage live in a contiguous block within the larger lineage territory.

The members of the same patrilineage address each other affectionately, and within this group, a headman maintains law and order. Killing within the lineage is considered a serious offense, and any fighting that takes place is done with sticks rather than lethal weapons such as spears. The sublineage headman tries to settle grievances within the sublineage as quickly and as peacefully as possible. If a sublineage mate commits a crime against outsiders, all members of the sublineage may be considered responsible and their property seized, or a member of the sublineage may be killed in revenge by the victim's kin.

The Kapauku also belong to larger and more inclusive patrilineal descent groups—clans and phratries. All the people of the same clan believe they are related to each other in the father's line, but they are unable to say how they are related. If a member of the patriclan eats the clan's plant or animal totem, it is believed that the person will become deaf. Kapauku are also forbidden to marry anyone from their clan. In other words, the clan is exogamous.

Unlike the members of the patrilineage, the male members of the patriclan do not all live together. Thus, the lineage is the largest group of patrilineal kinsmen that is localized. The lineage is also the largest group of kinsmen that acts together politically. Among clan members, there is no mechanism for resolving disputes, and members of the same patriclan (who belong to different lineages) may even go to war with one another.

The most inclusive patrilineal descent group among the Kapauku is the phratry, each of which is composed of two or more clans. The Kapauku believe that the phratry was originally one clan, but that, in a conflict between brothers of the founding family, the younger brother was expelled and he formed a new clan. The two resulting clans are viewed as patrilineally related, because their founders are said to have been brothers. The members of a phratry observe all the totemic taboos of the clans that belong to that phratry. Intermarriage of members of the same clan is forbidden, but members of the same phratry, if they belong to different clans, may marry.

The Kapauku, then, have lineages with demonstrated kinship links and two kinds of descent groups with unknown descent links (clans and phratries).

Matrilineal Organization

Although societies with matrilineal descent seem in many respects like mirror images of their patrilineal counterparts, they differ in one important way. That difference

new perspectives on gender

Variation in Residence and Kinship: What Difference Does It Make to Women?

When we say that residence and kinship have profound effects on people's lives, what exactly do we mean? We may imagine that it is hard for a woman in a patrilocal society to move at marriage into another village where her husband has plenty of relatives and she has few. But do we have evidence of that? Most ethnographies usually do not give details about people's feelings, but some do. For example, Leigh Minturn gives us the text of a letter that one new Rajput bride (who grew up in the village of Khalapur, India) sent to her mother shortly after she married into her husband's village. The letter was written when the bride had been gone six weeks, but she repeatedly asked if her mother, her father, and her aunts had forgotten her. She begged to be called home and said her bags were packed. She described herself as "a parrot in a cage" and complained about her in-laws. The bride's mother was not alarmed; she knew that such complaints were normal, reflections of her daughter's separation anxiety. Seven years later, when Minturn returned to India, the mother reported the daughter to be happy. Still, a few other brides did have more serious symptoms: ghost possession, 24- to 36-hour comas, serious depression, or suicide. What research has not told us is whether these serious symptoms are present more often in patrilocal, patrilineal societies than in other societies, particularly matrilocal, matrilineal societies. Conversely, do men have some symptoms in matrilocal, matrilineal societies that they do not have in patrilocal societies? We do not know.

What about the status of women? Some research suggests that matrilocality and matrilineality enhance some aspects of women's status, but perhaps not as much as we might think. Even in matrilineal societies, men are usually the political leaders. The main effect of matrilocality and matrilineality appears to be that women control property, but they also tend to have

more domestic authority in the home, more equal sexual restrictions, and more value placed on their lives. Alice Schlegel pointed out that women's status is not always relatively high in matrilineal societies, because they can be dominated by the husband or by brothers (because brothers play important roles in their kin groups). Only when neither the husband nor the brother dominates may women have considerable control over their own lives. Certainly the combination of matrilocality and matrilineality is better for women's status than patrilocality and patrilineality. Matrilocality and matrilineality might not enhance women's status because of the dominance of male matrilineal kin, but patrilocality and patrilineality are very likely to detract from women's status. Norma Diamond stated that, even after the Chinese Communist revolution, which abolished the landholding estates of patrilineages and gave women access to education as well as jobs outside the home, male dominance continued. The mode of production and labor changed, but patrilocality did not. Women were still usually the in-marrying strangers, and members of the patrilineage became a work team on the collective farm. Diamond pointed out that those few women who became local leaders were likely to have atypical marriages that allowed them to live in the villages of their birth.

Residence and descent also predict societal attempts to control reproduction. According to Suzanne Frayser, patrilineal societies have several sexual and reproductive dilemmas. One dilemma is the contradiction between the importance of males in kinship and the women's role in reproduction. If patrilineal societies denigrate women too much, women may try to decrease their reproduction. If patrilineal societies exalt women too much, that exaltation may detract from the value of men. A second dilemma has to do

with paternity, which is essential for patrilineal descent but harder than maternity to be certain of. Frayser argued that, because kin group links are traced through males in patrilineal societies, they will do more to ensure that the man a woman marries is the father. Frayser suggested that patrilineal societies therefore will be more restrictive about a woman's sexuality. Indeed, the results of her cross-cultural study indicate that patrilineal societies are more likely than other societies to prohibit premarital and extramarital sex for women, and they are more likely to make it very difficult for a woman to divorce her husband.

Of course, we have to remember that there is considerable variation within patrilocal/patrilineal societies and matrilocal/matrilineal societies. In the patrilineal society that Audrey Smedley studied—the Birom of the Jos Plateau in Nigeria—women were formally barred from owning property, from holding political offices, and from major decision making. Yet, her fieldwork revealed that they had considerable autonomy in their personal lives in everyday life, including the legal right to take on lovers. Indeed, they had considerable indirect influence on decision making and were strong supporters of the patrilineal system. Smedley speculates that women support patrilineality in some environmental circumstances because it serves their interests and those of their children too. For example, male crops are highly valued, but such crops are grown on the more dangerous plains where men risked death at the hands of raiders from other groups. Food was scarce, so it may have been adaptive for everyone, including women, to give special status to men for growing crops in dangerous places.

Sources: Minturn 1993, 54–71; M. K. Whyte 1978b, 132–34; Schlegel 2009; N. Diamond 1975; Smedley 2004; Frayser 1985, 338–47.

has to do with who exercises authority. In patrilineal systems, descent affiliation is transmitted through males, and it is also the males who exercise authority. Consequently, in the patrilineal system, lines of descent and of authority converge. In a matrilineal system, however, although the line of descent passes through females, females rarely exercise authority in their kin groups. Usually males do. Thus, the lines of authority and descent do not converge.[11] Anthropologists do not completely understand why this is so, but it is an ethnographic fact. In any case, because males exercise authority in the kin group, an individual's mother's brother becomes an important authority figure, because he is the individual's closest male matrilineal relative in the parental generation. The individual's father does not belong to the individual's own matrilineal kin group and thus has no say in kin group matters.

The divergence of authority and descent in a matrilineal system has some effect on community organization and marriage. Most matrilineal societies practice matrilocal residence. Daughters stay at home after marriage and bring their husbands to live with them; sons leave home to join their wives. But the sons who are required to leave will be the ones who eventually exercise authority in their kin groups. This situation presents a problem. The solution that seems to have been realized in most matrilineal societies is that, although the males move away to live with their wives, they usually do not move too far away; indeed, they often marry women who live in the same village. Thus, matrilineal societies tend not to be locally exogamous—that is, members often marry people from inside the village—whereas patrilineal societies are often locally exogamous.[12]

The matrilineal organization on Chuuk, a group of small islands in the Pacific, illustrates the general pattern of authority in matrilineal systems.[13] The Chuukese have both matrilineages and matriclans. The matrilineage is a property-owning group whose members trace descent from a known common ancestor in the female line. The female lineage members and their husbands occupy a cluster of houses on the matrilineage's land. The property of the lineage group is administered by the oldest brother of the group, who allocates the productive property of his matrilineage and directs the work of the members. He also represents the group in dealings with the district chief and all outsiders, and he must be consulted on any matter that affects the group. There is also a senior woman of the lineage who exercises some authority, but only insofar as the activities of the women are concerned. She may supervise the women's cooperative work (they usually work separately from the men) and manage the household.

Within the nuclear family, the father and mother have the primary responsibility for raising and disciplining their children. When a child reaches puberty, however, the father's right to discipline or exercise authority over the child ceases. The mother continues to exercise her right of discipline, but her brother may interfere. A woman's brother rarely interferes with his sister's child before puberty, but he may exercise some authority after puberty, especially because he is an elder in the child's own matrilineage. On Chuuk, men rarely move far from their birthplace. As Ward Goodenough pointed out: "Since matrilocal residence takes the men away from their home lineages, most of them marry women whose lineage houses are within a few minutes' walk of their own."[14]

Although there are some differences between patrilineal and matrilineal systems, there are many similarities. In both types of systems there may be lineages, clans, phratries, and moieties, alone or in any combination. These kin groups, in either matrilineal or patrilineal societies, may perform any number of functions. They may regulate marriage, they may come to each other's aid economically or politically, and they may perform rituals together.

FUNCTIONS OF UNILINEAL DESCENT GROUPS

Unilineal descent groups exist in societies at all levels of cultural complexity.[15] Apparently, however, they are most common in noncommercial food-producing, as opposed to food-collecting, societies.[16] Unilineal descent groups often have important functions in the social, economic, political, and religious realms of life.

Regulating Marriage

In unilineal societies, individuals are not usually permitted to marry within their own unilineal descent groups. In some, however, marriage may be permitted within more inclusive kin groups but prohibited within smaller kin groups. In a few societies, marriage within the kin group is actually preferred.

But, in general, the incest taboo in unilineal societies is extended to all presumed unilineal relatives. For example, on Chuuk, which has matriclans and matrilineages, people are forbidden to marry anyone from their matriclan by the rule of descent group exogamy. The matrilineage is included within the matriclan, so the rule of descent group exogamy also applies to the matrilineage. Among the Kapauku, who have patriphratries, patriclans, and patrilineages, the largest descent group that is exogamous is the patriclan. The phratry may once have been exogamous, but the exogamy rule no longer applies to it. Some anthropologists have suggested that rules of exogamy for descent groups may have developed because the alliances between descent groups generated by such rules may be selectively favored under the conditions of life most unilineal societies face.

Economic Functions

Members of a person's lineage or clan are often required to side with that person in any quarrel or lawsuit, to help him or her get established economically, to contribute to a bride price or fine, and to support the person in life crises. Mutual aid often extends to economic cooperation on a regular basis. The unilineal descent group may act as a corporate unit in landownership. For example, among the Chuukese and the Kapauku, a lineage owns house sites and farmland. Descent group members may also support one another in such enterprises as clearing virgin bush or forest for farmland and providing food and other items for feasts, potlatches, curing rites, and ceremonial occasions, such as births, initiations, marriages, and funerals.

The descent group sometimes views money earned—either by harvesting a cash crop or by leaving the community for a time to work for cash wages—as belonging to all. In recent times, however, young people in some places have shown an unwillingness to part with their money, viewing it as different from other kinds of economic assistance.

Political Functions

The word *political*, as used by members of an industrialized society, generally does not apply to the vague powers that may be entrusted to a headman or the elders of a lineage or clan. But these people may have the right to assign land for use by a lineage member or a clan member. Headmen or elders may also have the right to settle disputes between two members within a lineage, although they generally lack power to force a settlement. And they may act as intermediaries in disputes between a member of their own clan and a member of an opposing kin group.

Certainly one of the most important political functions of unilineal descent groups is their role in warfare—the attempt to resolve disputes within and outside the society by violent action. In societies without towns or cities, the organization of such fighting is often in the hands of descent groups. The Tiv of central Nigeria, for instance, know very well at any given moment which lineages they will fight against, which lineages they will join as allies in case of a fight, which they will fight against using only sticks, and which must be attacked using bows and arrows.

Religious Functions

A clan or lineage may have its own religious beliefs and practices, worshiping its own gods or goddesses and ancestral spirits. The Tallensi of West Africa revere and try to pacify their ancestors. They view life as we know it as only a part of human existence; for them, life existed before birth and will continue after death. The Tallensi believe that the ancestors of their descent groups have changed their form but have retained their interest in what goes on within their society. They can show their displeasure by bringing sudden disaster or minor mishap and their pleasure by bringing unexpected good fortune. But people can never tell what will please them; ancestral spirits are, above all, unpredictable. Thus, the Tallensi try to account for unexplainable happenings by attributing them to the ever-watchful ancestors. Belief in the presence of ancestors also provides security; if their ancestors have survived death, so will they. The Tallensi religion is thus a religion of that descent group. The Tallensi are not concerned with other people's ancestors; they believe only one's own ancestors can plague or protect one.[17]

In some cultures, people worship or give gifts to ancestral spirits, as is common in China.

AMBILINEAL SYSTEMS

Societies with ambilineal descent groups are far less numerous than unilineal or even bilateral societies. Ambilineal societies, however, resemble unilineal ones in many ways. For instance, the members of an ambilineal descent group believe that they are descended from a common ancestor, although frequently they cannot specify all the genealogical links. The descent group is commonly named and may have an identifying emblem or even a totem; the descent group may own land and other productive resources; and myths and religious practices are often associated with the group. Marriage is often regulated by group membership, just as in unilineal systems, although kin group exogamy is not nearly as common as in unilineal systems. Moreover, ambilineal societies resemble unilineal ones in having various levels or types of descent groups. They may have lineages and higher orders of descent groups, distinguished (as in unilineal systems) by whether or not all the genealogical links to the supposed common ancestors are specified.[18]

The Samoans of the South Pacific are an example of an ambilineal society.[19] Samoa has two types of ambilineal descent groups, corresponding to what would be called clans and subclans in a unilineal society. Both groups are exogamous. Associated with each ambilineal clan are one or more chiefs. A group takes its name from the senior chief; subclans, of which there are always at least two, may take their names from junior chiefs.

The distinctiveness of the Samoan ambilineal system, compared with unilineal systems, is that individuals could belong to a number of ambilineal groups because people may be affiliated with an ambilineal group through their father or mother (and the parents, in turn, could be affiliated with any of their parents' groups). Affiliation with a Samoan descent group is optional, and people may theoretically affiliate with any or all of the ambilineal groups to which they are related. In practice, however, people are primarily associated with one group—the ambilineal group whose land they actually live on and cultivate—although they may participate in the activities (e.g., house building) of several groups. Because a person may belong to more than one ambilineal group, the society is not divided into separate kin groups, in contrast with unilineal societies. Consequently, the core members of each ambilineal group cannot all live together, as they could in unilineal societies, because each person belongs to more than one group and cannot live in several places at once.

Not all ambilineal societies have the multiple descent group membership that occurs in Samoa. In some ambilineal societies, a person may belong to only one group at any one time. In such cases, the society can be divided into separate, nonoverlapping groups of kin.

EXPLAINING VARIATION IN RESIDENCE

Questions can be raised as to why different societies have different patterns of residence. If married couples in most societies live with or near kin, as in patrilocal, matrilocal, bilocal, and avunculocal patterns of residence, then why do couples in some societies, such as our own, typically live apart from kin? And, among the societies in which couples live with or near kin, why do most choose the husband's side (patrilocal residence), but some the wife's side (matrilocal residence)? Why do some non-neolocal societies allow a married couple to go to either the wife's or the husband's kin (bilocal residence), whereas most others do not allow a choice?

Neolocal Residence

Many anthropologists have suggested that neolocal residence is related to the presence of a money or commercial economy. They argue that, when people can sell their labor or their products for money, they can buy what they need to live, without having to depend on kin. Because money is not perishable, unlike crops and other foods in a world largely lacking refrigeration, it can be stored for exchange at a later time. Thus, a money-earning family can resort to its own savings during periods of unemployment or disability, or it might be able to rely on monetary aid from the government, as in our own society. This strategy is impossible in nonmonetary economies, where people must depend on relatives for food and other necessities if they cannot provide their own for some reason.

There is cross-cultural evidence to support this interpretation. Neolocal residence tends to occur in societies with monetary or commercial exchange, whereas societies without money tend to have patterns of residence that locate a couple near or with kin.[20] The presence of money, then, partially accounts for neolocal residence: Money seems to allow couples to live on their own. Still, this fact does not quite explain why they choose to do so.

One reason may be that couples in commercial societies do better on their own because the jobs available require physical or social mobility. Or perhaps couples prefer to live apart from kin because they want to avoid some of the interpersonal tensions and demands that may be generated by living with or near kin. But why couples, when given money, should *prefer* to live on their own is not completely understood.

Matrilocal versus Patrilocal Residence

It is traditionally assumed that, in societies in which married children live near or with kin, the pattern of residence will tend to be patrilocal if males contribute more to the economy and matrilocal if women contribute more. However plausible that assumption may seem, the cross-cultural evidence does not support it. Where men do most of the primary subsistence work, residence is patrilocal no more often than would be expected by chance. Conversely, where women do an equal amount or more of the subsistence work, residence is no more likely to be matrilocal than patrilocal.[21] And if we counted all work inside and outside the home, most societies should be matrilocal because women usually do more. But that is not true either; most societies are not matrilocal.

applied anthropology

From Cross-Cultural Research to Archaeology: Reconstructing Marital Residence in the Prehistoric U.S. Southwest

Applied anthropology uses anthropological knowledge to solve problems. Usually, the problem is a practical problem outside anthropology. For example, forensic anthropology applies biological anthropology to help solve murders and other crimes. But sometimes the application is from one subfield of anthropology to another.

Cross-cultural studies using ethnographic data indicate that sisters are very likely to live in the same household if marital residence is matrilocal. The family unit is likely to be larger therefore with matrilocal residence, and the living (nonstorage) floor area of the house is also likely to be larger. In contrast to patrilocal societies, where the average living floor area is less than 72 square yards (60 square meters), the living floor area in matrilocal societies tends to be larger than 120 square yards (100 square meters). Apparently, sisters have less trouble living together than non-sisters, perhaps because they have grown up together.

Most anthropologists would assume that a relationship derived from comparative ethnography on preindustrial societies would apply also to human behavior in the prehistoric past. If that's true, and there is no good reason to doubt it, archaeological sites with living floor areas totaling more than 120 square yards (100 square meters) are likely to have had matrilocal marital residence. This prediction has been applied to the transition from pit houses to great houses in the U.S. Southwest. The pit houses between A.D. 500 and A.D. 700 averaged 18 square yards (15 square meters) in floor area, in contrast to the multiroom households from A.D. 900 to A.D. 1100 (as in Pueblo Bonito in New Mexico's Chaco Canyon) that ranged in size from 84 square yards to more than 360 square yards (70 square meters to 300 square meters). The latter households were probably matrilocal. Archaeologists know that the households had

multiple rooms because there are double walls between adjacent households.

Years ago, some archaeologists suggested that a descent line of matrilineally related women, who would have occupied a site over time if couples lived matrilocally, should exhibit distinctive pottery design elements when compared with the pottery from other sites. After all, mothers would have taught daughters who would have taught their daughters. Perhaps because their calculations and measures were not simple counts such as number of potsherds found, the work by these pioneering archaeologists was ignored if not rejected. The study of kinship in archaeology, following the findings of cross-cultural research, is still wide open, particularly to investigators who are trained in statistical methods.

Sources: Peregrine 2001; M. Ember 1973; Divale 1977; Hill 1970; Longacre 1970.

We can predict whether residence will be matrilocal or patrilocal, however, from the type of warfare practiced in the society. In most societies known to anthropology, neighboring communities or districts are enemies. The type of warfare that breaks out periodically between such groups is called *internal*, because the fighting occurs between groups that speak the same language. In other societies, the warfare is never within the same society but only with other language groups. This pattern of warfare is referred to as purely *external*. Cross-cultural evidence suggests that, in societies where warfare is at least sometimes internal, residence is almost always patrilocal rather than matrilocal. In contrast, residence is usually matrilocal when warfare is purely external.[22]

How can we explain this relationship between type of warfare and matrilocal versus patrilocal residence? One theory is that patrilocal residence tends to occur with internal warfare because there may be concern over keeping sons close to home to help with defense. Because women do not usually constitute the fighting force in any society, having sons reside at home after marriage might be favored as a means of maintaining a loyal and quickly mobilized fighting force in case of surprise attack from nearby. If warfare is

purely external, however, people may not be so concerned about keeping their sons at home because families need not fear attack from neighboring communities or districts.

With purely external warfare, then, the pattern of residence may be determined by other considerations, especially economic ones. If the women do most of the primary subsistence work in societies with purely external warfare, families might want their daughters to remain at home after marriage, so the pattern of residence might become matrilocal. If warfare is purely external but men still do more of the primary subsistence work, residence should still be patrilocal. Thus, the need to keep sons at home after marriage when there is internal warfare may take precedence over any considerations based on division of labor. Perhaps only when internal warfare is nonexistent may a female-dominant division of labor give rise to matrilocal residence.[23]

The frequent absence of men because of long-distance trade or wage labor in distant places may also provide an impetus for matrilocal residence even after warfare ceases. For example, among the Miskito of eastern Central America, matrilocality allowed domestic and village life to continue without interruption when men were away from home for long periods of time, working as lumberers,

The Iroquois longhouses could house over 80 people. The female members of a matrilineage with their in-marrying husbands traditionally lived in one longhouse.

Parallel cousins always have terms different from those for cross-cousins and are sometimes, but not always, referred to by the same terms as one's brother and sister.

Like the Omaha and Crow systems, the Iroquois system has different terms for relatives on the father's and mother's sides. Such differentiation tends to be associated with unilineal descent, which is not surprising because unilineal descent involves affiliation with either mother's or father's kin. Why Iroquois, rather than Omaha or Crow, terminology occurs in a unilineal society requires explanation. One possible explanation is that Omaha or Crow is likely to occur in a developed, as opposed to a developing or decaying, unilineal system.[39] Another possibility is that Iroquois terminology emerges in societies that prefer marriage with both cross-cousins,[40] who are differentiated from other relatives in an Iroquois system.

Sudanese System

Unlike the Omaha, Crow, and Iroquois systems, the Sudanese system usually does not lump any relatives in the parents' and ego's generations. That is, the Sudanese system is usually a *descriptive system*, in which a different **descriptive term** is used for *each* of the relatives, as shown in Figure 22–11. What kinds of societies are likely to have such a system? Although societies with Sudanese terminology are likely to be patrilineal, they probably are different from most patrilineal societies that have Omaha or Iroquois terms. Sudanese terminology is associated with relatively great political complexity, class stratification, and occupational specialization. It has been suggested that, under such conditions, a kinship system may reflect the need to make fine distinctions among members of descent groups who have different opportunities and privileges in the occupational or class system.[41]

FIGURE 22–11 Sudanese Kinship Terminology System

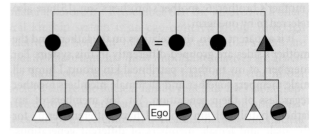

FIGURE 22–12 Hawaiian Kinship Terminology System

The Omaha, Crow, Iroquois, and Sudanese systems, although different from one another and associated with somewhat different predictors, share one important feature: The terms used for the mother's and father's side of the family are not the same. If you imagine folding the kinship terminology diagrams in half, the two sides would not be the same. As we have seen in the Inuit system, however, the terms on the mother's and father's side of the family are *exactly* the same. This feature suggests that the two sides of the family are equally important or equally unimportant. The Hawaiian system discussed next also has the same terms on both sides, but kinship outside the nuclear family is more important.

Hawaiian System

The Hawaiian system of kinship terminology is the least complex in that it uses the smallest number of terms. In this system, all relatives of the same sex in the same generation are referred to by the same term (see Figure 22–12). Thus, all my female cousins are referred to by the same term as my sister; all male cousins are referred to by the same term as my brother. Everyone known to be related to me in my parents' generation is referred to by one term if female (including my mother) and by another term if male (including my father).

The fact that societies with Hawaiian kin terminology tend not to have unilineal descent groups[42] helps explain why kinship terms are the same on both sides of the family. Why are the terms for mother, father, sister, and brother used for other relatives? Perhaps because societies with Hawaiian terminology are likely to have large extended families[43] to which every type of relative in Figure 22–12 may belong because of alternative (bilocal) residence patterns.[44] So, in contrast to our own society, many kin are very important, a fact that seems to be reflected in the practice of referring to other relatives with the same terms that are used for nuclear family members.

SUMMARY ● ○ ○

1. In our society, and in many other industrial societies, a newly married couple usually establishes a place of residence apart from parents or relatives (neolocal residence). But about 95 percent of the world's societies have some pattern of residence whereby the new couple settles within or very close to the household of the parents or some other close relative of the groom or bride.

2. The four major patterns in which married couples live with or near kinsmen are the following:

   a. Patrilocal residence: The couple lives with or near the husband's parents (67 percent of all societies).

   b. Matrilocal residence: The couple lives with or near the wife's parents (15 percent of all societies).

   c. Bilocal residence: The couple lives with or near either the husband's parents or the wife's parents (7 percent of all societies).

   d. Avunculocal residence: The son and his wife settle with or near his mother's brother (4 percent of all societies).

3. In most societies where kinship is important, rules of affiliation allocate each person to a particular and definable set of kin. The three main types of affiliation with kin are: *unilineal descent, ambilineal descent,* and *bilateral kinship.*

4. Unilineal descent and ambilineal descent are based on rules of descent, which are rules that connect individuals with particular sets of kin because of known or presumed common ancestry. Unilineal descent refers to the fact that a person is affiliated with a group of kin through descent links of one sex only—either males only or females only. Thus, unilineal descent can be either patrilineal or matrilineal.

   a. Patrilineal descent affiliates individuals with kin of both sexes related to them through men only. In each generation, then, children belong to the kin group of their father.

   b. Matrilineal descent affiliates individuals with kin related to them through women only. In each generation, then, children belong to the kin group of their mother.

5. Ambilineal descent affiliates individuals with kin related to them through either men or women. Consequently, the descent groups show both female and male genealogical links.

6. Societies without lineal descent rules are bilateral societies. Relatives on both the mother's and father's sides of the family are of equal importance or, more usually, unimportance. Kindreds are ego-centered sets of kin who may be called together temporarily for some purpose.

7. With unilineal descent, people usually refer to themselves as belonging to a particular unilineal group or set of groups because they believe they share common descent in either the male or the female line. These people form what is called a unilineal descent group. There are several types, and a society may have more than one type:

   a. Lineages are sets of kin whose members trace descent from a common ancestor through known links.

   b. Clans are sets of kin who believe they are descended from a common ancestor but cannot specify the genealogical links.

   c. Phratries are groups of supposedly related clans.

   d. Moieties are said to exist when the whole society is divided into two unilineal descent groups without specified links to the supposed common ancestor of each.

8. Unilineal descent groups are most common in societies in the middle range of cultural complexity—that is, in noncommercial food-producing, as opposed to food-collecting, societies. In such societies, unilineal descent groups often have important functions in the social, economic, political, and religious realms of life.

9. Societies differ markedly in how they group or distinguish relatives under the same or different kinship terms. The major systems of terminology are the Inuit (Eskimo), Omaha, Crow, Iroquois, Sudanese, and Hawaiian systems.

GLOSSARY TERMS ○ ● ○

affinal kin **404**
ambilineal descent **393**
avunculocal
   residence **389**
bilateral kinship **394**
bilocal residence **389**
clan or sib **395**
classificatory term **403**
consanguineal kin **404**
descriptive term **406**
double descent or double
   unilineal descent **393**
ego **394**
kindred **394**
lineage **394**
matriclans **395**

matrilineage **394**
matrilineal descent **392**
matrilocal residence **388**
moiety **396**
neolocal residence **389**
patriclans **395**
patrilineage **394**
patrilineal descent **392**
patrilocal residence **388**
phratry **396**
rules of descent **392**
siblings **405**
totem **395**
unilineal descent **392**
unilocal residence **389**

CRITICAL QUESTIONS ○ ○ ●

1. What other things about our society would change if we practiced other than neolocal residence?

2. Why does kinship provide the main structure of social action in noncommercial societies?

3. Why might it be important for unilineal descent groups to be nonoverlapping in membership?

PEARSON
myanthrolab

Read William L. Anderson's "Cherokee: The European Impact on the Cherokee Culture" on MyAnthroLab. Answer the following questions.

1. Describe the patterns of marital residence and descent practiced by the Cherokee.

2. What functions did the kin groups have?

3. How did European contact affect patterns of residence and descent?

Associations and Interest Groups

amuel Johnson, the 18th-century English author, was once asked to describe James Boswell, his companion and biographer. "Boswell," he boomed, "is a very clubable man." Johnson did not mean that Boswell deserved to be attacked with bludgeons. He was referring to Boswell's fondness for all sorts of clubs and associations, a fondness he shared with many of his contemporaries. The tendency to form associations was not unique to 18th-century England.

The notion of clubs may make us think of something extracurricular and not very important, but associations play very important roles in the economy and political life of many societies. Indeed, the associations we call non-governmental organizations (NGOs) have a lot of influence in our own and other modern societies (see the box on NGOs). In this chapter, we examine the various kinds of associations formed in different societies, how these groups function, and what general purposes they serve. When we speak of **associations,** we mean different kinds of groups that are not based on kinship, as discussed in the preceding chapter, or on territory, which we take up in the next chapter. Associations, then, are nonkin and nonterritorial groups; and, although they vary, they also have several common characteristics: (1) some kind of formal, institutionalized structure; (2) the exclusion of some people; (3) members with common interests or purposes; and (4) members with a discernible sense of pride and feeling of belonging. Contemporary American society has an abundance of *interest groups*—to use the terminology of the political scientist—that display these general characteristics of associations. Such groups vary considerably in size and social significance, ranging from national organizations such as the Democratic and Republican parties to more local organizations such as college sororities and fraternities.

But societies differ considerably in the degree to which they have such associations and, if they do have them, in what kind they have. To make our discussion somewhat easier, we focus on two dimensions of how associations vary from one society to another. One is whether or not recruitment into the association is voluntary. In U.S. society, with the exception of the government's right to draft men into the military, just about all associations are voluntary—that is, people can choose to join or not join. But in many societies, particularly the more egalitarian ones, membership is non-voluntary: All people of a particular category must belong.

A second dimension of variation in associations is what qualifies a person for membership. There are two possible kinds of qualifications: those that are achieved and those that are ascribed. **Achieved qualities** are those people acquire during their lifetime, such as superior skills in a sport or the skills required to be an electrician. **Ascribed qualities** are those determined for people at birth, either because of genetic makeup (e.g., sex) or because of family background (ethnicity, place of birth, religion, social class). We speak of two kinds of ascribed qualities or characteristics: **universally ascribed qualities,**

new perspectives on gender

Do Separate Women's Associations Increase Women's Status and Power?

Some women's associations, like those of the Ijaw of southern Nigeria, are reported to have considerable power. Do women generally have more power where women create and join their own associations? We might assume that the existence of such organizations would increase the status of women overall, or at least lead to more equality with men. But it could also be argued the other way around, that "separate" does not generally lead to more equality; it may just increase separateness. As far as we know, researchers have not yet tried to assess the cross-cultural effect of women's associations on female status in various domains of life, but there has been one cross-cultural attempt to see if the presence of women's associations predicts various aspects of women's participation in the political process.

Marc Howard Ross looked at four aspects of women's political participation: (1) the degree of inequality between women's and men's participation in public or community decision making; (2) the degree to which women participate in politics privately; (3) the degree to which women have access to positions of authority; and (4) the degree to which women have separate associations that are under their exclusive control. This last domain concerns us here. Does the presence of separate women's associations increase women's participation in public decision making and their access to positions of authority? Ross's cross-cultural data indicate that the answer is no. The presence of separate women's organizations *does not* generally increase the participation of women in public decision making, their access to positions of authority, or even their private participation in politics. This is not to say that women in organizations do not have influence. They do, but probably only or mainly within their organizations. The influence of women in their organizations, however, does not carry over into other political arenas.

Of course, we might need to consider other possible factors in future research. Perhaps women's participation in political arenas is more likely if female organizations control important economic resources. Such resources may give women more leverage politically. Also, some types of female organizations may have more power than others; for example, stand-alone organizations may have more power than those that are connected to male organizations. But it is also possible that these additional conditions would not change the basic finding: Separate female organizations—perhaps because they *are* separate—do not have any impact on women's participation in other political arenas.

Recently, people in the United States have started to discuss a related issue, the possible effects of female "separateness" on women's success. For example, do separate math and science classes for women lead to more equality between women and men in academic performance, in obtaining advanced degrees in math and science, and in access to high-paying positions in those areas? It is well known that women are very underrepresented in the math and physical science professions in the United States. Even though the percentages have been increasing, in 2006, women obtained only 20 percent of the doctorates in engineering, 28 percent in physical science, and 25 percent in mathematics and computer science; in contrast, women obtained 57 percent of the doctorates received in anthropology and 71 percent in psychology that year.

These differences could be mostly a result of social conditions that discourage females in various subjects and professions. Researchers have found that teachers of math and science pay more attention to boys. When boys give wrong answers, teachers are apt to challenge them; when girls give wrong answers, teachers tend to express sympathy. Boys are more likely to operate scientific equipment; girls are more likely to take notes. In the seventh grade, girls perform similarly to boys in math and

science, but girls display less confidence in their abilities. By the time they graduate from high school, women have taken fewer math and science courses, so they are at a disadvantage for continuing in those fields.

If the dampening effects on women are social, or mostly social, what can be done? Because current research suggests that girls do best in learning science and math without boys, some researchers have advocated separate math and science activities (classes and clubs). So, for example, voluntary girls' clubs (Operation SMART) have been set up in 240 locations to interest elementary and junior high school girls in science. A majority of the girls from those schools voluntarily attend. Moreover, many of them now say they want to go into science. Whether they stay in science, or how well they do if they stay, is not yet clear. But if these programs work, we would have to conclude that "separate" is more equal than "together."

The two situations we have described here do not seem to be parallel in their effects on women's status. Separate women's associations by themselves do not make for equality between the genders in political participation. But separate training for girls in math and science may make for more equality. What is different about the two situations? At least one thing is different. Separate women's associations are usually nonvoluntary; women more or less have to join because that's how the society structures what women can do. Separate training for females in math and science is usually voluntary; girls may opt for the separateness to acquire the skills and the confidence they need to move into arenas open to both genders. In other words, when achievement and not gender defines how far you can go, temporary separateness for women might increase the likelihood of gender equality in professions that do not have it now.

Sources: Ross 1986; "Women in Science" 1993; S. T. Hill 2000; National Science Foundation 2006.

keep secrets are they considered trustworthy for participation in political life.

The Poro leadership establishes the place where the initiates will undergo scarification and live in seclusion for about a year (formerly it was three or four years). The boys are taken out of town, where they engage in a mock battle with a *ngamu* (a member of the Poro masquerading as a forest devil), who incises marks on their necks, chests, and backs. These marks symbolize being killed and eaten by the devil; but then the initiates are "reborn." In the initiation "village" outside of town, the boys learn crafts, hunting, and the use of basic medicines. The children of the *Zo* are given special instruction so that they can take over the rituals from their fathers. Some are trained to perform as "devils." At the end of the year, the initiates are given Poro names, by which they will be known from then on. Secrecy is attached to events surrounding the initiates; everyone knows that the boys are not killed and eaten by the devil, but only some can speak of it. For example, women must say that the boys are in the devil's stomach; if they say otherwise, they might be killed in punishment.[9]

The initiation of females into the Sande (every seven years or so) also involves taking the initiates into the forest for a year (formerly three years). The girls not only undergo scarification; they also undergo a clitoridectomy, that is, the removal of the clitoris. Like the boys, the girls receive training in adult activities. In the years just before and during the Sande initiation, the women are responsible for the moral behavior of the community. People who commit crimes are first brought before the women. If a man is the accused, he is tried by the Poro *Zo*, but a portion of any fine is given to the women.[10]

The Poro and Sande *Zo* are held in great respect, and the devils are viewed with fear and awe for the powers they possess. Some authors suggest that fear of the Poro and the Sande strengthens the hands of secular political authority, because chiefs and landowners occupy the most powerful positions in the associations.[11]

Secret associations are common in many areas of the world—the Pacific, North and South America, as well as various parts of Africa—although they may be voluntary organizations in some places. In Africa, according to a recent cross-cultural study, secret associations are usually involved in political activities, as are the Poro and Sande. These activities punish people who, according to the secret society, have committed some wrongs. The fact that the punished people almost never seem to be members of the native elite or foreign rulers supports the observation about the Poro and Sande that they typically strengthen the hand of existing political authority.[12]

Ijaw Women's Associations Among the Ijaw of southern Nigeria, only women in the northern part of this society are organized into associations. In one northern Ijaw village, there are seven women's associations.[13] Once a married woman shows herself capable of supporting a household independent of her mother-in-law, which she does by engaging in marketing and trading, she has to belong to the women's association linked to her husband's patrilineage. Membership in such an association is

An N'jembe women's group in Gabon initiates young women into the group.

nonvoluntary; all eligible women must join, and members are fined if they do not come to meetings or arrive late.

The women's associations act as mediators in disputes and impose punishments even in cases that have gone to court. For example, an association may impose fines for "crimes" such as defaming a woman's character or adultery. An association may also adopt rules for proper behavior. Judgments and rules are arrived at by consensus of all the women members. If a punished member does not accept a judgment, the other members might get together and taunt the woman or take some important item from her house and refuse to have anything to do with her.

Some of the larger associations also act as lending institutions, using their cash reserves from fines to lend to members or nonmembers at an interest rate of 50 percent or more. Even a male in debt to the association might be held captive in his own house until he pays his debt. It is no wonder, then, that few resist an association's judgment for long. Although it is not clear why women's associations such as the Ijaw's are common in West Africa, one of the factors that may have been important is the women's participation in marketing and trade, which allows them to be financially independent of men. We shall see in the next section that women are increasingly forming voluntary self-help groups to improve themselves economically.

VOLUNTARY ASSOCIATIONS

Voluntary associations, such as the military associations of the Cheyenne of North America, may be found in some relatively simple societies. But voluntary associations tend to be more common in stratified and complex societies, presumably because stratified societies are composed of people with many different, and often competing, interests. We deal here with some examples of voluntary associations that are not familiar in North American experience.

Military Associations

Military associations in noncommercial societies may be compared to our own American Legion or Veterans of Foreign War posts. They all seem to exist to unite members

current research and issues

Why Do Street Gangs Develop, and Why Are They Often Violent?

The street gangs of young people that we read and hear about so often are voluntary associations. They are a little like age-sets in that the members are all about the same age, but they are unlike age-sets in being voluntary and they do not "graduate" through life stages together. Nobody has to join, although there may be strong social pressure to join the neighborhood gang. Gangs have a clear set of values, goals, roles, group functions, symbols, and initiations. Street gangs are also often like military associations in their commitment to violence in the defense of gang interests.

Violent street gangs are found in many U.S. cities, particularly in poor neighborhoods. But poverty alone does not appear sufficient to explain the existence of gangs. For example, there is plenty of poverty in Mexico, but gangs did not develop there. In Mexico, there was a *palomilla* (age-cohort) tradition; age-mates hung out together and continued their friendship well into adulthood, but there were no gangs as we know them. Mexican American gangs did develop in the *barrios* of cities such as Los Angeles. When we realize that *most* youths in poor neighborhoods do not join gangs, it is clear that poor neighborhoods cannot explain gangs. It is estimated that only 3 percent to 10 percent of Mexican American young people join gangs.

But why do some young people join and not others? If we look at who joins a gang, it seems to be those

children who are subject to the most domestic stress. The gang "joiners" are likely to come from poor families, have several siblings, and have no father in the household. They seem to have had difficulty in school and have gotten into trouble early. What about gangs appeals to them? Most adolescents in this country have a difficult time deciding who they are and what kind of person they want to be, but young people who join gangs seem to have more identity problems. One 18-year-old said he "joined the gang for my ego to go higher," reflecting a low self-esteem. Those who are raised in female-centered households seem to be looking for a way to show how "masculine" they are. They look up to the tough male street gang members and want to act like them. But getting into a gang requires initiation. Most gangs have their own stylized rituals; for example, Mexican American gangs physically beat the initiate, who must show bravery and courage. As happens in most initiation ceremonies, the gang initiate identifies even more strongly with the group afterward. So, belonging to a gang may make some youths feel as if they belong to something important. This is a kind of psychological adjustment, but is it adaptive? Does being in a gang help such youths survive in a neighborhood where young men are often killed? Or are gang members *less* likely to survive? We really don't know the answers to those questions.

Why did gangs develop in the United States and not in Mexico?

Were there some things different about life for Mexican Americans in the cities of the United States? Life in the United States was more difficult in several respects. First, many Mexican immigrants had to settle for very low pay and housing in marginal areas of the city. Second, they were subject to a lot of social and job discrimination. Third, they were immersed in a new culture that differed in many ways from their own. The young people who were least able to cope with these stresses were probably most likely to join gangs. But what explains the culture of violence of these gangs? Some scholars have suggested that the need to show exaggerated "masculine" behavior is a response to the absence of male models in the household. The association of many young men who have this same need may explain the violence of gangs. If aggressiveness is part of the male role (e.g., until recently only males were allowed to engage in military combat), then a young man who wants to exhibit his masculinity may be extremely aggressive.

We need much more research to uncover why gangs develop more often in some societies than in others and why they often are violent. Are there places where aggressiveness is not so much part of the male role, and are they therefore less likely to have violent gangs?

Sources: Vigil 1988, 2009; C. R. Ember and Ember 1994.

---

through their common experiences as warriors, to glorify the activities of war, and to perform certain services for the community. Membership in such associations is usually voluntary and based on the achieved criterion of participation in war. Among the North American Plains Indians, military societies were common. The Cheyenne, for example, had military associations that were not ranked by age but were open to any boy or man ready to go to war.[14]

In the beginning of the 19th century, the Cheyenne had five military associations: the Fox, Dog, Shield, Elk (or Hoof Rattle), and Bowstring (or Contrary). The last-named association was annihilated by the Pawnee in the

middle of the 19th century. Later, two new associations were established, the Wolf and Northern Crazy Dogs. Although the various associations may have had different costumes, songs, and dances, they were alike in their internal organization, each being headed by four leaders who were among the most important war chiefs.

When various Plains groups were confined to reservations, the military associations lost many of their old functions, but they did not entirely disappear. For example, among the Lakota, warrior societies continue to be an important part of social life because many men and women have engaged in military activity on behalf of the United States in

World Wars I and II, in Korea and Vietnam, and in the wars in the Persian Gulf. Returning soldiers continue to be welcomed with traditional songs of honor and victory dances.[15]

Regional Associations

Regional associations bring together migrants from a common geographic background. Thus, they are often found in urban centers, which traditionally have attracted settlers from rural areas. In the United States, for example, migrants from rural Appalachia have formed associations in Chicago and Detroit. Many of these organizations have become vocal political forces in municipal government. Regional associations often form even when migrants have come from a considerable distance. For example, in the Chinatowns of the United States and Canada, there are many associations based on district of origin in China as well as on surname. The regional and family organizations are in turn incorporated into more inclusive ethnic associations, as we shall see later in this chapter.[16]

William Mangin described the role of regional associations in helping rural migrants adapt to urban life in Lima, Peru.[17] During the 1950s, Mangin studied a group of migrants from the rural mountains, the *serranos* from Ancash. Typically these *serranos,* about 120,000 in number, lived in a slumlike urban settlement called a *barriada.* The *barriada* was not officially recognized by either the national government or the city authorities. Accordingly, it lacked all usual city services, such as water supply, garbage removal, and police protection. Its inhabitants had left their rural birthplaces for reasons typical of such population movements, wherever they occur. These reasons were social and economic; most were related to population and land pressure, but the higher expectations associated with the big city—better education, social mobility, wage labor—were also compelling considerations.

Typically, also, the *serranos* from Ancash formed a regional association. Club membership was open to both sexes. Men generally controlled the executive positions, and club leaders were often men who had achieved political power in their hometowns. Women, who had relatively less economic and social freedom, nevertheless played an important part in club activities.

The *serrano* regional association performed three main services for its members. First, it lobbied the central government on matters of community importance—for example, the supplying of sewers, clinics, and similar public services. A club member had to follow a piece of legislation through the channels of government to make certain it was not forgotten or abandoned. Second, the *serrano* association assisted in acculturating newly arrived *serranos* to the urban life in Lima. The most noticeable rural traits—coca chewing, hairstyle, and clothing peculiarities—were the first to disappear, with the men generally able to adapt faster than the women. The association also provided opportunities for fuller contact with the national culture. And finally, the group organized social activities such as fiestas, acted as the clearinghouse for information transmitted to and from the home area, and supplied a range of other services to help migrants adapt to their new environment while retaining ties to their birthplace.

The functions of regional associations may change over time as social conditions change. For example, during the plantation period in Hawaii, many Filipino migrants joined hometown associations that served as mutual aid societies. As more Filipinos went to Hawaii, however, more people had kin to whom they could turn. The hometown associations continue to have some economic functions, such as assistance in times of emergency, serious illness, or death, and some scholarship aid, but meetings are infrequent and most members do not attend. Those members who are active seem to want the recognition and prestige that can be attained through leadership positions in the hometown association, which is much more than they can achieve in the wider Hawaiian arena.[18]

Although regional clubs may help to integrate their members into a more complex urban or changing environment, the presence of many such groups may increase divisiveness and rivalry among groups. In some areas, the smaller groups have banded together and become quite powerful. For example, within each Chinatown of a major U.S. or Canadian city, the various regional and family associations formed a larger Chinese Benevolent Association.[19] Thus, by banding together, the regional and family associations formed ethnic associations (see the box on Chinatowns).

Ethnic Associations

Various types of ethnic associations or interest groups are found in cities all over the world. Membership in these associations is based largely on ethnicity. Ethnic associations are particularly widespread in urban centers of West Africa. There, accelerated cultural change, reflected in altered economic arrangements, in technological advances, and in new urban living conditions, has weakened kinship relations and other traditional sources of support and solidarity.[20] Sometimes it is difficult to say whether a particular association is ethnic or regional in origin; it may be both.

Tribal unions are frequently found in Nigeria and Ghana. These are typical of most such associations in that they are extraterritorial—that is, they recruit members

An ethnic association (Hop Sing Tong) in San Francisco was established in 1870.

migrants and immigrants

Ethnic Associations in "Chinatowns"

When immigrants come to a new country, they often first live in urban neighborhoods that mostly contain people like themselves, people from the same regions and even from the same towns and villages. These neighborhoods are called "Chinatowns," "Korea Towns," and the like. These ethnic neighborhoods often have associations, nonkin and nonterritorial groups that protect their members in a variety of ways, which is probably why people wanted to live in the neighborhood in the first place. R. H. Thompson pointed out that, according to the constitution of the Chinese Benevolent Association in Victoria, British Columbia (a ferry ride from Vancouver), that association was established "to undertake social welfare, to settle disputes, to aid the poor and the sick, to eliminate evils within the community, and to defend the community against external threat."

Many Chinatowns grew up in the United States and Canada since the middle of the 19th century. After perhaps working first on the railroads, for which they were recruited to come to North America, the Chinese immigrants would settle in San Francisco or Vancouver. Often they joined an association of people with the same surname. This set of people considered themselves vaguely related (after all, they did have the same surname), but they usually couldn't trace how or even *if* they were related. Or the neighborhood contained people from the same district in China, with the same dialect. Some people migrated eastward, to the urban centers of New York, Boston, Philadelphia, Montreal, and Toronto. Most if not all of the "Chinatowns" continue to exist, even if subsequent generations have moved away from them. Suburban Chinese Americans often come to Chinatown on the weekend to visit with relatives and to shop for traditional foods. They are not different from other immigrants in this respect; most immigrants retain their food preferences for generations.

The earliest Chinese immigrants established themselves in various kinds of small business—hand laundries, restaurants, groceries. Such businesses were cheap to start up, and workers who were family members did not have to be paid much to keep them. Hand laundries were the first to disappear as the immigrants and their descendants prospered, and as many people in the general population started to do their laundry in machines at home or in a nearby "laundromat." Now, instead of working in the old family businesses, the descendants of people who used to live in Chinatown often go to college and become doctors and other professionals. Their jobs could be anyplace. Upward mobility often means geographic mobility: people often have to chase the job rather than stay close to home, if they want to maximize their income. This is true for many immigrant groups, not just the people from "Chinatown." When people move away from the old neighborhood, the ethnic association loses its attraction and value. In a generation or two, it may be gone. Just as you may have less opportunity to see cousins and other relatives when you move away, you are also unlikely to participate in your ancestral ethnic association when your job requires you to live in a new place. Mobility has costs as well as benefits.

Sources: R. H. Thompson 1996; 2009; Brettell and Kemper 2002.

---

who have left their tribal locations; also, they have a formal constitution, and they have been formed to meet certain needs arising out of conditions of urban life. One such need is to keep members in touch with their traditional culture. The Ibo State Union, for example, in addition to providing mutual aid and financial support in case of unemployment, sickness, or death, performs the service of "fostering and keeping alive an interest in tribal song, history, language and moral beliefs and thus maintaining a person's attachment to his native town or village."[21] Some tribal unions collect money to improve conditions in their ancestral homes. Education, for example, is an area of particular concern. Others publish newsletters that report members' activities. Most unions have a young membership that exercises a powerful democratizing influence in tribal councils, and the organizations provide a springboard for those with national political aspirations.

West African occupational clubs also fall into the ethnic category. African versions of trade unions are organized along tribal as well as craft lines, and their principal concern is the status and remuneration of their members as workers. The Motor Drivers' Union of Keta, in Ghana, was formed to fund insurance and legal costs, to contribute to

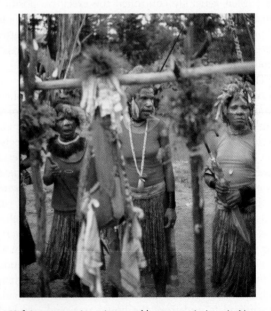

The Kafaina women's savings and loan associations in New Guinea often encourage relatives to start "daughter" organizations. At a ceremony for the new organization, a "daughter" doll is displayed.

medical care in case of accident or illness, and to help pay for funeral expenses.

Friendly societies differ from tribal unions in that their objectives are confined for the most part to mutual aid. Such a club was formed by the wives of Kru migrants in Freetown, Sierra Leone. Kru men normally go to sea, still a hazardous occupation. The club is classified into three grades. An admission fee permits entry into the lowest grade. Elevation to higher grades depends on further donations. At the death of a member or her husband, the family receives a lump sum commensurate with her status in the club.[22]

Rotating Credit Associations

A common type of mutual aid society is the *rotating credit association*. The basic principle is that each member of the group agrees to make a regular contribution, in money or in kind, to a fund, which is then handed over to each member in rotation.[23] The regular contributions promote savings by each member, but the lump sum distribution enables the recipient to do something significant with the money. These associations are found in many areas of East, South, and Southeast Asia, Africa (particularly West Africa), and the West Indies.[24] They usually include a small number of people, perhaps between 10 or 30, so that rotations do not take that long. The associations are usually informal and may last only as long as one rotation.

How do these systems work? What prevents someone from quitting after getting a lump sum? Ethnographic evidence indicates that defaulting on regular contributions is so rare that participants consider it unthinkable. Once a person joins a rotating credit association, there is strong social pressure to continue paying regularly. A person who joins does not have to fill out paperwork, as in a bank. All that is needed is a reputation for trustworthiness. There is often a social component to the association. Some have regular meetings with socializing and entertainment.[25] A rotating credit association may have one of three types of distribution. In some, a leader may decide the order of rotation, usually making the judgment on perceived need. In others, distribution is based on a random drawing or the roll of dice. The third method is based on who is willing to pay the highest interest.[26]

The principle of a rotating credit association often has roots in traditional sharing systems. For example, among the Kikuyu, related women would work together to weed or harvest each other's fields in turn. When a person had special expenses, such as a funeral, there would be a contribution party and everyone who came would make a contribution. Nici Nelson describes a very successful rotating credit association that developed in a squatter area of Nairobi. The founding woman organized a group of women of similar economic status who came from the Kiambu district of Kenya. Early in 1971, the group had about 20 members, but expanded to about 30. In a few years, the founder also started a land-buying cooperative. Although the rotating credit association remained embedded in the cooperative, eventually it lost its usefulness as members became wealthy enough to have bank accounts of their own. It disbanded in the 1990s. At one point, men tried to join, but the women refused to allow it. One woman said: "They will take over and not let us speak in our own cooperative."[27]

In Ghana, despite 30 years of national banking institutions, most saving methods are still informal. In 1991, an estimated 55 percent of the money in the country was saved informally. Rotating credit associations flourish. Women are more likely to join rotating credit associations than men, and the associations or clubs tend to be sex-segregated. The club names often reflect their emphasis on mutual aid. One club in the Accra Makola Market has a name that translates as "Our Well-Being Depends on Others."[28] Most of the savings are used to provide capital for trading activities.

In societies that depend on sharing, saving money is difficult. Others may ask you for money, and there may be an obligation to give it to them. However, if there is a rotating credit association, you can say that you are obliged to save for your contribution and people will understand. Rotating credit associations also appear to work well when people find it hard to delay gratification. The social pressure of the group appears sufficient to push people to save enough for their regular contribution and the windfall you get when your turn comes is gratifying.[29]

When people move far outside their homelands, they may make even more use of such associations. For example, rotating credit associations in Korea go back to 1633. In the Los Angeles area, Koreans are even more likely to use rotating credit associations, mostly to accumulate sums for business.[30]

Multiethnic Associations

Although many voluntary associations draw on people from the same regional or ethnic background, voluntary groups in the modern world increasingly draw members from many different backgrounds. For example, the Kafaina, or Wok Meri ("women's work"), associations in Papua New Guinea are savings and loan associations that link thousands of women from different tribal areas.[31] Originally, smaller groups started as savings associations in particular localities, but links between groups developed as women who married out of a village encouraged a relative back home or in another village to start a "daughter" group. "Mother-daughter" visits between groups can last for three days, as one group hosts another and the groups exchange money. All money received from another group is placed in a net bag that is hidden and cannot be touched, so the savings grow over time. When a group accumulates a certain amount, a building the size of a men's house is built for the association and a very large ceremony is held.

Does the development of these women's associations translate into new power for women in their traditionally male-dominated societies? That has yet to happen (see the box "Do Separate Women's Associations Increase Women's Status and Power?"). Apparently frustrated by their exclusion from local politics, the women are increasingly participating in the Kafaina movement. They may have intergroup exchanges and they may now engage in public speaking, but so far their arena is still separate from the men's arena.

Just as the Kafaina women's associations seem to be a response to perceived deprivation, the formation of associations with multiethnic or regional membership is not unusual where colonialism or other political domination is recognized as a common problem. For example, in Alaska in the 1960s, Native Americans felt threatened by proposals for economic development that they thought would threaten their subsistence resources. Many regional and ethnic associations formed during this crisis, but perhaps more significant from the point of view of achieving substantial compensation and titles to land was the formation of a pan-Alaska association called the Alaska Federation of Natives. What made the amalgamation possible? Like the leaders of multiethnic movements in many places, the leaders at the highest levels seem to have had a lot of things in common. They were educated, urban dwellers who worked at professional occupations. Perhaps most important, many of them had attended the same schools.[32]

Multiethnic and multiregional associations have often been involved in independence movements all over the world. Often, revolutionary political parties develop out of such associations and lead the efforts to gain independence. Why independence movements develop in some places but not in others is not yet understood.

Other Interest Groups

Societies such as the United States consist of people from many different ethnic backgrounds. Often there are voluntary ethnic and regional associations. But the majority of the voluntary associations in our own and other complex societies have members who belong because of common, achieved interests. These common interests include occupation (so we have trade unions and professional associations), political affiliation (as in national political parties and political action groups), recreation (sports and game clubs, fan clubs, music and theater groups), charities, and social clubs. The larger and more diversified the society, the more different kinds of associations there are. They bring together people with common interests, aspirations, or qualifications, and they provide opportunities to work for social causes, for self-improvement, or to satisfy a need for new and stimulating experiences. We join clubs and other interest groups because we want to achieve particular goals. Not the least of such goals is identification with a "corporate" group and, through it, the acquisition of status and influence.

Joining clubs is much more important in some societies than in others. Norway is an example of a society with a rich organizational life. Even in areas with small communities, there are many different clubs. For example, Douglas Caulkins found that in the municipality of Volda, a town of about 7,000, there were 197 organizations. People were expected to be active in at least a couple of organizations, and these groups met regularly. In fact, there were so many meetings that organizations were expected to coordinate their calendars so that the meetings would not interfere with one another.[33] Why some societies, like Norway, have so much involvement with voluntary associations is not well understood. Nor do we understand what the consequences of such involvement may be. Norway happens to have a particularly low crime rate and it scores high on other indicators of social and economic health.[34] Does the complexity of its organizational life and its many

overlapping involvements play a role in its social health? We don't know, because cross-cultural studies to test that possibility have not been done.

EXPLAINING VARIATION IN ASSOCIATIONS

Anthropologists are not content to provide descriptions of the structure and operation of human associations. They also seek to understand why different types of associations develop. For example, what may account for the development of age-set systems? S. N. Eisenstadt's comparative study of African age-sets led him to the hypothesis that, when kinship groups fail to carry out functions important to the integration of society—such as political, educational, and economic functions—age-set systems arise to fill the void. Age-set systems may provide a workable solution to a society's need for functional divisions among its members, because age is a criterion that can be applied to all members of society in the allocation of roles.[35] But it is not at all clear why age-set systems arise to fill the void left by lack of kinship organization. Many societies have kin structures that are limited in scope, yet the majority of them have not adopted an age-set system.

B. Bernardi, in his critical evaluation of Nilo-Hamitic age-set systems, also suggested that age-set systems arise to make up for a deficiency in social organization.[36] But, in contrast with Eisenstadt, Bernardi specifically suggested why more social organization is necessary and what particular deficiencies in the previous form of organization should favor development of age-sets. He hypothesized that age-set systems arise in societies that have a history of territorial rivalry, lack central authority, and have only dispersed kin groups. When all three factors are present, he argued, the need for a mechanism of territorial integration is supplied by an age-set system.

One cross-cultural study suggests that territorial rivalry, as indicated by warfare, may favor the development of age-set systems, but this study found no evidence to support Bernardi's hypothesis that age-sets develop in societies that lack central authority and have only dispersed kin groups.[37] So it does not seem that age-set societies are deficient in political or kinship organization. An alternative explanation, which is consistent with the cross-cultural evidence, is that age-set systems arise in societies that have both frequent warfare and local groups that change in size and composition throughout the year. In such situations, men may not always be able to rely on their kinsmen for cooperation in warfare because the kinsmen are not always nearby. Age-sets, however, can provide allies *wherever* one happens to be.[38] This interpretation suggests that age-set systems arise *in addition to*, rather than as alternatives to, kin-based and politically based forms of integration.[39]

As for voluntary associations whose membership is variably ascribed—that is, determined at birth but not found in all people of a given age-sex category—it is difficult to say exactly what causes them to arise. As already noted, there are suggestions that voluntary associations of all types become more numerous, and more important, as the society harboring them advances in technology, complexity, and scale. No definitive evidence is yet available to support this explanation, but the following trends seem to be sufficiently established to merit consideration.

First, there is urbanization. Developing societies are becoming urban, and as their cities grow, so does the number of people separated from their traditional kinship ties and local customs. It is not surprising, then, that the early voluntary associations should be mutual aid societies, established first to take over kin obligations in case of death and later broadening their benefits in other directions. In this respect, the recent associations of the developing African societies closely resemble the early English laboring-class associations. Those clubs also served to maintain the city migrants' contacts with former traditions and culture. The regional associations in Latin America resemble the regional associations of European immigrants in the United States. Such associations also seem to arise in response to the migrants' or immigrants' needs in the new home.

Second, there is an economic factor. Migrants and immigrants try to adapt to new economic conditions, and group interests in the new situations have to be organized, promoted, and protected.

Why, then, do variably ascribed associations tend to be replaced by clubs of the achieved category in highly industrialized societies? Perhaps the strong focus on specialization in industrialized societies is reflected in the formation of specialized groups. Possibly the emphasis on achievement in industrialized societies is another contributing factor. Perhaps, too, the trend toward uniformity, encouraged by mass marketing and the mass media, is progressively weakening the importance of regional and ethnic distinctions. The result seems to be that the more broadly based organizations are being replaced by more narrowly based associations that are more responsive to particular needs not being met by the institutions of mass society.

SUMMARY ● ○ ○

1. Associations or interest groups have the following characteristics in common: (a) some kind of formal, institutional structure exists; (b) some people are excluded from membership; (c) membership is based on commonly shared interests or purposes; and (d) there is a clearly discernible sense of mutual pride and belonging. Membership varies according to whether or not it is voluntary and whether the qualities of members are universally ascribed, variably ascribed, or achieved.

2. Age-sets are nonvoluntary associations whose members belong because of universally ascribed characteristics—that is, groups of people of similar age and sex who move through life's stages together. Entry into the

system is usually by an initiation ceremony. Transitions to new stages are usually marked by succession rituals. Unisex associations restrict membership to one sex. In noncommercial societies, membership in such associations (usually male) is generally nonvoluntary.

3. Regional and ethnic organizations are voluntary associations whose members belong because of variably ascribed characteristics. Both usually occur in societies where technological advance is accelerating, bringing with it economic and social complexity. Despite a variety of types, regional and ethnic associations have in common an emphasis on (a) helping members adapt to new conditions; (b) keeping members in touch with home area traditions; and (c) promoting improved living conditions for members who have recently migrated to urban areas.

4. Associations whose members belong because of variably ascribed characteristics tend to be replaced in highly industrialized societies by associations whose membership is based on achieved qualities.

GLOSSARY TERMS ○ ● ○

achieved qualities **408**	unisex association **412**
age-grade **411**	universally ascribed
age-set **411**	qualities **408**
ascribed qualities **408**	variably ascribed
associations **408**	qualities **410**

CRITICAL QUESTIONS ○ ○ ●

1. How could young people who might join gangs be encouraged not to?

2. What associations do you belong to, and why?

3. Many formerly unisex associations have opened their membership to the opposite sex. What might be the results of this change?

PEARSON
myanthrolab

Read Richard H. Thompson's "Chinatowns: Immigrant Communities in Transition" on MyAnthroLab. Answer the following questions.

1. Describe the role that associations played in the earliest Chinatowns.

2. According to Thompson, the traditional associations were more important to certain classes of Chinese Americans. Explain.

3. Describe some of the tensions between the generations.

chapter 24

Political Life: Social Order and Disorder

or people in the United States, the phrase *political life* has many connotations. It may call to mind the various branches of government: the executive branch, from the president on the national level to governors on the state level to mayors on the local level; legislative institutions, from Congress to state legislatures to city councils; and administrative bureaus, from federal government departments to local agencies.

Political life may also evoke thoughts of political parties, interest groups, lobbying, campaigning, and voting. In other words, when people living in the United States think of political life, they may think first of "politics," the activities (not always apparent) that influence who is elected or appointed to political office, what public policies are established, how they get established, and who benefits from those policies.

But in the United States and in many other countries, *political life* involves even more than government and politics. Political life also involves ways of preventing or resolving troubles and disputes both within and outside the society. Internally, a complex society such as ours may employ mediation or arbitration to resolve industrial disputes, a police force to prevent crimes or track down criminals, and courts and a penal system to deal with lawbreakers as well as with social conflict in general. Externally, such a society may establish embassies in other nations and develop and utilize its armed forces both to maintain security and to support domestic and foreign interests.

By means of all these informal and formal political mechanisms, complex societies establish social order and minimize, or at least deal with, social disorder.

Formal governments have become more widespread around the world over the last 100 years, as powerful colonizing countries have imposed political systems upon others or as people less formally organized realized that they needed governmental mechanisms to deal with the larger world. But many societies known to anthropology did not have political officials, political parties, courts, or armies. Indeed, the band or village was the largest autonomous political unit in 50 percent of the societies in the ethnographic record, as of the times they were first described. And those units were only informally organized; that is, they did not have individuals or agencies formally authorized to make and implement policy or resolve disputes. Does this mean they did not have political life? If we mean political life as we know it in our own society, then the answer has to be that they did not. But if we look beyond our formal institutions and mechanisms—if we ask what functions these institutions and mechanisms perform—we find that all societies have had political activities and beliefs to create and maintain social order and cope with social disorder.

Many of the kinds of groups we discussed in the three previous chapters, on families, descent groups, and associations, have political functions. But

when anthropologists talk about *political organization* or *political life,* they are particularly focusing on activities and beliefs pertaining to *territorial groups.* Territorial groups, on whose behalf political activities may be organized, range from small communities, such as bands and villages, to large communities, such as towns and cities, to multilocal groups, such as districts or regions, entire nations, or even groups of nations.

As we shall see, the different types of political organization, as well as how people participate in politics and how they cope with conflict, are often strongly linked to variation in food-getting, economy, and social stratification.

● ○ ●

VARIATION IN TYPES OF POLITICAL ORGANIZATION

Societies in the ethnographic record vary in *level of political integration*—that is, the largest territorial group on whose behalf political activities are organized—and in the degree to which political authority is centralized or concentrated in the integrated group. When we describe the political integration of particular societies, we focus on their traditional political systems. In many societies known to anthropology, the small community (band or village) was traditionally the largest territorial group on whose behalf political activities were organized. The authority structure in such societies did not involve any centralization; there was no political authority whose jurisdiction included more than one community. In other societies, political activities were traditionally organized sometimes on behalf of a multilocal group, but there was no permanent authority at the top. And in still other societies, political activities were often traditionally organized on behalf of multilocal territorial groups, and there was a centralized or supreme political authority at the top. In the modern world, however, every society has been incorporated into some larger, centralized political system.

Elman Service suggested that most societies can be classified into four principal types of political organization: bands, tribes, chiefdoms, and states.[1] Although Service's classification does not fit all societies, it is a useful way to show how societies vary in trying to create and maintain social order. We often use the present tense in our discussion, because that is the convention in ethnographic writing, but readers should remember that most societies that used to be organized at the band, tribe, or chiefdom level are now incorporated into larger political entities. With a handful of exceptions, there are no politically autonomous bands or tribes or chiefdoms in the world anymore.

Band Organization

Some societies were composed of fairly small and usually nomadic groups of people. Each of these groups is conventionally called a **band** and is politically autonomous. That is, in **band organization,** the local group or community is the largest group that acts as a political unit. Because most recent foragers had band organization, some anthropologists contend that this type of political organization characterized nearly all societies before the development of

agriculture, or until about 10,000 years ago. But we have to remember that almost all of the described food-collecting societies are or were located in marginal environments; and almost all were affected by more dominant societies nearby.[2] So it is possible that what we call "band organization" may not have been typical of foragers in the distant or prehistoric past.

Bands are typically small, with less than 100 people usually, often considerably less. Each small band occupies a large territory, so population density is low. Band size often varies by season, with the band breaking up or recombining according to the food resources available at a given time and place. Inuit bands, for example, are smaller in the winter, when food is hard to find, and larger in the summer, when there is sufficient food to feed a larger group.

Political decision making within the band is generally informal. The "modest informal authority"[3] that does exist can be seen in the way decisions affecting the group are made. Because the formal, permanent office of leader typically does not exist, decisions such as when camp has to be moved or how a hunt is to be arranged are either agreed upon by the community as a whole or made by the best qualified member. Leadership, when an individual exercises it, is not the consequence of bossing or throwing one's weight about. Each band may have its informal **headman,** or its most proficient hunter, or a person most accomplished in rituals. There may be one person with all these qualities, or several people, but such a person or people will have gained status through the community's recognition of skill, good sense, and humility. Leadership, in other words, stems not from power but from influence, not from office but from admired personal qualities.

In Inuit bands, each settlement may have its headman, who acquires his influence because the other members of the community recognize his good judgment and superior skills. The headman's advice concerning the movement of the band and other community matters is generally heeded, but he possesses no permanent authority and has no power to impose sanctions of any kind. Inuit leaders are male, but men often consult their wives in private, and women who hunt seem to have more influence than those who do not.[4] In any case, leadership exists only in a very restricted sense, as among the Iglulik Inuit, for example:

> Within each settlement . . . there is as a rule an
> older man who enjoys the respect of the others and
> who decides when a move is to be made to another

TABLE 24–1 Suggested Trends in Political Organization and Other Social Characteristics

Type of Organization	Highest Level of Political Integration	Specialization of Political Officials	Predominant Mode of Subsistence	Community Size and Population Density	Social Differentiation	Major Form of Distribution
Band	Local group or band	Little or none; informal leadership	Foraging or food collecting	Very small communities; very low density	Egalitarian	Mostly reciprocity
Tribe	Sometimes multilocal group	Little or none; informal leadership	Extensive (shifting) agriculture and/or herding	Small communities; low density	Egalitarian	Mostly reciprocity
Chiefdom	Multilocal group	Some	Extensive or intensive agriculture and/or herding	Large communities; medium density	Rank	Reciprocity and redistribution
State	Multilocal group; often entire language group	Much	Intensive agriculture and herding	Cities and towns; high density	Class and caste	Mostly market exchange

hunting center, when a hunt is to be started, how the spoils are to be divided, when the dogs are to be fed. . . . He is called *isumaitoq,* "he who thinks." It is not always the oldest man, but as a rule an elderly man who is a clever hunter or, as head of a large family, exercises great authority. He cannot be called a chief; there is no obligation to follow his counsel; but they do so in most cases, partly because they rely on his experience, partly because it pays to be on good terms with this man.[5]

A summary of the general features of band organization can be found in Table 24–1. Note, however, that there are exceptions to these generalizations. For example, not all known foragers are organized at the band level or have all the features of a band type of society. Classic exceptions are the Native American societies of the Northwest Pacific coast, who had enormous resources of salmon and other fish, relatively large and permanent villages, and political organization beyond the level of the typical band societies in the ethnographic record.

Tribal Organization

When local communities mostly act autonomously but there are kinship groups (such as clans or lineages) or associations (such as age-sets) that can potentially integrate several local groups into a larger unit (**tribe**), we say that the society has **tribal organization.** Unfortunately, the term *tribe* is sometimes used to refer to an entire society; that is, an entire language group may be called a tribe. But a tribal type of political system does not usually permit the entire society to act as a unit; all the communities in a tribal society may be linked only occasionally for some political (usually military) purpose. Thus, what distinguishes tribal from band political organization is the presence in the former of

some multilocal, but not usually societywide, integration. The multilocal integration, however, is *not permanent,* and it is *informal* in the sense that political officials do not head it. Frequently, the integration is called into play only when an outside threat arises; when the threat disappears, the local groups revert to self-sufficiency.[6] Tribal organization may seem fragile—and, of course, it usually is—but the fact that there are social ways to integrate local groups into larger political entities means that societies with tribal organization are militarily a good deal more formidable than societies with band organization.

In tribal societies, as among the Kayapo of Brazil, leadership tends not to be hereditary, but based on leadership qualities. There are no permanent chiefs of more than one community. Shown here is a Kayapo leader smoking a pipe.

Societies with tribal political organization are similar to band societies in their tendency to be egalitarian (see Table 24–1). At the local level, informal leadership is also characteristic. In those tribal societies where kinship provides the basic framework of social organization, the elders of the local kin groups tend to have considerable influence; where age-sets are important, a particular age-set is looked to for leadership. But, in contrast to band societies, societies with tribal organization generally are food producers. And because cultivation and animal husbandry are generally more productive than hunting and gathering, the population density of tribal societies is generally higher, local groups are larger, and the way of life is more sedentary than in hunter-gatherer bands.

Kinship Bonds Frequently communities are linked to each other by virtue of belonging to the same kin group, usually a unilineal group such as a lineage or clan. A **segmentary lineage system** is one type of tribal integration based on kinship. A society with such a system is composed of segments, or parts, each similar to the others in structure and function. Every local segment belongs to a hierarchy of lineages stretching farther and farther back genealogically. The hierarchy of lineages, then, unites the segments into larger and larger genealogical groups. The closer two groups are genealogically, the greater their general closeness. In the event of a dispute between members of different segments, people related more closely to one contestant than to another take the side of their nearest kinsman.

The Tiv of northern Nigeria offer a classic example of a segmentary lineage system, one that happens to link all the Tiv into a single genealogical structure or tribe. The Tiv are a large society, numbering more than 800,000. Figure 24–1 is a representation of the Tiv lineage structure as described by Paul Bohannan. In the figure, there are four levels of lineages. Each of the smallest lineages, symbolized by *a* through *h*, is in turn embedded in more inclusive lineages. So minimal lineages *a* and *b* are together in lineage *1*. Lineages *1* and *2* are embedded in lineage *A*. Territorial organization follows lineage hierarchy. As shown in the bottom of the figure, the most closely related lineages have territories near each other. Minimal lineages *a* and *b* live next to each other; their combined territory is the territory of their higher-order lineage, *1*. Lineage *A* in turn has a territory that is differentiated from lineage *B*. All of Tivland is said to descend from one ancestor, represented by *I*.[7]

Tiv lineage organization is the foundation of Tiv political organization. A look at Figure 24–1 helps to explain how. A dispute between lineages (and territories) *a* and *b* remains minor, because no more than "brother" segments are involved. But a dispute between *a* and *c* involves lineages *1* and *2* as well, with the requirement that *b* assist *a* and *d* support *c*. This process of mutual support, called **complementary opposition,** means that segments will unite only in a confrontation with some other group. Groups that will fight with each other in a minor dispute might coalesce at some later time against a larger group.

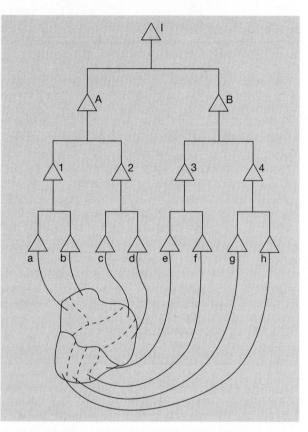

Figure 24–1 Tiv Lineage Segments and Their Territories

Source: Adapted from P. Bohannan 1954.

The segmentary lineage system was presumably very effective in allowing the Tiv to intrude into new territory and take land from other tribal societies with smaller descent groups. Individual Tiv lineage segments could call on support from related lineages when faced with border troubles. Conflicts within the society—that is, between segments—especially in border areas, were often turned outward, "releasing internal pressure in an explosive blast against other peoples."[8]

Segmentary lineage systems may have military advantages even when they do not unite the entire society. A classic example is the Nuer of the Upper Nile region, who had tribal, but not societywide, organization because of their segmentary lineages. In the early 1800s, the Nuer had a territory of about 8,700 square miles, and the neighboring Dinka had ten times that much. But by 1890, the Nuer had cut a 100-mile swath through Dinka territory, increasing Nuer territory to 35,000 square miles. Even though the Nuer and Dinka were culturally very similar, the segmentary lineage organization of the Nuer seems to have given them a significant military advantage in their incursions into Dinka territory.[9]

A segmentary lineage system may generate a formidable military force, but the combinations of manpower it produces are temporary, forming and dissolving as the occasion demands.[10] Tribal political organization does not make for a political system that more or less permanently integrates a number of communities.

Age-Set Systems In the previous chapter, we described age-set systems in general. Here we discuss how age-sets can function as the basis of a tribal type of political organization, as among the Karimojong of northeastern Uganda.[11]

The Karimojong age-set system has an important bearing on day-to-day tribal life. As herders, Karimojong adults are often separated from their usual settlements. Herders will meet, mingle for a while, then go their separate ways, but each may call upon other members of his age-set wherever he goes. The age-set system is important among the Karimojong because it immediately allocates to each individual a place in the system and thereby establishes for him an appropriate pattern of response. A quarrel in camp will be settled by the representatives of the senior age-set who are present, regardless of which section of the tribe they may belong to.

Among the Karimojong, political leaders are not elected from among the elders of a particular age-set, nor are they appointed; they acquire their positions informally. Usually a man's background, and the ability he has demonstrated in public debates over a period of time, will result in his being considered by the men of his neighborhood to be their spokesman. His function is to announce what course of action seems required in a particular situation, to initiate that action, and then to coordinate it after it has begun.

Most political leaders exercise their authority within the local sphere because the pastoral nature of the Karimojong economy, with its dispersed groups and movement from one feeding ground to another, offers no alternative. From time to time, an elder may acquire the status of a prophet and be awarded respect and obedience on a tribal scale. He will be called upon to lead sacrifices (to avert misfortune), to undertake rainmaking (to bring prosperity), and so on. Yet even a prophet's prestige and authority do not warrant him a position of overlord or chief.[12]

Chiefdom Organization

Whereas a tribe has some informal mechanism that can integrate more than one community, a **chiefdom** has some *formal* structure that integrates more than one community into a political unit. The formal structure could consist of a council with or without a chief, but most commonly there is a person—the **chief**—who has higher rank or authority than others. Most societies at the chiefdom level of organization contain more than one multicommunity political unit or chiefdom, each headed by a district chief or a council. There may also be more than one level of chief beyond the community, such as district chiefs and higher-level chiefs. Compared with tribal societies, societies with chiefdoms are more densely populated and their communities more permanent, partly as a consequence of their generally greater economic productivity (see Table 24–1).

The position of chief, which is sometimes hereditary and generally permanent, bestows high status on its holder. Most chiefdoms have social ranking and accord the chief and his family greater access to prestige. The chief may redistribute goods, plan and direct the use of public labor, supervise religious ceremonies, and direct military activities on behalf of the chiefdom. In South Pacific chiefdoms, the chiefs carried out most of these duties. In Fijian chiefdoms, for example, the chief was responsible for the redistribution of goods and the coordination of labor:

> [The chief] could summon the community's labor on his own behalf, or on behalf of someone else who requested it, or for general purposes. . . . Besides his right to summon labor he accumulated the greater proportion of the first fruits of the yam crop . . . and he benefited from other forms of food presentation, or by the acquisition of special shares in ordinary village distribution. . . . Thus, the paramount [chief] would collect a significant part of the surplus production of the community and redistribute it in the general welfare.[13]

In contrast to leaders in tribal societies, who generally have to earn their privileges by their personal qualities, hereditary chiefs are said to have those qualities in their "blood." A high-ranking chief in Polynesia, a huge triangular area of islands in the South Pacific, inherited special religious power called *mana*. *Mana* sanctified his rule and protected him.[14] Chiefs in Polynesia had so much religious power that missionaries could convert people to Christianity only after their chiefs had been converted.[15]

Samoan chiefs gather at an open meeting house for a *saofa'i*, or entitlement ceremony, during which a new chief gains his position.

In most chiefdoms, the chiefs did not have the power to compel people to obey them; people would act in accordance with the chief's wishes because the chief was respected and often had religious authority. But in the most complex paramount chiefdoms, such as those of Hawaii and Tahiti, the chiefs seemed to have more compelling sanctions than the "power" of respect or *mana*. Substantial amounts of goods and services collected by the chiefs were used to support subordinates, including specialists such as high priests, political envoys, and warriors who could be sent to quell rebellious factions.[16] When redistributions do not go to everybody—when chiefs are allowed to keep items for their own purposes—and when a chief begins to use armed force, the political system is on the way to becoming what we call a state.

State Organization

A state, according to one more or less standard definition, is "an autonomous political unit, encompassing many communities within its territory and having a centralized government with the power to collect taxes, draft men for work or war, and decree and enforce laws."[17] States, then, have a complex, centralized political structure that includes a wide range of permanent institutions with legislative, executive, and judicial functions and a large bureaucracy. Central to this definition is the concept of legitimate force used to implement policies both internally and externally. In states, the government tries to maintain a monopoly on the use of physical force.[18] This monopoly can be seen in the development of formal and specialized instruments of social control: a police force, a militia, or a standing army.

Just as a particular society may contain more than one band, tribe, or chiefdom, so may it contain more than one state. The contiguously distributed population speaking a single language may or may not be politically unified in a single state. Ancient Greece was composed of many city-states; so, too, was Italy until the 1870s. German speakers are also not politically unified; Austria and Germany are separate states, and Germany itself was not politically unified until the 1870s. We say that a society has **state organization** when it is composed of one or more political units that are states.

A state may include more than one society. Multisociety states are often the result of conquest or colonial control when the dominant political authority, itself a state, imposes a centralized government over a territory with many different societies and cultures, as the British did in Nigeria and Kenya.

Colonialism is a common feature of state societies. But not all colonialisms are alike. Archaeology and history tell us about various kinds of colonialism. The expanding state society may send people to build a new imperial settlement in some other place to trade or protect trade routes, like the British, Spanish, and others did. Or the colonial power may displace and move parts of the original population, as the Inka empire did.[19] Most of the expanding state societies we know about are usually called

empires. They incorporated other societies and states. The extension of U.S. power in modern times, for example, by persuading other countries to let the U.S. build military bases, has led some commentators to refer to an American empire, even though the United States did not always establish colonies where they had economic and political control.[20]

Nearly all of the multisociety states that emerged after World War II were the results of successful independence movements against colonial powers.[21] Most have retained their political unity despite the fact that they still contain many different societies. For example, Nigeria remains unified despite a civil war; the eastern section called Biafra (mostly populated by people of Ibo culture) tried unsuccessfully 30 years ago to secede, and subsequently there has been serious conflict among some of the constituent societies.

Multisociety or multiethnic states may also form voluntarily, in reaction to external threat. Switzerland comprises cantons, each of which speaks mainly French, German, Italian, or Romansch; the various cantons confederated originally to shake off control by the Holy Roman Empire. But some states have lost their unity recently, including the former Union of Soviet Socialist Republics (USSR) and much of Yugoslavia.

In addition to their strictly political features, intensive agriculture generally supports state-organized societies. The high productivity of the agriculture allows for the emergence of cities, a high degree of economic and other kinds of specialization, and market or commercial exchange. In addition, state societies usually have class stratification (see Table 24–1). Cities have grown tremendously in the last 100 years, largely as a result of migration and immigration. (See the Migrants and Immigrants box on the growth of cities.)

When states come into existence, people's access to scarce resources is radically altered. So, too, is their ability not to listen to leaders: You usually cannot refuse to pay taxes or avoid labor or military conscription and go unpunished. Of course, the rulers of a state do not maintain the social order by force alone. The people must believe, at least to some extent, that those in power have a legitimate right to govern. If the people think otherwise, history suggests that those in power may eventually lose their ability to control. Witness the recent downfall of Communist parties throughout most of eastern Europe and the former Soviet Union.

So force and the threat of force are not enough to explain the legitimacy of power, and the inequities that occur commonly, in state societies. But then what does? There are various theories. The rulers of early states often claimed divine descent to buttress their legitimacy, but this claim is rare nowadays. Another theory is that, if parents teach their children to accept all authority, such lessons may generalize to the acceptance of political authority. Some analysts think that people accept state authority for no good reason; the rulers are just able to fool them. Finally, some theorists think that states must provide people with real or rational advantages; otherwise,

migrants and immigrants

The Growth of Cities

Humans are a social bunch. They generally live in groups or communities. These groups range in size from bands to villages to town and cities. Each may function as a political entity; headmen, mayors, councils, and other political "officials" and groups organize activities on their behalf. Nearly half of the world's human population now lives in cities, which are usually defined as communities where few are directly involved in food getting. An even larger proportion of humanity will be urban dwellers 30 years from now.

The explosive growth of cities over the past century or so is not due to more births than deaths in the cities. Rather, cities have grown mostly because of migration from rural areas of the country, and from rural areas in other countries. Recall the exodus of the Irish to Britain and the United States because of the "potato famine," the massive migrations from the villages of Germany, Italy, and Greece in the 19th and 20th centuries, and the huge migrations particularly in the last 50 years from rural Mexico and China. It is probably safe to say that many millions of people in many parts of the world would move to the United States, Canada, and Western Europe tomorrow, if they could. Poverty is one "push" factor. Flight from persecution is another. Many parts of the world are not safe, particularly for poor people. Or other places look more promising. Think of the state of California in the United States. The vast majority of its inhabitants were born elsewhere. True, in the modern world, it is possible for some people to go "home" for a visit, even halfway around the world. But,

for many migrants now and in the recent past, the move was one way. Because you may have run away from poverty, persecution, and war, you couldn't (or wouldn't) go home again.

An increasing number of anthropologists call themselves "urban anthropologists." They study why people move, and how they adjust to new places. They do so because so many people are moving now. There are villages in rural Spain and France that are mostly empty during the week. The owners live and work in Barcelona or Paris, and they hardly ever go "home." Indeed, their village houses may not even be available to them much, because they are usually rented to tourists—from across the Atlantic, no less.

Cities everywhere have problems, even in the most developed countries. Providing water, power, sanitation, and other services to perhaps millions of city dwellers is difficult and expensive. Yet in every country, people are leaving rural areas and going to cities for a variety of reasons. Some are political refugees, like the Hmong from Laos who now live in St. Paul, Minnesota. Then there are the people from Congo and Sudan, from Kosovo and Northern Ireland, who have fled civil wars. There are other reasons to leave too. Technological improvements may have reduced the need for rural labor, which happened in the U.S. South after the 1930s. Or the rural opportunities cannot support the increased number of mouths to be fed. Where do they go? Usually not to other rural areas but rather to cities, often in other countries, where jobs are available. In the more urban-

ized countries, the cities have acquired "suburbs," where many of the people in a metropolitan area may actually live. But hardly anyone is left on the farm—only just a few percent of the population in the more developed countries.

In the last half of the 20th century, with the building of suburbs, there seems to have been a turning away from cities in many countries. Cities lost population as people moved to the suburbs to have more living space, a garden, "better" schools for their children, or to escape from the threat of violence. But recently, the flow has started to reverse in North America and elsewhere. The suburbanites are coming back to the cities, perhaps because people are getting tired of commuting longer distances to jobs and recreation. This is particularly so with wealthier people whose children have grown up and moved away, and with more people living until older ages, many want to move closer to the places where they mostly spend their time. Despite the social inequality and violence, cities have always been the places to go for jobs and other activities. Concerts, theaters, restaurants, museums, amusement parks, hospitals, and professional sports stadiums have always been located in cities or nearby.

The "push" out of the rural areas and the "pull" of the cities are hard to resist, despite the enormous political problems of urban living. As the old song laments, "Howya goin' keep 'em down on the farm after they've seen Paree?"

Source: M. Ember and Ember 2002.

---

people would not think that the rulers deserve to exercise authority. Legitimacy is not an all-or-none phenomenon; it varies in degree.[22]

A state society can retain its legitimacy, or at least its power, for a long time. For example, the Roman Empire was a complex state society that dominated the Mediterranean and Near East for hundreds of years. It began as a

city-state that waged war to acquire additional territory. At its height, the Roman Empire embraced more than 55 million people;[23] the capital city of Rome had a population of well over a million.[24] The empire included parts of what are now Great Britain, France, Spain, Portugal, Germany, Rumania, Turkey, Greece, Armenia, Egypt, Israel, and Syria.

Popular will can change governments. Massive protest in the Ukraine led a newly elected president to resign.

Another example of a state society was the kingdom of Nupe in West Africa, now part of the nation-state of Nigeria. Nupe society was rigidly stratified. At the top of the social system was the king, or *etsu*. Beneath the king, members of the royal family formed the highest aristocratic class. Next in order were two other classes of nobility, the local chiefs and the military leaders. At the bottom were the commoners, who had neither prestige nor power and no share in political authority.

The Nupe king possessed ultimate authority in many judicial matters. Local village councils handled minor disputes and civil cases, but serious criminal cases were the prerogative of the king. Such cases, referred to as "crimes for the king," were brought before the royal court by the king's local representatives. The king and his counselors judged the cases and determined suitable punishments.

The most powerful influence of the state over the Nupe people was in the area of taxation. The king was given the power to impose taxes and collect them from every household. Payment was made either in money (cowrie shells originally and, later, British currency) or certain gifts, such as cloth, mats, and slaves. The king kept much of the revenue collected, and his local representatives and lords shared the remainder. In return for the taxes they paid, the people received security—protection against invasion and domestic disorder.[25]

Although all state societies employ coercion or the threat of it, some states are more autocratic than others. This is not just today, or in the recent past, but also in the distant past. The less autocratic states are characterized by more "collective action." They produce more public goods, such as transportation systems and redistribution systems, in times of need. The rulers do not aggrandize themselves as much or live that luxuriously. And, the rulers must rule within limits and must respond to grievances. They are accountable. The Lozi state of central southern Africa had more collective action than the Nupe state described. The Lozi built an extensive system of drainage canals that also facilitated transportation. In hungry times, royal herds and the "state" gardens were used to feed distressed villages. And rulers were not that much more elevated in standard of living. In contrast, the Nupe state financed

very little in the way of public works, had little redistribution, and the rulers lived in elaborate palaces.[26] Collective action is a continuum; states at the higher end of that continuum have not been limited to a few world regions or particular time periods. Collection action theorists suggest that, when the state relies more heavily on resources from taxpayers, the rulers must give the public more in return or else face noncompliance and rebellion. Richard Blanton and Lane Fargher's comparative study of premodern states supports collection action theory.[27]

Factors Associated with Variation in Political Organization

The kinds of political organization we call band, tribal, chiefdom, and state are points on a continuum of levels of political integration or unification, from small-scale local autonomy to large-scale regional unification. There also is variation in political authority, from a few temporary and informal political leaders to large numbers of permanent, specialized political officials, from the absence of coercive political power to the monopoly of public force by a central authority. These aspects of variation in political organization are generally associated with shifts from foraging to more intensive food production, from small to large communities, from low to high population densities, from an emphasis on reciprocity to redistribution to market exchange, and from egalitarian to rank to fully stratified class societies.

The associations just outlined, which seem to be confirmed by the available cross-cultural evidence, are summarized in Table 24–1. With regard to the relation between level of subsistence technology and political complexity, one cross-cultural study employing a small random sample of societies found that the greater the importance of agriculture in a society, the larger the population that is politically unified and the greater the number and types of political officials.[28] A massive cross-cultural survey reported a similar trend: The more intensive the agriculture, the greater the likelihood of state organization; conversely, societies with no more than local political institutions are likely to depend on hunting, gathering, and fishing.[29]

With regard to community size, the first of these studies also suggested that the larger the leading community, the wider the range of political officials in the society.[30] Robert Textor presented a similar finding: Societies with state organization tend to have cities and towns, whereas those with only local political organization are more likely to have communities with an average population of fewer than 200 people.[31] Cross-cultural research also tends to confirm that societies with higher levels of political integration are more likely to exhibit social differentiation, especially in the form of class distinctions.[32]

Does this evidence provide us with an explanation for why political organization varies? Clearly, the data indicate that several factors are associated with political development, but exactly why changes in organization occur is not yet understood. Although economic development may be a necessary condition for political development,[33] that relation does not fully explain why political organization should become more complex just because the economy can support it. Some theorists have suggested that competition between groups may be a more important reason for political consolidation. For example, Elman Service suggested competition as a reason why a society might change from a band level of political organization to a tribal level. Band societies are generally hunter-gatherers. With a changeover to agriculture, population density and competition between groups may increase. Service believed that such competition would foster the development of some informal organization beyond the community—namely, tribal organization—for offense and defense.[34] Indeed, as we saw in the chapters on marital residence and kinship, and associations, both unilineal kinship groups and age-set systems seem to be associated with warfare.

Among agriculturalists, defensive needs might also be the main reason for switching from informal multivillage political organization to more formal chiefdom organization. Formally organized districts are probably more likely to defeat autonomous villages or even segmentary lineage systems.[35] In addition, there may be economic reasons for political development. With regard to chiefdoms, Service suggested that chiefdoms will emerge when redistribution between communities becomes important or when large-scale coordinated work groups are required. The more important these activities are, the more important—and hence more "chiefly"—the organizer and his family presumably become.[36] But redistribution is far from a universal activity of chiefs.[37]

Theory and research on the anthropology of political development have focused mostly on the high end of the scale of political complexity, and particularly on the origins of the first state societies. Those earliest states apparently rose independently of one another, after about 3500 B.C., in what are now southern Iraq, Egypt, northwestern India, northern China, and central Mexico. Several theories have been proposed to explain the rise of the earliest states, but no one theory seems to fit all the known archaeological sequences culminating in early state formation. The reason may be that different conditions in different places favored the emergence of centralized government. The state, by definition, implies the power to organize large populations for collective purposes. In some areas, the impetus may have been the need to organize necessary local or long-distance trade or both. In other areas, the state may have emerged as a way to control defeated populations that could not flee. In still other instances, other factors or a combination of factors may have fostered the development of states. It is still not clear what the specific conditions were that led to the emergence of the state in each of the early centers.[38]

THE SPREAD OF STATE SOCIETIES

The state level of political development has come to dominate the world. Societies with states have larger communities and higher population densities than do band, tribal, and chiefdom societies. They also have armies that are ready to fight at almost any time. State systems that have waged war against chiefdoms and tribes have almost always won, and the result has usually been the political incorporation of the losers. For example, the British and, later, the U.S. colonization of much of North America led to the defeat and incorporation of many Native American societies.

A meeting of European Union heads of state and government in Rome. The EU is an organization encompassing many nation-states.

The defeat and incorporation of the Native Americans was at least partly due to the catastrophic depopulations they suffered because of epidemic diseases, such as smallpox and measles, that European colonists introduced. Catastrophic depopulation was commonly the outcome of the first contacts between European Americans and the natives of North and South America, as well as the natives of the far islands in the Pacific. People in the New World and the Pacific had not been exposed, and therefore were not resistant to the diseases the European Americans carried with them when they began to colonize the world. Before the expansion of Europeans, the people of the New World and the Pacific had been separated for a long time from the people and diseases on the geographically continuous landmass we separate into Europe, Africa, and Asia. Smallpox, measles, and the other former scourges of Europe had largely become childhood diseases that most individuals of European ancestry survived.[39]

Whether by depopulation, conquest, or intimidation, the number of independent political units in the world has decreased strikingly in the last 3,000 years, and especially in the last 200 years. Robert Carneiro estimated that in 1000 B.C., there may have been between 100,000 and 1 million separate political units in the world; today, there are fewer than 200.[40] In the ethnographic record, about 50 percent of the 2,000 or so societies described within the last 150 years had only local political integration. That is, the highest level of political integration in one out of two recent societies was the local community.[41] Thus, most of the decrease in the number of independent political units has occurred fairly recently.

But the recent secessions from the former Soviet Union and Yugoslavia and other separatist movements around the world suggest that ethnic rivalries may make for departures from the trend toward larger and larger political units. Ethnic groups that have been dominated by others in multinational states may opt for political autonomy, at least for a while. On the other hand, the separate nations of western Europe are becoming more unified every day, both politically and economically. So the trend toward larger political units may be continuing, even if there are departures from it now and then.

Extrapolating from past history, a number of investigators have suggested that the entire world will eventually come to be politically integrated, perhaps as soon as the 23rd century and no later than A.D. 4850.[42] Only the future will tell if this prediction will come true. And only the future will tell if further political integration in the world will occur peacefully—with all parties agreeing—or by force or the threat of force, as has happened so often in the past.

VARIATION IN POLITICAL PROCESS

Anthropologists are increasingly interested in the politics, or political processes, of the societies they study: who acquires influence or power, how they acquire it, and how political decisions are made. But even though we have descriptive accounts of politics in many societies, there is still little comparative or cross-cultural research on what may explain variation in politics.[43]

Getting to Be a Leader

In those societies that have hereditary leadership, which is common in rank societies and in state societies with monarchies, rules of succession usually establish how leadership is inherited. Such leaders are often identifiable in some obviously visible way; they may be permanently marked or tattooed, as in chiefdoms in Polynesia, or they may wear elaborate dress and insignia, as in class-stratified societies (see the discussion of body adornment in the chapter on the arts). But for societies whose leaders are *chosen*, either as informal leaders or as political officials, we need a lot more research to understand why some kinds of people are chosen over others.

A few studies have investigated the personal qualities of leaders in tribal societies. One study, conducted among the Mekranoti-Kayapo of central Brazil, found that leaders, in contrast to followers, tend to be rated by their peers as higher in intelligence, generosity, knowledgeability, ambitiousness, and aggressiveness. Leaders also tend to be older and taller. And despite the egalitarian nature of Mekranoti society (at least with respect to sharing resources), sons of leaders are more likely than others to become leaders.[44]

Research in another Brazilian society, the Kagwahiv of the Amazon region, suggests another personal quality of leaders: They seem to have positive feelings about their fathers and mothers.[45] In many respects, studies of leaders in the United States show them to be not that different from their counterparts in Brazil. But there is one major difference: Mekranoti and Kagwahiv leaders are not wealthier than others; in fact, they give their wealth away. U.S. leaders are generally wealthier than others.[46]

"Big Men" In some egalitarian tribal societies, the quest for leadership seems quite competitive. In parts of New Guinea and South America, "big men" compete with other ambitious men to attract followers. Men who want to compete must show that they have magical powers, success in gardening, and bravery in war. But, most important, they have to collect enough goods to throw big parties at which the goods are given away. Big men have to work very hard to attract and keep their followings, for dissatisfied followers can always join other aspiring men.[47] The wives of big men are often leaders too. Among the Kagwahiv, for example, a headman's wife is usually the leader of the women in the community; she is responsible for much of the planning for feasts and often distributes the meat at them.[48]

Although the phenomenon of big men leaders is common throughout New Guinea, researchers are beginning to see variation in the type and extent of "bigmanship" in different areas of New Guinea. For example, in the southern Highlands, groups of men (not just big men) may engage in large-scale giveaways, so big men are not so different from ordinary men. In the northwestern Highlands, on the other hand, big men stand out from other men in striking ways. They make policy for groups of people and organize collective events, they have substantial access to pigs or to valuables acquired in exchanges, and they have control over a substantial amount of labor (more than one wife and fellow kin).[49]

We know that some big men are "bigger" than others, but how does a man get to be a big man? Among the Kumdi-Engamoi, a central Highlands group, a man who wants to be considered a *wua nium* (literally, a "great-important-wealthy man") needs to have many wives and daughters, because the amount of land controlled by a man and how much can be produced on that land depend on the number of women in his family. The more wives he has, the more land he is given to cultivate. He must also be a good speaker. Everyone has the right to speak and give speeches, but to get to be known as a big man requires speaking well and forcefully and knowing when to sum up a consensus. It usually takes a man until his thirties or forties to acquire more than one wife and to make his name through exchanges. When a man wants to inaugurate an exchange, he needs to get shells and pigs from his family and relatives. Once he has achieved a reputation as a *wua nium,* he can keep it only if he continues to perform well—that is, if he continues to distribute fairly, make wise decisions, speak well, and conduct exchanges.[50]

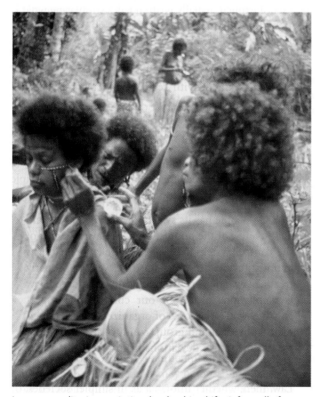

In many egalitarian societies, leadership shifts informally from one person to another. In much of New Guinea, there is more competition for achieving "big" status. On Vanatinai, the women compete as well as the men, so there are "big women" as well as "big men." Here a "big woman" paints the face of her cousin's widow for a feast honoring the dead man.

"Big Women"   In contrast to most of mainland New Guinea, the islands off the southeastern coast are characterized by matrilineal descent. But, like the rest of New Guinea, the islands also have a shifting system of leadership in which people compete for "big" status. Here, though, the people competing are women as well as men, and so there are "big women" as well as "big men." On the island of Vanatinai, for example, women and men compete with each other to exchange valuables. Women lead canoe expeditions to distant islands to visit male as well as female exchange partners, women mobilize relatives and exchange partners to mount large feasts, and the women get to keep the ceremonial valuables exchanged, at least for a while.[51]

The prominence of women on Vanatinai may be linked to the disappearance of warfare—the colonial powers imposed peace; we call this "pacification." Inter-island exchanges became frequent when war became rarer in the early 20th century, giving women and men more freedom to travel. For men, but not women, war provided a path to leadership; champion warriors would acquire great renown and influence. It is not that women did not participate in war; they did, which is unusual cross-culturally, but a woman could not become a war leader. Now, in the absence of war, women have an opportunity through exchanges to become leaders, or "big women."

In one respect, however, women have less of an opportunity to acquire influence now. There are local government councils now, but all the councillors are male. Why? Some women were nominated for the posts, but they withdrew in embarrassment because they could not speak English. Big men or big women do not automatically have a path to these new positions; mostly young males who know English become the councillors. But this situation may change. With the opening of a government primary school in 1984, both girls and boys are learning English, so women in the future may be more likely to achieve leadership by becoming councillors.

Researchers continue to explore other features that may enhance a person's ability to become leaders where leadership is not hereditary. One fascinating new finding is that in the United States, after controlling for age and perceived attractiveness, individuals who are judged prior to the election to be more "competent" from photographs of their faces are more likely to win in congressional elections.[52] What makes a face look more "competent"? It has fewer "babyish" features—it is less round, has a bigger chin, smaller eyes, and a smaller forehead.[53] Whether these facial features also predict leadership cross-culturally is not yet known.

Political Participation

Political scientist Marc Ross conducted cross-cultural research on variation in degree of political participation. Ross phrased the research question: "Why is it that in some polities there are relatively large numbers of persons involved in political life, while in others political action is the province of very few?"[54]

their dwellings to opposite ends of camp. Shifting horticulturalists may also split up when conflicts get too intense. Avoidance is obviously easier in societies, such as band societies, that are nomadic or seminomadic and in which people have temporary dwellings. And avoidance is more feasible when people live independently and self-sufficiently (e.g., in cities and suburbs).[62] But even if conditions in such societies may make avoidance easier, we still need to know why some societies use avoidance more than confrontation as a way of resolving conflict.

Community Action Societies have found various ways of resolving disputes peacefully. One such way involves action by a group or the community as a whole; collective action is common in simpler societies that lack powerful authoritarian leaders.[63] Many Inuit societies, for example, frequently resolve disputes through community action. An individual's failure to heed a taboo or to follow the suggestions of a shaman leads to expulsion from the group, because the community cannot accept a risk to its livelihood. People who fail to share goods voluntarily will find them confiscated and distributed to the community, and they may be executed in the process. A single case of murder, as an act of vengeance (usually because of the abduction of a wife or as part of a blood feud), does not concern the community, but repeated murders do. Franz Boas gave a typical example:

> There was a native of Padli by the name Padlu. He had induced the wife of a native of Cumberland Sound to desert her husband and follow him. The deserted husband, meditating revenge . . . visited his friends in Padli, but before he could accomplish his intention of killing Padlu, the latter shot him. . . . A brother of the murdered man went to Padli to avenge the death . . . but he also was killed by Padlu. A third native of Cumberland Sound, who wished to avenge the death of his relatives, was also murdered by him.
>
> On account of these outrages the natives wanted to get rid of Padlu, but yet they did not dare to attack him. When the *pimain* (headman) of the Akudmurmuit learned of these events he started southward and *asked every man in Padli whether Padlu should be killed. All agreed;* so he went with the latter deer hunting . . . and . . . shot Padlu in the back.[64]

The killing of an individual is the most extreme action a community can take—we call it *capital punishment.* The community as a whole or a political official or a court may decide to administer such punishment, but capital punishment seems to exist in nearly all societies, from the simplest to the most complex.[65] It is often assumed that capital punishment deters crime. If it did, we would expect the abolition of capital punishment to be followed by an increase in homicide rates. But that does not seem to happen. A cross-national study indicates that the abolition of capital punishment tends to be followed by a decrease in homicide rates.[66]

Negotiation and Mediation In many conflicts, the parties to a dispute may come to a settlement themselves by **negotiation.** There aren't necessarily any rules for how they will do so, but any solution is "good" if it restores peace.[67] Sometimes an outside or third party is used to help bring about a settlement between the disputants. We call it **mediation** when the outside party tries to help bring about a settlement, but that third party does not have the formal authority to force a settlement. Both negotiation and mediation are likely when the society is relatively egalitarian and it is important for people to get along.[68]

Among the Nuer of East Africa, a pastoral and horticultural people, disputes within the community can be settled with the help of an informal mediator called the "leopard-skin chief." His position is hereditary, and makes its holder responsible for the social well-being of the district. Matters such as cattle stealing rarely come to the attention of the leopard-skin chief. But if, for example, a murder has been committed, the culprit will go at once to the house of the leopard-skin chief. Immediately the chief cuts the culprit's arm so that blood flows; until the cut has been made, the murderer may not eat or drink. If the murderer is afraid of vengeance by the slain man's family, he will remain at the house of the leopard-skin chief, which is considered sanctuary. Then, within the next few months, the chief attempts to mediate between the parties to the crime. He tries to arrange compensation by the slayer's kin to avoid a feud, and he persuades the dead man's kin that they ought to accept the compensation, usually in the form of cattle. The chief then collects the cattle—40 to 50—and takes them

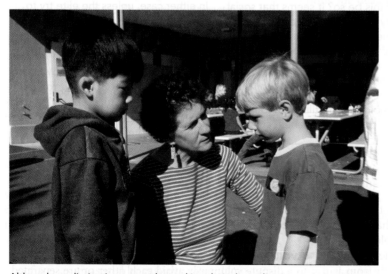

Although mediation is commonly used in relatively egalitarian societies, it is also used in societies with courts and other formal adjudication procedures for minor conflicts. A teacher in the United States tries to mediate a dispute between two boys.

to the dead man's home, where he performs various sacrifices of cleansing and atonement.[69] Throughout the process, the chief acts as a go-between. He has no authority to force either party to negotiate, and he has no power to enforce a solution once it has been arrived at. However, he is able to take advantage of the fact that both disputants are anxious to avoid a blood feud.

Ritual Reconciliation—Apology

The desire to restore a harmonious relationship may also explain ceremonial apologies. An apology is based on deference—the guilty party shows obeisance and asks for forgiveness. Such ceremonies tend to occur in recent chiefdoms.[70] For example, among the Fijians of the South Pacific, when a person offends someone of higher status, the offended person and other villagers begin to avoid, and gossip about, the offender. If offenders are sensitive to village opinion, they will perform a ceremony of apology called *i soro*. One of the meanings of *soro* is "surrender." In the ceremony, the offender bows the head and remains silent while an intermediary speaks, presents a token gift, and asks the offended person for forgiveness. The apology is rarely rejected.[71]

Oaths and Ordeals

Still another way of peacefully resolving disputes is through oaths and ordeals, both of which involve appeals to supernatural power. An **oath** is the act of calling upon a deity to bear witness to the truth of what one says. An **ordeal** is a means used to determine guilt or innocence by submitting the accused to dangerous or painful tests believed to be under supernatural control.[72]

A common kind of ordeal, found in almost every part of the world, is scalding. Among the Tanala of Madagascar, the accused person, having first had his hand carefully examined for protective covering, has to reach his hand into a cauldron of boiling water and grasp, from underneath, a rock suspended there. He then plunges his hand into cold water, has it bandaged, and is led off to spend the night under guard. In the morning, his hand is unbandaged and examined. If there are blisters, he is guilty.

Oaths and ordeals have also been practiced in Western societies. Both were common in medieval Europe. Even today, in our own society, vestiges of oaths can be found. Children can be heard to say, "Cross my heart and hope to die," and witnesses in courts of law are obliged to swear to tell the truth.

Why do some societies use oaths and ordeals? John Roberts suggested that their use tends to be found in fairly complex societies in which political officials lack sufficient power to make and enforce judicial decisions or would make themselves unnecessarily vulnerable were they to attempt to do so. So the officials may use oaths and ordeals to let the gods decide guilt or innocence.[73] In contrast, smaller and less complex societies probably have no need for elaborate mechanisms such as courts, oaths, and ordeals to ascertain guilt. In such societies, everyone

is aware of what crimes have been committed and who the guilty parties probably are.

Adjudication, Courts, and Codified Law

We call it **adjudication** when a third party acting as judge makes a decision that the disputing parties have to accept. Judgment may be rendered by one person (a judge), a panel of judges, a jury, or a political agent or agency (a chief, a royal personage, a council). Judges and courts may rely on codified law and stipulated punishments, but codified law is not necessary for decisions to be made. Codified laws and courts are not limited to Western societies. From the late 17th century to the early 20th century, for example, the Ashanti of West Africa had a complex political system with elaborate legal arrangements. The Ashanti state was a military-based empire possessing legal codes that resembled those of many ancient civilizations.[74] Ashanti law was based on a concept of natural law, a belief that there is an order of the universe whose principles lawmakers should follow in the decisions they make and in the regulations they design. In Ashanti court procedure, elders examined and cross-examined witnesses as well as parties to the dispute. There were also quasi-professional advocates, and appeals against a verdict could be made directly to a chief. Particularly noteworthy was the emphasis on intent when assessing guilt. Drunkenness constituted a valid defense for all crimes except murder and cursing a chief, and a plea of insanity, if proved, was upheld for all offenses. Ashanti punishments could be severe. Physical mutilation, such as slicing off the nose or an ear—even castration in sexual offenses—was often employed. Fines were more frequent, however, and death sentences could often be commuted to banishment and confiscation of goods.

Why do some societies have codified systems and others do not? One explanation, advanced by E. Adamson Hoebel, A. R. Radcliffe-Brown, and others, is that there is little need for formal legal guidelines in small, closely knit communities because competing interests are minimal. Hence, simple societies need little codified law. There are relatively few matters to quarrel about, and the general will of the group is sufficiently well known and demonstrated frequently enough to deter transgressors.

This point of view is echoed in Richard Schwartz's study of two Israeli settlements. In one communal kibbutz, a young man aroused a good deal of community resentment because he had accepted an electric teakettle as a gift. The general opinion was that he had overstepped the code about not having personal possessions, and he was so informed. Accordingly, he gave the kettle to the communal infirmary. Schwartz observed that "no organized enforcement of the decision was threatened, but had he disregarded the expressed will of the community, his life . . . would have been made intolerable by the antagonism of public opinion."[75]

In this community, where people worked and ate together, not only did everyone know about transgressions, but a wrongdoer could not escape public censure. Thus, yet understand why this change is happening. But it is possible that the global communication of ideas has a lot to do with it. Authoritarian governments can censor their own newspapers and prevent group meetings, and sophisticated technology can block Internet use and cell phone connections, but ultimately authoritarian governments really cannot stop the movement of ideas. The movement of ideas, of course, does not explain the acceptance of those ideas. Why democracy has recently diffused to more countries than ever before still requires explanation, as does why some countries do not find it appealing.

SUMMARY ● ○ ○

1. All societies have customs or procedures that, organized on behalf of territorial groups, result in decision making and the resolution of disputes. These ways of creating and maintaining social order and coping with social disorder vary from society to society.

2. Societies with a band type of political organization are composed of fairly small, usually nomadic groups. Each of these bands is politically autonomous, the band being the largest group that acts as a political unit. Authority within the band is usually informal. Societies with band organization generally are egalitarian hunter-gatherers. But band organization may not have been typical of foragers in the distant past.

3. Societies with tribal organization are similar to those with band organization in being egalitarian. But, in contrast with band societies, they generally are food producers, have a higher population density, and are more sedentary. Tribal organization is defined by the presence of groupings, such as clans and age-sets, that can integrate more than one local group into a larger whole.

4. The personal qualities of leaders in tribal societies seem to be similar to the qualities of leaders in the United States, with one major difference: U.S. leaders are generally wealthier than others in their society.

5. Chiefdom organization differs from tribal organization in having formal authority structures that integrate multicommunity political units. Compared with societies with tribal organization, societies with chiefdoms are more densely populated and their communities are more permanent. In contrast to "big men" in tribal societies, who generally have to earn their privileges by their personal qualities, chiefs generally hold their positions permanently. Most chiefdom societies have social ranking.

6. A state has been defined as a political unit composed of many communities and having a centralized government with the authority to make and enforce laws, collect taxes, and draft men for military service. In state societies, the government tries to maintain a monopoly on the use of physical force. In addition, states are generally characterized by class stratification, intensive agriculture (the high productivity of which presumably allows the emergence of cities), commercial exchange, a high degree of economic and other specialization, and extensive foreign trade. The rulers of a state cannot depend forever on the use or threat of force to maintain their power; the people must believe that the rulers are legitimate or have the right to govern.

7. Degree of political participation varies in the societies that anthropologists study, just as among modern nation-states. Degree of political participation seems to be high in small-scale societies, as well as in modern democratic nation-states, but not in those in between, such as feudal states and preindustrial empires.

8. Many societies lack specialized offices and institutions for dealing with conflict. Yet all societies have peaceful, regularized ways of handling at least certain disputes. Avoidance, community action, and negotiation and mediation are more common in simpler societies. Ritual apology occurs frequently in chiefdoms. Oaths and ordeals tend to occur in complex societies in which political officials lack power to enforce judicial decisions. Adjudication is more likely in stratified, more complex societies. Capital punishment seems to exist in nearly all societies, from the simplest to the most complex.

9. People are likely to resort to violence when regular, effective alternative means of resolving a conflict are not available. Violence can occur between individuals, within communities, and between communities. Violence that occurs between political entities such as communities, districts, or nations is generally referred to as warfare. The type of warfare varies in scope and complexity from society to society. Preindustrial societies with higher warfare frequencies are likely to have had a history of unpredictable disasters that destroyed food supplies. More often than not, societies with one type of violence have others.

10. One of the most striking types of political change in recent years is the spread of participatory forms of government—"democracy."

GLOSSARY TERMS ○ ● ○

adjudication **437**	mediation **436**
band **424**	negotiation **436**
band organization **424**	oath **437**
chief **427**	ordeal **437**
chiefdom **427**	raiding **440**
codified laws **434**	segmentary lineage
complementary	system **426**
opposition **426**	state organization **428**
crime **438**	tribal organization **425**
feuding **438**	tribe **425**
headman **424**	warfare **438**

CRITICAL QUESTIONS ○ ○ ●

1. When, if ever, do you think the world will be politically unified? Why do you think so?

2. Why don't informal methods of social control work well in societies like our own? Why don't formal methods work better than they do?

3. What does research on war and violence suggest about how to reduce their likelihood?

PEARSON myanthrolab

Read the chapter by Thomas Abler, "Iroquois: The Tree of Peace and the War Kettle" on MyAnthroLab and answer the following questions:

1. What was the Iroquois Confederacy? What kind of political organization was it?

2. What role did men and women play in making war and making peace?

3. What kinds of impacts did the Europeans have on the Iroquois?

Religion and Magic

s far as we know, all societies have possessed beliefs that can be grouped under the term *religion*. These beliefs vary from culture to culture and from time to time. Yet, despite their variety, we shall define **religion** as any set of attitudes, beliefs, and practices pertaining to *supernatural power*, whether that power be forces, gods, spirits, ghosts, or demons.

In our society, we divide phenomena into the natural and the supernatural, but not all languages or cultures make such a neat distinction. Moreover, what is considered **supernatural**—powers believed to be not human or not subject to the laws of nature—varies from society to society. Some of the variation is determined by what a society regards as natural. For example, some illnesses commonly found in our society are believed to result from the natural action of bacteria and viruses. In other societies, and even among some people in our own society, illness is thought to result from supernatural forces, and thus it forms a part of religious belief.

Beliefs about what is, or is not, a supernatural occurrence also vary within a society at a given time or over time. In Judeo-Christian traditions, for example, floods, earthquakes, volcanic eruptions, comets, and epidemics were once considered evidence of supernatural powers intervening in human affairs. It is now generally agreed that they are simply natural occurrences—even though many still believe that supernatural forces may be involved. Thus, the line between the natural and the supernatural varies in a society according to what people believe about the causes of things and events in the observable world. Similarly, what is considered sacred in one society may not be so considered in another.

In many cultures, what we would consider religious is embedded in other aspects of everyday life. That is, it is often difficult to separate the religious, economic, or political from other aspects of the culture. Such cultures have little or no specialization of any kind; there are no full-time priests, no purely religious activities. So the various aspects of culture we distinguish (e.g., in the chapter titles of this book) are not separate and easily recognized in many societies, as they are in complex societies such as our own. However, it is sometimes difficult even for us to agree whether or not a particular custom of ours is religious. After all, the categorizing of beliefs as religious, political, or social is a relatively new custom. The ancient Greeks, for instance, did not have a word for religion, but they did have many concepts concerning the behavior of their gods and their own expected duties to the gods.

When people's duties to their gods are linked with duty to their princes, it is difficult to separate religious from political ideas. As an example of our own difficulty in labeling a particular class of actions or beliefs as religious or social, consider our attitudes about wearing clothes. Is our belief that it is necessary to wear clothing, at least in the company of nonlovers, a religious principle, or is it something else? Recall that, in Genesis, the wearing of clothes or fig leaves is distinctly associated with the loss of innocence: Adam and Eve, after eating the apple, covered their nakedness. Accordingly,

445

when Christian missionaries first visited islands in the Pacific in the 19th century, they forced the native women to wear more clothes, particularly to cover their sexual parts. Were the missionaries' ideas about sex religious or social, or perhaps both?

● ○ ●

THE UNIVERSALITY OF RELIGION

Religious beliefs and practices are found in all known contemporary societies, and archaeologists think they have found signs of religious belief associated with *Homo sapiens* who lived at least 60,000 years ago. People then deliberately buried their dead, and many graves contain the remains of food, tools, and other objects that were probably thought to be needed in an afterlife. Some of the artistic productions of modern humans after about 30,000 years ago may have been used for religious purposes. For example, sculptures of females with ample secondary sex characteristics may have been fertility charms. Cave paintings in which the predominant images are animals of the hunt may reflect a belief that the image had some power over events. Perhaps early humans thought that their hunting would be more successful if they drew images depicting good fortune in hunting. The details of religions practiced in the distant past cannot be recovered. Yet evidence of ritual treatment of the dead suggests that early people believed in the existence of supernatural spirits and tried to communicate with, and perhaps influence, them.

We may reasonably assume the existence of prehistoric religion and we have evidence of the universality of religion in historic times, so we can understand why the subject of religion has been the focus of much speculation, research, and theorizing. As long ago as the 5th century B.C., Herodotus made fairly objective comparisons among the religions of the 50 or so societies he traveled to from his home in Greece. He noted many similarities among their gods and pointed out evidence of diffusion of religious worship. Since Herodotus's time some 2,500 years ago, scholars, theologians, historians, and philosophers have speculated about religion. Some have claimed superiority for their own forms of religion; others have derided the naive simplicity of others' beliefs; and some have expressed skepticism concerning all beliefs.

Speculation about which religion is superior is not an anthropological concern. What is of interest to anthropologists is why religion is found in all societies and how and why it varies from society to society. Many social scientists—particularly anthropologists, sociologists, and psychologists—have offered theories to account for the universality of religion. Most think that religions are created by humans in response to certain universal needs or conditions. We consider four such needs or conditions here: (1) a need for intellectual understanding, (2) reversion to childhood feelings, (3) anxiety and uncertainty, and (4) a need for community.

The Need to Understand

One of the earliest social scientists to propose a major theory of the origin of religion was Edward Tylor. In Tylor's view, religion originated in people's speculation about dreams, trances, and death. The dead, the distant, those in the next house, animals—all seem real in dreams and trances. Tylor thought that the lifelike appearances of these imagined people and animals suggest a dual existence for all things—a physical, visible body and a psychic, invisible soul. In sleep, the soul can leave the body and appear to other people; at death, the soul permanently leaves the body. Because the dead appear in dreams, people come to believe that the souls of the dead are still around.

Tylor thought that the belief in souls was the earliest form of religion; **animism** is the term he used to refer to belief in souls.[1] But many scholars criticized Tylor's theory for being too intellectual and not dealing with the emotional component of religion. One of Tylor's students, R. R. Marett, felt that Tylor's animism was too sophisticated an idea to be the origin of religion. Marett suggested that **animatism**—a belief in impersonal supernatural forces (e.g., the power of a rabbit's foot)—preceded the creation of spirits.[2] A similar idea is that, when people believe in gods, they are *anthropomorphizing*—attributing human characteristics and motivations to nonhuman, particularly supernatural, events.[3] Anthropomorphizing may be an attempt to understand what is otherwise incomprehensible and disturbing.

Reversion to Childhood Feelings

Sigmund Freud believed that early humans lived in groups, each of which was dominated by a tyrannical man who kept all the women for himself.[4] Freud postulated that, on maturing, the sons were driven out of the group. Later, they joined together to kill and eat the hated father. But then the sons felt enormous guilt and remorse, which they expressed (projected) by prohibiting the killing of a totem animal (the father substitute). Subsequently, on ritual occasions, the cannibalistic scene was repeated in the form of a totem meal. Freud believed that these early practices gradually became transformed into the worship of deities or gods modeled after the father.

Most social scientists today do not accept Freud's interpretation of the origin of religion. But there is widespread agreement with his idea that events in infancy can have long-lasting and powerful effects on beliefs and practices in adult life. Helpless and dependent on parents for many years, infants and children inevitably and unconsciously view their parents as all-knowing and all-powerful. When adults feel out of control or in need, they may unconsciously revert to their infantile and childhood feelings. They may then look to gods or magic to do what they cannot do for themselves, just as they looked to their parents to take care of their needs. As we shall see, there is evidence that feelings about the supernatural world parallel feelings in everyday life.

Anxiety and Uncertainty

Freud thought that humans would turn to religion during times of uncertainty, but he did not view religion positively, believing that humans would eventually outgrow the need for religion. Others viewed religion more positively. Bronislaw Malinowski noted that people in all societies are faced with anxiety and uncertainty. They may have skills and knowledge to take care of many of their needs, but knowledge is not sufficient to prevent illness, accidents, and natural disasters. The most frightening prospect is death itself. Consequently, there is an intense desire for immortality. As Malinowski saw it, religion is born from the universal need to find comfort in inevitable times of stress. Through religious belief, people affirm their convictions that death is neither real nor final, that people are endowed with a personality that persists even after death. In religious ceremony, humans can commemorate and communicate with those who have died, and achieve some measure of comfort in these ways.[5]

Theorists such as William James, Carl Jung, Erich Fromm, and Abraham Maslow have viewed religion even more positively: Religion is not just a way of relieving anxiety; it is thought to be therapeutic. James suggested that religion provides a feeling of union with something larger than oneself,[6] and Jung suggested that it helps people resolve their inner conflicts and attain maturity.[7] Fromm proposed that religion gives people a framework of values,[8] and Maslow argued that it provides a transcendental understanding of the world.[9]

The idea that religion relieves anxiety in times of greater stress is supported by a comparative study of fishermen. John Poggie and Richard Pollnac interviewed commercial fishermen from three New England ports about their ritual beliefs and practices. Most frequently mentioned were taboos such as "Don't turn a hatch cover upside down," "Don't whistle on a boat," and "Don't mention the word *pig* on board." When the fishermen were asked what these taboos meant, they talked about personal safety and preventing bad luck. Those fishermen who stay out for only a day at a time, fish closer to shore, or collect shellfish close to shore, report fewer taboos, consistent with the fact that they are less at risk from rough seas, storms, and inability to repair their boats if they break down.[10]

The Need for Community

All those theories of religion agree on one thing: Whatever the beliefs or rituals, religion may satisfy psychological needs common to all people. But some social scientists believe that religion springs from society and serves social, rather than psychological, needs. Émile Durkheim, a French sociologist, pointed out that living in society makes humans feel pushed and pulled by powerful forces. These forces direct their behavior, pushing them to resist what is considered wrong, pulling them to do what is considered right. These are the forces of public opinion, custom, and law. Because they are largely invisible and unexplained, people would feel them as mysterious forces and therefore come to believe in gods and spirits. Durkheim suggested that religion arises out of the experience of living in social groups; religious belief and practice affirm a person's place in society, enhance feelings of community, and give people confidence. He proposed that society is really the object of worship in religion.

Consider how Durkheim explained totemism, so often discussed by early religious theorists. He thought that nothing inherent in a lizard, rat, or frog—animal totems for some Australian aboriginal groups—would be sufficient to make them *sacred*. The totem animal therefore must be a symbol. But a symbol of what? Durkheim noted that the people are organized into clans, and each clan has its own totem animal; the totem distinguishes one clan

Fishermen working on a boat deck in choppy seas. The more danger involved in fishing, the more taboos fisherman seem to have.

from another. So the totem is the focus of the clan's religious rituals and symbolizes both the clan and the clan's spirits. It is the clan that is affirmed in ritual.[11]

Guy Swanson accepted Durkheim's belief that certain aspects or conditions of society generate the responses we call religious, but he thought that Durkheim was too vague about exactly what in society would generate the belief in spirits or gods. So what might? Swanson suggested that the belief in spirits derives from the existence of *sovereign groups* in a society. These are the groups that have independent jurisdiction (decision-making powers) over some sphere of life—the family, the clan, the village, the state. Such groups are not mortal; they persist beyond the lifetimes of their individual members. According to Swanson, then, the spirits or gods that people invent personify or represent the powerful decision-making groups in their society. Just like sovereign groups in a society, the spirits or gods are immortal and have purposes and goals that supersede those of individuals.[12]

VARIATION IN RELIGIOUS BELIEFS

There is no general agreement among scholars as to why people need religion, or how spirits, gods, and other supernatural beings and forces come into existence. (Any or all of the needs we have discussed, psychological or social, may give rise to religious belief and practice.) Yet there is general recognition of the enormous variation in the details of religious beliefs and practices. Societies differ in the kinds of supernatural beings or forces they believe in and the character of those beings. They also differ in the structure or hierarchy of those beings, in what the beings actually do, and in what happens to people after death. Variation exists also in the ways in which the supernatural is believed to interact with humans.

Types of Supernatural Forces and Beings

Supernatural Forces Some supernatural forces have no personlike character. As we discussed earlier, Marett referred to such religious beliefs as animatism. For example, a supernatural, impersonal force called **mana,** after its Malayo-Polynesian name, is thought to inhabit some objects but not others, some people but not others. A farmer in Polynesia places stones around a field; the crops are bountiful; the stones have mana. During a subsequent year, the stones may lose their mana and the crops will be poor. People may also possess mana, as, for example, the chiefs in Polynesia were said to do. However, such power is not necessarily possessed permanently; chiefs who were unsuccessful in war or other activities were said to have lost their mana.

The word *mana* may be Malayo-Polynesian, but a similar concept is also found in our own society. We can compare mana to the power that golfers may attribute to some but, unhappily not all, of their clubs. A ballplayer might think a certain sweatshirt or pair of pants has supernatural power or force, and that more runs or points will be scored when they are worn. A four-leaf clover has mana; a three-leaf clover does not.

Objects, people, or places can be considered **taboo.** Anthony Wallace distinguished mana from taboo by pointing out that things containing mana are to be touched, whereas taboo things are not to be touched, for their power can cause harm.[13] Thus, those who touch them may themselves become taboo. Taboos surround food not to be eaten, places not to be entered, animals not to be killed, people not to be touched sexually, people not to be touched at all, and so on. An Australian aborigine could not normally kill and eat the animal that was his totem; Hebrew tribesmen were forbidden to touch a woman during menstruation or for seven days afterward.

Supernatural Beings Supernatural beings fall within two broad categories: those of nonhuman origin, such as gods and spirits, and those of human origin, such as ghosts and ancestral spirits. Chief among the beings of nonhuman origin, **gods** are named personalities. They are often *anthropomorphic*—that is, conceived in the image of a person—although they are sometimes given the shapes of other animals or of celestial bodies, such as the sun or moon. Essentially, the gods are believed to have created themselves, but some of them then created, or gave birth to, other gods. Although some are seen as creator gods, not all peoples include the creation of the world as one of the acts of gods.

After their efforts at creation, many creator gods retire. Having set the world in motion, they are not interested in its day-to-day operation. Other creator gods remain interested in the ordinary affairs of human beings, especially the affairs of one small, chosen segment of humanity. Whether or not a society has a creator god, the job of running the creation is often left to lesser gods. The Maori of New Zealand, for example, recognize three important gods: a god of the sea, a god of the forest, and a god of agriculture. They call upon each in turn for help and try to get all three to share their knowledge of how the universe runs. The gods of the ancient Romans, on the other hand, specialized to a high degree. There were three gods of the plow, one god to help with the sowing, one for weeding, one reaping, one for storing grain, one for manuring, and so on.[14]

Beneath the gods in prestige, and often closer to people, are multitudes of unnamed **spirits.** Some may be guardian spirits for people. Some, who become known for particularly efficacious work, may be promoted to the rank of named gods. Some spirits who are known to the people but are never invoked by them are of the hobgoblin type. Hobgoblins delight in mischief and can be blamed for any number of small mishaps; still other spirits take pleasure in deliberately working evil on behalf of people.

Many Native American groups believed in guardian spirits that had to be sought out, usually in childhood. For example, among the Sanpoil of northeastern Washington, boys and sometimes girls would be sent out on overnight vigils to acquire their guardians. Most commonly the spirits were animals, but they could also be uniquely shaped

A Guatemalan Maya family visits a cemetery on the Day of the Dead. It is believed that the spirits of the dead return for a visit on that day.

rocks, lakes, mountains, whirlwinds, or clouds. The vigil was not always successful. When it was, the guardian spirit appeared in a vision or dream, and always at first in human form. Conversation with the spirit would reveal its true identity.[15]

Ghosts are supernatural beings who were once human, and **ancestor spirits** are ghosts of dead relatives. The belief that ghosts or their actions can be perceived by the living is almost universal.[16] The near-universality of the belief in ghosts may not be difficult to explain. There are many cues in everyday experience that are associated with a loved one, and even after the death, those cues might arouse the feeling that the dead person is still somehow present. The opening of a door or the smell of tobacco or cologne in a room may evoke the idea that the person is still present, if only for a moment. Then, too, loved ones live on in dreams. Small wonder, then, that most societies believe in ghosts. If the idea of ghosts is generated by these familiar associations, we might expect that ghosts in most societies would be close relatives and friends, not strangers—and they are.[17]

Although the belief in ghosts is nearly universal, the spirits of the dead do not play an active role in the life of the living in all societies. In his cross-cultural study of 50 societies, Swanson found that people are likely to believe in active ancestral spirits where descent groups are important decision-making units. The descent group is an entity that exists over time, back into the past as well as forward into the future, despite the deaths of individual members.[18] The dead feel concern for the fortunes, the prestige, and the continuity of their descent group as strongly as the living. As a Lugbara elder (in northern Uganda in Africa) put it, "Are our ancestors not people of our lineage? They are our fathers and we are their children whom they have begotten. Those that have died stay near us in our homes and we feed and respect them. Does not a man help his father when he is old?"[19]

The Character of Supernatural Beings

Whatever type they may be, the gods or spirits venerated in a given culture tend to have certain personality or character traits. They may be unpredictable or predictable, aloof from or interested in human affairs, helpful or punishing. Why do the gods and spirits in a particular culture exhibit certain character traits rather than others?

We have some evidence from cross-cultural studies that the character of supernatural beings may be related to the nature of child training. Melford Spiro and Roy D'Andrade suggested that the god-human relationship is a projection of the parent-child relationship, in which case child-training practices might well be relived in dealings with the supernatural.[20] For example, if a child was nurtured immediately by her parents when she cried or waved her arms about or kicked, she might grow up expecting to be nurtured by the gods when she attracted their attention by performing a ritual. On the other hand, if her parents often punished her, she would grow up expecting the gods to punish her if she disobeyed them. William Lambert, Leigh Minturn Triandis, and Margery Wolf, in another cross-cultural study, found that societies with hurtful or punitive child-training practices are likely to believe that their gods are aggressive and malevolent; societies with less punitive child training are more likely to believe that the gods are benevolent.[21] These results are consistent with the Freudian notion that the supernatural world should parallel the natural. It is worth noting in this context that some peoples refer to the god as their father and to themselves as his children.

Structure or Hierarchy of Supernatural Beings

The range of social structures in human societies from egalitarian to highly stratified has its counterpart in the supernatural world. Some societies have gods or spirits that are not ranked; one god has about as much power as another. Other societies have gods or spirits that are ranked in prestige and power. For example, on the Pacific islands of Palau, which was a rank society, gods were ranked as people were. Each clan worshiped a god and a goddess that had names or titles similar to clan titles. Although a clan god was generally important only to the members of that clan, the gods of the various clans in a village were believed to be ranked in the same order that the clans were. Thus, the god of the highest-ranking clan was respected by all the clans of the village. Its shrine was given the place of honor in the center of the village and was larger and more elaborately decorated than other shrines.[22]

Although the Palauans did not believe in a high god or supreme being who outranked all the other gods, some societies do. Consider Judaism, Christianity, and Islam, which we call **monotheistic** religions. Although *monotheism* means "one god," most monotheistic religions actually include more than one supernatural being (e.g., demons, angels, the Devil). But the supreme being or high god, as the creator of the universe or the director of events (or both), is believed to be ultimately responsible for all events.[23] A **polytheistic** religion recognizes many important gods, no one of which is supreme.

Why do some societies have a belief in a high god and others do not? Recall Swanson's suggestion that people invent gods who personify the important decision-making groups in their society. He therefore hypothesized that societies with hierarchical political systems should be more likely to believe in a high god. In his cross-cultural study of 50 societies (none of which practiced any of the major world religions), he found that belief in a high god is strongly associated with three or more levels of "sovereign" (decision-making) groups. Of the 20 sample societies that had a hierarchy of three or more sovereign groups—for instance, family, clan, and chiefdom—17 possessed the idea of a high god. Of the 19 societies that had fewer than three levels of decision-making groups, only two had a high god.[24] Consistent with Swanson's findings, societies dependent on food production are more likely to have a belief in a high god than are food-collecting societies.[25] These results strongly suggest, then, that the realm of the gods parallels and may reflect the everyday social and political worlds. In the past, many state societies had state religions in which the political officials were also the officials of the temples (e.g., the pharaohs in Egypt). In recent times, most state societies have separated church and state, as in the United States and Canada.

Intervention of the Gods in Human Affairs

According to Clifford Geertz, when people face ignorance, pain, and the unjustness of life, they explain the events by the intervention of the gods.[26] Thus, in Greek religion, the direct intervention of Poseidon as ruler of the seas prevented Odysseus from getting home for 10 years. In the Old Testament, the direct intervention of Yahweh caused the great flood that killed most of the people in the time of Noah. In other societies, people may search their memories for a violated taboo that has brought punishment through supernatural intervention.

In addition to unasked-for divine interference, there are numerous examples of requests for divine intervention, either for good for oneself and friends or for evil for others. Gods are asked to intervene in the weather and to make the crops grow, to send fish to the fisherman and game to the hunter, to find lost things, and to accompany travelers and prevent accidents. They are asked to stop the flow of lava down the side of a volcano, to stop a war, or to cure an illness.

The gods do not intervene in all societies. In some, they intervene in human affairs; in others, they are not the slightest bit interested; and in still others, they interfere only occasionally. We have little research on why gods are believed to interfere in some societies and not in others. We do, however, have some evidence suggesting when the gods will take an interest in the morality or immorality of human behavior. Swanson's study suggests that the gods are likely to punish people for immoral behavior when there are considerable differences in wealth in the society.[27] His interpretation is that supernatural support of moral behavior is particularly useful where inequalities tax the ability of the political system to maintain social order and minimize social disorder. Envy of others' privileges may motivate some people to behave immorally; the belief that the gods will punish such behavior might deter it. More generally, the concern of gods with moral behavior is more likely in large, complex societies (see the box "Religion: A Force for Harmony and Cooperation?").

Life after Death

In many societies, ideas about an afterlife are vague and seemingly unimportant, but many other peoples have very definite and elaborate ideas of what happens after death. The Lugbara of Uganda see the dead as joining the ancestors of the living and staying near the family homesite. They retain an interest in the behavior of the living, both rewarding and punishing them. The Zuni of the southwestern United States think the dead join the past dead, known as the *katcinas,* in a katcina village at the bottom of a nearby lake. There they lead a life of singing and dancing and bring rain to the living Zuni. Just as they are swift to punish the priest who fails in his duty, they also punish the people in masks who ineffectively impersonate the katcinas during the dance ceremonies.[28]

The Chamulas have merged the ancient Mayan worship of the sun and moon with the Spanish conquerors' Jesus and Mary. Their vision of life after death contains a blending of the two cultures. All souls go to the underworld, where they live a humanlike life except that they are incapable of sexual intercourse. After the sun travels over the world, it travels under the underworld, so that the dead have sunlight. Only murderers and suicides are punished, being burned by the Christ-sun on their journey.[29]

Many Christians believe that the dead are divided into two groups: The unsaved are sent to everlasting

applied anthropology

Religion: A Force for Cooperation and Harmony?

Most social science theories about religion suggest that religious beliefs and rituals promote social cohesion and cooperation within the group that shares them. Some religions, including the major religions in the modern world (Buddhism, Christianity, Islam, Hinduism, Judaism), are more explicit than others in their direct concern with moral behavior. Moralizing religions believe that the gods will reward moral behavior and punish immoral behavior, and are generally found in large and complex societies. Such societies are likely to have towns or cities and less reliance on kinship and reciprocity to encourage moral behavior. Neighbors may not know each other well and although there may be codified law and courts, these mechanisms may not be sufficient to promote social order. Complex societies are also likely to have a large amount of social inequality, which increases the likelihood of property-related crime. The cross-cultural evidence is consistent with the theory that morality-based religions and collective rituals minimize antisocial behavior in groups of unrelated individuals. Perhaps to promote solidarity among unrelated people, religions in complex societies often extend kin terms to members of the religious communities, calling each other "brothers" and "sisters" or sometimes "God's children." Experimental evidence suggests individuals are more generous toward strangers if their religious feelings have been aroused. Religious communes are also four times as likely to survive compared with secular communes.

These studies raise important questions about exactly why and when moralizing religions came into existence and whether the spread of these religions had to do with their adaptive consequences. But there are also questions raised about mechanisms. For example, religious communes, as compared with secular communes, usually impose more requirements from members, such as food taboos, fasts, constraints on sex and possessions, and so on. A comparative study of communes suggests that the religious elements are more important than the commitments themselves. However, in experimental research, there are some hints that nonreligious conditions could also make people more cooperative. Experimental reminders of secular morality had as much effect as reminders of God. Also, there are examples of modern societies, especially in northern Europe, that are very cooperative, but not very religious.

But, even if religious belief and ritual promote greater in-group trust and cooperation, there is a dark side to strongly held religious belief—the potential for greater out-group conflict. History is replete with examples of people hurting others in the name of religion. Christianity and Islam are the two largest religions, possibly because of their zeal to convert others. Some of the biggest conflicts have occurred where the two largest religions meet. The Christian Crusades of the 11th century through 13th century were attempts to "liberate" sites in the Holy Land controlled by Muslims. Osama bin Laden cited the establishment of U.S. bases in Saudi Arabia, which "defiled" sacred lands in his view, as justification for the September 11, 2001, attacks on the United States. Religions, or, more precisely, religious groups, do not necessarily promote violence. After all, some of the founders of various religions preached nonviolence and harmony. Exactly what persuades a religious group to commit violence is not well understood. There are five warning signs. One is when leaders act as if only they know the truth. A second is a call to blind obedience to a religious leader. A third is when the people believe it is possible to establish an "ideal world." A fourth is acting as if "the end justifies the means." Lastly, and perhaps the clearest, is a call for "a holy war."

In the globalized world today, there is more admixture of all types— heterogeneous cities full of people of different colors, dress, ethnicities, and religions. This situation has two potential outcomes—the potential for different groups to live together peacefully, or a greater potential for violence. Whether the major religions will adapt to create a new morality for the new global circumstances remains to be seen. Research has not told us enough yet about how to achieve more harmony across different religions or across different ethnicities. We can hope that simply learning more about other individuals and groups—their hopes, dreams, and expectations, how they have adapted to their environments—may enhance tolerance.

Sources: Winkelman and Baker 2010, 259–65; 314-318; Norenzayan and Shariff 2008; Sosis and Bressler 2003; Stark 2001; Roes and Raymond 2003.

punishment and the saved to everlasting reward. Accounts differ, but hell is often associated with torture by fire, heaven with mansions. Several societies see the dead as returning to earth to be reborn. The Hindus use this pattern of reincarnation to justify one's caste in this life and to promise eventual release from the pain of life through the attainment of *nirvana*, or inclusion into the One.

A recent cross-cultural study asks why some societies judge where you will go after death and others do not. Support was found for the idea that judgmental beliefs parallel the society's economic practices. Some societies have considerable delay between labor inputs and return of food. For example, intensive agriculturalists need considerable labor input to plow, fertilize, or create irrigation systems, and many months go by until crops can be

A ghost festival in Thailand. The belief in ghosts is practically a cross-cultural universal.

harvested. Not planning ahead has dire long-term consequences. In contrast, mistakes by hunter-gatherers are realized more quickly and can be corrected more quickly. Religions that foster the idea that actions in the present will be judged after death reinforce the need for long-term planning. Consistent with this idea, societies with intensive agriculture are the most likely to believe that their actions in life affect where their souls will go after death.[30] This finding is consistent with Swanson's conclusion discussed previously that the gods are generally likely to punish people for immoral behavior when there are considerable differences in wealth in the society. Intensive agricultural societies tend to have considerable differences in wealth.

In many respects, the afterworld in many religions may resemble the everyday world, but we still have only a few comparative studies that show exactly how.

VARIATION IN RELIGIOUS PRACTICES

Beliefs are not the only elements of religion that vary from society to society. Societies vary in the kinds of religious practitioners they have. There is also variation in how people interact with the supernatural. The manner of approach to the supernatural varies from supplication—requests, prayers, and so on—to manipulation. Many of these interactions are highly *ritualized*. **Rituals** are repetitive sets of behaviors that occur in essentially the same patterns every time they occur. Religious rituals involve the supernatural in some way. They are generally collective, follow customary patterns, and are thought to strengthen faith.[31]

Ways to Interact with the Supernatural

How to get in touch with the supernatural has proved to be a universal problem. Wallace identified a number of

ways people the world over use, though not necessarily all together, including, but not limited to, prayer (asking for supernatural help), physiological experience (doing things to the body and mind), simulation (manipulating imitations of things), feasts, and sacrifices.[32] Prayer can be spontaneous or memorized, private or public, silent or spoken. The Lugbara do not say the words of a prayer aloud, for doing so would be too powerful; they simply think about the things that are bothering them. The gods know all languages.

Doing things to the body or mind may involve drugs (hallucinogenics such as peyote or opiates) or alcohol; social isolation or sensory deprivation; dancing or running until exhausted; being deprived of food, water, and sleep; and listening to repetitive sounds such as drumming. Such behaviors may induce trances or altered states of consciousness.[33] Erika Bourguignon found that achieving these altered states, which she generally referred to as *trances*, is part of religious practice in 90 percent of the world's societies.[34] In some societies, trances are thought to involve the presence of a spirit or power inside a person that changes or displaces that person's personality or soul. These types are referred to as possession trances. Other types of trances may involve the journey of a person's soul, experiencing visions, or transmitting messages from spirits. Possession trances are especially likely in societies that depend on agriculture and have social stratification, slavery, and more complex political hierarchies. Nonpossession trances are most likely to occur in food-collecting societies. Societies with moderate levels of social complexity have both possession and nonpossession trances.[35]

One puzzle is why there is a preponderance of women thought to be possessed. Alice Kehoe and Dody Giletti suggested that women are more likely than men to suffer from nutritional deficiencies because of pregnancy, lactation, and men's priority in gaining access to food. Calcium deficiency in particular can cause muscular spasms, convulsive seizures, and disorientation, all of which may foster the belief that an individual is possessed.[36] Douglas

Raybeck and his colleagues suggest that women's physiology makes them more susceptible to calcium deficiency even with an equivalent diet. In addition, women are subject to more stress because they are usually less able to control their lives. Higher levels of stress, they suggest, lower the body's reserves of calcium.[37] Erika Bourguignon suggests a more psychological explanation of women's preponderance in possession trances. In many societies, women are brought up to be submissive. But when possessed, women are taken over by spirits and they are not responsible for what they do or say—therefore, they can unconsciously do what they are not able to do consciously.[38] Although intriguing, these suggestions need to be tested on individuals in field situations.

Voodoo employs simulation, or the imitation of things. Dolls are made in the likeness of an enemy and then are maltreated in hopes that the original enemy will experience pain and even death.

Divination seeks practical answers from the supernatural about anything that is troublesome—decisions to be made, interpersonal problems, or illness. (We discuss divination's role in curing illness in the chapter on medical anthropology.) Diviners use a variety of methods, including altered states of consciousness and simulation through the use of objects such as Ouija boards or tarot cards.[39]

Omar Moore suggested that, among the Naskapi hunters of Labrador, divination is an adaptive strategy for successful hunting. The Naskapi consult the diviner every three or four days when they have no luck in hunting. The diviner holds a caribou bone over the fire, as if the bone were a map, and the burns and cracks that appear in it indicate where the group should hunt. Moore, unlike the Naskapi, did not believe that the diviner really can find out where the animals will be; the cracks in the bones merely provide a way of randomly choosing where to hunt. Because humans are likely to develop customary patterns of action, they might be likely to look for game according to some plan. But game might learn to avoid hunters who operate according to a plan. Thus, any method of ensuring against patterning or predictable plans—any random strategy—may be advantageous. Divination by "reading" the bones would seem to be a random strategy. It also relieves any individual of the responsibility of deciding where to hunt, a decision that might arouse anger if the hunt failed.[40]

The eating of a sacred meal is found in many religions. For instance, Holy Communion is a simulation of the Last Supper. Australian aborigines, normally forbidden to eat their totem animal, have one totem feast a year at which they eat the totem. Feasts are often part of marriage and funeral ceremonies, as well as a fringe benefit of the sacrifice of food to the gods.

Some societies make sacrifices to a god in order to influence the god's action, either to divert anger or to attract goodwill. Characteristic of all sacrifices is that something of value is given up to the gods, whether it be food, drink, sex, household goods, or the life of an animal or person. Some societies feel that the god is obligated to act on their behalf if they make the appropriate sacrifice.

A woman with offerings at a Hindu temple in Bali.

Others use the sacrifice in an attempt to persuade the god, realizing there is no guarantee that the attempt will be successful.

Of all types of sacrifice, we probably think that the taking of human life is the ultimate. Nevertheless, human sacrifice is not rare in the ethnographic and historical records. Why have some societies practiced it? One cross-cultural study found that, among preindustrial societies, those with full-time craft specialists, slavery, and the corvée are most likely to practice human sacrifice. The suggested explanation is that the sacrifice mirrors what is socially important: Societies that depend mainly on human labor for energy (rather than animals or machines) may think of a human life as an appropriate offering to the gods when people want something very important.[41] Later studies found that societies with human sacrifice were at a mid-range level of political complexity, having alliances and confederacies with other polities, but only weak political integration. Such societies also seemed to be subject to population pressure and frequently carried out warfare for land and other resources. Human sacrifice, with humans from the outside groups, may have been an attempt to terrorize people from the other polities.[42]

Magic

All these modes of interacting with the supernatural can be categorized in various ways. One dimension of variation is how much people in society rely on pleading, asking, or trying to persuade the supernatural to act on their behalf, as opposed to whether they believe they can compel the supernatural to help by performing certain acts. For example, prayer is asking; performing voodoo is presumably compelling. When people believe their action can compel the supernatural to act in some particular and intended way, anthropologists often refer to the belief and related practice as **magic.**

Magic may involve manipulation of the supernatural for good or for evil. Many societies have magical rituals designed to ensure good crops, the replenishment of game, the fertility of domestic animals, and the avoidance and cure of illness in humans. We tend to associate the belief in magic with societies simpler than our own, but some people in complex societies take magic seriously and many follow some magical practices.

People who engage in risky activities may try to ensure their safety by carrying or wearing lucky charms. They believe the charms protect them by invoking the help of supernatural beings or forces. We might also believe we can protect ourselves by not doing some things. For example, baseball players on a hitting streak may choose not to change their socks or sweatshirt for the next game (to continue their luck). Why magic appeals to some individuals but not others in our own society may help us explain why magic is an important part of religious behavior in many societies.

As we will see, the witch doctor and the shaman often employ magic to effect a cure. But the use of magic to bring about harm has evoked perhaps the most interest.

Sorcery and Witchcraft Sorcery and witchcraft are attempts to invoke the spirits to work harm against people. Although the words *sorcery* and *witchcraft* are often used interchangeably, they are also often distinguished. **Sorcery** may include the use of materials, objects, and medicines to invoke supernatural malevolence. **Witchcraft** may be said to accomplish the same ills by means of thought and emotion alone. Evidence of witchcraft can never be found. This lack of visible evidence makes an accusation of witchcraft both harder to prove and harder to disprove.

To the Azande of Zaire, in central Africa, witchcraft was part of everyday living. It was not used to explain events for which the cause was known, such as carelessness or violation of a taboo, but to explain the otherwise unexplainable. A man is gored by an elephant. He must have been bewitched, because he had not been gored on other elephant hunts. A man goes to his beer hut at night, lights some straw, and holds it aloft to look at his beer. The thatch catches fire and the hut burns down. The man has been bewitched, for huts did not catch fire on hundreds of other nights when he and others did the same thing. Some of the pots of a skilled potter break; some of the bowls of a skilled carver crack. Witchcraft. Other pots, other bowls treated exactly the same have not broken.[43]

The witch craze in Europe during the 16th and 17th centuries and the witch trials in 1692 in Salem, Massachusetts, remind us that the fear of others, which the belief in witchcraft presumably represents, can increase and decrease in a society within a relatively short period of time. Many scholars have tried to explain these witch hunts. One factor often suggested is political turmoil, which may give rise to widespread distrust and a search for scapegoats. In the case of Europe during the 16th and 17th cen-

turies, small regional political units were being incorporated into national states, and political allegiances were in flux. In addition, as Swanson noted, the commercial revolution and related changes were producing a new social class, the middle class, and "were promoting the growth of Protestantism and other heresies from Roman Catholicism."[44] In the case of Salem, the government of Massachusetts colony was unstable and there was much internal dissension. In 1692, the year of the witchcraft hysteria, Massachusetts was left without an English governor, and judicial practices broke down. These extraordinary conditions saw the accusation of a single person for witchcraft become the accusation of hundreds and the execution of 20 people. Swanson suggested that the undermining of legitimate political procedures may have generated the widespread fear of witches.[45]

It is also possible that epidemics of witchcraft accusation, like in Salem as well as other New England and European communities, may be the result of real epidemics—epidemics of disease. The disease implicated in Salem and elsewhere is the fungus disease called ergot, which can grow on rye plants. (The rye flour that went into the bread that the Salem people ate may have been contaminated by ergot.) It is now known that people who eat grain products contaminated by ergot suffer from convulsions, hallucinations, and other symptoms, such as crawling sensations in the skin. We also now know that ergot contains LSD, the drug that produces hallucinations and other delusions that resemble those occurring in severe mental disorders.

The presumed victims of bewitchment in Salem and other places had symptoms similar to victims of ergot poisoning today. They suffered from convulsions and the sensations of being pricked, pinched, or bitten. They had visions and felt as if they were flying through the air. We cannot know for sure that ergot poisoning occurred during those times when witchcraft accusations flourished. There is no direct evidence, of course, because the "bewitched" were not medically tested. But we do have some evidence that seems to be consistent with the ergot theory. Ergot is known to flourish on rye plants under certain climatic conditions—particularly a very cold winter followed by a cool, moist spring and summer. Tree-ring growth indicates that the early 1690s were particularly cold in eastern New England, and the outbreaks of witchcraft accusation in Europe seem to have peaked with colder winter temperatures.[46] Interestingly, too, when witchcraft hysteria was greatest in Europe, Europeans were using an ointment containing a skin-penetrating substance that we now know produces hallucinations and a vivid sensation of flying.[47] It may not be cause for wonder, then, that our popular image of witches is of people flying through the air on broomsticks.

But whether or not epidemics of witchcraft hysteria are due to epidemics of ergot poisoning or episodes of political turmoil or both, we still have to understand why so many societies in the ethnographic record believe in witchcraft and sorcery in the first place. Why do so many societies believe that there are ways to invoke the spirits to work harm against people? One possible explanation, suggested by Beatrice Whiting, is that sorcery or witchcraft will be found in societies that lack procedures or judicial authorities to deal with crime and other offenses. Her theory is that all societies need some form of social control—some way of deterring most would-be offenders and of dealing with actual offenders. In the absence of judicial officials who, if present, might deter and deal with antisocial behavior, sorcery may be a very effective mechanism for social control. If you misbehave, the person you mistreated might cause you to become ill or even die. The cross-cultural evidence seems to support this theory. Sorcery is more important in societies that lack judicial authorities than in those that have them.[48]

Types of Practitioners

Individuals may believe that they can directly contact the supernatural, but almost all societies also have part-time or full-time religious or magical practitioners. Research suggests there are four major types of practitioners: shamans, sorcerers or witches, mediums, and priests. As we shall see, the number of types of practitioners in a society seems to vary with degree of cultural complexity.[49]

The Shaman   The word *shaman* may come from a language that was spoken in eastern Siberia. The **shaman** is usually a part-time male specialist who has fairly high status in his community and is often involved in healing.[50] We discuss the role of the shaman as healer in the chapter on applied, practicing, and medical anthropology. More generally, the shaman deals with the spirit world to try to get their help or to keep them from causing harm.[51] Here we focus on the methods shamans use to help others.

The shaman enters into a trance, or some other altered state of consciousness, and then journeys to other worlds to get help from guardians or other spirits. Dreams may be used to provide insight or as a way for shamans to commune with spirits. People may seek help for practical matters, such as where to get food resources or whether to relocate, but solving a health problem is most often the goal of the shaman.[52] Shamans may also bring news from spirits, such as a warning about an impending disaster.[53]

Someone may receive a "call" to the role of shaman in recovering from an illness, through a vision quest, or in a dream. Shamans-in-training may enhance the vividness of their imagery by using hallucinogens, sleep or food deprivation, or engaging in extensive physical activity such as dancing. An important part of the process of being a shaman is learning to control the imagery and the spirit powers. Shamanistic training can take several years under the guidance of a master shaman.[54]

Sorcerers and Witches   In contrast with shamans, who have fairly high status, sorcerers and witches of both sexes tend to have very low social and economic status in their societies.[55] Suspected sorcerers and witches are usually feared because they are thought to know how to invoke the supernatural to cause illness, injury, and death. Because sorcerers use materials for their magic, evidence of sorcery can be found, and suspected sorcerers are often killed for their malevolent activities. Because witchcraft supposedly is accomplished by thought and emotion alone, it may be harder to prove that someone is a witch, but the difficulty of proving witchcraft has not prevented people from accusing and killing others for being witches.

Mediums   **Mediums** tend to be females. These part-time practitioners are asked to heal and divine while in possession trances—that is, when they are thought to be possessed by spirits. Mediums are described as having tremors, convulsions, seizures, and temporary amnesia.

Priests   **Priests** are generally full-time male specialists who officiate at public events. They have very high status

Shamans are usually male. Here, female shamans in Korea perform a healing ritual.

and are thought to be able to relate to superior or high gods who are beyond the ordinary person's control. In most societies with priests, the people who get to be priests obtain their offices through inheritance or political appointment.[56] Priests are sometimes distinguished from other people by special clothing or a different hairstyle. The training of a priest can be vigorous and long, including fasting, praying, and physical labor, as well as learning the dogma and the ritual of his religion. Priests in the United States complete four years of theological school and sometimes serve first as apprentices under established priests. Priests do not receive a fee for their services but are supported by donations from parishioners or followers. Priests often have some political power as a result of their office—the chief priest is sometimes also the head of state or is a close adviser to the chief of state—and their material well-being is a direct reflection of their position in the priestly hierarchy.

The dependence on memorized ritual both marks and protects the priest. If a shaman repeatedly fails to effect a cure, he will probably lose his following, for he has obviously lost the support of the spirits. But if a priest performs his ritual perfectly and the gods choose not to respond, the priest will usually retain his position and the ritual will preserve its assumed effectiveness. The nonresponse of the gods will be explained in terms of the people's unworthiness of supernatural favor.

Practitioners and Social Complexity   More complex societies tend to have more types of religious or magical practitioners. If a society has only one type of practitioner, it is almost always a shaman; such societies tend to be nomadic or seminomadic food collectors. Societies with two types of practitioners (usually shaman healers and priests) have agriculture. Those with three types of practitioners are agriculturalists or pastoralists with political integration beyond the community (the additional practitioner type tends to be either a sorcerer or witch or a medium). Finally, societies with all four types of practitioners have agriculture, political integration beyond the community, and social classes.[57]

RELIGION AND ADAPTATION

Following Malinowski, many anthropologists take the view that religions are adaptive because they reduce the anxieties and uncertainties that afflict all peoples. We do not really know that religion is the only means of reducing anxiety and uncertainty, or even that individuals or societies *have* to reduce their anxiety and uncertainty. Still, it seems likely that certain religious beliefs and practices have directly adaptive consequences. For example, the Hindu belief in the sacred cow has seemed to many to be the very opposite of a useful or adaptive custom. Their religion does not permit Hindus to slaughter cows. Why do the Hindus retain such a belief? Why do they allow all those cows to wander around freely, defecating all over the place, and not slaughter any of them? The contrast with our own use of cows could hardly be greater.

Marvin Harris suggested that the Hindu use of cows may have beneficial consequences that some other use of cows would not have. Harris pointed out that there may be a sound economic reason for not slaughtering cattle in India. The cows, and the males they produce, provide resources that could not easily be gotten otherwise. At the same time, their wandering around to forage is no strain on the food-producing economy.

The resources provided by the cows are varied. First, a team of oxen and a plow are essential for the many small farms in India. The Indians could produce oxen with fewer cows, but to do so, they would have to devote some of their food production to feeding those cows. In the present system, they do not feed the cows, and even though poor nutrition makes the cows relatively infertile, males, which are castrated to make oxen, are still produced at no cost to the economy. Second, cow dung is essential as a cooking fuel and fertilizer. The National Council of Applied Economic Research estimated that an amount of dung equivalent to 45 million tons of coal is burned annually. Moreover, it is delivered practically to the door each day at no cost. Alternative sources of fuel, such as wood, are scarce or costly. In addition, about 340 million tons of dung are used as manure—essential in a country obliged to derive three harvests a year from its intensively cultivated land. Third, although Hindus do not eat beef, cattle that die naturally or are butchered by non-Hindus are eaten by the lower castes, who, without the upper-caste taboo against eating beef, might not get this needed protein. Fourth, the hides and horns of the cattle that die are used in India's enormous leather industry. Therefore, because the cows do not themselves consume resources needed by people and it would be impossible to provide traction, fuel, and fertilizer as cheaply by other means, the taboo against slaughtering cattle may be very adaptive.[58]

RELIGIOUS CHANGE

In any society, religious beliefs and practices change over time, but some types of change are quite dramatic. Perhaps the most dramatic is religious conversion, particularly when large numbers of people switch to a completely new religion presented by missionaries or other proselytizers. Changing religion so drastically is perplexing to many scholars of religion who believe that religious beliefs are deeply connected to one's sense of identity, one's family, one's community, and ideas about the world.[59] Within the last few centuries, conversion has sometimes followed Western expansion and exploration. Contact with Westerners and other outsiders has also produced religious change in more indirect ways. In some native societies, contact has led to a breakdown of social structure and the growth of feelings of helplessness and spiritual demoralization. *Revitalization movements* have arisen as apparent attempts to restore such societies to their former confidence and prosperity. In recent times, religious *fundamentalist* movements have flourished. Some scholars have argued that such movements are also responses to the stress of rapid social change.

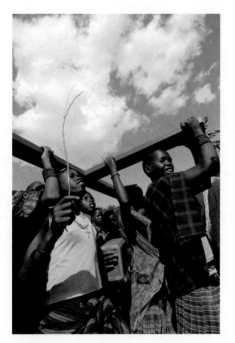

A Catholic mass under open skies conducted by missionaries among the Karamojong of Uganda.

As we will see, religious change, particularly of the dramatic kind, usually does not occur in a vacuum, but is often associated with other dramatic changes—economic, political, and demographic.

Religious Conversion

The two world religions with the greatest interest now in obtaining converts have been Christianity and Islam. Christian missionaries, supported by their churches back home, have been some of the earliest Western settlers in interior regions and out-of-the-way places. Traders have been the main proselytizers of Islam. Conversion to one of the world religions has often been associated with colonization and the expansion of state societies (see the box on colonialism and religious affiliation). The presence of people from other religions does not necessarily mean that people convert to the new religion. For example, missionaries have not met with equal success in all parts of the world. In some places, large portions of the native population have converted to the new religion with great zeal. In others, missionaries have been ignored, forced to flee, or even killed. We do not fully understand why missionaries have been successful in some societies and not in others.

We now examine the process of conversion on the island of Tikopia, as an example of religious change brought about by direct contact with missionaries.

Christianity on Tikopia Tikopia was one of the few Polynesian societies to retain its traditional religious system into the first decades of the 20th century. An Anglican mission was first established on the island in 1911. With it came a deacon and the founding of two schools for about 200 pupils. By 1929, approximately half the population had converted, and in the early 1960s, almost all of Tikopia gave at least nominal allegiance to Christianity.[60]

Traditional Tikopian belief embraced a great number of gods and spirits of various ranks who inhabited the sky, the water, and the land. One god in particular—the original creator and shaper of the culture—was given a place of special importance, but he was in no way comparable to the all-powerful God of Christianity. Unlike Christianity, Tikopian religion made no claim to universality. The Tikopian gods did not rule over all creation, only over Tikopia. It was thought that if one left Tikopia, one left the gods behind.

The people of Tikopia interacted with their gods and spirits primarily through religious leaders who were also the heads of descent groups. Clan chiefs presided over rituals associated with the everyday aspects of island life, such as house construction, fishing, planting, and harvesting. The chief was expected to intercede with the gods on the people's behalf, to persuade them to bring happiness and prosperity to the group. Indeed, when conditions were good, it was assumed that the chief was doing his job well. When disaster struck, the prestige of the chief often fell in proportion. Why did the Tikopia convert to Christianity? Firth suggested several contributing factors.

First, the mission offered the people the prospect of acquiring new tools and consumer goods. Although conversion alone did not provide such benefits, attachment to the mission made them more attainable. Later, it became apparent that education, particularly in reading and writing English, was helpful in getting ahead in the outside world. Mission schooling became valued and provided a further incentive for adopting Christianity.

Second, conversion may have been facilitated by the ability of chiefs, as religious and political leaders, to bring over entire descent groups to Christianity. Should a chief decide to transfer his allegiance to Christianity, the members of his kin group usually followed him. In 1923, when Tafua, chief of the Faea district of Tikopia, converted to the new religion, he brought with him his entire group—nearly half the population of the island. The ability of the chiefs to influence their kin groups, however, was both an asset and a hindrance to missionary efforts, because some chiefs steadfastly resisted conversion.

A final blow to traditional Tikopian religion came in 1955, when a severe epidemic killed at least 200 people in a population of about 1,700. According to Firth, "the epidemic was largely interpreted as a sign of divine discrimination," because three of the outstanding non-Christian religious leaders died.[61] Subsequently, the remaining non-Christian chiefs voluntarily converted to Christianity, and so did their followers. By 1966, all Tikopia, with the exception of one old woman, had converted to the new faith.

Although many Tikopians feel their conversion to Christianity has been a unifying, revitalizing force, the changeover from one religion to another has not been without problems. Christian missionaries on Tikopia have succeeded in eliminating the traditional Tikopian population-control devices of abortion, infanticide, and male

migrants and immigrants

Colonialism and Religious Affiliation

Many of us might like to think that we belong to a particular religious group because we prefer its beliefs and practices. And that may be true for people who have chosen to switch their religious affiliation. But many religious people affiliate with the religion they grew up with, or one very much like it.

Clearly, religious affiliation is a complex issue. But one thing stands out. You are not likely to choose an affiliation you have never been exposed to. This goes for people who believe in religion and also for people who don't. Most North Americans say they are Christians. But how come?

Would so many in North America be Christians if Europeans (mostly Christian) hadn't established colonies here and elsewhere in the last 500 years? Would there be Muslims in Indonesia, the Philippines, and North Africa if Arab kingdoms hadn't established colonies in those places after the 7th century? Would there have been Hindus in Sumatra if South Asians hadn't migrated and established the Srivijayan kingdom in Sumatra before the time of Christ? Would there have been Jews in

Yemen (until their emigration to Israel 50 years ago) if King Solomon's state had not colonized in the land of the Queen of Sheba more than 2,000 years ago? An expanding state society can directly or indirectly force a change in people's religious affiliation. It is not coincidental that the new religious affiliation usually matches the dominant society's.

Religion in some form may be a cultural universal. People may worship the supernatural, pray to it for help and guidance, and even try to control it (with "lucky charms" and other magic). But religion is not the same everywhere, as is evident in this chapter. Why people convert to a major religion carried by an expanding state society is still not completely understood. Sometimes the people do not convert, or do not convert right away. Anthropologist Elizabeth Brusco has written that one primary motivation for conversion, long recognized by scholars, is the desire to maximize advantages. In recent times, missionaries have offered new beliefs and practices that may be appealing, but they have also offered what

Brusco calls "protection, access to food and other desirable goods, medical care, literacy, technology, status, and, at times, political power." Was the same true, at least somewhat, in the past? Was adopting the new religion the best way to survive colonialism and its consequences?

Even if people adopt a religion, they often change important parts of it. For example, the Lahu of southwest China became Buddhist but the Buddha became a male-female couple rather than just a male. The Lahu were a stateless society (prior to the expansion of the Han Chinese) with a strong emphasis on gender equality. By identifying Buddha with their indigenous god, Xeul Sha, the image of the Buddha was changed. According to Lahu origin myths, Xeul Sha is a male-female pair of twins. They marry and propagate humanity. The identification of Xeul Sha with Buddha means that Buddha is considered a pair of male-female gods by most Lahu Buddhist villagers.

Sources: Brusco 1996; Stevens 1996; Du 2003.

---

celibacy. It is very possible that the absence of these controls will continue to intensify population pressure. The island, with its limited capacity to support life, can ill afford this outcome. Firth summed up the situation Tikopian society faced:

> In the history of Tikopia complete conversion of the people to Christianity was formerly regarded as a solution to their problems; it is now coming to be realized that the adoption and practice of Christianity itself represents another set of problems. As the Tikopia themselves are beginning to see, to be Christian Polynesians in the modern technologically and industrially dominated world, even in the Solomon Islands, poses as many questions as it supplies answers.[62]

Unfortunately, not all native peoples have made the transition to Christianity as painlessly as the Tikopia. In fact, the record is dismal in most cases. All too frequently, missionary activity tends to destroy a society's culture and self-respect. It offers nothing in return but an alien, repressive system of values ill suited to the people's real needs and aspirations. Phillip Mason, a critic of European evangelists in Africa, pointed out some of the psychological damage inflicted by missionary activity.[63] The missionaries repeatedly stressed sin and guilt; they used the color black to represent evil and the color white to signify good; and they showed hostility toward pagan culture. Most damaging of all was their promise that Africans, provided they adopted the European's ways, would gain access both to the European's heaven and to European society. But no matter how diligently Africans attempted to follow missionary precepts or climb the socioeconomic ladder, they were soon blocked from entry into European homes, clubs, and even churches and seminaries.

Explaining Conversion Anthropologists have just begun to try to understand religious conversion. As the box on colonialism and religious affiliation and the Tikopia case suggest, some of the motivation for switching to a new religion may have to do with economic and political advantages associated with converting to the new religion. With regard to the recent spread of Islam in Africa, Jean Ensminger suggests that Islam provided opportunities for those who wanted to engage in trade—"Islam brought a common language of trade (Arabic), a monetary system, an accounting system, and a legal code to adjudicate financial contracts and disputes."[64] These institutions were shared across ethnic groups, making it possible to engage in long-distance trade. But what increased the attractiveness of Islamic trade? Ensminger's study of the Orma, a pastoralist group in Kenya, is instructive, for despite the presence of Islam for 300 years, it did not appear to be of interest to them. The Orma chiefs did trade, but the Orma were mostly self-sufficient and the need for trade appeared to be relatively low. However, the Orma were in serious trouble after successful attacks by the Masai and Somali in the late 1800s, which almost decimated them and depleted their cattle. After 1920, as they began to recover their population somewhat and their cattle began to be replenished, there was rapid conversion to Islam, mostly led by the young, who perhaps were attracted by the economic opportunities.[65]

Loss of population and the demoralization that it brings may also have played a significant role in conversion. Daniel Reff, comparing widespread conversion to Christianity in the Roman Empire after A.D. 150 and in northern Mexico after A.D. 1593, notes the parallels in both. In both situations, there were ravaging epidemics along with the presence of Christian personnel ready to help heal the sick. In Europe, about 8 percent of the population died before smallpox epidemics subsided in A.D. 190, and population continued to decline into the Middle Ages, perhaps to half of what it was. Population losses might have been more extreme in Mexico. In northern Mexico, an estimated 75 percent of the native populations died from disease. In Europe, Christians provided charity, food, and shelter for the ill, without regard to their status. The Jesuit missions in Mexico did not have that many personnel, but they did what they could to provide food, water, and "medicine."[66] Do epidemics play a role in other places? An exploratory cross-cultural study suggests that rapid population loss, usually from introduced diseases, predicts religious conversion, particularly when people believe that their traditional gods could help them.[67] If gods could have helped but didn't and people are dying in unusual numbers, people may think that the "gods have failed." In such circumstances, it is not surprising that people would be receptive to a new religion, particularly if it is preached by missionaries who are not dying.

Revitalization

The long history of religion includes periods of strong resistance to change as well as periods of radical change. Anthropologists have been especially interested in the founding of new religions or sects. The appearance of new religions is one of the things that may happen when cultures are disrupted by contact with dominant societies. Various terms have been suggested for these religious movements—cargo cults, nativistic movements, messianic movements, millenarian cults. Wallace suggested that they are all examples of **revitalization movements,** efforts to save a culture by infusing it with a new purpose and new life.[68] We turn to examples of such movements from North America and Melanesia.

The Seneca and the Religion of Handsome Lake The Seneca reservation of the Iroquois on the Allegheny River in New York State was a place of "poverty and humiliation" by 1799.[69] Demoralized by whiskey and dispossessed from their traditional lands, unable to compete with the new technology because of illiteracy and lack of training, the Seneca were at an impasse. In this setting, Handsome Lake, the 50-year-old brother of a chief, had the first of a number of visions. In them, he met with emissaries of the Creator who showed him heaven and hell and commissioned him to revitalize Seneca religion and society. This he set out to do for the next decade and a half. As his principal text, he used the *Gaiwiio,* or "Good Word," a gospel that contains statements about the nature of religion and eternity and a code of conduct for the righteous. The *Gaiwiio* is interesting both for the influence of Quaker Christianity it clearly reveals,[70] and for the way the new material was merged with traditional Iroquois religious concepts.

The first part of the "Good Word" has three main themes, one of which is the concept of an apocalypse. Handsome Lake offered many signs by which the faithful could recognize impending, cosmic doom. Great drops of fire would rain from the skies and a veil would be cast over the earth. False prophets would appear, witch women would openly cast spells, and poisonous creatures from the underworld would seize and kill those who had rejected the *Gaiwiio*. Second, the *Gaiwiio* emphasized sin. The great sins were disbelief in the "good way," drunkenness, witchcraft, and abortion. Sins had to be confessed and repented. Finally, the *Gaiwiio* offered salvation. Salvation could be won by following a code of conduct, attending certain important traditional rites, and performing public confession.

The second part of the *Gaiwiio* sets out the code of conduct. This code seems to orient the Seneca toward advantageous European American practices without separating them from their culture. The code has five main sections:

1. **Temperance.** All Seneca leaders were fully aware of the social disorders arising out of abuse of liquor. Handsome Lake went to great lengths to illustrate and explain the harmfulness of alcohol.

2. **Peace and social unity.** Seneca leaders were to cease their futile bickering, and all were to be united in their approach to the larger society.

3. **Preservation of tribal lands.** Handsome Lake, fearing the piecemeal alienation of Seneca lands, was far ahead of his contemporaries in demanding a halt in land sales to non-Seneca.

A revitalization movement that became known as the Ghost Dance spread eastward from the Northwest from the 1870s to the 1890s. It was generally believed that, if people did the dance correctly, ghosts would come to life with sufficient resources to allow the people to return to their old ways, and, as a result of some cataclysm, the whites would disappear.

Source: Ogallala Sioux performing the Ghost Dance at the Pine Ridge Indian Agency, South Dakota. Illustration by Frederic Remington, 1890.

4. **Proacculturation (favoring external culture traits).** Though individual property and trading for profit were prohibited, the acquisition of literacy in English was encouraged so that people would be able to read and understand treaties and to avoid being cheated.

5. **Domestic morality.** Sons were to obey their fathers, mothers should avoid interfering with daughters' marriages, and husbands and wives should respect the sanctity of their marriage vows.

Handsome Lake's teaching seems to have led to a renaissance among the Seneca. Temperance was widely accepted, as were schooling and new farming methods. By 1801, corn yields had been increased tenfold, new crops (oats, potatoes, flax) had been introduced, and public health and hygiene had improved considerably. Handsome Lake himself acquired great power among his people. He spent the remainder of his life fulfilling administrative duties, acting as a representative of the Iroquois in Washington, and preaching his gospel to neighboring tribes. By the time of Handsome Lake's death in 1815, the Seneca clearly had undergone a dramatic rebirth, attributable at least in part to the new religion. Later in the

century, some of Handsome Lake's disciples founded a church in his name that, despite occasional setbacks and political disputes, survives to this day.

Although many scholars believe cultural stress gives rise to these new religious movements, it is still important to understand exactly what the stresses are and how strong they have to become before a new movement emerges. Do different kinds of stresses produce different kinds of movements? And does the nature of the movement depend on the cultural elements already present? Let us consider some theory and research on the causes of the millenarian cargo cults that began to appear in Melanesia from about 1885 on.

Cargo Cults The *cargo cults* can be thought of as religious movements "in which there is an expectation of, and preparation for, the coming of a period of supernatural bliss."[71] Thus, an explicit belief of the cargo cults was the notion that some liberating power would bring all the Western goods (cargo in pidgin English) the people might want. For example, around 1932, on Buka in the Solomon Islands, the leaders of a cult prophesied that a tidal wave would sweep away the villages and a ship would arrive

current research and issues

One Appeal of Religion May Be the Wish for a Better World

There are many religions in the United States today, and new sects, often derisively called cults, emerge regularly. Few of us realize that nearly all of the major churches or religions in the world began as minority sects or cults. Indeed, some of the most established and prestigious Protestant churches were considered radical social movements at first. For example, what we now know as the United Church of Christ, which includes the Congregational Church, was founded by radicals in England who wanted church governance to be in the hands of the local congregation. Many of these radicals became the people we call Pilgrims, who had to flee to the New World. But they were very fundamentalist in their beliefs; for example, as late as the 1820s, Congregationalist-dominated towns in Connecticut prohibited celebrations of Christmas outside of church because such celebrations were not mentioned in the Bible. Nowadays, Congregationalists are among the most liberal Protestants.

We should not be surprised to learn that most of the various Protestant churches today, including some considered very conservative, began as militant sects that set out to achieve a better world. After all, that's why we call them "Protestant." At first, the rebellion was against Rome and the Catholic Church. Later, sects developed in opposition to church and government hierarchies. And remember that Christianity itself began as a radical group in the hinterland of the Roman Empire. So new sects or cults were probably always political and social, as well as religious, movements. Recall that the word *millennium*, as used in discussions of religious movements, refers to a wished-for or expected future time when human life and society will be perfect and free of troubles; the world will then be prosperous, happy, and peaceful. Nowadays, the wish for a better world may or may not be religiously inspired. Some people who seek a more perfect world believe that humans alone must achieve it.

How should we categorize this wish for a better world? Should we call it "conservative" because the imagined world may have existed in the past? If the imagined world does not yet exist, is it "radical" to believe it can be achieved? Maybe the wish for a more perfect world is neither conservative nor radical. Maybe it is just that people who are not satisfied with the world as it is think that something can be done to improve things, with or without divine assistance. However it will come, the "millennium" will be different from now, and better.

Ideas about the millennium, and the origins of new cults and religions, might best be viewed then as human hopes: Which ones do people have? Do they vary from culture to culture, and why? Are some hopes universal? And how might they be achieved?

Sources: Stark 1985; Trompf 1990.

---

with iron, axes, food, tobacco, cars, and arms. Work in the gardens ceased, and wharves and docks were built for the expected cargo.[72]

What may explain such cults? Peter Worsley suggested that an important factor in the rise of cargo cults and millenarian movements in general is the existence of oppression—in the case of Melanesia, colonial oppression. He suggested that the reactions in Melanesia took religious rather than political forms because they were a way of pulling together people who previously had no political unity and who lived in small, isolated social groups.[73] Other scholars, such as David Aberle, suggested that *relative deprivation* is more important than oppression in explaining the origins of cults; when people feel that they could have more, and they have less than what they used to have or less than others, they may be attracted to new cults.[74] Consistent with Aberle's general interpretation, Bruce Knauft's comparative study of cargo cults found that such cults were more important in Melanesian societies that had had decreasing cultural contact with the West, and presumably *decreasing* contact with valued goods, within the year prior to the cult's emergence.[75]

Fundamentalism For some scholars, one of the main attributes of fundamentalism is the literal interpretation of a sacred scripture. But recent scholars have suggested that fundamentalist movements need to be understood more broadly as religious or political movements that appear in response to the rapidly changing environment of the modern world. In this broader view, fundamentalism occurs in many religions, including those of Christians, Jews, Islamics, Sikhs, Buddhists, and Hindus. Although each movement is different in content, Richard Antoun suggests that fundamentalist movements have the following elements in common: the selective use of scripture to inspire and assert proof of particular certainties; the quest for purity and traditional values in what is viewed as an impure world; active opposition to what is viewed as a permissive secular society and a nation-state that separates religion from the state; and an incorporation of selected modern elements such as television to promote the movements' aims.[76]

Fundamentalist religious movements do appear to be linked to the anxieties and uncertainties associated with culture change in general and globalization in particular. Many people in many countries are repelled by new behaviors and attitudes, and react in a way that celebrates the old. As Judith Nagata puts it, fundamentalism is a "quest for certainty in an uncertain world."[77] Protestant fundamentalism flourished at the end of the 19th century in the United States as immigrant groups came into the country in great numbers and the country became industrialized and increasingly urbanized. The fundamentalists denounced foreign influences, the decline of the Bible as a guide to moral behavior, the teaching of evolution, and they succeeded in getting the country to prohibit the sale of alcoholic beverages. Recent Islamic fundamentalist movements seem to be responses to a different kind of challenge to the social order—increasing Westernization. Westernization may have first arrived in conjunction with colonial rule. Later, it may have been promoted by Western-educated native elites.[78] Antoun suggests that fundamentalist movements deliberately push certain practices because the leaders know they will outrage the secular opposition. Examples in recent Islamic fundamentalist movements are the extreme punishment of cutting off a hand for theft and requiring women to be covered by veils or head-to-toe covering in public.[79] Unfortunately, in present-day discourse, fundamentalism tends to be equated by Westerners with Islam itself. But, in historical perspective, all major religions have had fundamentalist movements in times of rapid culture change.

If the recent as well as distant past is any guide, we can expect religious belief and practice to be revitalized periodically, particularly during times of stress. As we discussed in the chapter on culture change and globalization, change associated with globalization appears to be accompanied by the rise of fundamentalist religious movements. Paradoxically, globalization has increased the spread of world religions but it has also increased the worldwide interest in shamanism and other features of religion that are different from the dominant religions. Thus, we can expect the world to continue to have religious variation.

SUMMARY ● ○ ○

1. Religion is any set of attitudes, beliefs, and practices pertaining to supernatural power. Such beliefs may vary within a culture as well as among societies, and they may change over time.

2. Religious beliefs are evident in all known cultures and are inferred from artifacts associated with *Homo sapiens* since at least 60,000 years ago.

3. Theories to account for the universality of religion suggest that humans create religion in response to certain universal needs or conditions, including a need for understanding, reversion to childhood feelings, anxiety or uncertainty, and a need for community.

4. There are wide variations in religious beliefs. Societies vary in the number and kinds of supernatural entities in which they believe. There may be impersonal supernatural forces (e.g., mana and taboo), supernatural beings of nonhuman origin (gods and spirits), and supernatural beings of human origin (ghosts and ancestor spirits). The religious belief system of a society may include any or all such entities.

5. Gods and spirits may be unpredictable or predictable, aloof from or interested in human affairs, helpful or punishing. In some societies, all gods are equal in rank; in others, there is a hierarchy of prestige and power among gods and spirits, just as among the humans in those societies.

6. A monotheistic religion is one in which there is one high god, as the creator of the universe or the director of events (or both); all other supernatural beings are either subordinate to, or function as alternative manifestations of, this god. A high god is generally found in societies with a high level of political development.

7. Faced with ignorance, pain, and injustice, people frequently explain events by claiming intervention by the gods. Such intervention has also been sought by people who hope it will help them achieve their own ends. The gods are likely to punish the immoral behavior of people in societies that have considerable differences in wealth.

8. Various methods have been used to attempt communication with the supernatural. Among them are prayer, taking drugs or otherwise affecting the body and mind, simulation, feasts, and sacrifices.

9. When people believe that their actions can compel the supernatural to act in a particular and intended way, anthropologists refer to the belief and related practice as magic. Sorcery and witchcraft are attempts to make the spirits work harm against people.

10. Almost all societies have part-time or full-time religious or magical practitioners. Recent cross-cultural research suggests that there are four major types of practitioners: shamans, sorcerers or witches, mediums, and priests. The number of types of practitioners seems to vary with degree of cultural complexity: The more complex the society, the more types of practitioners.

11. The history of religion includes periods of strong resistance to change and periods of radical change. Perhaps the most dramatic is religious conversion, particularly when large numbers of people switch to a completely new religion presented by missionaries or other proselytizers. In some native societies, contact has led to a breakdown of social structure and the growth of feelings of helplessness and spiritual demoralization. *Revitalization movements* have arisen as apparent attempts to restore such societies to their former confidence and prosperity. In recent times, religious *fundamentalist* movements have flourished. Religious change, particularly of the dramatic kind, usually does not occur in a vacuum, but is often associated with other dramatic changes—economic, political, and demographic.

GLOSSARY TERMS ○ ● ○

CRITICAL QUESTIONS ○ ○ ●

1. How does your conception of God compare with beliefs about supernatural beings in other religious systems?

2. What do you think is the future of religion? Explain your answer.

3. Could any of the religious practices you know about be classified as magic? Are they associated with anxiety-arousing situations?

PEARSON
myanthrolab

Read the chapter by Debra Picchi titled "Bakairí: The Death of an Indian" on MyAnthroLab, and answer the following questions:

1. How come the Bakairi did not ask whether Western medicine works, but Westerners asked whether shamanism works?

2. Why would a shaman be able to settle disputes?

The Arts

ost societies do not have a word for art.[1] Perhaps that is because art, particularly in societies with relatively little specialization, is often an integral part of religious, social, and political life. Indeed, most of the aspects of culture we have already discussed—economics, kinship, politics, religion—are not easily separated from the rest of social life.[2]

The oldest art found so far comes from caves in South Africa. Pieces of red ochre were engraved there more than 77,000 years ago. In Australia, people painted on walls of rock shelters and on cliff faces between 70,000 and 60,000 years ago. And in southern Africa, Spain, and France, people painted slabs of rock 28,000 years ago (see the box on rock art on page 467). Art is clearly an old feature of human cultures. We say that those earliest paintings are art, but what do we mean by "art"? A stone spear point and a bone fishhook obviously require skill and creativity to make. But we do not call them art. Why do we feel that some things are art and others are not?

Some definitions of art emphasize its evocative quality. From the viewpoint of the person who creates it, art expresses feelings and ideas; from the viewpoint of the observer or participant, it evokes feelings and ideas. The feelings and ideas on each side may or may not be exactly the same. And they may be expressed in a variety of ways—drawing, painting, carving, weaving, body decoration, music, dance, or story. An artistic work or performance is intended to excite the senses, to stir the emotions of the beholder or participant. It may produce feelings of pleasure, awe, repulsion, or fear, but usually not indifference.[3]

But emphasizing the evocative quality of art may make it difficult to compare the art of different cultures because what is evocative in one culture may not be evocative in another. For example, a humorous story in one culture may not be funny in another. Thus, most anthropologists agree that art is more than an attempt by an individual to express or communicate feelings and ideas. There is also some cultural patterning or meaning; societies vary in their characteristic kinds and styles of art.[4]

Artistic activities are always cultural in part, involving shared and learned patterns of behavior, belief, and feeling. What are some of the ideas about art in our own culture? We tend to think that anything useful is not art. If a basket has a design that is not necessary to its function, we may possibly consider it art, especially if we keep it on a shelf; but the basket with bread on the table would probably not be considered art. The fact that such a distinction is not made in other societies strongly suggests that our ideas about art are cultural. Among Native Americans in the Pacific Northwest, elaborately carved totem poles not only displayed the crests of the lineages of their occupants, they also supported the house.[5] The fact that artistic activities are partly cultural is evident when we compare how people in different societies treat the outsides of their houses. Most North Americans share the value of decorating the interiors of their homes with pictures—paintings, prints, or photographs hung on the walls.

But they do not share the value of painting pictures on the outside walls of their houses, as Native Americans did in the Pacific Northwest.

In our society, we also insist that a work must be unique to be considered art. This aspect is clearly consistent with our emphasis on the individual. However, even though we require that artists be unique and innovative, the art they produce must still fall within some range of acceptable variation. Artists must communicate to us in a way we can relate to, or at least learn to relate to. Often, they must follow certain current styles of expression that other artists or critics have set, if they hope to have the public accept their art. The idea that an artist should be original is a cultural idea; in some societies, the ability to replicate a traditional pattern is more valued than originality.

So, art seems to have several qualities: It expresses as well as communicates. It stimulates the senses, affects emotions, and evokes ideas. It is produced in culturally patterned ways and styles. It has cultural meaning. In addition, some people are thought to be better at it than others.[6] Art does not require some people to be full-time artistic specialists; many societies in the ethnographic record had no full-time specialists of any kind. But, although everyone in some societies may participate in some arts (dancing, singing, body decoration), it is usually thought that certain individuals have superior artistic skill.

To illustrate the cross-cultural variation that exists in artistic expression, we will consider first the art of body decoration and adornment.

● ○ ●

BODY DECORATION AND ADORNMENT

In all societies, people decorate or adorn their bodies. The decorations may be permanent—scars, tattoos, or changes in the shape of a body part. Or they may be temporary, in the form of paint or objects such as feathers, jewelry, skins, and clothing that are not strictly utilitarian. Much of this decoration seems to be motivated by aesthetic considerations, which, of course, vary from culture to culture. The actual form of the decoration depends on cultural traditions. Body ornamentation includes the pierced noses of some women in India, the elongated necks of the Mangebetu of central Africa, the tattooing of North American males and females, the body painting of the Caduveo of South America, and the variety of ornaments found in almost every culture.

However, in addition to satisfying aesthetic needs, body decoration or adornment may be used to delineate social position, rank, sex, occupation, local and ethnic identity, or religion within a society. Along with social stratification come visual means of declaring status. The symbolic halo (the crown) on the king's head, the scarlet hunting jacket of the English gentleman, the eagle feathers of the Native American chief's bonnet, the gold-embroidered jacket of the Indian rajah—each mark of high status is recognized in its own society. Jewelry in the shape of a cross or the Star of David indicates Christian or Jewish inclinations. Clothes may set apart the priest, nun, or member of a sect such as the Amish.

The erotic significance of some body decoration is also apparent. Women draw attention to erogenous zones of the body by painting, as on the lips, and by attaching some object—an earring, a flower behind the ear, a necklace, bracelet, brooch, anklet, or belt. Men draw attention, too, by beards, tattoos, and penis sheaths (in some otherwise naked societies) that point upward. We have only to follow the fashion trends for women of Europe and North America during the past 300 years, with their history of pinched waists, ballooned hips, bustled rumps, exaggerated breasts, painted faces, and exposed bosoms, to realize the significance of body adornment for sexual provocation. Why some societies emphasize the erotic adornment of women and others emphasize it in men is not yet understood.

Type of body adornment may reflect politics. Polynesians decorate their bodies with tattoos, which are permanent. In Samoa, for example, tattoos distinguished the chiefly class from commoners. Bands and stripes were restricted to people of high status; low-status people could have tattoos only of solid black and only from waist to knees. Within the ruling class, the number of tattooed triangles down a man's leg indicated his relative rank. Because tattooing is permanent, it is a form of body decoration well suited to a society with inherited social stratification. On the other hand, in Melanesia, typically with "big men" type of leadership which is somewhat fluid, Melanesians paint their bodies, and the painting is ephemeral. It disappears within a short time, or after the first wash.[7]

A need to decorate the human body seems universal. We have noted some of the various methods people have used to adorn themselves in different societies. We are also aware of body-decoration practices that raise questions to which we have no ready answers. What explains adornment of the body by permanent marking such as scarification, bound feet, elongated ears and necks, shaped heads, pierced ears and septums, and filed teeth? Why do different societies

applied anthropology

Rock Art: Preserving a Window into the Past

If the art of an ancient or earlier culture reflects the preoccupations and ideas of the culture, and if we are interested in understanding what the creators of the art thought, the art of the past and its surroundings must be preserved as much as possible. One type of ancient art frequently found is what anthropologists call "rock art," drawings and paintings on cliff faces and the walls of caves. Some of the most famous are the cave paintings of Europe, dating from about 30,000 years ago, but a large number of other rock art sites are in danger and in need of preserving.

Unlike a painting or a decorated object, rock art is part of its environment, and the environmental area as well as the rock art needs to be preserved. Excavation of the area may provide information that not only allows us to date the drawings and paintings, it may also tell us what the people did to produce the art and why they produced it. For example, in one French cave, analysis of charcoal indicates that the artists made fires to produce the charcoal they would use in their drawings. In another cave in Montana, pollen found below the paintings came from a number of plants. Many of the plants have known medicinal properties, and the pollens may indicate what shamans had in their medicine bags. Talking to the descendants of the creators of the rock art is also essential. Sometimes anthropologists learn things that surprise them. For instance, near Alice Springs, Australia, some branches were knocking against some rock art and the preservers considered cutting some of the branches. The aboriginal elders were horrified at the idea because the trees were believed to harbor the souls of the deceased, and it would have been a crime to cut them.

Although there are natural threats to rock art, the greatest threats come from humans. Religious change with European contact often lessened the interest of indigenous populations in their earlier sacred sites, making for less protest when development projects are proposed. Tours to previously isolated sites often lead to more destruction from graffiti or unauthorized attempts to reproduce or photograph the art. Ironically though, making the rock art the center of a park helps protect it.

Raising awareness of rock art is one of the most important ways of protecting it in its environment. Although nothing beats seeing rock art in its natural setting, modern methods (holograms, laser recording, 3D imagery) and computer-assisted enhancement have made it possible to have life-size replicas, allowing the public to see more than they can in some mostly inaccessible caves. These replicas and images also give anthropologists and other scientists materials for appreciation and study. The greater the number of displays in public facilities (museums, parks) that expose tourists to rock art, the more valuable it may become. Anthropologists or not, we all seem to be fascinated by the ancient graphics. We try to imagine what motivated the original artists. If we could reconstruct those motives, they might suggest why we choose subjects and techniques in our own art, as well as in our "graffiti."

The archaeological context of rock art can help us understand the rock art. Teaching people how to preserve rock art is applied anthropology that will help to preserve a priceless heritage and a source of knowledge about humans in the past.

Source: Clottes 2008.

---

adorn, paint, or otherwise decorate different parts of the body for sexual or other reasons? And what leads some members of our society to transfer body decoration to their animals? Why the shaped hair of the poodle, the braided manes of some horses, and diamond collars, painted toenails, coats, hats, and even boots for some pets?

EXPLAINING VARIATION IN THE ARTS

In our society, we stress the freedom of the artist, so it may seem to us that art is completely free to vary. But our emphasis on uniqueness obscures the fact that different cultures not only use or emphasize different materials and have different ideas of beauty, but they also may have characteristic styles and themes. It is easy to see styles when we look at art that is different from our own; it is harder to see similarity when we look at the art of our own culture. If we look at dance styles, for example, we may think that the dance style of the 1940s is completely different from the dance style of today. It might take an outsider to notice that, in our culture, we still generally see couples dancing as a pair rather than in a group line or circle, as in dances we call "folk dances." And, in our culture, females and males dance together rather than separately. Furthermore, our popular music still has a beat or combination of beats and is made by many of the same kinds of instruments as in the past.

But where do these similarities in form and style come from? Much of the recent research on variation in the arts supports the idea that form and style in visual art, music, dance, and folklore are very much influenced by other aspects of culture. Some psychological anthropologists, as we saw in the chapter on culture and the individual, would go even further, suggesting that art, like religion, expresses the typical feelings, anxieties, and experiences of people in a culture. And the typical feelings and anxieties in turn are influenced by basic institutions such as childrearing, economy, social organization, and politics.

Consider how the physical form of art a society prefers may reflect its way of life. For example, Richard Anderson pointed out that the art of traditionally nomadic people such as the !Kung, Inuit, and Australian aborigines is mostly carryable.[8] Song, dance, and oral literature are very important in those societies and are as portable as they can be. Those societies decorate useful objects that they carry with them—harpoons for the Inuit, boomerangs for the Australian aborigines, ostrich egg "canteens" for the !Kung. But they don't have bulky things such as sculpture or elaborate costumes. And what about the presence of artists or art critics? Although some people in small-scale societies are more artistic than others, specialized artists, as well as critics or theoreticians of art, tend to be found only in societies with a complex, specialized division of labor.

Visual Art

Perhaps the most obvious way artistic creations reflect how we live is by mirroring the environment—the materials and technologies available to a culture. Stone, wood, bones, tree bark, clay, sand, charcoal, berries for staining, and a few mineral-derived ochers are generally available materials. In addition, depending on the locality, other resources are accessible: shells, horns, tusks, gold, copper, and silver. The different uses to which societies put these materials are of interest to anthropologists, who may ask, for example, why a people chooses to use clay and not copper when both items are available. Although we have no conclusive answers as yet, such questions have important ramifications. The way in which a society views its environment is sometimes apparent in its choice and use of artistic materials. Certain metals, for example, may be reserved for ceremonial objects of special importance. Or the belief in the supernatural powers of a stone or tree may cause a sculptor to be sensitive to that particular material.[9]

The traditional political systems of Africa ranged from centralized kingdoms (on the complex end of the continuum) to village-based or segmentary lineage systems in which leadership was ephemeral or secret (tied to secret societies). Masks that conceal identity are often used in the uncentralized systems; crowns or other headdresses indicating high status are frequent in the kingdoms. Among the uncentralized Ibo of eastern Nigeria, masks are often worn by the young men of a village when they criticize the

behavior of the village elders. In the kingdom of Ngoyo, in western Zaire, the king's status is indicated by his special cap as well as by his special three-legged stool.

What is particularly meaningful to anthropologists is the realization that, although the materials available to a society may to some extent limit or influence what it can do artistically, the materials by no means determine what is done. Why does the artist in Japanese society rake sand into patterns, the artist in Navajo society paint sand, and the artist in Roman society melt sand to form glass? Moreover, even when the same material is used in the same way in different societies, the form or style of the work varies enormously from culture to culture.

A society may choose to represent objects or phenomena that are especially important to the people or elite. An examination of the art of the Middle Ages tells us something about the medieval preoccupation with theological doctrine. In addition to revealing the primary concerns of a society, the content of that society's art may also reflect the culture's social stratification. Authority figures may be represented in obvious ways. In the art of ancient Sumerian society, the sovereign was portrayed as being much larger than his followers, and the most prestigious gods were given oversized eyes. Also, differences in clothing and jewelry styles within a society usually reflect social stratification.

Art historians have always recognized certain possible relationships between the art of a society and other aspects of its culture. Much of this attention has been concentrated on the content of art, because European art has been representational for such a long time. But the style of the art may reflect other aspects of culture. John Fischer, for example, examined the stylistic features of art with the aim of discovering "some sort of regular connection between some artistic feature and some social situation."[10] He argued that the artist expresses a form of social fantasy. In other words, in a stable society, artists will respond to those conditions in the society that bring security or pleasure to them and the society.

The same materials may be used artistically in different ways. In Japan (on the left), sand is raked into patterns. In the Northern Territory of Australia (on the right), the Yuendumu paint the sand.

Assuming that "pictorial elements in design are, on one psychological level, abstract, mainly unconscious representations of persons in the society,"[11] Fischer reasoned that egalitarian societies would tend to have different stylistic elements in their art as compared with stratified societies. Egalitarian societies are generally composed of small, self-sufficient communities that are structurally similar and have little differentiation between people. Stratified societies, on the other hand, generally have larger and more interdependent, and dissimilar, communities and great differences among people in prestige, power, and access to economic resources. Fischer hypothesized, and found in a cross-cultural study, that certain elements of design were strongly related to the presence of social hierarchy. His findings are summarized in Table 26–1.

Repetition of a simple element, for example, tends to be found in the art of egalitarian societies, which have little political organization and few authority positions. If each element unconsciously represents individuals within the society, the relative sameness of people seems to be reflected in the repetitiveness of design elements. Conversely, the combinations of different design elements in complex patterns that tend to be found in the art of stratified societies seem to reflect the high degree of social differentiation that exists in such societies.[12]

According to Fischer, the egalitarian society's empty space in a design represents the society's relative isolation. Because egalitarian societies are usually small and self-sufficient, they tend to shy away from outsiders, preferring to find security within their own group. In contrast, the art of stratified societies is generally crowded. The hierarchical society does not seek to isolate individuals or communities within the group because they must be interdependent, each social level ideally furnishing services for those above it and help for those beneath it. As Fischer suggested, we can, in general, discern a lack of empty space in the designs of societies in which security is not sought by avoiding strangers, but rather "security is produced by incorporating strangers into the hierarchy, through dominance or submission as the relative power indicates."[13]

Symmetry, the third stylistic feature related to type of society, is similar to the first. Symmetry may suggest likeness or an egalitarian society; asymmetry suggests difference and perhaps stratification. The fourth feature of interest here, the presence or absence of enclosures or boundaries—"frames" in our art—may indicate the presence or absence of hierarchically imposed rules circumscribing individual behavior. An unenclosed design may reflect free access to most property; in egalitarian societies, the fencing off of a piece of property for the use of only one person is unknown. In the art of stratified societies, boundaries or enclosures may reflect the idea of private property. Or they may symbolically represent the real differences in dress, occupation, type of food allowed, and manners that separate the different classes of people.

Studies such as Fischer's offer anthropologists new tools with which to evaluate ancient societies that are known only by a few pieces of pottery or a

TABLE 26–1 Artistic Differences in Egalitarian and Stratified Societies	
Egalitarian Society	**Stratified Society**
Repetition of simple elements	Integration of unlike elements
Much empty or irrelevant space	Little empty space
Symmetrical design	Asymmetrical design
Unenclosed figures	Enclosed figures

Source: Based on Fischer 1961.

few tools or paintings. If art reflects certain aspects of a culture, then the study of whatever art of a people has been preserved may provide a means of testing the accuracy of the guesses we make about their culture on the basis of more ordinary archaeological materials. For example, even if we did not know from classical Greek writings that Athens became much more socially stratified between 750 B.C. and 600 B.C., we might guess that such a transformation had occurred because of the changes we can see over time in the way the Athenians decorated vases. Consistent with Fischer's cross-cultural findings, as Athens became more stratified, its vase painting became more complex, more crowded, and more enclosed.[14]

Music

When we hear the music of another culture, we often don't know what to make of it. We may say it does not "mean" anything to us, not realizing that the "meaning" of music has been programmed into us by our culture. In music as well as in art, our culture largely determines what we consider acceptable variation, what we say has "meaning" to us. Even a trained musicologist, listening for the first time to music of a different culture, will not be able to hear the subtleties of tone and rhythm that members of the culture hear with ease. This predicament is similar to that of the linguist who, exposed to a foreign language,

Changes in Greek vases show how increasing stratification is associated with integration of unlike elements as well as more crowded design. The one on the left dates from around 1000 B.C. when there was less stratification. The vase on the right dates from the time period between 750 B.C. and 600 B.C., when stratification was at its maximum.

Masks with V shapes represent threat. There are many such shapes on the masked individual from Panama shown on the right—the placement of the horns, the green spikes on the outside of the mask, over the eyes, the ears, the pointed chin, and of course the many pointed teeth. The nonthreatening Iroquois mask on the left has more curved lines and generally lacks any angles.

The kinds of stress Ayres looked for in ethnographic reports were those that would be applied to all children or to all of one sex—for example, scarification; piercing of the nose, lips, or ears; binding, shaping, or stretching of feet, head, ears, or any limb; inoculation; circumcision; or cauterization. The results showed that, in societies in which infants are stressed before the age of 2, music is marked by a wider tonal range than in societies in which children are not stressed or are stressed only at a later age. Also, a firm accent or beat is characteristic of music more often in societies that subject children to stress than in societies that do not.[20]

Cultural emphasis on obedience or independence in children is another variable that may explain some aspects of musical performance. In societies in which children are generally trained for compliance, cohesive singing predominates; where children are encouraged to be assertive, singing is mostly individualized. Moreover, assertive training of children is associated with a raspy voice or harsh singing. A raspy voice seems to be an indication of assertiveness and is most often a male voice quality. Interestingly enough, in societies in which women's work predominates in subsistence production, the women sing with harsher voices.

Other voice characteristics may also be associated with elements of culture. For example, sexual restrictions in a society seem to be associated with voice restrictions, especially with a nasalized or narrow, squeezed tone. These voice qualities are associated with anxiety and are especially noticeable in sounds of pain, deprivation, or sorrow. Restrictive sexual practices may be a source of pain and anxiety, and the nasal tone in song may reflect such emotions.[21]

The cross-cultural results about music should be able to explain change over time as well as variation within a society. Future research in a variety of societies may help test the theories of Lomax and Ayres.[22]

Folklore

Folklore is a broad category comprising all the myths, legends, folktales, ballads, riddles, proverbs, and superstitions of a cultural group.[23] In general, folklore is transmitted orally, but it may also be written. Games are also sometimes considered folklore, although they may be learned by imitation as well as transmitted orally. All societies have a repertoire of stories that they tell to entertain each other and teach children. Examples of our folklore include fairy tales and the legends we tell about our folk heroes, such as George Washington's confessing that he chopped down the cherry tree. Folklore is not always clearly separable from the other arts, particularly music and dance; stories often are conveyed in those contexts.

Although some folklore scholars emphasize the traditional aspects of folklore and the continuity between the present and the past, more recently attention has been paid to the innovative and emergent aspects of folklore. In this view, folklore is constantly created by any social group that has shared experiences. So, for example, computer programmers may have their jokes and their own proverbs (e.g., "Garbage in, garbage out!").[24] Jan Brunvand compiled a set of recently arisen *urban legends*. One such legend is "The Hook." The story, which has many versions, is basically about a young couple parked on Lover's Lane with the radio on. There is an announcement that a killer with an artificial hand is loose, so the girl suggests that they leave. The boy starts the car and drives her home. When he walks around the car to open her door, he finds a bloody hook attached to the door handle.[25] There are even legends on college campuses. What is the answer to the question of how long students should wait for a tardy professor? Students have an answer, ranging from 10 to 20 minutes. Is this a rule, or only a legend? Brunvand reported that he never found a regulation about how long to wait for the professor on any campus that tells this story![26]

Some folklore scholars are interested in universal or recurrent themes. Clyde Kluckhohn suggested that five themes occur in the myths and folktales of all societies: catastrophe, generally through flood; the slaying of monsters; incest; sibling rivalry, generally between brothers; and castration, sometimes actual but more commonly symbolic.[27]

Just as in art and song, dance style seems to reflect societal complexity. In less complex societies, everyone participates in dances in much the same way, as among the Huli of New Guinea. In more complex societies, there tend to be leading roles and minor roles, as in a Japanese Geisha show.

migrants and immigrants

The Spread of Popular Music

Music is a very visceral art. You feel it in your gut. Hearing a piece of music can make your belly vibrate and give you goosebumps. You don't forget that experience. The ideas expressed in a song can get to you, but you're mostly moved by the sound. You feel it. Music can lift you up or make you sad.

But we wouldn't know about lots of music if not for migration. Would there be "country music" radio stations in the United States if lots of people hadn't moved out of the South in the 20th century? Country music itself was an amalgam of Appalachian folk music heavily influenced by music from the British Isles and also by African music. The banjo, adapted by country musicians, was created by African Americans who modeled the banjo on the African stringed musical instrument called a banjar. Though the fiddle, an important instrument in country music, was European in origin, many of the fiddlers in the South were African American, and country music incorporated African rhythmic styles and improvisation. There were other influences also—the guitar came from Spain, and yodeling from the Swiss. African American music also influenced much of popular American music—ragtime, the blues, jazz, rhythm and blues, rock

and roll, disco and rap, to name just a few. African influences also came to the United States via the Caribbean and South America where people from different cultures created a creolized music. Would we like "salsa" dancing, a form of Afro-Cuban music, or reggae and hip-hop from Jamaica, if there were no immigration? The answer is probably not. If people didn't migrate, it is unlikely that we would know so many styles of music. To get to know music, you need personal contact with it through your own ears. Of course, it is possible that you learn to like music from concerts, on CDs, the radio, or now on the Internet, without hearing it from migrants or immigrants. But most people don't listen to everything; they need to know something about the music before they listen to it further.

Probably no place imports or accepts all kinds of music. The movement of popular music is not guaranteed. For example, although there are many immigrants and migrants of Chinese or South Asian descent in the United States and Canada, Chinese or South Asian music has not become popular. Of course, it might in the future. Why the music of some immigrants and migrants is adopted or incorporated whereas other music is not is not yet

understood. The spread of music is quite different from the spread of technology. The computer and the automobile, like many technologies, can and do spread widely, as people earn more and can afford to buy them. In the case of technologies, there is an easy test of usefulness; a steel ax is better than a stone ax (which is why we don't see people making stone axes anymore). Music is not something that is or is not useful—the ideas and feelings communicated answer our needs. Although young people, the most frequent consumers of popular music, are often looking for something "new," the latest style is probably not that different in some respects from the last style. Cultures have musical preferences, and musical styles that are very different are not readily accepted. And there are those who still like their "golden oldies."

With all the migration and immigration in the modern world, it is likely that the market demand for new popular music will continue to expand. In a few years, we may have Internet-based radio for every demographic niche. Wouldn't that be a blast!

Sources: Nicholls 1998; D. R. Hill 2005, 363–73.

Edward Tylor, who proposed that religion is born from the human need to explain dreams and death, suggested that hero myths follow a similar pattern the world over—the central character is exposed at birth, is subsequently saved by others (humans or animals), and grows up to become a hero.[28] Joseph Campbell argued that hero myths resemble initiations—the hero is separated from the ordinary world, ventures forth into a new world (in this case, the supernatural world) to triumph over powerful forces, and then returns to the ordinary world with special powers to help others.[29]

Myths may indeed have universal themes, but few scholars have looked at a representative sample of the world's societies, and therefore we cannot be sure that current conclusions about universality are correct. Indeed, most folklore researchers have not been interested in universal themes but in the particular folktales told in specific societies or regions. For example, some scholars have

focused on the "Star Husband Tale," a common Native American story. Stith Thompson presented 84 versions of this tale; his goal was to reconstruct the original version and pinpoint its place of origin. By identifying the most common elements, Thompson suggested that the basic story (and probably the original) is the following:

> Two girls sleeping out of doors wish that stars would be their husbands. In their sleep the girls are taken to the sky where they find themselves married to stars, one of which is a young man and the other an old man. The women are warned not to dig, but they disregard the warning and accidentally open up a hole in the sky. Unaided they descend on a rope and arrive home safely.[30]

The tale, Thompson suggested, probably originated in the Plains and then spread to other regions of North America.

Alan Dundes has concentrated on the structure of folktales; he thinks that Native American folktales, including the "Star Husband Tale," have characteristic structures. One is a movement away from disequilibrium. Equilibrium is the desirable state; having too much or too little of anything is a condition that should be rectified as soon as possible. Disequilibrium, which Dundes calls *lack,* is indicated by the girls in the "Star Husband Tale" who do not have husbands. The lack is then corrected, in this case by marriage with the stars. This tale has another common Native American structure, says Dundes—a sequence of prohibition, interdiction, violation, and consequence. The women are warned not to dig, but they do—and as a consequence, they escape for home.[31] It should be noted that the consequences in folktales are not always good. Recall the Garden of Eden tale. The couple are warned not to eat the fruit of a tree; they eat the fruit; they are cast out of their paradise. Similarly, Icarus in the Greek tale is warned not to fly too high or low. He flies too high; the sun melts the wax that holds his feathered wings, and he falls and drowns.

As useful as it might be to identify where certain tales originated, or what their common structures might be, many questions remain. What do the tales mean? Why did they arise in the first place? Why are certain structures common in Native American tales? We are still a long way from answering many of these questions, and trying to answer them is difficult. How does one try to understand the meaning of a tale?

It is easy for people to read different meanings into the same myth. For example, consider the myth the Hebrews told of a paradise in which only a man was present until Eve, the first woman, arrived and ate the forbidden fruit of knowledge. One might conclude that men in that society had some grudge against women. If the interpreter were a psychoanalyst, he, or especially she, might assume that the myth reflected the male's deeply hidden fears of female sexuality. A historian might believe that the myth reflected actual historical events and that men were living in blissful ignorance until women invented agriculture—the effect of Eve's "knowledge" led to a life of digging rather than gathering.

It is clearly not enough to suggest an interpretation. Why should we believe it? We should give it serious consideration only if some systematic test seems to support it. For example, Michael Carroll suggested a Freudian interpretation of the "Star Husband Tale"—that the story represents repressed sentiments in the society. Specifically, he suggested that incestuous intercourse is the underlying concern of this myth, particularly the desire of a daughter to have intercourse with her father. He assumed that the stars symbolize fathers. Fathers, like stars, are high above, in children's eyes. Carroll predicted that, if the "Star Husband Tale" originated on the Plains, and if it symbolizes intercourse, then the Plains groups should be more likely than other societies to have intercourse imagery in their versions of the tale. That seems to be the case. Analyzing 84 versions of the tale, Carroll found that Plains societies are the Native American groups most likely to have imagery suggesting intercourse, including the lowering of a rope or ladder—symbolizing the penis—through a sky hole—symbolizing the vagina.[32]

Few studies have investigated why there is cross-cultural variation in the frequency of certain features in folktales. One feature of folktale variation that has been investigated cross-culturally is aggression. George Wright found that variation in childrearing patterns predicted some aspects of how aggression is exhibited in folktales. Where children are severely punished for aggression, more intense aggression appears in the folktales. And in such societies, strangers are more likely than the hero or friends of the hero to be the aggressors in the folktales. It seems that where children may be afraid to exhibit aggression toward their parents or those close to them because of fear of punishment, the hero or close friends in folktales are also not likely to be aggressive.[33]

Other kinds of fears may be reflected in folktales. A cross-cultural study by Alex Cohen found that unprovoked aggression is likely in folktales of societies that are subject to unpredictable food shortages. Why? One possibility is that the folktales reflect reality; after all, a serious drought may seem capricious, not possibly provoked by any human activity, brought on by the gods or nature "out of the blue." Curiously, however, societies with a history of unpredictable food shortages hardly mention natural disasters in their folktales, perhaps because disasters are too frightening. In any case, the capriciousness of unpredictable disasters seems to be transformed into the capricious aggression of characters in the folktales.[34]

Folklore, just like other aspects of art, may at least partly reflect the feelings, needs, and conflicts that people acquire as a result of growing up in their culture.

VIEWING THE ART OF OTHER CULTURES

Sally Price raised some critical questions about how Western museums and art critics look at the visual art of less complex cultures. Why is it that when artworks from Western or Oriental civilizations are displayed in a museum here, they carry the artist's name? In contrast, art from less complex cultures, often labeled "primitive art," tends to be displayed without the name of the artist; instead, it is often accompanied by a description of where it came from, how it was constructed, and what it may be used for. More words of explanation seem to accompany displays of unfamiliar art. Price suggested that the art pieces that we consider the most worthy require the least labeling, subtly conveying that the viewer needs no help to judge a real work of art.[35] In addition, art acquired from less complex cultures tends to be labeled by the name of the Westerner who acquired it. It is almost as if the fame of the collector, not the art itself, sets the value of such art.[36]

Just as the art from less complex cultures tends to be nameless, it also tends to be treated as timeless. We recognize that Western art and the art from classical civilizations change over time, which is why it must be dated, but the art from other places seems to be viewed as representing a timeless cultural tradition.[37] Do we know that the art of peoples with simpler technology changes less, or is this assumption a kind of ethnocentrism? Price, who has studied the art of the Saramakas of Suriname, points out that

Navajo rugs have changed over time. On the left are rugs from 1905; on the right, rugs from a modern trading post.

although Westerners think of Saramakan art as still representing its African ancestry, Saramakans themselves can identify shifts in their art styles over time. For example, they describe how calabashes used to be decorated on the outside, then the style changed to decorating the inside. They can also recognize the artist who made particular carved calabashes as well as identify those who were innovators of designs and techniques.[38]

When Westerners do notice changes over time in the art of less complex societies, it seems to be because they are concerned about whether the art represents traditional forms or is "tourist art." Tourist art is often evaluated negatively, perhaps because of its association with money. But famous Western artists often also worked for fees or were supported by elite patrons, and yet the fact that they were paid does not seem to interfere with our evaluation of their art.[39]

Although it seems that individual artists can usually be recognized in any community, some societies do appear to be more "communal" than others in their art style. For example, let us compare the Puebloan peoples of the Southwest with native peoples of the Great Plains. Traditionally, women Puebloan potters did not sign their pots, and they largely followed their pueblo's characteristic style. In contrast, each Plains warrior stressed his individual accomplishments by painting representations of those accomplishments on animal hides. Either the warrior would do it himself or he would ask someone else to do it for him. These hides were worn by the warrior or displayed outside his tipi.[40]

ARTISTIC CHANGE AND CULTURE CONTACT

It is unquestionably true that contact with the West did alter some aspects of the art of other cultures, but that does not imply that their art was changeless before. What kinds of things changed with contact? In some places, artists began to represent European contact itself. For example, in Australia, numerous rock paintings by aborigines portray sailing ships, men on horseback carrying pistols, and even cattle brands. With encouragement from Europeans,

indigenous artists also began drawing on tree bark, canvas, and fiberboard to sell to Europeans. Interestingly, the art for sale mostly emphasizes themes displayed before contact and does not include representations of ships and guns.[41] As aboriginal populations were decimated by European contact, a lot of their traditional art forms disappeared, particularly legends and rock paintings that were associated with the sacred sites of each clan. The legends described the creation of the sacred places, and art motifs with painted human or animal heroes marked the sites.[42]

In North America, contact between native groups produced changes in art even before the Europeans came. Copper, sharks' teeth, and marine shells were traded extensively in precontact times and were used in the artwork of people who did not have access to those materials locally. Ceremonies were borrowed among groups, and with the new ceremonies came changes in artistic traditions. Borrowing from other native groups continued after European contact. The Navajo, who are well known today for their rug weaving, were not weavers in the 17th century. They probably obtained their weaving technology from the Hopi and then began to weave wool and herd sheep. European contact also produced material changes in art; new materials, including beads, wool cloth, and silver, were introduced. Metal tools such as needles and scissors could now be used to make more tailored and more decorated skin clothing. In the Northwest, the greater availability of metal tools made it possible to make larger totem poles and house posts.[43]

After they were placed on reservations, virtually all Native Americans had to change their ways of making a living. Selling arts and crafts earned some of them supplementary income. Most of these crafts used traditional techniques and traditional designs, altered somewhat to suit European expectations. Outsiders played important roles in encouraging changes in arts and crafts. Some storekeepers became patrons to particular artists who were then able to devote themselves full time to their craft. Traders would often encourage changes, such as new objects—for example, ashtrays and cups made of pottery. Scholars have played a role too. Some have helped artisans learn about styles of the past that had disappeared. For example, with the encouragement of anthropologists and others in the Santa Fe area,

Maria and Julian Martinez of San Ildefonso Pueblo brought back a polished black-on-black pottery style originally produced by nearby ancient peoples.[44]

Some of the artistic changes that have occurred after contact with the West are partly predictable from the results of cross-cultural research on artistic variation. Remember that Fischer found that egalitarian societies typically had less complex designs and more symmetry than did stratified societies. With the loss of traditional ways of making a living and with the increase in wage labor and commercial enterprises, many Native American groups have become more socially stratified. Extrapolating from Fischer's results, we would predict that designs on visual art should become more complex and asymmetrical as social stratification increases. Indeed, if early reservation art (1870–1901) among the Shoshone-Bannock of southeastern Idaho is compared with their recent art (1973–1983), it is clear that the art has become more complex as social stratification has increased.[45] It could also be true that the art changed because the artists came to realize that more asymmetry and complexity would sell better to people who collect art.

SUMMARY ● ○ ○

1. Not all societies have a word for art, but art universally seems to have several qualities. It expresses as well as communicates. It stimulates the senses, affects emotions, and evokes ideas. It is produced in culturally patterned ways and styles. It has cultural meaning. And some people are thought to be better at it than others.

2. All societies decorate or adorn the body, temporarily or permanently. But there is enormous cultural variation in the parts decorated and how. Body decoration may be used to delineate social position, gender, or occupation. It may also have an erotic significance, as, for example, in drawing attention to erogenous zones of the body.

3. The materials used to produce visual art, the way those materials are used, and the natural objects the artist may choose to represent all vary from society to society and reveal much about a particular society's relation to its environment. Some studies indicate a correlation between artistic design and social stratification.

4. Like the visual arts, music is subject to a remarkable amount of variation from society to society. Some studies suggest correlations between musical styles and cultural complexity. Other research shows links between childrearing practices and a society's preference for certain rhythmical patterns, tonal ranges, and voice quality.

5. Folklore is a broad category including all the myths, legends, folktales, ballads, riddles, proverbs, and superstitions of a cultural group. In general, folklore is transmitted orally, but it may also be written. Some anthropologists have identified basic themes in myths—catastrophe, slaying of monsters, incest, sibling rivalry, and castration. Myths may reflect a society's deepest preoccupations.

6. Art is always changing, but recent culture contact has had some profound effects on art in various parts of the world. With the decimation of many indigenous populations, many areas have lost some of their artistic traditions. But the art also changed as individuals began to sell arts and crafts.

GLOSSARY TERMS ○ ● ○

folklore   472   polyphony   470

CRITICAL QUESTIONS ○ ○ ●

1. How innovative or original can a successful artist be? Explain your answer.

2. What kind of art do you prefer, and why?

3. Do you think art made for tourists is inferior? Whatever you think, why do you think so?

PEARSON myanthrolab

Read the chapter by Donald Mitchell titled "Nimpkish: Complex Foragers on the Northwest Coast of North America" on MyAnthroLab, and answer the following questions:

1. The art form of dance was important to the Nimpkish. Why do you think?

2. In what season were the dances held, and why do you think they occurred then?

chapter 27

Applied, Practicing, and Medical Anthropology

nthropology is no longer a merely academic subject. A large number of anthropologists in the United States are applied and practicing anthropologists. Some estimates suggest that more than half of those with graduate degrees in anthropology are now employed outside of colleges and universities.[1] The fact that so many organizations hire anthropologists suggests an increasing realization that anthropology, what it has discovered and can discover about humans, is useful. Anthropologists who call themselves applied or practicing anthropologists work for a large variety of organizations, government agencies, international development agencies, private consulting firms, public health organizations, medical schools, public interest law firms, community development agencies, charitable foundations, and profit-seeking corporations (see the box on anthropology and business).

● ○ ●

Applied or **practicing anthropology** as a profession is explicitly concerned with making anthropological knowledge useful. Applied or practicing anthropologists may be involved in one or more phases of a project: assembling relevant knowledge, developing plans and policies, assessing the likely social and environmental impacts, implementation, and evaluating the project and its effects.[2] Anthropologists are most often involved in gathering information, rather than constructing policy or initiating action.[3] The organizations that hire the applied anthropologists usually set policy and have staff to execute projects. However, anthropologists are increasingly finding themselves involved in policy making and action. The field of applied or practicing anthropology is very diverse. In this chapter, we first focus on general issues: ethics; evaluating the effects of planned change; and the difficulties of implementing change. In the course of this discussion, we cover a variety of projects, mostly development projects. We then turn to several other kinds of applications: *cultural resource management*, the "social impact" studies required in connection with many government or private programs, and *forensic anthropology*—the use of physical anthropology to help identify human remains and assist in solving crimes. The chapter concludes with an extensive discussion of the application of anthropological knowledge to the study of health and illness. In the chapter that follows, we describe how anthropology has been, or could be, used to solve global problems.

ETHICS OF APPLIED ANTHROPOLOGY

Anthropologists have usually studied people who are disadvantaged—by imperialism, colonialism, and other forms of exploitation—and so it is no wonder that we care about the people's lives we have shared. But caring is not enough to improve others' lives. We may need basic research that allows us to understand how a condition might be successfully treated. A particular proposed "improvement" might actually not be an improvement; well-meaning efforts have sometimes produced harmful consequences. And even if we know that a change would be an improvement, there is still the problem of how to make

As part of a study funded by USAID, a multidisciplinary team consisting of anthropologists, engineers and agricultural experts from the United States met with villagers in Senegal to assess how the Manantali Dam might affect them.

that change happen. The people to be affected may not want to change. Is it ethical to try to persuade them? And, conversely, is it ethical *not* to try? Applied anthropologists must take all of these matters into consideration in determining whether and how to act in response to a perceived need.

Anthropology as a profession has adopted certain principles of responsibility. Above all, an anthropologist's first responsibility is to those who are being studied; everything should be done to ensure that their welfare and dignity will be protected. Anthropologists also have a responsibility to those who will read about their research; research findings should be reported openly and truthfully.[4] But because applied anthropology often deals with planning and implementing changes in some population, ethical responsibilities can become complicated. Perhaps the most important ethical question is: Will the change truly benefit the potentially affected population?

In May 1946, the Society for Applied Anthropology established a committee to draw up a specific code of ethics for professional applied anthropologists. After many meetings and revisions, a statement on ethical responsibilities was finally adopted in 1948, and in 1983, the statement was revised.[5] According to the code, the targeted community should be included as much as possible in the formulation of policy,

so that people in the community may know in advance how the program will affect them. Perhaps the most important aspect of the code is the pledge not to recommend or take any action that is harmful to the interests of the community. The National Association for the Practice of Anthropology goes further: If the work the employer expects of the employee violates the ethical principles of the profession, the practicing anthropologist has the obligation to try to change those practices or, if change cannot be brought about, to withdraw from the work.[6]

Ethical issues are often complicated. Thayer Scudder described the situation of Gwembe Tonga villagers who were relocated after a large dam was built in the Zambezi Valley of central Africa. Economic conditions improved during the 1960s and early 1970s, as the people increasingly produced goods and services for sale. But then conditions deteriorated. By 1980, the villagers were in a miserable state; rates of mortality, alcoholism, theft, assault, and murder were up. Why? One reason was that they had cut back on producing their own food in favor of producing for the world market. Such a strategy works well when world market prices are high; however, when prices fall, so does the standard of living.[7] The situation described by Scudder illustrates the ethical dilemma for many

479

applied anthropology

Anthropology and Business

Only relatively recently have business-people come to realize that anthropologists have useful knowledge to contribute, particularly with regard to the globalization of trade, the increase in international investments and joint ventures, and the spread of multinational corporations. What can anthropology offer? One of the most important contributions of anthropology is the understanding of how much culture can influence relationships between people of different cultures. For example, anthropologists know that communication is much more than the formal understanding of another language. People in some countries, such as the United States, expect explicit, straightforward verbal messages, but people in other countries are more indirect in their verbal messages. In Japan and China, for example, negative messages are less likely than messages expressing politeness and harmony. Many Eastern cultures have ways of saying no without saying the word.

It is also important to understand that different cultures may have different values. People in the United States place a high value on the individual, but as we discussed in the chapter on culture and the individual, the importance of relationships with others may take precedence over individual needs in other places. People in the United States emphasize the future, youth, informality, and competitiveness, but the emphases in other societies are often the opposite. In any business arrangement, perhaps no difference is as salient as the value a culture places on time. As we say, "Time is money." If a meeting is arranged and the other person is late, say, 45 minutes, people from the United States consider it rude; but such a delay is well within the range of acceptable behavior in many South American countries.

Anthropologists have helped businesses become aware of their own "cultures" (sometimes referred to as *organizational cultures*). The organizational culture of a business may interfere with the acceptance of new kinds of workers, or it may interfere with changing business needs. If parts of that culture need to be changed, it is necessary first to identify what the culture involves and to understand how and why it developed the way it did. Anthropologists know how to identify cultural patterns on the basis of systematic observation and interviewing individuals.

Anthropologist Jill Kleinberg studied six Japanese-owned firms in the United States to understand the impact of both the larger culture and the organizational culture of the workplace. All six firms employed both Japanese and Americans, although the Japanese dominated the managerial positions. The main goal of the study was to discover why there was considerable tension in the six firms. Kleinberg's first order of business was to interview people about their views of work and their jobs. She found clear differences between the Japanese and the American employees that seemed to reflect broader cultural differences. Americans wanted a clear definition of the job and its attached responsibilities, and they also wanted their job titles, authority, rights, and pay to match closely. The Japanese, on the other hand, emphasized the need to be flexible in their responsibilities as well as their tasks. They also felt that part of their responsibility was to help their co-workers. (See the box "Schools: Values and Expectations" in the chapter on culture and the individual, in which we discussed Japanese preschools and their emphasis on the good of the group.) Americans were uncomfortable because the Japanese managers did not indicate exactly what the workers were supposed to do; even if there was a job description, the manager did not appear to pay attention to it. Americans were given little information, were left out of decision making, and were frustrated by the lack of

opportunity to advance. The Japanese thought that the Americans were too hard to manage, too concerned with money and authority, and too concerned with their own interests.

Dissatisfaction is a problem in any business. Absenteeism, high turnover, and lack of incentive on the job all detract from job performance and business capability. Kleinberg recommended giving all employees more information about the company as well as conducting training sessions about cross-cultural differences in business cultures. She also recommended making the Japanese philosophy of management more explicit during the hiring process so that the company would be able to find Americans who were comfortable with that philosophy. But she also suggested that the managerial structure be somewhat "Americanized" so that American employees could feel at ease. Finally, she recommended that Americans be given more managerial positions and contact with their Japanese counterparts overseas. These suggestions might not eliminate all problems, but they would increase mutual understanding and trust.

In a way, then, as Andrew Miracle notes, the work of the practicing anthropologist is similar to the shaman's in traditional societies. The people who call on shamans for help believe in their abilities to help, and the shaman tries to find ways to empower the client to think positively. To be sure, there are profound differences between shamans and applied anthropologists. Perhaps the most important is that applied anthropologists use research, not trance or magic, to effect an organizational cure. Like shamans, however, applied anthropologists must make an understandable diagnosis and help clients see the way to health and restored power.

Sources: Ferraro 2002; Kleinberg 1994; Miracle 2009.

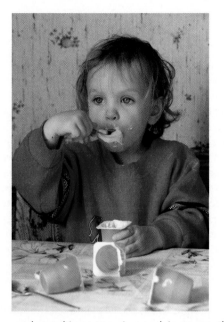

Businesses and consulting companies are doing more ethnographic research. Such research in the United States among families during the morning suggests that "breakfast" has become an intermittent series of snacks throughout the morning as families struggle with their time schedules and finding the right foods for their children.

applied anthropologists. As he said: "So how is it that I can still justify working for the agencies that fund such projects?" He points out that large-scale projects are almost impossible to stop. The anthropologist can choose to stand on the sidelines and complain or try to influence the project to benefit the affected population as much as possible.[8]

The problem described by Scudder comes about in part because the anthropologist is not often involved until after a decision is made to go ahead with a change program. This situation has begun to change as applied anthropologists are increasingly asked to participate in earlier stages of the planning process. Anthropologists are also increasingly asked to help in projects initiated by the affected party. Such requests may range from help in solving problems in corporate organizations to helping Native Americans with land claims. Because the project is consistent with the wishes of the affected population, the results are not likely to put the anthropologist into an ethical dilemma.

When physical anthropologists and archaeologists work with skeletal and even fossil materials, the ethical complications can become extremely complex. Consider the case of "Kennewick Man," a 9,200-year-old skeleton found in July 1996, along the Columbia River in Washington State. Before anthropologists could study the skeleton, the U.S. Army Corps of Engineers decided to turn the remains over to the Umatilla Indians, as the remains were found on Corps land within their reservation. The physical anthropologists and archaeologists who wanted to study this very old skeleton faced an ethical quandary: A group claiming to be related to the individual did not

want the study to be undertaken, but, without the study, the group's claim of relationship could not be firmly established.[9] The physical anthropologists and archaeologists filed a lawsuit under the Native American Graves Protection and Repatriation Act of 1900, which provides absolute protection to Native American graves on federal land, and which makes it a felony to collect, possess, or transfer human remains of known affinity to an existing Native American culture, except if approved by the members of that culture.[10]

At the core of the legal case was this question: To whom does this skeleton belong? If this is an individual who is related to contemporary Native Americans, then do the Umatilla get to speak for all Native American groups, even though 9,000 years separate them? Or should other Native American groups, who may also be descended from this individual or his group, also have a say in what happens? If this is an individual who appears not to be related to contemporary Native Americans, then should the U.S. government decide what happens to his remains? Underlying these questions was a deeper struggle between anthropologists and Native Americans over historic preservation and whose wishes and ideas carry the most weight. Archaeologists and physical anthropologists feel ethical responsibilities that can be in conflict when dealing with human remains. As part of the archaeological record, archaeologists and physical anthropologists have an ethical responsibility to protect and preserve human remains. As anthropologists, they have the ethical responsibility to consult with and follow the wishes of local groups with whom they are working. The "Kennewick Man" case highlights this ethical conflict, for which there seems no easy answer.

EVALUATING THE EFFECTS OF PLANNED CHANGE

The decision as to whether a proposed change would benefit the affected population is not always easy to make. In certain cases, as when improved medical care is involved, the benefits offered to the target group would seem to be unquestionable—we all feel sure that health is better than illness. However, what about the long-term effects? Consider a public health innovation such as inoculation against disease. Once the inoculation program was begun, the number of children surviving would probably increase. But will there be enough food for the additional population? Given the level of technology, capital, and land resources possessed by the population, there might not be enough resources to feed more people. Thus, the death rate, because of starvation, might rise to its previous level and perhaps even exceed it. Without additional changes to increase the food supply, the inoculation program in the long term might merely change the causes of death. This example shows that, even if a program of planned change has beneficial consequences in the short run, a great deal of thought and investigation has to be given to its long-term effects.

Debra Picchi raised questions about the long-term effects on the Bakairí Indians of a program by the Brazilian National Indian Foundation (FUNAI) to produce rice with machine technology.[11] The Bakairí of the Mato Grosso region largely practice slash-and-burn horticulture in gallery forests along rivers, with supplementary cattle raising, fishing, and hunting. In the early part of the 20th century, their population had declined to 150 people and they were given a relatively small reserve, much of it parched and infertile (*cerrado*). When the Bakairí population began to increase, FUNAI introduced a scheme to plant rice on formerly unused *cerrado* land, using machinery, insecticides, and fertilizer. FUNAI paid the costs for the first year and expected that the scheme would be self-supporting by the third year. The project did not go so well because FUNAI did not deliver all the equipment needed and did not provide adequate advice. Only half the expected rice was produced. Still, it was more food than the Bakairí had previously, so the program should have been beneficial to them.

But there were unanticipated negative side effects. Using *cerrado* land for agriculture reduced the area on which cattle could be grazed; cattle are an important source of high-quality protein. Mechanization also makes the Bakairí more dependent on cash for fuel, insecticides, fertilizer, and repairs. But cash is hard to come by. Only some individuals can be hired—usually men with outside experience who have the required knowledge of machinery. So the cash earned in the now-mechanized agriculture goes mainly to a relatively small number of people, creating new inequalities of income.

The benefits of programs or applied efforts are sometimes obvious. For example, Haiti has experienced serious deforestation. The process began in colonial times when the Spanish exported wood and the French cleared forests to grow sugarcane, coffee, and indigo. After Haiti's independence, foreign lumber companies continued to cut and sell hardwood. Wood is needed by the local population for fuel and for construction, but rapid population increases have increased the demand for fuel and wood, and the trees were rapidly diminishing. The loss of tree cover also speeds up erosion of topsoil. Forestry experts, environmentalists, and anthropologists all agree about the need to stop this trend. How to bring about the appropriate change is not so easy. The poorer people become, the more likely they are to cut down trees to sell.[12]

These failures were not the fault of anthropologists—indeed, most instances of planned change by governments and other agencies usually have begun without the input of anthropologists at all. Applied anthropologists have played an important role in pointing out the problems with programs like these that fail to evaluate long-term consequences. Such evaluations are an important part of convincing governments and other agencies to ask for anthropological help in the first place. Ironically, failure experiences are learning experiences: Applied anthropologists who study previous examples of planned change can often learn a great deal about what is likely or not likely to be beneficial in the long run.

DIFFICULTIES IN INSTITUTING PLANNED CHANGE

After numerous reforestation projects failed in Haiti, an anthropologist, Gerald Murray, was asked to help design a program that would work.[13] Understanding why previous projects failed was the first step in helping Murray design an effective project. One problem seems to have been that previous projects were run through the government's Ministry of Agriculture. The seedling trees that were given away were referred to as "the state's trees." So, when project workers told farmers not to cut the new trees down so as to protect the environment, farmers took this statement to mean that the land on which the trees were planted might be considered government land, which the farmers could not care less about. In the project proposed by Murray, private voluntary organizations rather than the Haitian government were used to distribute trees and the farmers were told that they were the tree owners. Ownership included the right to cut the trees and sell the wood, just as they could sell crops. In previous projects, farmers were given heavy, hard-to-transport seedlings that took a long time to mature. They were told to plant in a large communal woodlot, an idea inconsistent with the more individualistic Haitian land tenure arrangements. In the new plan, the tree seedlings given away were fast-growing species that matured in as little as four years. In addition, the new seedlings were very small and could be planted quickly. Perhaps most important of all, the new trees could be planted in borders or interspersed with other crops, interfering little with traditional crop patterns. To Murray's great surprise, by the end of two years, 2,500 Haitian households had planted 3 million seedlings. Over 20 years, the estimate is that over a 100 million trees were planted and over 350,000 farm families were involved in the project, more than 40 percent of rural households.[14] Also, farmers were not rushing to cut down trees. Because growing trees do not spoil, farmers were postponing their cutting and sales until they needed cash. So even though farmers were told that it was all right to cut down trees, a statement contrary to the message of previous reforestation projects, the landscape was filling up with trees.

People cut down trees in Haiti for firewood and to clear fields, resulting in severe deforestation. The need for reforestation is clear, but how to bring about change was not so clear.

Murray's lengthy participant observation and interviewing had helped him predict what might overcome the previous implementation difficulties and fit in with the Haitian farmers' needs. The idea that wood could be an important marketable cash crop was much more consistent with farmers' existing behavior—they already sold crops for cash when they needed it. The difference now was that, instead of cutting down naturally grown wood, they were raising wood just as they raised other crops.

Whether a program of planned change can be successfully implemented depends largely on whether the people want the proposed change and like the proposed program. Before an attempt can be made at cultural innovation, the innovators must determine whether the population is aware of the benefits of the proposed change. Lack of awareness can be a temporary barrier to solving the problem at hand. For example, health workers have often had difficulty convincing people that they were becoming ill because something was wrong with their water supply. Many people do not believe that disease can be transmitted by water. At other times, the population is perfectly aware of the problem. A case in point involved Taiwanese women who were introduced to family-planning methods beginning in the 1960s. The women knew they were having more children than they wanted or could easily afford, and they wanted to control their birth rate. They offered no resistance—they merely had to be given the proper devices and instructions, and the birth rate quickly fell to a more desirable, and more manageable, level.[15]

Overcoming Resistance

Many change projects experience resistance, and most of the time the change agents try to figure out how to overcome the resistance. But not all proposed change programs are beneficial to the recipients. Sometimes resistance is rational. Applied anthropologists have pointed to cases where the judgment of the affected population has been better than that of the agents of change. One such example occurred during a Venezuelan government–sponsored program to give infants powdered milk. The mothers rejected the milk, even though it was free, on the grounds that it implied that the mothers' milk was no good.[16] But who is to say that the resistance was not in fact intuitively smart, reflecting an awareness that such a milk program would not benefit the children? Medical research now indicates quite clearly that mothers' milk is far superior to powdered milk or formula. First, human milk best supplies the nutrients needed for human development. Second, it is now known that the mother, through her milk, is able to transmit antibodies (disease resistances) to the baby. And third, nursing delays ovulation and usually increases the spacing between births.[17]

The switchover to powdered milk and formula in many underdeveloped areas has been nothing short of a disaster, resulting in increased malnutrition and misery. For one thing, powdered milk must be mixed with water, but if the water and the bottles are not sterilized, more sickness is introduced. Then, too, if powdered milk has to be purchased, mothers without cash are forced to dilute the milk to stretch it. And if a mother feeds her baby formula or powder for even a short time, the process is tragically irreversible, for her own milk dries up and she cannot return to breast-feeding even if she wants to.

As the Venezuelan example suggests, individuals may be able to resist proposed medical or health projects because acceptance is ultimately a personal matter. Large development projects planned by powerful governments or agencies rarely are stoppable, but even they can be resisted successfully. The Kayapo of the Xingu River region of Brazil were able to cancel a plan by the Brazilian government to build dams along the river for hydroelectric power. The Kayapo gained international attention when some of their leaders appeared on North American and European television and then successfully organized a protest in 1989, by members of several tribal groups. Their success seemed to come in part from their ability to present themselves to the international community as guardians of the rain forest—an image that resonated with international environmental organizations that supported their cause. Although to outsiders it might seem that the Kayapo want their way of life to remain as it was, the Kayapo are not opposed to all change. In fact, they want greater access to medical care, other government services, and manufactured goods from outside.[18]

Even if a project is beneficial to a population, it may still meet with resistance, as the tree reforestation project in Haiti illustrated. Factors that may hinder acceptance can be divided roughly into three, sometimes overlapping, categories: *cultural, social,* and *psychological* barriers.

Cultural barriers are shared behaviors, attitudes, and beliefs that tend to impede the acceptance of an innovation. For example, members of different societies may view gift giving in different ways. Particularly in commercialized societies, things received for nothing are often believed to be worthless. When the government of Colombia instituted a program of giving seedling orchard trees to

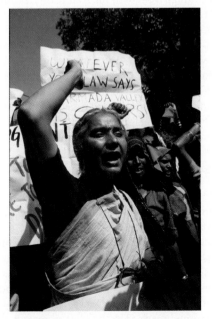

Medha Patkar leading a protest rally in New Delhi against Narmada dams.

farmers to increase fruit production, the farmers showed virtually no interest in the seedlings, many of which proceeded to die of neglect. When the government realized that the experiment had apparently failed, it began to charge each farmer a nominal fee for the seedlings. Soon the seedlings became immensely popular and fruit production increased.[19] Other examples of cultural resistance to change, which we discuss more when we discuss medical anthropology, are beliefs about sex that make it difficult for people to follow medical guidelines for safer sex.

It is very important for agents of change to understand what the shared beliefs and attitudes are. First, indigenous cultural concepts or knowledge can sometimes be used effectively to enhance educational programs. For instance, in a program in Haiti to prevent child mortality from diarrhea, change agents used the terminology for traditional native herbal tea remedies (*rafrechi*, or cool refreshment) to identify the new oral rehydration therapy, which is a very successful medical treatment. In native belief, diarrhea is a "hot" illness and appropriate remedies have to have cooling properties.[20] Second, even if indigenous beliefs are not helpful to the campaign, not paying attention to contrary beliefs can undermine the campaign. But uncovering contrary beliefs is not easy, particularly when they do not emerge in ordinary conversation.

The acceptance of planned change may also depend on social factors. Research suggests that acceptance is more likely if the change agent and the target or potential adopter are similar socially. But change agents may have higher social status and more education than the people they are trying to influence. So change agents may work more with higher-status individuals because they are more likely to accept new ideas. If lower-status individuals also have to be reached, change agents of lower status may have to be employed.[21]

Finally, acceptance may depend on psychological factors—that is, how the individuals perceive both the innovation and the agents of change. In the course of trying to encourage women in the southeastern United States to breast-feed rather than bottle-feed their infants, researchers discovered a number of reasons why women were reluctant to breast-feed their infants, even though they heard it was healthier. Many women did not have confidence that they would produce enough milk for their babies; they were embarrassed about breast-feeding in public; and their family and friends had negative attitudes.[22] In designing an educational program, change agents may have to address such psychological concerns directly.

Discovering and Utilizing Local Channels of Influence

In planning a project involving cultural change, the administrator of the project should find out what the normal channels of influence are in the population. In most communities, there are preestablished networks for communication, as well as people of high prestige or influence who are looked to for guidance and direction. An understanding of such channels of influence is extremely valuable when deciding how to introduce a program of change. In addition, it is useful to know at what times, and in what

sorts of situations, one channel is likely to be more effective in spreading information and approval than another.

An example of the effective use of local channels of influence occurred when an epidemic of smallpox broke out in the Kalahandi district of the state of Orissa in India. The efforts of health workers to vaccinate villagers against the disease were consistently resisted. The villagers, naturally suspicious and fearful of these strange men with their equally strange medical equipment, were unwilling to offer themselves, and particularly their babies, to the peculiar experiments the strangers wished to perform. Afraid of the epidemic, the villagers appealed for help to their local priest, whose opinions on such matters they trusted. The priest went into a trance, explaining that the illness was the result of the goddess Thalerani's anger with the people. She could be appeased, he continued, only by massive feasts, offerings, and other demonstrations of the villagers' worship of her. Realizing that the priest was the village's major opinion leader, at least in medical matters, the frustrated health workers tried to get the priest to convince his people to undergo vaccination. At first, the priest refused to cooperate with the strange men, but when his favorite nephew fell ill, he decided to try any means available to cure the boy. He thereupon went into another trance, telling the villagers that the goddess wished all her worshipers to be vaccinated. Fortunately, the people agreed, and the epidemic was largely controlled.[23]

If channels of influence are not stable, using influential people in a campaign can sometimes backfire. In the educational campaign in Haiti to promote the use of oral rehydration therapy to treat diarrhea in children, Madame Duvalier, the first lady of Haiti at the time, lent her name to the project. Because there were no serious social or cultural barriers to the treatment and mothers reported that children took to the solutions well, success was expected. But in the middle of the campaign, Haiti became embroiled in political turmoil and the first lady's husband was overthrown. Some of the public thought that the oral rehydration project was a plot by the Duvaliers to sterilize children, and this suspicion fueled resistance.[24] As the earlier discussion of Haiti deforestation shows, people in Haiti were suspicious of any government-sponsored program.

Applied anthropologists often advocate integrating indigenous healers into medical change programs. This idea may encounter considerable resistance by the medical profession and by government officials who view such healers negatively. But this strategy may be quite effective in more isolated areas where indigenous healers are the only sources of health care. If they are involved in medical change programs, indigenous healers are likely to refer patients to hospitals when they feel unable to cope with an illness, and the hospitals choose sometimes to refer patients to the healers.[25]

Need for More Collaborative Applied Anthropology

Most large-scale programs of planned change originate with governments, international aid organizations, or other agencies. Even if the programs are well intentioned and even if the appropriate evaluations are made to ensure that the population will not be harmed, the population targeted for the change is usually not involved in the decision making. Some anthropologists, like Wayne Warry, think that applied anthropology should be more collaborative. Warry explains that he was asked by a Native Canadian elder whether he (Warry) would tolerate his own methods and interpretations if he were the native.[26] This question prompted him to involve himself in a project with Native Canadian collaborators, directed by the Mamaweswen Tribal Council. The project assesses health care needs and develops plans to improve local community health care. Funding is provided by the Canadian government as part of a program to transfer health care to the First Nations. Native researchers are conducting the surveys and workshops to keep the community informed about the project. The tribal council also reviews any publications and shares in any profits resulting from those publications.

Applied anthropologists may be increasingly asked to work on behalf of indigenous grassroots organizations. As we saw in the chapter on associations, the developing world has seen a proliferation of such groups. In some cases, these small groups and networks of such groups are starting to hire their own technical assistance.[27] When such organizations do the hiring, they control the decision making. There is increasing evidence that grassroots organizations are the key to effective development. For example, Kenyan farmers who belong to grassroots organizations produce higher farm yields than those farmers who do not belong, even though the latter group is exposed to more agricultural extension agents.[28] Grassroots organizations can succeed where government or outside projects fail. We have plenty of instances of people effectively resisting projects. Their willingness to change, and their participation in crucial decision making, may be mostly responsible for the success of a change project.

There is another kind of collaboration that is becoming increasingly important. Many projects require team efforts, working with people from other disciplines. Anthropologists increasingly have to be conversant with the theory and methods in other fields to understand and negotiate with other members of their team. Earlier anthropologists might have been more likely to work alone. Now that is less likely.[29]

Commuters look at 4th century ruins uncovered as part of a large scale CRM project associated with construction of the Athens metro system.

CULTURAL RESOURCE MANAGEMENT

Large-scale programs of planned change like those discussed earlier in this chapter have an impact not only on living people. They can also have an impact on the archaeological record left by the ancestors of living people. Recovering and preserving the archaeological record before programs of planned change disturb or destroy it is called **cultural resource management (CRM).** CRM work is carried out by archaeologists who are often called "contract archaeologists" because they typically work under contract to a government agency, a private developer, or a native group.

What kinds of impact can programs of planned change have on the archaeological record? In the 1960s, a large number of hydroelectric dam projects were initiated to provide flood control and to bring a stable source of electrical power to developing nations. In Egypt, a dam was built on the Nile River at a site called Aswan. Archaeologists realized that once the dam was in place a huge lake would form behind it, submerging thousands of archaeological sites, including the massive temple of Rameses II. Something needed to be done; the archaeological record had to be salvaged or protected. In the language of CRM, there needed to be a *mitigation plan* put into action. And there was. As the Aswan dam was being built, archaeologists went to work excavating sites that would be flooded. Archaeologists and engineers designed a way to take apart the temple of Rameses II and rebuild it, piece by piece, on higher ground where it would not be flooded. By the time the dam was completed in 1965, hundreds of sites had been investigated and two entire temple complexes moved.

Large-scale development projects are not the only projects that involve CRM archaeologists. In many nations, including the United States and Canada, historic preservation laws require any project receiving federal funds to ensure that archaeological resources are protected or their damage mitigated. Highway construction projects in the United States are common places to find CRM archaeologists at work. Virtually all highway projects rely on federal funding, and before a highway can be built, a complete archaeological survey of the proposed right-of-way has to be made. If archaeological sites are found, potential damage to them must be mitigated. A CRM archaeologist will work with the construction company, the state archaeologist, and perhaps a federal archaeologist to decide on the best course of action. In some cases, the archaeological site will be excavated. In others, the right-of-way may be moved. In still others, the decision is to allow the archaeological site to be destroyed, because it would be too costly to excavate or the site may not be significant enough to warrant excavation. Regardless of the decision, the CRM archaeologist plays a crucial role in assessing and protecting the archaeological record.

CRM archaeologists do not work only for state or federal agencies. In many nations today, CRM archaeologists are also working with native peoples to protect, preserve, and manage archaeological materials for them. Indeed, archaeologist John Ravesloot recently stated that "the future of American archaeology is with Indian communities functioning as active, not passive, participants in the

A forensic anthropologist digs out a body, apparently a victim of state-sponsored violence in Argentina between 1976 and 1983.

interpretation, management, and preservation of their rich cultural heritage."[30] One example of such a working relationship is the Zuni Heritage and Historic Preservation Office. During the 1970s, the Pueblo of Zuni decided it needed to train tribal members in archaeology to ensure that Zuni cultural resources and properties were managed properly. It hired three professional archaeologists and, with additional assistance from the National Park Service and the Arizona State Museum, initiated a program to train and employ tribal members in cultural resource management. Working with these non-Zuni archaeologists, the Pueblo of Zuni were able to establish their own historic preservation office that today manages and coordinates all historic preservation on the Zuni reservation, a task that the federal government managed until 1992. The Pueblo also established the Zuni Cultural Resource Enterprise, a Zuni-owned CRM business that employs both Zuni and non-Zuni archaeologists and carries out contract archaeology projects both on and off the Zuni reservation.[31]

Cultural resource management accounts for the majority of archaeology jobs in the United States.[32] As development and construction projects continue to affect the archaeological record, the need for well-trained CRM archaeologists is likely to persist.

FORENSIC ANTHROPOLOGY

Many of us are fascinated by detective stories. We are interested in crimes and why they occur, and we like to read about them, fictional or not. **Forensic anthropology** is the specialty in anthropology that is devoted to helping solve crimes and identifying human remains, usually by applying knowledge of physical anthropology.[33] It is attracting increasing attention by the public, and an increasing number of practitioners. One forensic anthropologist says she is called "the bone lady" by law enforcement personnel.[34] Like others in her line of work, she is asked to dig up or

examine human bones to help solve crimes. Narrowing down identification is one of the first priorities, but it is not as simple as on television shows. Are these the bones of a man or woman? How old was the person? How well the forensic anthropologist can answer these seemingly simple questions depends upon whether the remains include most bones of the skeleton. Identification of an adult's sex from remains is easier if the pelvis is present, but establishing sex in nonadult remains is not reliable from skeletal remains.[35] With regard to estimating age, only a wide age range can be estimated for adults, but a much narrower range can be estimated for nonadult remains. Forensic anthropologists are often asked for "race" as well. As we discussed in earlier chapters, "race" is not a useful biological category when applied to humans, but it is a significant social category. Forensic anthropologists can estimate with fairly high accuracy whether a person's ancestors came from Asia, Europe, or Africa, but they cannot detect skin color.[36] The police files may suggest that an adult male with Asian ancestry disappeared five years ago. The forensic anthropologist could say with a high probability that the remains were of an Asian male adult. Dental, surgical, or hospital records from that individual might lead to unique features that could be matched for more precise identification. Sometimes the forensic anthropologist can suggest the cause of death when the law enforcement people are stumped.

Some cultural anthropologists have also done forensic work, often in connection with legal cases involving Native Americans. For example, in 1978, Barbara Joans was asked to advise the defense in a trial of six older Bannock-Shoshoni women from the Fort Hall reservation who were accused of fraud. They had received "supplemental security income (SSI)," which the social service agency claimed they had no right to receive because they had not reported receiving rent money on land that they owned. Joans presented evidence that the women, although they spoke some English, did not have enough proficiency to understand the nuances of what the SSI people told them. The judge agreed with the defense and ruled that the SSI would have to use a Bannock-Shoshoni interpreter in the future when they went to the reservation to describe the requirements of the program.[37]

In recent years, Clyde Snow and other forensic anthropologists have been called on to confirm horrendous abuses of human rights. Governments have been responsible for the systematic killing of their citizens, and forensic anthropologists have helped to bring the perpetrators to justice. For example, Snow and other forensic anthropologists helped to confirm that the military dictatorship in Argentina in the 1980s was responsible for the deaths of many Argentine civilians who had "disappeared." The forensic anthropologists were also able to determine the location of mass graves and the identity of victims of state-organized brutality in Guatemala. In addition to bringing the perpetrators to justice, confirming the massacres and identifying the victims help the families of the "disappeared" put their anguish behind them. A special session (called "Uncovering the 'Disappeared': Clyde Snow and Forensic Anthropologists Work for Justice"[38]) at the annual meeting of the American Anthropological Association in November 2000 honored Snow and other forensic anthropologists.

MEDICAL ANTHROPOLOGY

Illness and death are significant events for people everywhere. No one is spared. So it should not be surprising that how people understand the causes of illness and death, how they behave, and what resources they marshal to cope with these events are extremely important parts of culture. Some argue that we will never completely understand how to treat illness effectively until we understand the cultural behaviors, attitudes, values, and the larger social and political milieu in which people live. Others argue that society and culture have little to do with the outcome of illness—the reason that people die needlessly is that they do not get the appropriate medical treatment.

But anthropologists, particularly those in **medical anthropology,** who are actively engaged in studying health and illness, are increasingly realizing that biological *and* social factors need to be considered if we are to reduce human suffering. For instance, some populations have an appalling incidence of infant deaths due to diarrhea. The origin of this situation is mostly biological, in the sense that the deaths are caused by bacterial infection. But why are so many infants exposed to those bacteria? Usually, the main reason is social. The affected infants are likely to be poor. Because they are poor, they are likely to live with infected drinking water. Similarly, malnutrition may be the biological result of a diet poor in protein, but such a diet is usually also a cultural phenomenon, reflecting a society with classes of people with very unequal access to the necessities of life. In many ways, therefore, medical anthropology, and anthropology in general, are developing in the direction of a "biocultural synthesis."[39]

Medical anthropology is part of this developing synthesis. Indeed, the growth of jobs in medical anthropology is one of the more striking developments in contemporary anthropology. Medical anthropology has developed into a very popular specialty, and the Society for Medical Anthropology is now the second largest unit in the American Anthropological Association.[40]

The medical profession's ways of treating illness may be able to treat some conditions well, but by itself the medical profession cannot tell us why some groups are more affected than others, or why the effectiveness of treatment varies from group to group. This section discusses cultural variation in conceptions of health and illness, cultural universals and variables in how illness is treated, the political and social forces that affect health, and contributions of medical anthropology to the study and treatment of some diseases and health conditions.

CULTURAL UNDERSTANDINGS OF HEALTH AND ILLNESS

Medical researchers and medical practitioners in the United States and other Western societies do not exist in a social vacuum. Many of their ideas and practices are influenced by the culture in which they live. We may think of medicine as purely based on "fact," but it is clear on reflection that many ideas stem from the culture in which the researchers reside. Consider the recent shift in attitudes toward birth. Not so long ago in the United States, fathers were excluded from

In China and elsewhere, tai chi exercises are believed to bring harmony and balance.

the birth, hospitals whisked the baby away from the mother and only brought the baby to her infrequently, and visitors (but not attending nurses and doctors) had to wear masks when holding the baby. Rationalizations were given for those practices, but looking back at them, they do not appear to be based on scientific evidence. Many medical anthropologists now argue that the *biomedical paradigm* (the system in which physicians are trained) itself needs to be understood as part of the culture.

Discovering the health-related beliefs, knowledge, and practices of a cultural group—its **ethnomedicine**—is one of the goals of medical anthropology. How do cultures view health and illness? What are their theories about the causes of illness? Do those theories impact on how illnesses are treated? What is the therapeutic process? Are there specialized medical practitioners, and how do they heal? Are there special medicines, and how are they administered? These are just some of the questions asked by the anthropological study of ethnomedicine.

Concepts of Balance or Equilibrium

Many cultures have the view that the body should be kept in equilibrium or balance. The balance may be between hot and cold, or wet and dry, as in many cultures of Latin America and the Caribbean.[41] The notion of balance is not limited to opposites. For example, the ancient Greek system of medicine, stemming from Hippocrates, assumed that there were four "humors"—blood, phlegm, yellow bile, and black bile—that must be kept in balance. These humors have hot and cold as well as wet and dry properties. The Greek medical system was widely diffused in Europe and spread to parts of the Islamic world. In Europe, the humoral medical system was dominant until the germ theory replaced it in the 1900s.[42] In the Ayurvedic system, whose practice dates back 4,000 years in North India, Pakistan, Bangladesh, Sri Lanka, and in the Arab world, there are three humors (phlegm, bile, and flatulence), and a balance between hot and cold is also important.[43] The Chinese medical system, which dates back about 3,500 years, initially stressed the balance between the contrasting forces of *yin* and *yang* and later added the concept of humors, which were six in number in Chinese medicine.[44]

Placebos do not just have psychological effects. Although the mechanisms are not well understood, they may also alter body chemistry and bolster the immune system.[67]

Shamans may coexist with medical doctors. Don Antonio, a respected Otomi Indian shaman in central Mexico, has many patients, perhaps not as many as before modern medicine, but still plenty. In his view, when he was born, God gave him his powers to cure, but his powers are reserved for removing "evil" illnesses (those caused by sorcerers). "Good" illnesses can be cured by herbs and medicine, and he refers patients with those illnesses to medical doctors; he believes that doctors are more effective than he could be in those cases. The doctors, however, do not seem to refer any patients to Don Antonio or other shamans.[68]

Physicians The most important full-time medical practitioner in the biomedical system is the physician, and the patient-physician relationship is central. In the ideal scheme of things, the physician is viewed as having the ability, with some limits, of being able to treat illness, alleviate suffering, and prolong the life of the patient, as well as offering promises of patient confidentiality and privacy. The patient relies on the physician's knowledge, skill, and ethics. Consistent with the biomedical paradigm, doctors tend to treat patients as having "conditions" rather than as complete people. Physicians presumably rely on science for authoritative knowledge, but they place a good deal of importance on the value of their own clinical experience. Often, physicians consider their own observations of the patient to be more valuable than the reports by the patient. Because patients commonly go to physicians to solve a particular condition or sickness, physicians tend to try to do something about it even in the face of uncertainty. Physicians tend to rely on technology for diagnoses and treatment and place relatively low value on talking with patients. In fact, physicians tend to give patients relatively little information, and they may not listen very well.[69]

Despite the importance of physicians in biomedicine, patients do not always seek physician care. In fact, one-third of the population of the United States regularly consults with alternative practitioners, such as acupuncturists or chiropractors, often unbeknownst to the physician. Somewhat surprisingly, individuals with more education are more likely to seek alternative care.[70]

POLITICAL AND ECONOMIC INFLUENCES ON HEALTH

People with more social, economic, and political power in a society are generally healthier.[71] Inequality in health in socially stratified societies is not surprising. The poor usually have more exposure to disease because they live in more crowded conditions. And the poor are more likely to lack the resources to get quality care. For many diseases, health problems, and death rates, incidence or relative frequency varies directly with social class. In the United Kingdom, for example, people in the higher social classes are less likely to have headaches, bronchitis, pneumonia, heart disease, arthritis, injuries, and mental disorders, to name just a few of the differences.[72] Ethnic differences also predict health

inequities. In South Africa under apartheid, the 14 percent minority population, referred to as "white," controlled most of the income of the country and most of the high-quality land. "Blacks" were restricted to areas with shortages of housing, inadequate housing, and little employment. To get a job, families often had to be disrupted; usually the husband would have to migrate to find work. "Blacks" lived, on average, about nine years less than "whites" in 1985, and "black" infants died at about seven times the rate of "white" infants. In the United States recently, the differences between African Americans and European Americans in health are not as stark as in South Africa, but those favoring European Americans are still substantial. As of 1987, the difference in life expectancy was seven years, and African American infant mortality was about twice the rate for European American infants. Robert Hahn has estimated that poverty accounts for about 19 percent of the overall mortality in the United States.[73]

Inequities, because of class and ethnicity, are not limited to within-society differences. Power and economic differentials *between* societies also have profound health consequences. Over the course of European exploration and expansion, indigenous peoples died in enormous numbers from introduced diseases, wars, and conquests; they had their lands expropriated and diminished in size and quality. When incorporated into colonial territories or into countries, indigenous people usually become minorities and they are almost always very poor. These conditions of life not only affect the incidence of disease, they also tend to lead to greater substance abuse, violence, depression, and other mental pathologies.[74]

HEALTH CONDITIONS AND DISEASES

Medical anthropologists have studied an enormous variety of conditions. What follows is only a small sampling.

AIDS

Epidemics of infectious disease have killed millions of people within short periods of time throughout recorded history. The Black Death—bubonic plague—killed between 25 percent and 50 percent of the population of Europe, perhaps 75 million people, during the 14th century; an epidemic during the 6th century killed an estimated 100 million people in the Middle East, Asia, and Europe. Less noted in our history books, but also devastating, was the enormous depopulation that accompanied the expansion of Europeans into the New World and the Pacific from the 1500s on. Not only were people killed directly by European conquerors, millions also died from introduced diseases to which the natives had little or no resistance, diseases such as smallpox and measles that the Europeans brought with them but were no longer dying from.

The current state of medical science and technology may lull us into thinking that epidemics are a thing of the past. But the recent and sudden emergence of the disease we call **AIDS (acquired immune deficiency syndrome)** reminds us that new diseases, or new varieties of

Millions of children in sub-Saharan Africa are orphaned because of AIDS. These orphaned children in Uganda look on during a visit by Britain's Queen Elizabeth to their center.

old diseases, can appear at any time. Like all other organisms, disease-causing organisms also evolve. The human immunodeficiency virus (HIV) that causes AIDS emerged only recently. Viruses and bacteria are always mutating, and new strains emerge that are initially a plague on our genetic resistance and on medical efforts to contain them.

Millions of people around the world already have the symptoms of AIDS, and millions more are infected with HIV but do not know they are infected. As of December 2007, 33 million adults and children in the world were living with HIV/AIDS.[75] There are a few signs of improvement since 2001. The percentage of people infected globally is now stable; some countries have improved with prevention efforts, and the number of new cases each year has gone down. However, AIDS is the major cause of death in sub-Saharan Africa and is still a leading cause of death worldwide.[76] There is still no cure. AIDS is a frightening epidemic not only because of its death toll. It is also frightening because it takes a long time (on average, four years) after exposure for symptoms to appear. This means that many people who have been infected by HIV but do not know they are infected may continue, unknowingly, to transmit the virus to others.[77]

Transmission occurs mostly via sexual encounters, through semen and blood. Drug users may also transmit HIV by way of contaminated needles. Transmission by blood transfusion has been virtually eliminated in this and other societies by medical screening of blood supplies. In many countries, however, there is still no routine screening of blood prior to transfusions. HIV may be passed from a pregnant woman to her offspring through the placenta and after birth through her breast milk. The rate of transmission between a mother and her baby is 20 percent to 40 percent. Children are also at great risk because they are likely to be orphaned by a parent's death from AIDS. At the turn of the 21st century, approximately 14 million children were parentless because of AIDS.[78]

Many people think of AIDS as only a medical problem that requires only a medical solution, without realizing

that behavioral, cultural, and political issues need to be addressed as well. It is true that developing a vaccine or a drug to prevent people from getting AIDS and finding a permanent cure for those who have it will finally solve the problem. But, for a variety of reasons, we can expect that the medical solution alone will not be sufficient, at least not for a while. First, to be effective worldwide, or even within a country, a vaccine has to be inexpensive and relatively easy to produce in large quantities; the same is true of any medical treatment. Second, governments around the world have to be willing and able to spend the money and hire the personnel necessary to manage an effective program.[79] Third, future vaccination and treatment will require the people at risk to be willing to get vaccinated and treated, which is not always the case. Witness the fact that the incidence of measles is on the rise in the United States because many people are not having their children vaccinated.

There are now expensive drug treatments that significantly reduce the degree of HIV infection, but we do not know if an effective and inexpensive vaccine or treatment will be developed soon. In the meantime, the risk of HIV infection can be reduced only by changes in social, particularly sexual, behavior. But to persuade people to change their sexual behavior, it is necessary to find out exactly what they do sexually, and why they do what they do.

Research so far suggests that different sexual patterns are responsible for HIV transmission in different parts of the world. In the United States, England, northern Europe, Australia, and Latin America, the recipients of anal intercourse, particularly men, are the most likely individuals to acquire HIV infection; vaginal intercourse can also transmit the infection, usually from the man to the woman. Needle sharing can transmit the infection, too. In Africa, the most common mode of transmission is vaginal intercourse, and so women get infected more commonly in Africa than elsewhere.[80] In fact, in Africa there are slightly more cases of HIV in women as compared with men.[81]

Some researchers are arguing that, although the immediate cause of HIV infection may be mostly related to sexual practice, larger political and social issues, such as poverty and gender inequality, increase the likelihood of such infection. For example, sexually transmitted diseases increase the risk of HIV infection three to five times, but those who are poor are less likely to get adequate treatment. And, in the developing world, rural and poorer areas are also more likely to get tainted blood transfusions. Gender inequality is likely to increase the likelihood that women have to submit to unsafe sex, and women are even less likely than men to have access to adequate medical care.[82]

As of now, there are only two known ways to reduce the likelihood of sexual HIV transmission. One way is to abstain from sexual intercourse; the other is to use condoms. Male circumcision now appears to decrease the risk of HIV infection, but studies have not yet evaluated long-term effects.[83] Educational programs that teach how AIDS spreads and what one can do about it may reduce the spread somewhat, but such programs may fail where people have incompatible beliefs and attitudes about sexuality. For example, people in some central African societies believe that deposits of semen after conception are necessary for a successful pregnancy and generally enhance a woman's health and ability to reproduce. It might be expected then that people who have these beliefs about semen would choose not to use condoms; after all, condoms in their view are a threat to public health.[84] Educational programs may also emphasize the wrong message. Promiscuity may increase the risk of HIV transmission, so hardly anyone would question the wisdom of advertising to reduce the number of sexual partners. And, at least in the homosexual community in the United States, individuals report fewer sexual partners than in the past. What was not anticipated, however, was that individuals in monogamous relationships, who may feel safe, are less likely to use condoms or to avoid the riskiest sexual practices. Needless to say, sex with a regular partner who is infected is not safe![85] In what may seem like something of a paradox, the United Nations observed that, for most women in the world today, the major risk factor for being infected with HIV is being married.[86] It is not marriage, *per se,* that heightens the risk of HIV infection; rather, the proximate cause may be the lower likelihood of condom use or less abstinence by a married couple.

The stigmas associated with AIDS also hinder efforts to reduce its spread. In some societies, there is the widespread belief that homosexual men are particularly likely to get infected.[87] In other societies, AIDS may be thought to be due to promiscuity. If a woman asks a man to use a condom, she may be assumed to be a prostitute. In addition, many people mistakenly fear even proximity to AIDS victims, as if any kind of contact could result in infection.

To solve the problem of AIDS, we may hope that medical science will develop an effective and inexpensive vaccination or treatment that all can afford. There is a vaccine that seems to reduce HIV infection in monkeys to hardly detectable levels.[88] Perhaps soon there will be a similar vaccine for humans. In the meantime, we can try to understand why people engage in certain risky sexual practices. Such understanding may allow us to design educational and other programs that would help inhibit the spread of AIDS.

Mental and Emotional Disorders

Diagnosing mental or emotional disorders in one culture is difficult enough; diagnosing them in others poses much greater difficulty. Many researchers start with Western categories of mental illness and try to apply them elsewhere, without first trying to understand native conceptions of mental disorder. In addition, "mental" and "physical" disorders are rarely separate. For example, a host of illnesses can produce a loss of energy that some may see as depression; and fear or anger can produce physical symptoms such as a heart attack.[89]

When Western anthropologists first started describing mental illness in non-Western societies, there seemed to be unique illnesses in different cultures. These are referred to as *culture-bound syndromes.* For example, a mental disorder called *pibloktoq* occurred among some Eskimo adults of Greenland, usually women, who became oblivious to their surroundings and acted in agitated, eccentric

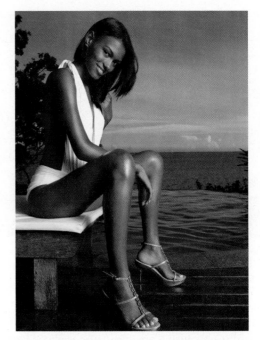

Cultures vary in their ideals of beauty, and ideals change over time. In the United States in the 1950s, "somewhat plump" was idealized. Beginning in the 1960s, thinness became idealized.

ways. They might strip themselves naked and wander across the ice and over hills until they collapsed of exhaustion. Another disorder, *amok,* occurred in Malaya, Indonesia, and New Guinea, usually among males. John Honigmann characterized it as a "destructive maddened excitement . . . beginning with depression and followed by a period of brooding and withdrawal [culminating in] the final mobilization of tremendous energy during which the 'wild man' runs destructively berserk."[90] *Anorexia nervosa,* the disorder involving aversion to food, may be unique to the relatively few societies that idealize slimness.[91] (See the box "Eating Disorders, Biology, and the Cultural Construction of Beauty.")

Some scholars think that each society's views of personality and concepts of mental illness have to be understood in their own terms. Western understandings and concepts cannot be applied to other cultures. For example, Catherine Lutz suggested that the Western concept of depression cannot be applied to the Pacific island of Ifaluk. The people there have many words for thinking or feeling about "loss and helplessness," but all their words are related to a specific need for someone, such as when someone dies or leaves the island. Such thoughts and feelings of loss are considered perfectly normal, and there is no word in their language for general hopelessness or "depression."[92] Therefore, Lutz questioned the applicability of the Western concept of depression as well as other Western psychiatric categories.

Other researchers are not so quick to dismiss the possible universality of psychiatric categories. Some think they have found a considerable degree of cross-cultural uniformity in conceptions of mental illness. Jane Murphy studied descriptions by the Inuit and the Yoruba, in Nigeria, of severely disturbed people. She found that their

applied anthropology

Eating Disorders, Biology, and the Cultural Construction of Beauty

Cultures differ about what they consider beautiful, including people. In many cultures, fat people are considered more beautiful than thin people. Melvin Ember did fieldwork years ago on the islands of American Samoa. When he returned to the main island after three months on a distant island, he ran into a Samoan acquaintance, a prominent chief. The chief said: "You look good. You gained weight." In reality, he had lost 30 pounds! The chief may not have remembered how heavy the anthropologist had been, but he clearly thought that fat was better than thin. Among the Azawagh Arabs of Niger, fatness was not merely valued and considered beautiful; great care was taken to ensure that young girls became fat by insisting and sometimes forcing them to drink large quantities of milk-based porridge.

Around the world, fatness is generally considered more desirable than thinness, particularly for women. Fatness is widely valued in these cultures not only because it is considered more beautiful, but also because it is thought to be a marker of health, fertility, and higher status in societies with social stratification. This view is in strong contrast to the ideal in the United States and many other Western societies, where fatness is thought to be unattractive, and to reflect laziness, a lack of self-control, and poor health. Thinness, particularly in the upper classes, is considered beautiful. How can we explain these differences in what is considered beautiful?

Recent cross-cultural research suggests that the picture is more complicated. It appears that societies with unpredictable resources actually value thinness, particularly in societies that have no way of storing food. At first glance, this seems puzzling. Shouldn't an individual who stores calories on the body be better off than an individual who is thin when facing starvation, particularly if there is no food storage? Perhaps. But 10 thin individuals will generally consume less than 10 heavier people, so perhaps there is a group advantage to being thin. Indeed, many societies with frequent episodes of famine encourage fasting or eating very light meals, as among the Gurage of Ethiopia. The strongest cross-cultural predictor of valuing fatness in women is what is often referred to as "machismo" or "protest masculinity." Societies with a strong emphasis on male aggression, strength, and sexuality are the most likely to value fatness in women; those with little machismo value thinness. Why machismo is associated with valuing fatness in women is far from clear. One suggestion is that machismo actually reflects male insecurity and fear of women. Such men may not be looking for closeness or intimacy with their wives, but they may want to show how potent they are by having lots of children. If fatness suggests fertility, men may look for wives who are fatter. Consistent with this idea, the ideal of thinness in women became more common in North America with the rise of women's movements in the 1920s and late 1960s. Consider that Marilyn Monroe epitomized beauty in the 1950s; she was well-rounded, not thin. Thin became more popular only when women began to question early marriage and having many children.

Behaviors associated with machismo became less acceptable at those times.

Cultural beliefs about what is considered a beautiful body can impose enormous pressures on females to achieve the ideal body type—whether it be fat or thin. In the United States and other Western countries, the effort to be thin can be carried to an extreme, resulting in the eating disorders anorexia and bulimia. If you suffer from these often fatal illnesses, you may regularly eat little and you may regularly force yourself to throw up, thus depriving your body of nutrients in your quest to be thinner and thinner. The irony of "thinness" being idealized in the United States and other Western countries is that obesity is becoming more common in those societies. In 2001, the incidence of obesity increased in the United States to 31 percent, and medical researchers worried about the increase in heart disease and diabetes resulting from obesity. Whether or not obesity is a result of an eating disorder (in the psychological sense) is more debatable. Researchers are finding biological causes of obesity, such as resistance to the hormone leptin, which regulates appetite, suggesting that much of the obesity "epidemic" has biological causes. Still, fast food, increasing sedentariness, and extremely large portion sizes are probably contributing factors also.

Sources: P. J. Brown 1997, 100; Loustaunau and Sobo 1997, 85; N. Wolf 1991; R. Popenoe 2004; C. R. Ember et al. 2005: J. L. Anderson et al. 1992; J. M. Friedman 2003.

---

descriptions not only were similar to each other but also corresponded to North American descriptions of schizophrenia. The Inuit word for "crazy" is *nuthkavihak*. They use this word when something inside a person seems to be out of order. *Nuthkavihak* people are described as talking to themselves, believing themselves to be animals, making strange faces, becoming violent, and so on. The Yoruba have a word, *were*, for people who are "insane." People described as *were* sometimes hear voices, laugh when there is nothing to laugh at, and take up weapons and suddenly hit people.[93]

Robert Edgerton found similarities in conceptions of mental illness in four East African societies. He noted not only that the four groups essentially agreed on the symptoms of psychosis but also that the symptoms they described were the same ones that are considered psychotic here.[94] Edgerton believed that the lack of exact translation in different cultures, such as the one pointed out by Lutz regarding Ifaluk, does not make comparison impossible. If researchers can come to understand another culture's views of personality and if the researchers can manage to communicate these views to people of other cultures, we can compare the described cases and try to discover what may be universal and what may be found only in some cultures.[95]

Some mental illnesses, such as schizophrenia and depression, seem so widespread that many researchers think they are probably universal. Consistent with this idea is the fact that schizophrenic individuals in different cultures seem to share the same patterns of distinctive eye movements.[96] Still, cultural factors may influence the risk of developing such diseases, the specific symptoms that are expressed, and the effectiveness of different kinds of treatment.[97] There may be some truly culture-bound (nearly unique) syndromes, but others thought at one time to be unique may be culturally varying expressions of conditions that occur widely. *Pibloktoq,* for example, may be a kind of hysteria.[98]

Biological but not necessarily genetic factors may be very important in the etiology of some of the widespread disorders such as schizophrenia.[99] With regard to hysteria, Anthony Wallace theorized that nutritional factors such as calcium deficiency may cause hysteria and that dietary improvement may account for the decline of this illness in the Western world since the 19th century.[100] By the early 20th century, the discovery of the value of good nutrition, coupled with changes in social conditions, had led many people to drink milk, eat vitamin-rich foods, and spend time in the sun (although spending a lot of time in the sun is no longer recommended because of the risk of skin cancer). These changes in diet and activity increased the intake of vitamin D and helped people to maintain a proper calcium level. Consequently, the number of cases of hysteria declined.

Regarding *pibloktoq,* Wallace suggested that a complex set of related variables may cause the disease. The Inuit live in an environment that supplies only a minimum amount of calcium. A diet low in calcium could result in two different conditions. One condition, rickets, would produce physical deformities potentially fatal in the Inuit hunting economy. People whose genetic makeup made them prone to rickets would be eliminated from the population through natural selection. A low level of calcium in the blood could also cause muscular spasms known as tetany. Tetany, in turn, may cause emotional and mental disorientation similar to the symptoms of *pibloktoq.* Such attacks last for only a relatively short time and are not fatal, so people who developed *pibloktoq* would have a far greater chance of surviving in the Arctic environment with a calcium-deficient diet than would people who had rickets.

Although researchers disagree about the comparability of mental illnesses among cultures, most agree that effective treatment requires understanding a culture's ideas about a mental illness—why people think it occurs, what treatments are believed to be effective, and how families and others respond to those afflicted.[101]

Susto   *Susto* is often described as a "folk illness" or a culture-bound syndrome because there doesn't seem to be any direct counterpart in biomedical terms. In many areas of Latin America, it is believed that a person suffers susto, or becomes *astudado,* when a nonmaterial essence from the body becomes detached during sleep, or after suffering a fright. This essence is either held captive by supernatural forces or wanders freely outside the body.[102] Susto patients are described as restless during sleep, and listless, depressed, debilitated, and indifferent to food and hygiene during the day. Some researchers have suggested that people labeled as suffering from susto may in fact be suffering from mental illness. Believing that such conclusions were incomplete or premature, Arthur Rubel, Carl O'Nell, and Rolando Collado-Ardón designed a three-culture comparative study to evaluate whether susto victims were suffering from social, psychological, or organic problems. They compared individuals suffering from susto to other individuals matched by culture, age, and sex who defined themselves as "sick" when they came to health clinics (but who did not claim susto as their illness). The three cultures were Chichimec, Zapotec, and a Spanish-speaking mestizo community.[103]

From previous study of susto victims, Rubel and his colleagues hypothesized that susto was likely to strike people in socially stressful situations where they may think they are inadequate in required roles. For example, two cases of susto occurred among women who desperately wanted more children, but each had had a number of miscarriages (one had seven, the other two). In addition to measuring social stress, the researchers also had physicians evaluate organic problems with reference to the World Health Organization's *International Classification of Diseases.* Degree of psychiatric impairment was judged in an interview based on questions other researchers had previously developed. And seven years after the study, the researchers found out which, if any, of the studied individuals had died.

The research results supported the social stress hypothesis: Susto victims were significantly more likely to feel inadequate about social roles. The researchers did not expect to find evidence that susto victims had more psychiatric impairment or more organic disease. However, to their surprise, susto victims were also more likely to have had serious physical health problems. In fact, susto victims were more likely to have died in the seven years after the study. It is hard to say whether the susto victims had more disease because they were debilitated by susto or they were more prone to susto because they were physically sicker. The researchers guess that, because many of the conditions that created social role impairment were of long duration (such as many miscarriages), it seemed likely that susto itself put its victims at risk for biological diseases.[104]

Depression   Just as one kind of stress seems to be involved in the folk illness susto, researchers have considered the role of other kinds of stress in producing various other forms of mental illness. One of the most important stressors may be economic deprivation. Many studies have found that the lower classes in socially stratified societies have much higher proportions of all kinds of mental illness. Acute stressors like death of a loved one, divorce, loss of a job, or a natural disaster predict higher rates of mental illness for all social classes; however, these events take more of a toll in lower-class families.[105]

In a study designed to evaluate the effect of these and other stressors on the prevalence of depression in an African American community in a southern city, William Dressler combined fieldwork methods and hypothesis testing to try to better understand depression.[106] Although many studies rely on treatment or hospitalization rates, Dressler decided that such rates drastically underestimate the incidence of depression, inasmuch as many people do not seek treatment. He decided to rely on a symptom checklist, which asked such questions as how often in the last week a person felt like crying, felt lonely, or felt hopeless about the future. Although such checklists do not provide clear divisions for characterizing someone as mildly depressed or seriously depressed, they do allow researchers to compare people along a continuum.

Dressler measured a variety of different possible stressors, including life crises, economic worries, perceived racial inequality, and problems in social roles, and found that some of the objective stressors, like life crises and unemployment, predict depression in the expected direction only in the lower classes. That is, for lower-class African Americans, unemployment and other life crises predicted more depression, but that result was not found among middle- and upper-class individuals. These results are consistent with previous findings that many stressors take more of a toll among poorer individuals. On the other hand, more subjective economic stressors, such as feeling you are not making enough money, predict depression across all class lines. So does "social role" stress, such as thinking you are missing promotions because you are African American or thinking that your spouse expects too much.[107]

Undernutrition

What people eat is intrinsically connected to their survival and the ability of a population to reproduce itself, so we would expect that the ways people obtain, distribute, and consume food have been generally adaptive.[108] For example, the human body cannot synthesize eight amino acids. Meat can provide all of these amino acids, and combinations of particular plants can also provide them for a complete complement of protein. The combination of maize and beans in many traditional Native American diets, or *tortillas* and *frijoles* in Mexico, can provide all the needed amino acids. In places where wheat (often made into bread) is the staple, dairy products combined with wheat also provide complete protein.[109] Even the way that people have prepared for scarcity, such as breaking up into mobile bands, cultivating crops that can better withstand drought, and preserving food in case of famine, are probably adaptive practices in unpredictable environments. Geneticists have proposed that populations in famine-prone areas may have had genetic selection for "thrifty genes"—genes

A sisal plant in Bahia, Brazil. The switch to sisal production led to undernutrition in children.

that allow individuals to need a minimum of food and store the extra in fatty tissue to get them past serious scarcity.[110] Customary diets and genetic changes may have been selected over a long stretch of time, but many serious nutritional problems observed today are due to rapid culture change. For instance, although "thrifty genes" may be adaptive during famine, they may become maladaptive when food is readily available. The high prevalence of diabetes and obesity in many populations today may be linked to such genes.

Often the switch to commercial or cash crops has harmful effects in another direction—creating undernutrition. For example, when the farmer-herders of the arid region in northeastern Brazil started growing sisal, a drought-resistant plant used for making twine and rope, many of them abandoned subsistence agriculture. The small landholders used most of their land for sisal growing and, when the price of sisal fell, they had to work as laborers for others to try to make ends meet. Food then had to be mostly bought, but if a laborer or sisal grower didn't earn enough, there was not enough food for the whole family.

Analysis of allocation of food in some households by Daniel Gross and Barbara Underwood suggests that the laborer and his wife received adequate nutrition, but the children often received much less than required. Lack of adequate nutrition usually results in retarded weight and height in children. As is commonly the case when there is substantial social inequality, the children from lower-income groups weigh substantially less than those from higher-income groups. But even though there were some economic differences before sisal production, the effects on nutrition appeared negligible before, judging from the fact that there was little or no difference in weight among adults from higher and lower socioeconomic positions who grew up prior to sisal production. But more recently, 45 percent of the children from lower economic groups were undernourished as compared with 23 percent of those children from the higher economic groups.[111]

This is not to say that commercialization is always deleterious to adequate nutrition. For example, in the Highlands of New Guinea, there is evidence that the nutrition of children improved when families started growing coffee for sale. However, in this case, the families still had land to grow some crops for consumption. The extra money earned from coffee enabled them to buy canned fish and rice, which provided children with higher amounts of protein than the usual staple of sweet potatoes.[112]

Nutritional imbalances for females have a far-reaching impact on reproduction and the health of the infants they bear. In some cultures, the lower status of women has a direct bearing on their access to food. Although the custom of feeding males first is well known, it is less often realized that females end up with less nutrient-dense food such as meat. Deprivation of food sometimes starts in infancy where girl babies, as in India, are weaned earlier than boy babies.[113] Parents may be unaware that their differential weaning practice has the effect of reducing the amount of high-quality protein that girl infants receive. Indeed, in Ecuador, Lauris McKee found that parents thought that earlier weaning of girls was helpful to them. They believed that mothers' milk transmitted sexuality and aggression, both ideal male traits, to their infants and so it was important that girl babies be weaned early. Mothers weaned their girls at about 11 months and their boys at about 20 months, a 9-month difference. McKee found that girl infants had a significantly higher mortality than boy infants in their second year of life, suggesting that the earlier weaning time for girls and their probable undernutrition may have been responsible.[114]

Malnutrition and AIDS are biological and social problems. In the next chapter, we turn to other global social problems and how anthropology and other social sciences may contribute to their solution.

SUMMARY ● ○ ○

1. Applied or practicing anthropology as a profession is explicitly concerned with making anthropological knowledge useful. Applied or practicing anthropologists may be involved in one or more phases of programs that are designed to change peoples' lives: assembling relevant knowledge, constructing alternative plans, assessing the likely social and environmental impact of particular plans, implementing the programs, and monitoring the programs and their effects.

2. Applied or practicing anthropologists work for a large variety of organizations, government agencies, international development agencies, private consulting firms, public health organizations, medical schools, public interest law firms, community development agencies, charitable foundations, and profit-seeking corporations.

3. The code of ethics for those who work professionally as applied anthropologists specifies that the target population should be included as much as possible in the formulation of policy, so that people in the community may know in advance how the program may affect them. But perhaps the most important aspect of the code is the pledge not to be involved in any plan whose effect will not be beneficial. It is often difficult to evaluate the effects of planned changes. Long-term consequences may be detrimental even if the changes are beneficial in the short run.

4. Even if a planned change will prove beneficial to the targeted population, the people may not accept it. And if the proposed innovation is not utilized by the intended population, the project cannot be considered a success. Affected populations may reject or resist a proposed innovation for cultural, social, or psychological reasons. It is important to understand what the reasons are. The population may also resist the proposed change because they unconsciously or consciously know it is not good for them.

5. To be effective, change agents may have to discover and use the traditional channels of influence in introducing their projects.

6. Cultural resource management usually takes the form of "contract archaeology" to record and/or conserve the archaeology of a building site.

7. Forensic anthropology is the specialty in anthropology that is devoted to helping solve crimes and identifying human remains, usually by applying knowledge of physical anthropology.

8. Medical anthropologists suggest that biological and social factors need to be considered if we are to understand how to treat illness effectively and reduce the suffering in human life.

9. Many of the ideas and practices of medical practitioners are influenced by the culture in which they reside. Understanding ethnomedicine—the medical beliefs and practices of a society or cultural group—is one of the goals of medical anthropology.

10. Many cultures have the view that the body should be kept in equilibrium or balance. The balance may be between hot and cold, or wet and dry, or there may be other properties that need to be balanced.

11. The belief that gods or spirits can cause illness is a near universal. The belief in sorcery or witchcraft as a cause of illness is also very common.

12. Some anthropologists think that there are few cultural universals about conceptions of illness or its treatment, but some researchers are finding evidence that many of the plant remedies that indigenous peoples use contain chemicals that are the same as, or similar in effect to, chemicals used in Western biomedicine remedies.

13. In the biomedical system, medical practitioners emphasize disease and cures, focusing on the body of the patient, not the mind or the social circumstances of the patient. In some societies, healers are more

"personalistic," and illness may be viewed as something out of order in one's social life. Shamans are perhaps the most important medical practitioners in societies lacking full-time specialization. Biomedical practitioners are becoming more aware of the psychological factors involved in healing.

14. People with more social, economic, and political power in a society are generally healthier. In socially stratified societies, the poor usually have increased exposure to disease because they are more likely to live in crowded and unsafe conditions and they are less likely to get access to quality care. Power and economic differentials between societies also have had profound health consequences.

15. The enormous death toll of AIDS, the leading cause of adult death in many countries today, will be reduced when medical science develops effective and inexpensive medicines to treat victims of HIV or AIDS and a vaccine to prevent individuals from getting HIV. In the meantime, if the death toll from AIDS is to be reduced, changes in attitudes, beliefs, and practices regarding sexual activity are needed.

16. Anthropologists debate the extent to which mental and emotional disorders are comparable across cultures. Some illnesses such as schizophrenia and depression seem so widespread as to be probably universal. Others, such as susto or anorexia nervosa, appear to be culture-bound syndromes.

17. The ways that people obtain, distribute, and consume food have been generally adaptive. Geneticists have proposed that populations in famine-prone areas may have had genetic selection for "thrifty genes." Now these populations with regular food supplies may be prone to diabetes and obesity. Many of the serious nutritional problems of today are due to rapid culture change, particularly those making for an increasing degree of social inequality.

GLOSSARY TERMS ○ ● ○

AIDS (acquired immune deficiency syndrome) **492**
applied or practicing anthropology **478**
biomedicine **488**
cultural resource management (CRM) **485**
ethnomedicine **487**
forensic anthropology **486**
medical anthropology **487**

CRITICAL QUESTIONS ○ ○ ●

1. What particular advantages do anthropologists have in trying to solve practical problems?

2. Is it ethical to try to influence people's lives when they have not asked for help? Explain your answer.

3. Why do native remedies often contain chemicals that are the same as, or similar in effect to, chemicals used in Western biomedicine remedies?

4. Why might people engage in sexual practices that increase their likelihood of contracting AIDS?

PEARSON myanthrolab

Read the chapter by Andrew W. Miracle titled "A Shaman for Organizations" on MyAnthroLab. Answer the following questions:

1. Why does Miracle call himself a "shaman"?

2. According to Miracle, what skills are useful to an applied anthropologist? Why does he think so?

Read the chapter by Ruthbeth Finerman titled "Saraguro: Medical Choices, Medical Changes" on MyAnthroLab. Answer the following questions:

1. Why do the Saraguros continue mostly to rely on mothers to treat illness in the household?

2. How are Saraguro herbal treatments like your use of medicines? How are they unlike yours?

chapter 28

Global Problems

The news on television and in the newspapers makes us aware every day that terrible social problems threaten people around the world. War, crime, family violence, natural disasters, poverty, famine—all these and more are the lot of millions of people in many places. And now there is an increasing threat of terrorism. Can anthropological and other research help us solve these global social problems? Many anthropologists and other social scientists think so.

High-tech communications have increased our awareness of problems all over the world, and we seem to be increasingly more aware of, and bothered by, problems in our own society. For these two reasons, and perhaps also because we know much more than we used to about human behavior, we may be more motivated now to try to solve those problems. We call them "social problems" not just because a lot of people worry about them but also because they have social causes and consequences, and treating or solving them requires changes in social behavior. Even AIDS, which we discussed in the previous chapter, is partly a social problem. It may be caused by a virus, but it is mostly transmitted by social (sexual) contact with another person. And the main ways to avoid it—abstinence and "safe" sex—require changes in social behavior.

The idea that we can solve social problems, even the enormous ones such as war and family violence, is based on two assumptions. First, we have to assume that it is possible to discover the causes of a problem. And two, we have to assume that we may be able to do something about the causes, once they are discovered, and thereby eliminate or reduce the problem. Not everyone would agree with these assumptions. Some would say that our understanding of a social problem cannot ever be sufficient to suggest a solution guaranteed to work. To be sure, no understanding in science is perfect or certain; there is always some probability that even a well-supported explanation is wrong or incomplete. But the uncertainty of knowledge does not rule out the possibility of application. With regard to social problems, the possible payoff from even incomplete understanding could be a better and safer world. This possibility is what motivates many researchers who investigate social problems. After all, the history of the various sciences strongly supports the belief that scientific understanding can often allow humans to control nature, not just predict and explain it. Why should human behavior be any different?

So what do we know about some of the global social problems, and what policies or solutions are suggested by what we know?

● ○ ●

NATURAL DISASTERS AND FAMINE

Natural events such as floods, droughts, earthquakes, and insect infestations are usually but not always beyond human control, but their effects are not.[1] We call such events accidents or emergencies when only a few people are affected, but we call them disasters when large numbers of people or large areas are affected. The harm caused is not just a function of the

magnitude of the natural event. Between 1960 and 1980, 43 natural disasters in Japan killed an average of 63 people per disaster. During the same period, 17 natural disasters in Nicaragua killed an average of 6,235 people per disaster. In the United States, between 1960 and 1976, the average flood or other environmental disturbance killed just one person, injured a dozen, and destroyed fewer than five buildings. These comparative figures demonstrate that climatic and other events in the physical environment become disasters because of events or conditions in the social environment.

If people live in houses that are designed to withstand earthquakes—if governing bodies require such construction and the economy is developed enough so that people can afford such construction—the effects of an earthquake will be minimized. If poor people are forced to live in deforested floodplains to be able to find land to farm (as in coastal Bangladesh), if the poor are forced to live in shanties built on precarious hillsides (like those of Rio de Janeiro), the floods and landslides that follow severe hurricanes and rainstorms can kill thousands and even hundreds of thousands.

Thus, natural disasters can have greater or lesser effects on human life, depending on social conditions. And therefore disasters are also social problems, problems that have social causes and possible social solutions. Legislating safe construction of a house is a social solution. The 1976 earthquake in Tangsham, China, killed 250,000 people, mostly because they lived in top-heavy adobe houses that could not withstand severe shaking, whereas the 1989 Loma Prieta earthquake in California, which was of comparable intensity, killed 65 people.

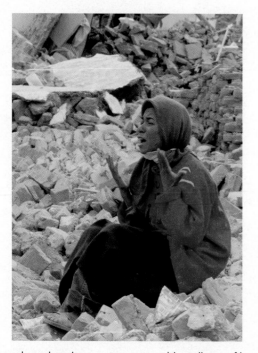

Although earthquakes are not preventable, collapse of houses is mostly preventable by building houses to withstand earthquakes. In Bam, Iran, 20,000 people were killed during a 2003 earthquake and most of the houses collapsed. This woman sits amid the ruins of her house.

One might think that floods, of all disasters, are the least influenced by social factors. After all, without a huge runoff from heavy rains or snow melt, there cannot be a flood. But consider why so many people have died from Hwang River floods in China. (One such flood, in 1931, killed nearly 4 million people, making it the deadliest single disaster in history.) The floods in the Hwang River basin have occurred mostly because the clearing of nearby forests for fuel and farmland has allowed enormous quantities of silt to wash into the river, raising the riverbed and increasing the risk of floods that burst the dams that normally would contain them. The risk of disastrous flooding would be greatly reduced if different social conditions prevailed—if people were not so dependent on firewood for fuel, if they did not have to farm close to the river, or if the dams were higher and more numerous.

Famines, episodes of severe starvation and death, often appear to be triggered by physical events such as a severe drought or a hurricane that kills or knocks down food trees and plants. But famines do not inevitably follow such an event. Social conditions can prevent a famine or increase the likelihood of one. Consider what is likely to happen in Samoa after a hurricane.[2] Whole villages that have lost their coconut and breadfruit trees, as well as their taro patches, pick up and move for a period of time to other villages where they have relatives and friends. The visitors stay and are fed until some of their cultivated trees and plants start to bear food again, at which point they return home. This kind of intervillage reciprocity probably could occur only in a society that has relatively little inequality in wealth. Nowadays, the central government or international agencies may also help out by providing food and other supplies.

Researchers point out that famine rarely results from just one bad food production season. During one bad season, people can usually cope by getting help from relatives, friends, and neighbors or by switching to less desirable foods. The 1974 famine in the African Sahel occurred after eight years of bad weather; a combination of drought, floods, and a civil war in 1983 to 1984 contributed to the subsequent famine in the Sahel, Ethiopia, and Sudan.[3] Famine almost always has some social causes. Who has rights to the available food, and do those who have more food distribute it to those who have less? Cross-cultural research suggests that societies with individual property rights rather than shared rights are more likely to suffer famine.[4] Nonetheless, government assistance can lessen the risk of famine in societies with individual property.

Relief provided by government may not always get to those who need it the most. In India, for example, the central government provides help in time of drought to minimize the risk of famine. But the food and other supplies provided to a village may end up being unequally distributed, following the rules of social and gender stratification. Members of the local elite arrange to function as distributors and find ways to manipulate the relief efforts to their advantage. Lower-class and lower-caste families still suffer the most. Within the family, biases against females, particularly young girls and elderly women, translate into their getting less food. It is no wonder, then, that in times of food shortage and famine, the poor and other socially disadvantaged people are especially likely to die.[5]

Thus, the people of a society may not all be equally at risk in case of disaster. In socially stratified societies, the poor particularly suffer. They are likely to be forced to overcultivate, overgraze, and deforest their land, making it more susceptible to degradation. A society most helps those it values the most.

People in the past, and even recently in some places, viewed disasters as divine retribution for human immorality. For example, the great flood described in the Old Testament was understood to be God's doing. But scientific research increasingly allows us to understand the natural causes of disasters, and particularly the social conditions that magnify or minimize their effects. To reduce the impact of disasters, then, we need to reduce the social conditions that magnify the effects of disasters. If humans are responsible for those social conditions, humans can change them. If earthquakes destroy houses that are too flimsy, we can build stronger houses. If floods caused by overcultivation and overgrazing kill people directly (or indirectly by stripping their soils), we can grow new forest cover and provide new job opportunities to floodplain farmers. If prolonged natural disasters or wars threaten famine, social distribution systems can lessen the risk. In short, we may not be able to do much about the weather or other physical causes of disasters, but we can do a lot—if we want to— about the social factors that make disasters disastrous.

INADEQUATE HOUSING AND HOMELESSNESS

In most nations, those who are poor typically live in inadequate housing, in areas we call *slums*. In many of the developing nations, where cities are growing very rapidly, squatter settlements emerge as people build dwellings (often makeshift) that are typically declared illegal, either because the land is illegally occupied or because the dwellings violate building codes. Squatter settlements are often located in degraded environments that are subject to flooding and mudslides or have inadequate or polluted water. The magnitude of the problem is made clear in some statistics. As of the 1980s, 40 percent of the population in Nairobi, Kenya, lived in unauthorized housing, and 67 percent of the people in five of El Salvador's major cities lived in illegal dwellings.[6] In 2001, an estimated 32 percent of city-dwellers in the world lived in slums. The overall picture has not improved in the last ten years.[7]

But contrary to what some people have assumed, not all dwellers in illegal settlements are poor; all but the upper-income elite may be found in such settlements.[8] Moreover, although squatter settlements have problems, they are not chaotic and unorganized places that are full of crime. Most of the dwellers are employed, aspire to get ahead, live in intact nuclear families, and help each other.[9] People live in such settlements because they cannot find affordable housing and they house themselves as best they can. Many researchers think that such self-help tendencies should be assisted to improve housing, because governments in developing countries can seldom afford costly public housing projects. But they could invest somewhat in infrastructure—sewers, water supplies, roads—and provide construction materials to those who are willing to do the work required to improve their dwellings.[10]

Housing in slum areas or shantytowns does provide shelter, minimal though it may be. But many people in many areas of the world have no homes at all. Even in countries such as the United States, which are affluent by world standards, large numbers of people are homeless. They sleep in parks, over steam vents, in doorways, subways, and cardboard boxes. Homelessness is difficult to measure. In 1987, more than 1 million people were estimated to be homeless in the United States.[11] Homelessness has increased in the last few decades. About 3.5 million people experienced homelessness in 2000, almost 40 percent of them children.[12]

Who are the homeless, and how did they get to be homeless? We have relatively little research on these questions, but what we do have suggests differences in the causes of homelessness in different parts of the world. In the United States, unemployment and the shortage of decent low-cost housing appear to be at least partly responsible for the large number of homeless people.[13] But there is also another factor: the deliberate policy to reduce the number of people hospitalized for mental illness and other disabilities. For example, from the mid-1960s to the mid-1990s, New York State released thousands of patients from mental hospitals. Many of these ex-patients had to live in cheap hotels or poorly monitored facilities with virtually no support network. With very little income, they found it especially hard to cope with their circumstances. Ellen Baxter and Kim Hopper, who studied the homeless in New York City, suggest that one event is rarely sufficient to render a person homeless. Rather, poverty and disability

A homeless boy in Calcutta, India with his belongings.

current research and issues

Global Warming, Air Pollution, and Our Dependence on Oil

Scientists are increasingly sure that the world is heating up. And they are worried about the consequences. The more the temperature rises, the more the Greenland and Arctic ice will melt. The resulting higher sea level will flood many low-lying coastal areas, including many world cities. Storms, floods, and droughts will intensify. Places at high latitudes are likely to see increased rainfall and snow; places at low latitudes are likely to have less rainfall and more drought.

The world is warming probably for several reasons. One of them is our increasing use of fossil fuels, particularly oil. We burn those fuels to make electricity, to power our cars (with the gasoline made from oil), to heat our homes, and to cook food. The emissions from all that burning may contribute to a "greenhouse effect": The atmosphere reflects the warmth produced on earth, and temperatures rise. And the air gets dirtier, resulting in other harmful consequences such as a higher incidence of breathing disorders.

Can people do anything about global warming and air pollution? Surely the answer is yes. If at least some of the problem is of human making, we could change our behavior and at least partly solve the problem. One way would be to reduce our use of oil as fuel. But how could we do that?

In the year 2000, the first hybrid cars were sold in the United States. These cars are powered by an electric motor and a small gasoline engine. The combination reduces the amount of fuel needed, because the electric motor moves the car much of the time. The battery that powers the electric motor is recharged by braking and when the gasoline engine is on, which is not much of the time. (For example, at a stop light, the gasoline engine turns off.) So a hybrid car allows a gallon of gasoline to go a lot farther. If most cars were hybrid cars, we would need much less oil to make the gasoline needed.

It is estimated that hybrid cars could cut greenhouse emissions by up to half, which would help alleviate or even reverse global warming and air pollution. So, given this rosy scenario, what is discouraging the world from switching to hybrid cars?

The answer is probably economics and politics. There is money to be made from the dependence on oil, particularly when supplies are short. The shorter the supplies, the more the oil producers abroad and the refiners at home can charge their customers. And the more the oil comes from abroad, the more the U.S. and other governments may feel that they have to keep the foreign producers happy. But this obligation runs counter to a foreign policy that would encourage democracy in the world; many of the countries that produce our oil are dictatorships. So the oil companies are dependent on those regimes to keep their refineries going, and they lobby governments (ours included) to maintain friendly relations with many of those regimes. Can we expect the oil companies to want to escape their dependence on foreign suppliers, if they are making a lot of money from that dependence? Hardly.

Our market economy does offer a way out of this dilemma. If hybrid cars and other ways to reduce the need for fossil fuels become more economical, the marketplace will turn the tide. Ironically, the capitalist laws of supply and demand may reduce the influence of oil companies on politics and help us solve the problems of global warming and air pollution. Even if the automobile manufacturers wanted to continue doing business as usual, they will not be able to resist making more fuel-efficient cars. As the recent "cash for clunkers" program in the United States shows, consumers want to reduce their gasoline expenses. No car company will be able to ignore that kind of pressure from the marketplace. There is more interest in making and buying hybrid vehicles, and there is the possibility of transforming organic garbage into oil. Other solutions to our dependency on foreign oil are also being tested. So our consumption of oil may decrease significantly in the near future.

Sources: Oerlemans 2005; M. L. Wald 2000; Ambient Corporation 2000; Duane 2003; Baer and Singer 2009.

(mental or physical) seem to lead to one calamity after another and, finally, homelessness.[14]

Many people cannot understand why homeless individuals do not want to go to municipal shelters. But observations and interviews with the homeless suggest that violence pervades the municipal shelters, particularly the men's shelters. Many feel safer on the streets. Some private charities provide safe shelters and a caring environment. These shelters are filled, but the number of homeless they can accommodate is small.[15] Even single-room-occupancy hotels are hardly better. Many of them are infested with vermin, the common bathrooms are filthy, and they, like the shelters, are often dangerous.[16]

Some poor individuals may be socially isolated, with few or no friends and relatives and little or no social contact. But a society with many such individuals does not necessarily have much homelessness. Socially isolated individuals, even mentally ill individuals, could still have housing, or so the experience of Melbourne, Australia, suggests. Universal health insurance there pays for health care as well as medical practitioners' visits to isolated and ill individuals, wherever they live. Disabled individuals receive a pension or sickness benefits sufficient to allow them to live in a room or apartment. And there is still a considerable supply of cheap housing in Melbourne. Research in Melbourne suggests that a severe mental disorder often precedes living in marginal accommodations—city shelters, commercial shelters, and cheap single rooms. About 50 percent of the people living in such places were diagnosed as previously having some form of mental illness; this percentage is similar to what seems to be the case for homeless people and people living in marginal accommodations in the United States.

The contrast between the United States and Australia makes it clear that social and political policies cause homelessness. Individuals with similar characteristics live in both Australia and the United States, but a larger percentage of them are homeless in the United States.[17]

Because homelessness cannot occur if everybody can afford housing, some people would say that homelessness can happen only in a society with great extremes in income. Statistics on income distribution in the United States clearly show that, since the 1970s, the rich have gotten much richer and the poor have gotten much poorer.[18] The United States now has more income inequality than any country in western Europe and more than most high-income countries. In fact, the profile of inequality in the United States more closely resembles that of developing countries, such as Cambodia and Morocco[19] (see the discussion in the chapter on social stratification).

In the United States and many other countries, most homeless people are adults. Whereas adults are "allowed" to be homeless, public sensibilities in the United States appear to be outraged by the sight of children living in the streets; when authorities discover homeless children, they try to find shelters or foster homes for them. But many countries have "street children." In the late 1980s, 80 million of the world's children lived in the streets; 40 million in Latin America, 20 million in Asia, 10 million in Africa and the Middle East, and 10 million elsewhere.[20] In the 2000s, the estimated number grew to about 150 million worldwide.[21]

Lewis Aptekar, who studied street children in Cali, Colombia, reported some surprises.[22] Whereas many of the homeless in the United States and Australia are mentally disabled, the street children in Cali, ranging in age from 7 to 16, are mostly free of mental problems; by and large, they also test normally on intelligence tests. In addition, even though many street children come from abusive homes or never had homes, they usually seem happy and enjoy the support and friendship of other street children. They cleverly and creatively look for ways to get money, frequently through entertaining passersby.

Although observers might think that the street children must have been abandoned by their families, most of them in actuality have at least one parent they keep in touch with. Street life begins slowly, not abruptly; children usually do not stay on the streets full time until they are about 13 years old. Though street children in Cali seem to be in better physical and mental shape than their siblings who stay at home, they often are viewed as a "plague." The street children come from poor families and cope with their lives as best they can, so why are they not viewed with pity and compassion? Aptekar suggests that well-off families see the street children as a threat because a life independent of family may appeal to children, even those from well-off families, who wish to be free of parental constraint and authority.

Whether people become homeless, whether they have shantytowns, seems to depend on a society's willingness to share wealth and help those in need. The street children of Cali may remind us that children as well as adults need companionship and care. Addressing physical needs without responding to emotional needs may get people off the streets, but it won't get them a "home."

FAMILY VIOLENCE AND ABUSE

In U.S. society, we hear regularly about the abuse of spouses and children, which makes us think that such abuse is increasing—but is it? This seems to be a simple question, but it is not so simple to answer. We have to decide what we mean by *abuse*.

Is physical punishment of a child who does something wrong child abuse? Not so long ago, teachers in public schools in the United States were allowed to discipline children by hitting them with rulers or paddles, and many parents used switches or belts. Many would consider these practices to be child abuse, but were they abusive when they were generally accepted? Some would argue that abuse is going beyond what a culture considers appropriate behavior. Others would disagree and would focus on the violence and severity of parents' or teachers' behavior, not the cultural judgment of appropriateness. And abuse need not involve physical violence. It could be argued that verbal aggression and neglect may be just as harmful as physical aggression. Neglect presents its own problems of definition. People from other cultures might argue that we act abusively when we put an infant or child alone in a room to sleep.[23] Few would disagree about severe injuries that kill a child or spouse or require medical treatment, but other disciplinary behaviors are more difficult to judge.

To avoid having to decide what is or is not abuse, many researchers focus their studies on variation in the frequencies of specific behaviors. For example, one can ask which societies have physical punishment of children without calling physical punishment abusive.

According to four national interview surveys of married or cohabiting couples in the United States conducted from 1975 to 1995, physical violence against children appears to have decreased in frequency over time, as did serious assaults by husbands against wives. But serious assaults by wives on husbands did not decrease.[24] The decreasing rates of abuse may be mostly due to reporting differences: wife and child beating is less acceptable now. For example, men report dramatically fewer assaults on their wives, but wives report only slight declines.[25] However, the United States remains a society with a lot of physical violence in families. In 1992 alone, one out of 10 couples had a violent assault episode and one out of 10 children was severely assaulted by a parent.[26] A survey conducted in the mid-1990s found that about 75 percent of the violence against women comes from a male intimate partner, such as a husband. In contrast, most of the violence men experience comes from strangers and

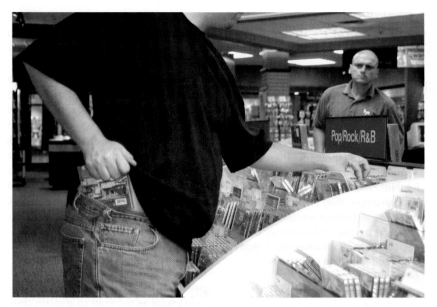

Theft tends to be more prevalent with social inequality and with higher unemployment. This man is stealing CDs from a music store in the United States.

example, surges in violent crime rates occurred during the 1860s and 1870s (during and after the Civil War), after World War I, after World War II, and during the Vietnam War.[43] But recently the homicide rate in the United States has declined.[44]

In the types of societies that anthropologists have typically studied, homicide statistics were not usually available; so cross-cultural studies of homicide usually measure homicide rates by comparing and rank-ordering ethnographers' statements about the frequency of homicide. For example, the statement that murder is "practically unheard of" is taken to mean that the murder rate is lower than where it is reported that "homicide is not uncommon." Despite the fact that the data on cultural homicide rates are not quantitative, the cross-cultural results are consistent with the cross-national results; more war is usually associated with more homicide and assault, as well as with socially approved aggressive behaviors (as in aggressive games) and severe physical punishment for wrongdoing.[45] A cross-cultural study suggests that the more war a society has, the more the society socializes or trains boys in aggression, and such socialization strongly predicts higher rates of homicide and assault.[46]

Capital punishment—execution of criminals—is severe physical punishment for wrongdoing. It is commonly thought that the prospect of capital punishment deters would-be murderers. Yet, cross-national research suggests otherwise. More countries show murder rates going down rather than up after capital punishment was abolished.[47] Capital punishment may legitimize violence rather than deter it.

Research conducted in the United States suggests that juvenile delinquents (usually boys) are likely to come from broken homes, with the father absent for much of the time the boy is growing up. The conclusion often drawn is that father absence somehow increases the likelihood of delinquency and adult forms of physical violence. But other conditions that may cause delinquency are also associated with broken homes, conditions such as the stigma of not having a "regular" family and the generally low standard of living of such families. It is therefore important to conduct research in other societies, in which father absence does not occur in concert with these other factors, to see if father absence by itself is related to physical violence.

For example, in many polygynous societies, children grow up in a mother-child household; the father lives separately and is seldom around the child. Does the father absence explanation of delinquency and violence fit such societies? The answer is apparently yes: Societies in which children are reared in mother-child households or the father spends little time caring for the child tend to have more physical violence by males than do societies in which fathers spend time with children.[48] The rate of violent crime is also more frequent in nations that have more women than men, which is consistent with the theory that father absence increases violence.[49]

More research is needed to discover exactly what accounts for these relationships. It is possible, as some suggest, that boys growing up without fathers are apt to act "supermasculine," to show how "male" they are. But it is also possible that mothers who rear children alone have more frustration and more anger, and therefore are likely to provide an aggressive role model for the child. In addition, high male mortality in war predicts polygyny, as we saw in the chapter on marriage and the family; therefore, boys in polygynous societies are likely to be exposed to a warrior tradition.[50]

Trying to act supermasculine, however, may be likely to involve violence only if aggression is an important component of the male gender role in society. If men were expected by society to be sensitive, caring, and nonviolent, boys who grew up without fathers might try to be supersensitive and supercaring. So society's expectations for males probably shape how growing up in a mother-child household affects behavior in adolescence and later.[51] The media may also influence the expectations for males. Numerous studies in the United States show that, even controlling for other factors like parental neglect, family income, and mental illness, more television watching in childhood and adolescence predicts more overt aggression later. Estimates show that an hour of prime-time television depicts 3 to 5 violent acts, and an hour of children's television depicts 20 to 25 violent acts.[52]

One widely held idea is that poor economic conditions increase the likelihood of crime, but the relationship does not appear to be strong. Also, the findings are somewhat different for different types of crime. For example, hundreds of studies in this and other countries do not show a clear relationship between changes in economic well-being as measured by unemployment rates and changes in violent crime as measured by homicide. The rate of homicide does not appear to increase in bad times. Property crimes, however, do increase with increases in unemployment. Violent crime does appear to be associated with one economic characteristic: Homicide is usually highest in nations or societies with high income inequality.[53] Why income inequality predicts homicide but downturns in the economy do not is something of a puzzle.[54]

The fact that property crime is linked to unemployment is consistent with the cross-cultural finding that theft (but not violent crime) tends to occur less often in egalitarian societies than in stratified ones. Societies with equal access to resources usually have distribution mechanisms that offset any differences in wealth. Hence, theft should be less of a temptation and therefore less likely in an egalitarian society. Theft rates are higher in socially stratified societies despite the fact that they are more likely than egalitarian societies to have police and courts to punish crime. Societies may try to deter property and other crimes when the rates of such are high, but we do not know that these efforts actually reduce the rates.

So what does the available research suggest about how we might be able to reduce crime? The results so far indicate that homicide rates are highest in societies that socialize their boys for aggression. Such socialization is linked to war and other forms of socially approved violence—capital punishment, television and movie violence by heroes, violence in sports. The statistical evidence suggests that war encourages socialization for aggression, which in turn results unintentionally in high rates of violence. The policy implication of these results is that, if we can reduce socialization for aggression by reducing the risk of war and therefore the necessity to produce effective warriors, and if we can reduce other forms of socially approved violence, we may thereby reduce the rates of violent crime. The reduction of inequalities in wealth may also help to reduce crime, particularly theft. And although it is not yet clear why, it appears that raising boys with a male role model around may reduce the likelihood of male violence in adulthood.

Evidence indicates that violence on TV encourages violence in real life.

WAR

War is an unfortunate fact of life in most societies known to anthropology, judging by the cross-cultural research we referred to in the chapter on political life. Almost every society had at least occasional wars when it was first described, unless it had been pacified (usually by Western colonial powers).[55] Since the Civil War, the United States has not had any wars on its territory, but it is unusual in that respect. Before pacification, most societies in the ethnographic record had frequent armed combat between communities or larger units that spoke the same language. That is, most warfare was internal to the society or language group. Even some wars in modern times involved speakers of the same language; recall the wars between Italian states before the unification of Italy and many of the "civil" wars of the last two centuries. Although people in some societies might fight against people in other societies, such "external" wars were usually not organized on behalf of the entire society or even a major section of it.[56] That is, warfare in the ethnographic record did not usually involve politically unified societies. The absolute numbers of people killed may have been small, but this does not mean that warfare in nonindustrial societies was a trivial matter. Indeed, it appears that nonindustrial warfare may have been even more lethal *proportionately* than modern warfare, judging by the fact that wars killed 25 percent to 30 percent of the males in some nonindustrial societies.[57]

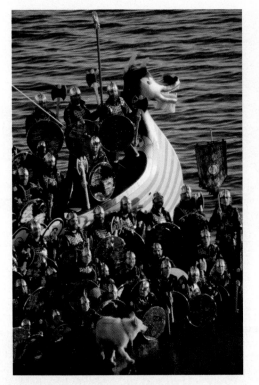

Although warfare has occurred frequently in societies at all levels of complexity, changes over time tell us that war is not inevitable. For example, Norway is one of the world's most peaceful countries. The Viking age, as shown in this reenactment, was an era of militarism.

In the chapter on political life, we discussed the possibility that people in nonindustrial societies go to war mostly out of fear, particularly a fear of expectable but unpredictable natural disasters (droughts, floods, hurricanes, among others) that destroy food supplies.[58] People with more of a history of such disasters have more war. It seems as if people go to war to protect themselves ahead of time from disasters, inasmuch as the victors in war almost always take resources (land, animals, other things) from the defeated, even when the victors have no current resource problems. Another factor apparently making for more war is teaching children to mistrust others. People who grow up to be mistrustful of others may be more likely to go to war than to negotiate or seek conciliation with "enemies." Mistrust or fear of others seems to be partly caused by threat or fear of disasters.[59]

Is warfare in and between modern state societies explainable in much the same way that nonindustrial warfare seems to be explainable? If the answer to that question turns out to be yes, it will certainly be a modified yes, because the realities of industrialized societies require an expanded conception of disasters. In the modern world, with its complex economic and political dependencies among nations, we may not be worried only about weather or pest disasters that could curtail food supplies. Possible curtailments of other resources, particularly oil, may also scare us into going to war. According to some commentators, the decision in 1991 to go to war against Iraq after it invaded Kuwait fits this theory of war.

But even if the "threat-to-resources" theory is true, we may be coming to realize (since the end of the Cold War) that war is not the only way to ensure access to resources. There may be a better way in the modern world, a way that is more cost-effective as well as more preserving of human life. If it is true that war is most likely when people fear unpredictable disasters of any kind, the risk of war should lessen when people realize that the harmful effects of disasters could be reduced or prevented by international cooperation. Just as we have the assurance of disaster relief within our country, we could have the assurance of disaster relief worldwide. That is, the fear of unpredictable disasters and the fear of others, and the consequent risk of war, could be reduced by the assurance ahead of time that the world would help those in need in case of disaster. Instead of going to war out of fear, we could go to peace by agreeing to share. The certainty of international cooperation could compensate for the uncertainty of resources.

Consider how Germany and Japan have fared in the years since their "unconditional surrender" in World War II. They were forbidden to participate in the international arms race and could rely on others, particularly the United States, to protect them. Without a huge burden of armaments, Germany and Japan thrived. But countries that competed militarily, particularly the United States and the Soviet Union at the height of the Cold War, experienced economic difficulties. Doesn't that scenario at least suggest the wisdom of international cooperation, particularly the need for international agreements to ensure worldwide disaster relief? Compared with going to war and its enormous costs, going to peace would be a bargain!

Recent research in political science and anthropology suggests an additional way to reduce the risk of war. Among the societies known to anthropology, studies indicate that people in more participatory—that is, more "democratic"—political systems rarely go to war with each other.[60] Thus, if authoritarian governments were to disappear from the world because the powerful nations of the world stopped supporting them militarily and otherwise, the world could be more peaceful for this reason too.

Although democratically governed states rarely go to war with each other, it used to be thought that they are not necessarily more peaceful in general, that they are as likely to go to war as are other kinds of political systems, but not so much with each other. For example, the United States has gone to war with Grenada, Panama, and Iraq—all authoritarian states—but not with democratic Canada, with which the United States has also had disputes. But now a consensus is emerging among political scientists that democracies are not only unlikely to go to war with each other, they are also less warlike in general.[61] The theory suggested by the cross-national and cross-cultural results is that democratic conflict resolution within a political system generalizes to democratic conflict resolution between

current research and issues

Ethnic Conflicts: Ancient Hatreds or Not?

Ethnic conflicts appear to be on the rise. In recent years, violent conflicts have erupted between ethnic groups in the former Yugoslavia, Russia, and Spain (in Europe), in Rwanda and Sierra Leone (in Africa), and in Sri Lanka and Indonesia (in Asia)—to name just a few of the many instances. Such conflicts are often thought to be intractable and inevitable because they are supposedly based on ancient hatreds. But is that true?

Social scientists are a long way from understanding the conditions that predict ethnic conflicts, but they do know that ethnic conflicts are not necessarily ancient or inevitable. For example, anthropologists who did fieldwork in the former Yugoslavia in the 1980s described villages where different ethnic groups had lived side by side for a long time without apparent difficulty. The differences between them were hardly emphasized. Mary Kay Gilliland worked in a midsize town (Slavonski Brod) in the Slavonian region of Croatia, which was part of Yugoslavia. The people in the town identified themselves as from Slavonia, rather than as Croats, Serbs, Hungarians, Czechs, Muslims (from Bosnia or from Albania), or Roma (Gypsies). Mixed marriages were not uncommon and people discussed differences in background without anger. But in 1991, when Gilliland returned to Croatia, people complained about Serb domination of the Yugoslav government and there was talk of Croatia seceding. Symbols of Croat national-

ism had appeared—new place names, a new flag—and Croats were now said to speak Croatian, rather than the language they shared with the Serbs (Serbo-Croatian or Croato-Serbian). Later in 1991, violence broke out between Serbs and Croats, and atrocities were committed on both sides. Ethnicity became a matter of life or death, and Croatia seceded from Yugoslavia. At the same time, Tone Bringa, a Norwegian anthropologist who worked in Bosnia (which was then still a region of Yugoslavia), reported that the people there also paid little attention to ethnicity. A few years later, however, ethnic violence erupted among Bosnian Serbs, Muslims, and Croats, and only the intervention of the United Nations established a precarious peace.

Ethnic conflict is frequently associated with secessionist movements. That is, secession often occurs after the eruption of ethnic conflict. Remember the American Revolution? The region that became the United States of America seceded from Great Britain and declared independence. To be sure, the ethnic differences between the Americans and the British were not great. After all, not too many years had passed since the first British colonizers had come to America. But there still was a secessionist movement, and there was violence. Ethnic differences do not always lead to violence. Sometimes, probably even most of the time, people of different ethnic backgrounds live in peace with each other. So the

basic question is why do some places with ethnic differences erupt in violence, but not all? Why do different ethnic groups get along in some places?

We need research to answer this question. With all of the forced and voluntary immigration in the world, many countries are becoming more multiethnic or multicultural. The possibility of ethnic violence has become a global social problem. Gilliland suggests, among other things, that discontent over economic and political power (inequitable access to resources and opportunities) drove the Croatians to violence and secession. Other scholars have suggested other possible answers to the question of why ethnic relations do not always become ethnic conflict and violence. Violence may erupt in the absence of strong unifying interests (cross-cutting ties) between the parties. Another suggested factor is the absence of constitutional ways to resolve conflict. What we need now is cross-cultural, cross-national, and cross-historical studies to measure each of the possible explaining factors, so that we can compare how well (or poorly) they predict ethnic conflict throughout the world, controlling for the effects of the other factors. If we knew which factors generally give rise to ethnic violence, we might be able to think of ways to reduce or eliminate the causal conditions.

Sources: Gilliland 1995; Bringa 1995; M. H. Ross 2009a.

---

political systems, particularly if the systems are both democratic. If our participatory institutions and perceptions allow us to resolve our disputes peacefully, internally and externally, we may think that similarly governed people would also be disposed to settle things peacefully. Therefore, disputes between participatory political systems should be unlikely to result in war.

The understanding that participatory systems rarely fight each other, and knowing why they do not, would

have important consequences for policy in the contemporary world. The kinds of military preparations believed necessary and the costs people would be willing to pay for them might be affected. On the one hand, understanding the relationship between democracy and peace might encourage war making against authoritarian regimes to overturn them—with enormous costs in human life and otherwise. On the other hand, understanding the consequences of democracy might encourage us to assist the emergence and consolidation of more participatory systems of government in the countries of eastern Europe, the former Soviet Union, and elsewhere. In any case, the relationship between democracy and peace strongly suggests that it is counterproductive to support any undemocratic regimes, even if they happen to be enemies of our enemies, if we want to minimize the risk of war in the world. The latest cross-national evidence suggests that extending democracy around the world would minimize the risk of war. Encouraging nations to be more interdependent economically, and encouraging the spread of international nongovernmental organizations (like professional societies and trade associations) to provide informal ways to resolve conflicts, would also minimize the risk of war, judging by results of recent research by political scientists.[62]

TERRORISM

Ever since September 11, 2001, when terrorists crashed airliners into the World Trade Center towers in New York City and into the Pentagon in Arlington, Virginia, people all over the world realize that terrorism has become a social problem globally. It is now painfully clear that organized groups of terrorists can train their people to kill themselves and thousands of others half a world away, not only by hijacking airliners and flying them into skyscrapers, but also by using easily transported explosives and biological weapons. Social scientists are now actively trying to understand terrorism, in the hope that research may lead to ways to minimize the likelihood of future attacks. But there are lots of questions to answer. What is terrorism and how shall it be defined?

How long has terrorist activity been around? What are the causes of terrorism? What kind of people are likely to become terrorists? And what are the consequences of terrorism?

Answering these questions is not so simple. Most people can point to instances that hardly anyone would have trouble calling terrorism—spraying nerve gas in a Japanese subway, Palestinian suicide bombers targeting Israeli civilians, Ku Klux Klan members lynching African Americans.[63] It is harder to identify the boundaries between terrorism, crime, political repression, and warfare.[64] Most researchers agree that terrorism involves the threat or use of violence against civilians. Terrorism is usually also politically or socially organized, in contrast to most crimes, which are usually perpetrated by individuals acting on their own. (To be sure, crime can be socially organized too, as, for example, in what we call "organized crime.") One marker of the difference between most crime and terrorism is that criminals rarely take public credit for their activities, because they want to avoid being caught. In terrorism, the perpetrators usually proclaim their responsibility. In terrorism also, the violence is directed mostly at unarmed people, including women and children. It is intended to frighten the "enemy," to *terrorize* them, to scare them into doing something that the terrorists want to see happen. Generally, then, **terrorism** may be defined as the use or threat of violence to create terror in others, usually for political purposes.[65] Some define terrorism as perpetrated by groups that are not formal political entities. However, this criterion presents some difficulty. What are we to call it when governments support death squads and genocide against their own civilians? Some scholars call this "state terror."[66] And what are

A candlelight vigil after the terrorist attack in 2008 on the Taj Mahal Hotel in Mumbai, India.

migrants and immigrants

Refugees Are a Global Social Problem

The continuing turmoil in many countries throughout the world has created a flow of refugees that is much larger than ever before in world history. Refugees have become a worldwide social problem; their numbers are so high. In the past, thousands of people might have had to flee persecution and war. Now the refugees number in the millions. They flee to other parts of the country, to neighboring countries, and to countries on the other side of the world. As many as an estimated 140 million people became refugees in the 20th century. For example, the refugees from the civil wars in Somalia are not unusual; 10 percent of the Somali population is now living outside of Somalia, perhaps a million people altogether.

Conceivably, the problem could be handled with less suffering if countries were willing to accept any and all refugees. Shouldn't governments accept them for humanitarian reasons, just because the refugees could die otherwise? Or does there have to be an acknowledged or felt need in the accepting country for cheap labor? There is a fine line between people who want to migrate to have a better or safer life, and people who have to migrate because they would be killed if they don't flee. Refugees are a problem not just because they are

suffering, and the world should do something. They are also a problem because countries may refuse to accept them, because their numbers are so large. Governments and charitable agencies have to provide support until the refugees acquire the skills for making a living on their own.

Compare how we think of refugees from different places. Some are accepted (however grudgingly), whereas others are not. The United States only half-heartedly tries to prevent poor Mexicans from entering the country. But people from Africa who are threatened with genocide are rejected much more. Why? Is it because Mexicans and others from Latin America have skills that we need, and they are willing to take jobs that no one else wants because the pay is low and the benefits nil? Who benefits from this state of affairs? Too many! Think of the employers who would otherwise have to pay their workers more or invest in labor-saving machinery. Think of the Chinese "coolies" who were brought in 150 years ago to build the railroads that linked the eastern and western United States. And, of course, think of the refugee laborers. If they didn't "cross the border" looking for work, their children left at home would suffer or even die from malnutrition and other consequences of poverty.

So, what are countries to do? Should they throw open their doors to everyone who wants to come in? Humanitarians might say yes. But this too would make for problems. Some would say that we should not accept and support refugees when we already have lots of poor people. Don't we owe them more than we owe poor people from somewhere else? Shouldn't our tax money go to improve the lives of people already here? What are taxes for, anyway?

How to help refugees is clearly a complex issue. But if we don't do anything to help them, is that ethical? Refugees are the consequences of social inequality and persecution. They are a global social problem that won't go away, as long as the world contains governments that persecute their own citizens, or allow some groups to persecute others. If the solution is not to rely on those governments because they are not likely to change what they are doing, it would seem that we will have to rely for the near future on international organizations (like the United Nations and charitable foundations) if we want to reduce or eliminate the worldwide problem of refugees.

Sources: Harrell-Bond 1996; Van Hear 2004.

---

we to call the activities of some governments that support secret operations against other countries (often referred to as "state-sponsored terrorism")? Finally, although some nations conducting war explicitly try to avoid civilian casualties and focus primarily on combatants (armed soldiers), their weapons, and resources or "assets" such as factories, air strips, and fuel depots, many attacks in wartime throughout history have purposefully targeted civilians (e.g., the United States dropped atomic bombs on Hiroshima and Nagasaki to persuade the Japanese to end World War II).

One thing is certain about terrorism: It is not a new development. Some of the words we use for terrorists—for example, "zealots" and "assassins"—derive from terrorist

movements in the past. The Zealots, Jewish nationalists who revolted against the Romans occupying Judea in the first century, would hide in crowds and stab officials and priests as well as soldiers. In the 11th and 12th centuries in southwest Asia, the Fedayeen (a group of Muslim Isma'ili Shi'ites) undertook to assassinate Sunni rulers despite the almost certainty of their own capture or death. The rulers said that the Fedayeen were under the influence of hashish and called them "Hashshashin," which is the root of the later term *assassin*.[67] In the late 18th and early 19th centuries, the "reign of terror" occurred during and after the French Revolution. In the early and middle 20th century, the dictator Joseph Stalin ordered the execution of many millions of people who were considered enemies of the Soviet state. Six million Jews and millions of other innocents were exterminated by the German Third Reich in the 1930s and 1940s.[68] And many Latin American regimes, such as that in Argentina, terrorized and killed dissidents in the 1970s and 1980s.[69] Now there is a heightened fear of terrorists who may have access to weapons of mass destruction. In a world made smaller by global transportation, cell phones, and the Internet, terrorism is a greater threat than ever before.

We still lack systematic research that explains why terrorism occurs and why people are motivated to become terrorists. But there is a good deal of research about state terrorism. Political scientist R. J. Rummel estimates that governments have killed nearly 262 million people in the 20th century (he calls this kind of terrorism "democide"). State terrorism has been responsible for four times more deaths than all the wars, civil and international, that occurred in the 20th century. Regimes in the Soviet Union (1917–1987), China (1923–1987), and Germany (1933–1945) were responsible for killing more than a total of 190 million civilians. Proportionately the Khmer Rouge regime in Cambodia topped them all, killing over 30 percent of its population from 1975 to 1978.[70] What predicts state terrorism against one's own people? Rummel finds one clear predictor—totalitarian governments. By far, they have the highest frequencies of domestic state terrorism, controlling for factors such as economic wealth, type of religion, and population size. As Rummel puts it, "power kills; absolute power kills absolutely."[71] Democratic countries are less likely to practice state terrorism, but when they do, it occurs during or after a rebellion or a war.[72]

We know relatively little so far about what predicts who will become a terrorist. We do know that terrorists often come from higher social statuses and generally have more education than the average person.[73] If state terrorism is more likely to occur in totalitarian regimes, terrorists and terrorist groups may be more likely to occur in such societies. If so, the spread of democracy may be our best hope of minimizing the risk of terrorism in the world, just as the spread of democracy seems to minimize the likelihood of war between countries.

MAKING THE WORLD BETTER

Many social problems afflict our world, not just the ones discussed in this chapter.[74] We don't have the space to discuss the international trade in drugs and how it plays out in violence, death, and corruption. We haven't talked about the negative effects of environmental degradations such as water pollution, ozone depletion, and destruction of forests and wetlands. We haven't said much, if anything, about overpopulation, the energy crisis, and a host of other problems we should care and do something about, if we hope to make this a safer world. But we have tried in this chapter to encourage positive thinking about global social problems; we have suggested how the results of past and future scientific research could be applied to solving some of those problems.

We may know enough now that we can do something about our problems, and we will discover more through future research. Social problems are mostly of human making and are therefore susceptible to human unmaking. There may be obstacles on the road to solutions, but we can overcome them if we want to. So let's go for it!

SUMMARY ● ○ ○

1. We may be more motivated now to try to solve social problems because worldwide communication has increased our awareness of them elsewhere, because we seem to be increasingly bothered by problems in our own society, and because we know more than we used to about various social problems that afflict our world.

2. The idea that we can solve global social problems is based on two assumptions. We have to assume that it is possible to discover the causes of a problem, and we have to assume that we will be able to do something about the causes once they are discovered and thereby eliminate or reduce the problem.

3. Disasters such as earthquakes, floods, and droughts can have greater or lesser effects on human life, depending on social conditions. Therefore, disasters are partly social problems, with partly social causes and solutions.

4. Whether people become homeless, whether they have shantytowns, seems to depend on a society's willingness to share wealth and to help those in need.

5. Promoting the equality of men and women and the sharing of childrearing responsibilities may reduce family violence.

6. We may be able to reduce rates of violent crime if we can reduce socialization and training for aggression. To do that, we would have to reduce the likelihood of war, the high likelihood of which predicts more socialization for aggression and other forms of socially approved aggression. The reduction of inequalities in wealth may also help to reduce crime, particularly theft. And raising boys with a male role model around may reduce the likelihood of male violence in adulthood.

7. People seem to be most likely to go to war when they fear unpredictable disasters that destroy food supplies or curtail the supplies of other necessities. Disputes between more participatory (more "democratic") political systems are unlikely to result in war. Therefore, the more democracy spreads in the world, and the more people all over the world are assured of internationally organized disaster relief, the more they might go to peace rather than to war to solve their problems.

8. Terrorism has occurred throughout history. State terrorism has killed more than all wars in the 20th century and seems to be predicted mostly by totalitarianism.

GLOSSARY TERM ○ ● ○

terrorism **512**

CRITICAL QUESTIONS ○ ○ ●

1. What particular advantages do anthropologists have in trying to solve practical problems?

2. Select one of the social problems discussed in this chapter and suggest what you think could be done to reduce or eliminate it.

3. Do global problems require solutions by global agencies? If so, which?

PEARSON
myanthrolab

Read the chapter by Paul C. Rosenblatt titled "Human Rights Violations" on MyAnthroLab. Answer the following questions:

1. Rosenblatt states that human rights may be enhanced by "promoting more respectful, peaceful, and non-exploitive relations among different groups within countries." Explain why he thinks so.

2. Why does he say that "saints can be sinners and sinners can be saints"?

3. Rosenblatt asks: "Is it moral for the United States and a handful of other powerful nations to impose their will on other nations?" What do you think, and why do you think so?

glossary

Absolute dating   A method of dating fossils in which the actual age of a deposit or specimen is measured. Also known as **chronometric dating.**

Accent   Differences in pronunciation characteristic of a group.

Acclimatization   Impermanent physiological changes that people make when they encounter a new environment.

Acculturation   The process of extensive borrowing of aspects of culture in the context of superordinate-subordinate relations between societies; usually occurs as the result of external pressure.

Acheulian   A stone toolmaking tradition dating from 1.5 million years ago. Compared with the Oldowan tradition, Acheulian assemblages have more large tools created according to standardized designs or shapes. One of the most characteristic and prevalent tools in the Acheulian tool kit is the so-called hand axe, which is a teardrop-shaped bifacially flaked tool with a thinned sharp tip. Other large tools might have been cleavers and picks.

Achieved qualities   Those qualities people acquire during their lifetime.

Adapid   A type of prosimian with many lemurlike features; appeared in the early Eocene.

Adaptation   Refers to genetic changes that allow an organism to survive and reproduce in a specific environment.

Adaptive customs   Cultural traits that enhance survival and reproductive success in a particular environment.

Adjudication   The process by which a third party acting as judge makes a decision that the parties to a dispute have to accept.

Aegyptopithecus   An Oligocene anthropoid and probably the best-known propliopithecid.

Affinal kin   One's relatives by marriage.

Age-grade   A category of people who happen to fall within a particular, culturally distinguished age range.

Age-set   A group of people of similar age and the same sex who move together through some or all of life's stages.

Agriculture   The practice of raising domesticated crops.

AIDS (Acquired Immune Deficiency Syndrome)   A disease caused by the HIV virus.

Allele   One member of a pair of genes.

Allen's rule   The rule that protruding body parts (particularly arms and legs) are relatively shorter in the cooler areas of a species' range than in the warmer areas.

Ambilineal descent   The rule of descent that affiliates individuals with groups of kin related to them through men or women.

Ancestor spirits   Supernatural beings who are the ghosts of dead relatives.

Animatism   A belief in supernatural forces.

Animism   A belief in a dual existence for all things—a physical, visible body and a psychic, invisible soul.

Anthropoids   One of the two suborders of primates; includes monkeys, apes, and humans.

Anthropological linguistics   The anthropological study of languages.

Anthropology   A discipline that studies humans, focusing on the study of differences and similarities, both biological and cultural, in human populations. Anthropology is concerned with typical biological and cultural characteristics of human populations in all periods and in all parts of the world.

Anthropometry   Refers to the study of variation in the size and shape of the human body.

Applied (practicing) anthropology   The branch of anthropology that concerns itself with applying anthropological knowledge to achieve practical goals, usually in the service of an agency outside the traditional academic setting.

^{40}Ar–^{39}Ar dating   Used in conjunction with potassium-argon dating, this method gets around the problem of needing different rock samples to estimate potassium and argon. A nuclear reactor is used to convert the ^{39}Ar to ^{39}K, on the basis of which the amount of ^{40}K can be estimated. In this way, both argon and potassium can be estimated from the same rock sample.

Arboreal   Adapted to living in trees.

Archaeology   The branch of anthropology that seeks to reconstruct the daily life and customs of peoples who lived in the past and to trace and explain cultural changes. Often lacking written records for study, archaeologists must try to reconstruct history from the material remains of human cultures. See also **Historical archaeology.**

Archaic   Time period in the New World during which food production first developed.

Ardipithecus ramidus   Perhaps the first hominid, dating to about 4.5 million years ago. Its dentition combines apelike and australopithecine-like features, and its skeleton suggests it was bipedal.

Artifact   Any object made by a human.

Ascribed qualities   Those qualities that are determined for people at birth.

Association   An organized group not based exclusively on kinship or territory.

Atlatl   Aztec word for "spear thrower."

Australopithecus   Genus of Pliocene and Pleistocene hominids.

Australopithecus aethiopicus   An early robust australopithecine.

Australopithecus afarensis   A species of *Australopithecus* that lived 4 million to 3 million years ago in East Africa and was definitely bipedal.

Australopithecus africanus   A species of *Australopithecus* that lived between about 3 million and 2 million years ago.

Australopithecus anamensis   A species of *Australopithecus* that lived perhaps 4.2 million years ago.

Australopithecus bahrelghazali   An early gracile australopithecine, dating to about 3 million years ago, and currently represented by only a single jaw. It is an interesting species because it is found in western Chad, distant from the East African Rift Valley where all other early australopithecines have been found.

Australopithecus boisei An East African robust australopithecine species dating from 2.2 million to 1.3 million years ago with somewhat larger cranial capacity than *A. africanus*. No longer thought to be larger than other australopithecines, it is robust primarily in the skull and jaw, most strikingly in the teeth. Compared with *A. robustus*, *A. boisei* has even more features that reflect a huge chewing apparatus.

Australopithecus garhi A gracile australopithecine, dating to about 2.5 million years ago.

Australopithecus robustus A robust australopithecine species found in South African caves dating from about 1.8 million to 1 million years ago. Not as large in the teeth and jaws as *A. boisei*.

Avunculocal residence A pattern of residence in which a married couple settles with or near the husband's mother's brother.

Balanced reciprocity Giving with the expectation of a straightforward immediate or limited-time trade.

Balancing selection A type of selection that occurs when a heterozygous combination of alleles is positively favored even though a homozygous combination is disfavored.

Band A fairly small, usually nomadic local group that is politically autonomous.

Band organization The kind of political organization where the local group or band is the largest territorial group in the society that acts as a unit. The local group in band societies is politically autonomous.

Behavioral ecology Typically tries to understand contemporary human behavior using evolutionary principles. In addition to the principle of individual selection, behavioral ecologists point to the importance of analyzing economic tradeoffs because individuals have limited time and resources.

Bergmann's rule The rule that smaller-sized subpopulations of a species inhabit the warmer parts of its geographic range and larger-sized subpopulations the cooler areas.

Bifacial tool A tool worked or flaked on two sides.

Bilateral kinship The type of kinship system in which individuals affiliate more or less equally with their mother's and father's relatives; descent groups are absent.

Bilocal residence A pattern of residence in which a married couple lives with or near either the husband's parents or the wife's parents.

Bilophodont Having four cusps on the molars that form two parallel ridges. This is the common molar pattern of Old World monkeys.

Biological (physical) anthropology The study of humans as biological organisms, dealing with the emergence and evolution of humans and with contemporary biological variations among human populations.

Biomedicine The dominant medical paradigm in Western societies today.

Bipedalism Locomotion in which an animal walks on its two hind legs.

Blade A thin flake whose length is usually more than twice its width. In the blade technique of toolmaking, a core is prepared by shaping a piece of flint with hammerstones into a pyramidal or cylindrical form. Blades are then struck off until the core is used up.

Brachiators Animals that move through the trees by swinging hand over hand from branch to branch. They usually have long arms and fingers.

Bride price A substantial gift of goods or money given to the bride's kin by the groom or his kin at or before the marriage. Also called **bride wealth.**

Bride service Work performed by the groom for his bride's family for a variable length of time either before or after the marriage.

Burin A chisel-like stone tool used for carving and for making such artifacts as bone and antler needles, awls, and projectile points.

Canines The cone-shaped teeth immediately behind the incisors; used by most primates to seize food and in fighting and display.

Carpolestes A mouse-sized arboreal creature living about 56 million years ago; a strong candidate for the common primate ancestor.

Cash crop A cultivated commodity raised for sale rather than for personal consumption by the cultivator.

Caste A ranked group, often associated with a certain occupation, in which membership is determined at birth and marriage is restricted to members of one's own caste.

Catarrhines The group of anthropoids with narrow noses and nostrils that face downward. Catarrhines include monkeys of the Old World (Africa, Asia, and Europe), as well as apes and humans.

Ceramics Objects shaped from clay and baked at high temperature (fired) to make them hard. Containers such as pots and jars are typical ceramics, though they can take on many forms and uses.

Cercopithecoids Old World monkeys.

Cerebral cortex The "gray matter" of the brain; the center of speech and other higher mental activities.

Chief A person who exercises authority, usually on behalf of a multicommunity political unit. This role is generally found in rank societies and is usually permanent and often hereditary.

Chiefdom A political unit, with a chief at its head, integrating more than one community but not necessarily the whole society or language group.

Chromosomes Paired rod-shaped structures within a cell nucleus containing the genes that transmit traits from one generation to the next.

Chronometric dating See **Absolute dating.**

Civilization Urban society, from the Latin word for "city-state."

Clan A set of kin whose members believe themselves to be descended from a common ancestor or ancestress but cannot specify the links back to that founder; often designated by a totem. Also called a **sib.**

Class A category of people who have about the same opportunity to obtain economic resources, power, and prestige.

Classificatory terms Kinship terms that merge or equate relatives who are genealogically distinct from one another; the same term is used for a number of different kin.

Class societies Societies containing social groups that have unequal access to economic resources, power, and prestige.

Cline The gradually increasing (or decreasing) frequency of a gene from one end of a region to another.

Code-switching Using more than one language in the course of conversing.

Codified laws Formal principles for resolving disputes in heterogeneous and stratified societies.

Cognates Words or morphs that belong to different languages but have similar sounds and meanings.

Commercial exchange See **Market (or commercial) exchange.**

Commercialization The increasing dependence on buying and selling, with money usually as the medium of exchange.

Complementary opposition The occasional uniting of various segments of a segmentary lineage system in opposition to similar segments.

Consanguineal kin One's biological relatives; relatives by birth.

Context The relationships between and among artifacts, ecofacts, fossils, and features.

Continental drift The movement of the continents over the past 135 million years. In the early Cretaceous (circa 135 million years ago), there were two "supercontinents": *Laurasia,* which included North America and Eurasia; and *Gondwanaland,* which included Africa, South America, India, Australia, and Antarctica. By the beginning of the Paleocene (circa 65 million years ago), Gondwanaland had broken apart, with South America drifting west away from Africa, India drifting east, and Australia and Antarctica drifting south.

Core vocabulary Nonspecialist vocabulary.

Corvée A system of required labor.

Cretaceous Geological epoch 135 million to 65 million years ago, during which dinosaurs and other reptiles ceased to be the dominant land vertebrates, and mammals and birds began to become important.

Crime Violence not considered legitimate that occurs within a political unit.

Cro-Magnons Humans who lived in western Europe about 35,000 years ago, they were once thought to be the earliest specimens of modern-looking humans, or *Homo sapiens sapiens.* But it is now known that modern-looking humans appeared earlier outside of Europe; the earliest so far found lived in Africa.

Cross-cousins Children of siblings of the opposite sex. One's cross-cousins are the father's sisters' children and mother's brothers' children.

Cross-cultural researcher An ethnologist who uses ethnographic data about many societies to test possible explanations of cultural variation to discover general patterns about cultural traits—what is universal, what is variable, why traits vary, and what the consequences of the variability might be.

Crossing-over Exchanges of sections of chromosomes from one chromosome to another.

Cultural anthropology The study of cultural variation and universals in the past and present.

Cultural ecology The analysis of the relationship between a culture and its environment.

Cultural relativism The attitude that a society's customs and ideas should be viewed within the context of that society's problems and opportunities.

Cultural resource management (CRM) The branch of applied anthropology that seeks to recover and preserve the archaeological record before programs of planned change disturb or destroy it.

Culture The set of learned behaviors, beliefs, attitudes, values, and ideals that are characteristic of a particular society or other social group.

Culture history A history of the cultures that lived in a given area over time. Until the 1950s, building such culture histories was a primary goal of archaeological research.

Cuneiform Wedge-shaped writing invented by the Sumerians around 3000 B.C.

Descriptive (structural) linguistics The study of how languages are constructed.

Dialect A variety of a language spoken in a particular area or by a particular social group.

Diastema A gap between the canine and first premolar found in apes.

Diffusion The borrowing by one society of a cultural trait belonging to another society as the result of contact between the two societies.

Directional selection A type of natural selection that increases the frequency of a trait (the trait is said to be positively favored, or adaptive).

Diurnal Active during the day.

Divination Getting the supernatural to provide guidance.

DNA Deoxyribonucleic acid; a long, two-stranded molecule in the genes that directs the makeup of an organism according to the instructions in its genetic code.

Domestication Modification or adaptation of plants and animals for use by humans. When people plant crops, we refer to the process as cultivation. It is only when the crops cultivated and the animals raised have been modified—are different from wild varieties—that we speak of plant and animal domestication.

Dominant The allele of a gene pair that is always phenotypically expressed in the heterozygous form.

Double descent or double unilineal descent A system that affiliates individuals with a group of matrilineal kin for some purposes and with a group of patrilineal kin for other purposes.

Dowry A substantial transfer of goods or money from the bride's family to the bride.

Dryopithecus Genus of ape from the later Miocene found primarily in Europe. It had thin tooth enamel and pointed molar cusps very similar to those of the fruit-eating chimpanzees of today.

Dual-inheritance theory In contrast to other evolutionary ecological perspectives, this theory gives much more importance to culture as part of the evolutionary process. Dual inheritance refers to both genes and culture playing different, but nonetheless important and interactive roles in transmitting traits to future generations.

Ecofacts Natural items that humans have used; things such as the remains of animals eaten by humans or plant pollens found on archaeological sites are examples of ecofacts.

Economic resources Things that have value in a culture, including land, tools and other technology, goods, and money.

Egalitarian societies Societies in which all people of a given age-sex category have equal access to economic resources, power, and prestige.

Ego In the reckoning of kinship, the reference point or focal person.

Enculturation See **Socialization.**

Endogamy The rule specifying marriage to a person within one's own group (kin, caste, community).

Eocene   A geological epoch 55 million to 34 million years ago during which the first definite primates appeared.

Epipaleolithic   Time period during which food production first developed in the Near East.

Ethnicity   The process of defining ethnicity usually involves a group of people emphasizing common origins and language, shared history, and selected aspects of cultural difference such as a difference in religion. Because different groups are doing the perceiving, ethnic identities often vary with whether one is inside or outside the group.

Ethnocentric   Refers to judgment of other cultures solely in terms of one's own culture.

Ethnocentrism   The attitude that other societies' customs and ideas can be judged in the context of one's own culture.

Ethnogenesis   Creation of a new culture.

Ethnographer   A person who spends some time living with, interviewing, and observing a group of people to describe their customs.

Ethnographic analogy   Method of comparative cultural study that extrapolates to the past from recent or current societies.

Ethnography   A description of a society's customary behaviors and ideas.

Ethnohistorian   An ethnologist who uses historical documents to study how a particular culture has changed over time.

Ethnology   The study of how and why recent cultures differ and are similar.

Ethnomedicine   The health-related beliefs, knowledge, and practices of a cultural group.

Ethnoscience   An approach that attempts to derive rules of thought from the logical analysis of ethnographic data.

Eugenics   Selectively breeding humans with desirable characteristics and preventing those with undesirable ones from having offspring.

Evolutionary psychology   A type of evolutionary ecological approach that is particularly interested in universal human psychology. It is argued that human psychology was primarily adapted to the environment that characterized most of human history—the hunting-gathering way of life.

Excavation   The careful removal of the archaeological deposits; the recovery of artifacts, ecofacts, fossils, and features from the soil in which those deposits have been buried.

Exogamy   The rule specifying marriage to a person from outside one's own group (kin or community).

Explanation   An answer to a *why* question. In science, there are two kinds of explanation that researchers try to achieve: associations and theories.

Extended family   A family consisting of two or more single-parent, monogamous, polygynous, or polyandrous families linked by a blood tie.

Extensive cultivation   A type of horticulture in which the land is worked for short periods and then left to regenerate for some years before being used again. Also called **shifting cultivation.**

Falsification   Showing that a theory seems to be wrong by finding that implications or predictions derivable from it are not consistent with objectively collected data.

Family   A social and economic unit consisting minimally of a parent and a child.

Fayum   A site southwest of Cairo, Egypt, where the world's best record of Oligocene primate fossils has been found.

Features   Artifacts of human manufacture that cannot be removed from an archaeological site. Hearths, storage pits, and buildings are examples of features.

Feuding   A state of recurring hostility between families or groups of kin, usually motivated by a desire to avenge an offense against a member of the group.

Fieldwork   Firsthand experience with the people being studied and the usual means by which anthropological information is obtained. Regardless of other methods that anthropologists may use (e.g., censuses, surveys), fieldwork usually involves participant-observation for an extended period of time, often a year or more. See **Participant-observation.**

Folklore   Includes all the myths, legends, folktales, ballads, riddles, proverbs, and superstitions of a cultural group. Generally, folklore is transmitted orally, but it may also be written.

Food production   The form of subsistence technology in which food-getting is dependent on the cultivation and domestication of plants and animals.

Foragers   People who subsist on the collection of naturally occurring plants and animals. Also referred to as **hunter-gatherers** or *food collectors.*

Foraging   May be generally defined as a food-getting strategy that obtains wild plant and animal resources through gathering, hunting, scavenging, or fishing; also known as food collection.

Foramen magnum   Opening in the base of the skull through which the spinal cord passes en route to the brain.

Forensic anthropology   The application of anthropology, usually physical anthropology, to help identify human remains and assist in solving crimes.

Fossils   The hardened remains or impressions of plants and animals that lived in the past.

Fraternal polyandry   The marriage of a woman to two or more brothers at the same time.

Functionalism   The theoretical orientation that looks for the part (function) that some aspect of culture or social life plays in maintaining a cultural system.

Gender differences   Differences between females and males that reflect cultural expectations and experiences.

Gender roles   Roles that are culturally assigned to genders.

Gender stratification   The degree of unequal access by the different genders to prestige, authority, power, rights, and economic resources.

Gene   Chemical unit of heredity.

Gene flow   The process by which genes pass from the gene pool of one population to that of another through mating and reproduction.

General evolution   The notion that higher forms of culture arise from and generally supersede lower forms.

Generalized reciprocity   Gift giving without any immediate or planned return.

General-purpose money   A universally accepted medium of exchange.

Genetic drift   The various random processes that affect gene frequencies in small, relatively isolated populations.

Genotype   The total complement of inherited traits or genes of an organism.

Genus   A group of related species; pl., genera.

Ghosts   Supernatural beings who were once human; the souls of dead people.

Globalization   The ongoing spread of goods, people, information, and capital around the world.

Gloger's rule The rule that populations of birds and mammals living in warm, humid climates have more melanin (and therefore darker skin, fur, or feathers) than populations of the same species living in cooler, drier areas.

Gods Supernatural beings of nonhuman origin who are named personalities; often anthropomorphic.

Gracile australopithecines The earliest group of australopithecines, usually differentiated from the robust australopithecines by their lighter dentition and smaller faces.

Group marriage Marriage in which more than one man is married to more than one woman at the same time; not customary in any known human society.

Group selection Natural selection of group characteristics.

Half-life The time it takes for half of the atoms of a radioactive substance to decay into atoms of a different substance.

Hand axe A teardrop-shaped stone tool characteristic of Acheulian assemblages.

Hard hammer A technique of stone tool manufacture where one stone is used to knock flakes from another stone. Flakes produced through hard hammer percussion are usually large and crude.

Headman A person who holds a powerless but symbolically unifying position in a community within an egalitarian society; may exercise influence but has no power to impose sanctions.

Hermeneutics The study of meaning.

Heterozygous Possessing differing genes or alleles in corresponding locations on a pair of chromosomes.

Hieroglyphics "Picture writing," as in ancient Egypt and in Mayan sites in Mesoamerica (Mexico and Central America).

Historical archaeology A specialty within archaeology that studies the material remains of recent peoples who left written records.

Historical linguistics The study of how languages change over time.

Holistic Refers to an approach that studies many aspects of a multifaceted system.

Hominids The group of hominoids consisting of humans and their direct ancestors. It contains at least two genera: *Homo* and *Australopithecus*.

Hominoids The group of catarrhines that includes both apes and humans.

Homo Genus to which modern humans and their ancestors belong.

Homo antecessor Refers to a group of hominid fossils found in the Atapuerca region of Spain that appear to be transitional between Neandertals and modern humans. They are closely related to *Homo heidelbergensis*, and many scholars believe they are the same species.

Homo erectus The first hominid species to be widely distributed in the Old World. The earliest finds are possibly 1.8 million years old. The brain (averaging 895–1,040 cc) was larger than that found in any of the australopithecines or *H. habilis* but smaller than the average brain of a modern human.

Homo floresiensis A dwarf species of hominid that lived on the Indonesian island of Flores until about 12,000 years ago and probably descended from an isolated *Homo erectus* population.

Homo habilis Dating from about 2 million years ago, an early species belonging to our genus, *Homo*, with cranial capacities averaging about 630–640 cc, about 50 percent of the brain capacity of modern humans.

Homo heidelbergensis A transitional species between *Homo erectus* and *Homo sapiens*.

Homo neandertalensis The technical name for the Neandertals, a group of robust and otherwise anatomically distinct hominids that are close relatives of modern humans—so close that some believe they should be classified as *Homo sapiens neandertalensis*.

Homo rudolfensis Early species belonging to our genus, *Homo*. Similar enough to *Homo habilis* that some paleoanthropologists make no distinction between the two.

Homo sapiens All living people belong to one biological species, *Homo sapiens*, which means that all human populations on earth can successfully interbreed. The first *Homo sapiens* may have emerged about 200,000 years ago.

Homo sapiens sapiens Modern-looking humans, undisputed examples of which appeared about 50,000 years ago; may have appeared earlier.

Homozygous Possessing two identical genes or alleles in corresponding locations on a pair of chromosomes.

Horticulture Plant cultivation carried out with relatively simple tools and methods; nature is allowed to replace nutrients in the soil, in the absence of permanently cultivated fields.

Human paleontology The study of the emergence of humans and their later physical evolution. Also called **paleoanthropology.**

Human variation The study of how and why contemporary human populations vary biologically.

Hunter-gatherers People who collect food from naturally occurring resources, that is, wild plants, animals, and fish. The term *hunter-gatherers* minimizes sometimes heavy dependence on fishing. Also referred to as **foragers** or *food collectors.*

Hybridization The creation of a viable offspring from the mating of two different species.

Hylobates The family of hominoids that includes gibbons and siamangs; often referred to as the lesser apes (as compared with the great apes such as gorillas and chimpanzees).

Hypotheses Predictions, which may be derived from theories, about how variables are related.

Hypoxia A condition of oxygen deficiency that often occurs at high altitudes. The percentage of oxygen in the air is the same as at lower altitudes, but because the barometric pressure is lower, less oxygen is taken in with each breath. Often, breathing becomes more rapid, the heart beats faster, and activity is more difficult.

Incest taboo Prohibition of sexual intercourse or marriage between mother and son, father and daughter, and brother and sister; often extends to other relatives.

Incisors The front teeth; used for holding or seizing food and preparing it for chewing by the other teeth.

Independent family A family unit consisting of one monogamous (nuclear) family, or one polygynous or one polyandrous family.

Indirect dowry Goods given by the groom's kin to the bride (or her father, who passes most of them to her) at or before her marriage.

Indicator artifacts and ecofacts Items that changed relatively rapidly and which, thus, can be used to indicate the relative age of associated items.

Indirect percussion A toolmaking technique common in the Upper Paleolithic. After shaping a core into a pyramidal or cylindrical form, the toolmaker can put a punch of antler or wood or another hard material into position and strike it with a hammer. Using a hammer-struck punch enabled toolmakers to strike off consistently shaped blades.

Individual selection Natural selection of individual characteristics.

Insectivore The order or major grouping of mammals, including modern shrews and moles, that is adapted to feeding on insects.

Intensive agriculture Food production characterized by the permanent cultivation of fields and made possible by the use of the plow, draft animals or machines, fertilizers, irrigation, water-storage techniques, and other complex agricultural techniques.

Kenyanthropus platyops A nearly complete 3.5 million year old skull found in western Kenya. It is thought by some scholars to be a species of gracile australopithecine (and hence should not be regarded as a separate genus).

Kenyapithecus An apelike primate from the middle Miocene found in East Africa. It had very thickly enameled teeth and robust jaws, suggesting a diet of hard, tough foods. Probably somewhat terrestrial.

Kindred A bilateral set of close relatives.

Kinesics The study of communication by nonvocal means, including posture, mannerisms, body movement, facial expressions, and signs and gestures.

Knuckle walking A locomotor pattern of primates such as the chimpanzee and gorilla in which the weight of the upper part of the body is supported on the thickly padded knuckles of the hands.

Laws (scientific) Associations or relationships that almost all scientists accept.

Levalloisian method A method that allowed flake tools of a predetermined size to be produced from a shaped core. The toolmakers first shaped the core and prepared a "striking platform" at one end. Flakes of predetermined and standard sizes could then be knocked off. Although some Levallois flakes date from as far back as 400,000 years ago, they are found more frequently in Mousterian tool kits.

Levirate A custom whereby a man is obliged to marry his brother's widow.

Lexical content Vocabulary or lexicon.

Lexicon The words and morphs, and their meanings, of a language; approximated by a dictionary.

Lineage A set of kin whose members trace descent from a common ancestor through known links.

Lithics The technical name for tools made from stone.

Lower Paleolithic The period of the Oldowan and Acheulian stone tool traditions.

Magic The performance of certain rituals that are believed to compel the supernatural powers to act in particular ways.

Maladaptive customs Cultural traits that diminish the chances of survival and reproduction in a particular environment.

Mana A supernatural, impersonal force that inhabits certain objects or people and is believed to confer success and/or strength.

Manumission The granting of freedom to a slave.

Market (or commercial) exchange Transactions in which the "prices" are subject to supply and demand, whether or not the transactions occur in a marketplace.

Marriage A socially approved sexual and economic union, usually between a man and a woman, that is presumed, both by the couple and by others, to be more or less permanent, and that subsumes reciprocal rights and obligations between the two spouses and their future children.

Matriclan A clan tracing descent through the female line.

Matrilineage A kin group whose members trace descent through known links in the female line from a common female ancestor.

Matrilineal descent The rule of descent that affiliates individuals with kin of both sexes related to them through women only.

Matrilocal residence A pattern of residence in which a married couple lives with or near the wife's parents.

Measure To describe how something compares with other things on some scale of variation.

Mediation The process by which a third party tries to bring about a settlement in the absence of formal authority to force a settlement.

Mediums Part-time religious practitioners who are asked to heal and divine while in a trance.

Meiosis The process by which reproductive cells are formed. In this process of division, the number of chromosomes in the newly formed cells is reduced by half, so that when fertilization occurs the resulting organism has the normal number of chromosomes appropriate to its species, rather than double that number.

Mesolithic The archaeological period in the Old World beginning about 12,000 B.C. Humans were starting to settle down in semipermanent camps and villages, as people began to depend less on big game (which they used to have to follow over long distances) and more on relatively stationary food resources such as fish, shellfish, small game, and wild plants rich in carbohydrates, proteins, and oils.

Messenger RNA A type of ribonucleic acid that is used in the cell to copy the DNA code for use in protein synthesis.

Microlith A small, razorlike blade fragment that was probably attached in a series to a wooden or bone handle to form a cutting edge.

Middle Paleolithic The time period of the Mousterian stone tool tradition.

Miocene The geological epoch from 24 million to 5.2 million years ago.

Mitosis Cellular reproduction or growth involving the duplication of chromosome pairs.

Moiety A unilineal descent group in a society that is divided into two such maximal groups; there may be smaller unilineal descent groups as well.

Molars The large teeth behind the premolars at the back of the jaw; used for chewing and grinding food.

Monogamy Marriage between only one man and only one woman at a time.

Monotheistic Believing that there is only one high god and that all other supernatural beings are subordinate to, or are alternative manifestations of, this supreme being.

Morph The smallest unit of a language that has a meaning.

Morpheme One or more morphs with the same meaning.

Morphology The study of how sound sequences convey meaning.

Mousterian tool assemblage   Named after the tool assemblage found in a rock shelter at Le Moustier in the Dordogne region of southwestern France. Compared with an Acheulian assemblage, the Middle Paleolithic (40,000–300,000 years ago) Mousterian has a smaller proportion of large core tools such as hand axes and cleavers and a bigger proportion of small flake tools such as scrapers. Flakes were often altered or "retouched" by striking small flakes or chips from one or more edges.

Mutation   A change in the DNA sequence, producing an altered gene.

Natural selection   The outcome of processes that affect the frequencies of traits in a particular environment. Traits that enhance survival and reproductive success increase in frequency over time.

Neandertal   The common name for the species *Homo neandertalensis*.

Negotiation   The process by which the parties to a dispute try to resolve it themselves.

Neolithic   Originally meaning "the new stone age," now meaning the presence of domesticated plants and animals. The earliest evidence of domestication comes from the Near East about 8000 B.C.

Neolocal residence   A pattern of residence whereby a married couple lives separately, and usually at some distance, from the kin of both spouses.

Nocturnal   Active during the night.

Nonfraternal polyandry   Marriage of a woman to two or more men who are not brothers.

Nonsororal polygyny   Marriage of a man to two or more women who are not sisters.

Normalizing selection   The type of natural selection that removes harmful genes that arose by mutation.

Nuclear family   A family consisting of a married couple and their young children.

Oath   The act of calling upon a deity to bear witness to the truth of what one says.

Obsidian   A volcanic glass that can be used to make mirrors or sharp-edged tools.

Occipital torus   A ridge of bone running horizontally across the back of the skull in apes and some hominids.

Oldowan   The earliest stone toolmaking tradition, named after the tools found in Bed I at Olduvai Gorge, Tanzania, from about 2.5 million years ago. The stone artifacts include core tools and sharp-edged flakes made by striking one stone against another. Flake tools predominate. Among the core tools, so-called choppers are common.

Oligocene   The geological epoch 34 million to 24 million years ago during which definite anthropoids emerged.

Omnivorous   Eating both meat and vegetation.

Omomyid   A type of prosimian with many tarsierlike features that appeared in the early Eocene.

Operational definition   A description of the procedure that is followed in measuring a variable.

Opposable thumb   A thumb that can touch the tips of all the other fingers.

Optimal foraging theory   The theory that individuals seek to maximize the returns (in calories and nutrients) on their labor in deciding which animals and plants they will go after.

Ordeal   A means of determining guilt or innocence by submitting the accused to dangerous or painful tests believed to be under supernatural control.

Orrorin tugenensis   An apparently bipedal primate dating to between 5.8 and 6 million years, making it possibly the earliest known hominid.

Osteology   Refers to the study of bones.

Paleoanthropology   See **Human paleontology.**

Paleocene   The geological epoch 65 million to 55 million years ago.

Paralanguage   Refers to all the optional vocal features or silences apart from the language itself that communicate meaning.

Parallel cousins   Children of siblings of the same sex. One's parallel cousins are the father's brothers' children and the mother's sisters' children.

Parapithecids   Small monkeylike Oligocene primates found in the Fayum area of Egypt.

Participant-observation   Living among the people being studied—observing, questioning, and (when possible) taking part in the important events of the group. Writing or otherwise recording notes on observations, questions asked and answered, and things to check out later are parts of participant-observation.

Pastoralism   A form of subsistence technology in which food-getting is based directly or indirectly on the maintenance of domesticated animals.

Patriclan   A clan tracing descent through the male line.

Patrilineage   A kin group whose members trace descent through known links in the male line from a common male ancestor.

Patrilineal descent   The rule of descent that affiliates individuals with kin of both sexes related to them through men only.

Patrilocal residence   A pattern of residence in which a married couple lives with or near the husband's parents.

Peasants   Rural people who produce food for their own subsistence but who must also contribute or sell their surpluses to others (in towns and cities) who do not produce their own food.

Percussion flaking   A toolmaking technique in which one stone is struck with another to remove a flake.

Personality integration of culture   The theory that personality or psychological processes may account for connections between certain aspects of culture.

Pierolapithecus   A middle Miocene ape that has wrists and vertebrae that would have made it capable of brachiation, but also has relatively short fingers like modern monkeys.

Phenotype   The observable physical appearance of an organism, which may or may not reflect its genotype or total genetic constitution.

Phone   A speech sound in a language.

Phoneme   A sound or set of sounds that makes a difference in meaning to the speakers of the language.

Phonology   The study of the sounds in a language and how they are used.

Phratry   A unilineal descent group composed of a number of supposedly related clans (sibs).

Physical (biological) anthropology   See **Biological (physical) anthropology.**

Platyrrhines   The group of anthropoids that have broad, flat-bridged noses, with nostrils facing outward; these monkeys are currently found only in the New World (Central and South America).

Pleistocene   A geological epoch that started 1.6 million years ago and, according to some, continues into the present. During this period, glaciers have often covered much of the earth's surface and humans became the dominant life form.

Plesiadipis   The most well known of the plesiadipiforms, possibly an archaic primate.

Pliocene   The geological epoch 5.2 million to 1.6 million years ago during which the earliest definite hominids appeared.

Political economy   The study of how external forces, particularly powerful state societies, explain the way a society changes and adapts.

Polyandry   The marriage of one woman to more than one man at a time.

Polygamy   Plural marriage; one individual is married to more than one spouse simultaneously. **Polygyny** and **polyandry** are types of polygamy.

Polygyny   The marriage of one man to more than one woman at a time.

Polyphony   Two or more melodies sung simultaneously.

Polytheistic   Recognizing many gods, none of whom is believed to be superordinate.

Pongids   Hominoids whose members include both the living and extinct apes.

Potassium-argon (K-Ar) dating   A chronometric dating method that uses the rate of decay of a radioactive form of potassium (^{40}K) into argon (^{40}Ar) to date samples from 5,000 years to 3 billion years old. The K-Ar method dates the minerals and rocks in a deposit, not the fossils themselves.

Postpartum sex taboo   Prohibition of sexual intercourse between a couple for a period of time after the birth of their child.

Potlatch   A feast among Pacific Northwest Native Americans at which great quantities of food and goods are given to the guests in order to gain prestige for the host(s).

Power   The ability to make others do what they do not want to do or influence based on the threat of force.

Practicing anthropology   See **Applied anthropology**.

Prairie   Grassland with a high grass cover.

Prehensile   Adapted for grasping objects.

Prehistory   The time before written records.

Premolars   The teeth immediately behind the canines; used in chewing, grinding, and shearing food.

Pressure flaking   Toolmaking technique whereby small flakes are struck off by pressing against the core with a bone, antler, or wooden tool.

Prestige   Being accorded particular respect or honor.

Priests   Generally full-time specialists, with very high status, who are thought to be able to relate to superior or high gods beyond the ordinary person's access or control.

Primary institutions   The sources of early experiences, such as family organization and subsistence techniques, that presumably help form the basic, or typical, personality found in a society.

Primary subsistence activities   The food-getting activities: gathering, hunting, fishing, herding, and agriculture.

Primate   A member of the mammalian order Primates, divided into the two suborders of prosimians and anthropoids.

Primatologists   People who study primates.

Primatology   The study of primates.

Probability value (*p*-value)   The likelihood that an observed result could have occurred by chance.

Proconsul   The best-known genus of proto-apes from the early Miocene.

Prognathic   A physical feature that is sticking out or pushed forward, such as the faces in apes and some hominid species.

Projective tests   Tests that utilize ambiguous stimuli; test subjects must project their own personality traits in order to structure the ambiguous stimuli.

Propliopithecids   Apelike anthropoids dating from the early Oligocene, found in the Fayum area of Egypt.

Prosimians   Literally "pre-monkeys," one of the two suborders of primates; includes lemurs, lorises, and tarsiers.

Protolanguage   A hypothesized ancestral language from which two or more languages seem to have derived.

Quadrupeds   Animals that walk on all fours.

Race   In biology, race refers to a subpopulation or variety of a species that differs somewhat in gene frequencies from other varieties of the species. All members of a species can interbreed and produce viable offspring. Many anthropologists do not think that the concept of race is usefully applied to humans because humans do not fall into geographic populations that can be easily distinguished in terms of different sets of biological or physical traits. Thus, race in humans is largely a culturally assigned category.

Rachis   The seed-bearing part of a plant. In the wild variety of grain, the rachis shatters easily, releasing the seeds. Domesticated grains have a tough rachis, which does not shatter easily.

Racism   The belief, without scientific basis, that some "races" are inferior to others.

Radiocarbon (or carbon-14, ^{14}C) dating   A dating method uses the decay of carbon-14 to date organic remains. It is reliable for dating once-living matter up to 50,000 years old.

Raiding   A short-term use of force, generally planned and organized, to realize a limited objective.

Random sample   A sample in which all cases selected have had an equal chance to be included.

Rank societies   Societies that do not have any unequal access to economic resources or power, but with social groups that have unequal access to status positions and prestige.

Recessive   An allele phenotypically suppressed in the heterozygous form and expressed only in the homozygous form.

Reciprocity   Giving and taking (not politically arranged) without the use of money.

Redistribution   The accumulation of goods (or labor) by a particular person or in a particular place and their subsequent distribution.

Relative dating   A method of dating fossils that determines the age of a specimen or deposit relative to a known specimen or deposit.

Religion   Any set of attitudes, beliefs, and practices pertaining to supernatural power, whether that power rests in forces, gods, spirits, ghosts, or demons.

Revitalization movements   New religious movements intended to save a culture by infusing it with a new purpose and life.

Revolution   A usually violent replacement of a society's rulers.

Ribosome   A structure in the cell used in making proteins.

Rituals   Repetitive sets of behaviors that occur in essentially the same patterns every time they occur. Religious rituals involve the supernatural in some way.

Robust australopithecines   A later group of australopithecines usually differentiated from the gracile australopithecines by their heavier dentition and larger faces.

Rules of descent   Rules that connect individuals with particular sets of kin because of known or presumed common ancestry.

Sagittal crest   A ridge of bone running along the top of the skull in apes and early hominids.

Sagittal keel   An inverted V-shaped ridge running along the top of the skull in *Homo erectus.*

Sahelanthropus tchadensis   A hominoid found in Chad dating to around 7 million years ago.

Sampling universe   The list of cases to be sampled from.

Savanna   Tropical grassland.

Secondary institutions   Aspects of culture, such as religion, music, art, folklore, and games, which presumably reflect or are projections of the basic, or typical, personality in a society.

Secondary subsistence activities   Activities that involve the preparation and processing of food either to make it edible or to store it.

Sedentarism   Settled life.

Segmentary lineage system   A hierarchy of more inclusive lineages; usually functions only in conflict situations.

Segregation   The random sorting of chromosomes in meiosis.

Sex differences   The typical differences between females and males that are most likely due to biological differences.

Sexually dimorphic   A marked difference in size and appearance between males and females of a species.

Shaman   A religious intermediary, usually part-time, whose primary function is to cure people through sacred songs, pantomime, and other means; sometimes called witch doctor by Westerners.

Shifting cultivation   See **Extensive cultivation.**

Sib   See **Clan.**

Siblings   A person's brothers and sisters.

Sickle-cell anemia (sicklemia)   A condition in which red blood cells assume a crescent (sickle) shape when deprived of oxygen, instead of the normal (disk) shape. The sickle-shaped red blood cells do not move through the body as readily as normal cells, and thus cause damage to the heart, lungs, brain, and other vital organs.

Sites   Locations where the material remains of human activity have been preserved in a way that archaeologists or paleoanthropologists can recover them.

Sivapithecus   A genus of ape from the later Miocene known for its thickly enameled teeth, suggesting a diet of hard, tough, or gritty items. Found primarily in western and southern Asia and now thought to be ancestral to orangutans.

Slash-and-burn   A form of shifting cultivation in which the natural vegetation is cut down and burned off. The cleared ground is used for a short time and then left to regenerate.

Slaves   A class of people who do not own their own labor or the products thereof.

Socialization   A term anthropologists and psychologists use to describe the development, through the direct and indirect influence of parents and others, of children's patterns of behavior (and attitudes and values) that conform to cultural expectations. Also called **enculturation.**

Society   A group of people who occupy a particular territory and speak a common language not generally understood by neighboring peoples. By this definition, societies do not necessarily correspond to nations.

Sociobiology   Systematic study of the biological causes of human behavior. Compare with **behavioral ecology, evolutionary psychology**, and **dual-inheritance theory.**

Sociolinguistics   The study of cultural and subcultural patterns of speaking in different social contexts.

Soft hammer   A technique of stone tool manufacture in which a bone or wood hammer is used to strike flakes from a stone.

Sorcery   The use of certain materials to invoke supernatural powers to harm people.

Sororal polygyny   The marriage of a man to two or more sisters at the same time.

Sororate   A custom whereby a woman is obliged to marry her deceased sister's husband.

Special-purpose money   Objects of value for which only some goods and services can be exchanged.

Speciation   The development of a new species.

Species   A population that consists of organisms able to interbreed and produce viable and fertile offspring.

Specific evolution   The particular sequence of change and adaptation of a society in a given environment.

Spirits   Unnamed supernatural beings of nonhuman origin who are beneath the gods in prestige and often closer to the people; may be helpful, mischievous, or evil.

State   An autonomous political unit with centralized decision making over many communities with power to govern by force (e.g., to collect taxes, draft people for work and war, and make and enforce laws). Most states have cities with public buildings; full-time craft and religious specialists; an "official" art style; a hierarchical social structure topped by an elite class; and a governmental monopoly on the legitimate use of force to implement policies.

State organization   A society is described as having state organization when it includes one or more states.

Statistical association   A relationship or correlation between two or more variables that is unlikely to be due to chance.

Statistically significant   Refers to a result that would occur very rarely by chance. The result (and stronger ones) would occur fewer than 5 times out of 100 by chance.

Steppe   Grassland with a dry, low grass cover.

Stratified   An archaeological deposit that contains successive layers or strata.

Stratigraphy   The study of how different rock formations and fossils are laid down in successive layers or strata. Older layers are generally deeper or lower than more recent layers.

Structuralism   The theoretical orientation that human culture is a surface representation of the underlying structure of the human mind.

Structural linguistics   See **Descriptive (structural) linguistics.**

Subculture   The shared customs of a subgroup within a society.

Subsistence economies   Economies in which almost all able-bodied adults are largely engaged in getting food for themselves and their families.

Supernatural   Believed to be not human or not subject to the laws of nature.

Symbolic communication   An arbitrary (not obviously meaningful) gesture, call, word, or sentence that has meaning even when its *referent* is not present.

Syntax   The ways in which words are arranged to form phrases and sentences.

Taboo A prohibition that, if violated, is believed to bring supernatural punishment.

Taphonomy The study of how natural processes form and disturb archaeological sites.

Taurodontism Having teeth with an enlarged pulp cavity.

Taxonomy The classification of extinct and living organisms.

Terrestrial Adapted to living on the ground.

Terrorism The use or threat of violence to create terror in others, usually for political purposes.

Theoretical construct Something that cannot be observed or verified directly.

Theoretical orientation A general attitude about how phenomena are to be explained.

Theories Explanations of associations or laws.

Totem A plant or animal associated with a clan (sib) as a means of group identification; may have other special significance for the group.

Tribal organization The kind of political organization in which local communities mostly act autonomously but there are kin groups (such as clans) or associations (such as age-sets) that can temporarily integrate a number of local groups into a larger unit.

Tribe A territorial population in which there are kin or nonkin groups with representatives in a number of local groups.

Typology A way of organizing artifacts in categories based on their particular characteristics.

Unifacial tool A tool worked or flaked on one side only.

Unilineal descent Affiliation with a group of kin through descent links of one sex only.

Unilocal residence A pattern of residence (patrilocal, matrilocal, or avunculocal) that specifies just one set of relatives that the married couple lives with or near.

Unisex association An association that restricts its membership to one sex, usually male.

Universally ascribed qualities Those ascribed qualities (age, sex) that are found in all societies.

Upper Paleolithic The time period associated with the emergence of modern humans and their spread around the world.

Variable A thing or quantity that varies.

Variably ascribed qualities Those ascribed qualities (such as ethnic, religious, or social class differences) that are found only in some societies.

Vertical clinging and leaping A locomotor pattern characteristic of several primates, including tarsiers and galagos. The animal normally rests by clinging to a branch in a vertical position and uses its hind limbs alone to push off from one vertical position to another.

Warfare Violence between political entities such as communities, districts, or nations.

Witchcraft The practice of attempting to harm people by supernatural means, but through emotions and thought alone, not through the use of tangible objects.

"Y-5" pattern Refers to the pattern of cusps on human molars. When looked at from the top, the cusps of the molars form a Y opening toward the cheek.

notes

Chapter 1

1. Harrison 1975; Durham 1991, 228–37.
2. Chimpanzee Sequencing and Analysis Consortium 2005.
3. Nolan 2003, 2.
4. Van Willigen 2002, 7.
5. Kedia and van Willigen 2005; Miracle 2009.
6. White 1968.
7. Hall 1966, 144–53.

Chapter 2

1. Lovejoy 1964, 58–63.
2. Lovejoy 1964, 63.
3. Mayr 1982, 339–60.
4. Wallace 1858/1970.
5. Mayr 1982, 423.
6. Darwin had a still longer title. It continued, *Or the Preservation of the Favoured Races in the Struggle for Life.* Darwin's notion of "struggle for life" is often misinterpreted to refer to a war of all against all. Although animals may fight with each other at times over access to resources, Darwin was referring mainly to their metaphorical "struggle" with the environment, particularly to obtain food.
7. Darwin 1970/1859.
8. Futuyma 1982 provides an overview of this long controversy.
9. Huxley 1970.
10. Tylor 1971/1958.
11. Morgan 1877/1964.
12. Peregrine 2007a.
13. Lewontin 1972.
14. Ceci and Williams 2009.
15. Harris 1968, 380–84; Langness 1974, 50–53.
16. Ibid.
17. Langness 1974, 53–58; Harris 1968, 304–77.
18. Langness 1974, 50.
19. Boas 1940, 270–80.
20. Langness 1974, 85–93; Bock 1980, 57–82.
21. Kardiner and Linton 1946/1939; Whiting and Child 1953; Whiting and Whiting 1975.
22. Bock 1996, 1044.
23. Bock 1996, 1042.
24. Malinowski 1939.
25. Radcliffe-Brown 1952.
26. Ibid.
27. White 1949, 368–69.
28. Steward 1955b.
29. Sahlins and Service 1960.
30. Lévi-Strauss 1969a, 75.
31. Lévi-Strauss 1966; Lévi-Strauss 1969b.
32. Ortner 1984.
33. Douglas 1975.
34. Colby 1996.
35. Ibid.
36. Steward 1955a, 30–42.
37. Vayda and Rappaport 1968. For a selection of recent studies in human ecology, see Bates and Lees 1996.
38. Vayda and Rappaport 1968, 493.

39. Rappaport 1967.
40. Kottak 1999.
41. Ortner 1984, 141–42.
42. Sanderson 1995.
43. Roseberry 1988, 163; see also Wolf 1956 and Mintz 1956.
44. Roseberry 1988, 164; see also Leacock 1954.
45. Roseberry 1988, 166; see also Frank (1967).
46. Roseberry 1988, 166–67; see also Wallerstein (1974).
47. Gray 1996.
48. Gray 1996; Boyd and Richerson 1996; Richerson and Boyd 2005.
49. Irons 1979, 10–12.
50. Low 2009.
51. Richerson and Boyd 2005, 9.
52. Gray 1996; Richerson and Boyd 2005, 9.
53. Boyd and Richerson 2005, 103–04.
54. Lamphere 2006, x; Stockett and Geller 2006, 17.
55. Weiner 1987.
56. Slocum 1975.
57. Behar and Gordon 1995.
58. Clifford 1986, 3.
59. Geertz 1973c, 3–30, 412–53; see also Marcus and Fischer 1986, 26–29.
60. Geertz 1973b.
61. Sperber 1985, 34.
62. Bishop 1996, 993.
63. Foucault 1970.
64. Rubel and Rosman 1996.
65. Bishop 1996; Rubel and Rosman 1996.

Chapter 3

1. Salzman 2001, 135.
2. Whiting 1964.
3. Nagel 1961, 88–89.
4. Ibid., 83–90.
5. Ibid., 85. See also McCain and Segal 1988, 75–79.
6. McCain and Segal 1988, 62–64.
7. Caws 1969, 1378.
8. McCain and Segal 1988, 114.
9. Ibid., 56–57, 131–32.
10. Whiting 1964, 519–20.
11. McCain and Segal 1988, 67–69.
12. Blalock 1972, 15–20; and Thomas 1986, 18–28. See also M. Ember 1970, 701–03.
13. For examples, see Murdock 1967 and Murdock and White 1969, 329–69.
14. Sets of the HRAF in paper or microfiche format, and now on the Web, are found in more than 400 universities and research institutions around the world. See the HRAF Web site: www.yale.edu/hraf.
15. Ogburn 1922, 200–80.
16. Bernard 2001, 323.
17. Peacock 1986, 54.
18. Lawless et al. 1983, xi–xxi; Peacock 1986, 54–65.
19. Romney et al. 1986.
20. Bernard 2001, 190.
21. See Murdock and White 1969 for a description of the SCCS sample; the HRAF Collection of Ethnography is described at www.yale.edu/hraf; for a description of many different cross-cultural samples, see C. R. Ember and M. Ember 2009.
22. Helms 2009.
23. Trigger 1989.

24. Martin 1990, 42.
25. Etienne 1992.
26. Isaac 1997.
27. Leakey 1965, 73–78.
28. F. H. Brown 1992.
29. Gentner and Lippolt 1963.
30. F. H. Brown 2000, 225.
31. American Anthropological Association 1991.
32. Szklut and Reed 1991.
33. Lambert et al. 2000, 405.
34. Hill and Hurtado 2004.
35. Waldbaum 2005.

Chapter 4

1. Sagan 1975.
2. R. N. Brandon 1990, 6–7.
3. G. Williams 1992, 7.
4. J. M. Smith 1989, 42–45.
5. Hooper 2002.
6. Grant 2002.
7. Devillers and Chaline 1993, 22–23.
8. Beadle and Beadle 1966, 216.
9. Golden et al. 2000; Hayden 2000; Marshall 2000; Pennisi 2000; Travis 2000.
10. Daiger 2005.
11. Olsen 2002.
12. Dobzhansky 1962, 138–40.
13. Relethford 1990, 94.
14. G. A. Harrison et al. 1988, 198–200.
15. Brace 1996.
16. Grant and Grant 2002.
17. Rennie 2002, 83.
18. Chatterjee 1997.
19. Paley 1810.
20. Center for Renewal of Science and Culture, "The Wedge Strategy," cited in Forrest 2001, 16.
21. McMullin 2001, 174.
22. Rennie 2002.
23. Barash 1977.
24. Krebs and Davies 1984; 1987.
25. Badcock 2000.
26. Boyd and Richerson 2005.
27. Schaller 1972.
28. Hare et al. 2002.
29. E. O. Wilson 1975.
30. B. Low 2009.
31. D. Campbell 1965.
32. Nissen 1958.
33. Boyd and Richerson 1985/1996.
34. Durham 1991.

Chapter 5

1. See Durham 1991, 154–225, for an extensive discussion of the relationship between genes and culture.
2. Stewart 1950.
3. *Genesis* 17: 9–15.
4. Hanna, Little, and Austin 1989, 133–36; G. A. Harrison et al. 1988, 504–07.
5. D. F. Roberts 1953. Cited in Garn 1971, 73. See also Roberts 1978.
6. D. F. Roberts 1953.
7. G. A. Harrison et al. 1988, 505.
8. Riesenfeld 1973, 427–59.
9. Riesenfeld 1973, 452–53.
10. J. S. Weiner 1954, 615–18; Steegman 1975. See also Larsen 2009.
11. G. A. Harrison et al. 1988, 308–10.
12. Polednak 1974, 49–57. See also Branda and Eaton 1978.
13. Loomis 1967.
14. Post, Daniels, and Binford 1975, 65–80.
15. Holden 2000; Jablonski and Chaplin 2000.
16. Stini 1975, 53.
17. Mazess 1975.
18. Greksa and Beall 1989, 223.
19. Greksa and Beall 1989, 226.
20. Frisancho and Greksa 1989, 204.
21. Eveleth and Tanner 1990, 176–79.
22. Eveleth and Tanner 1990, 205–06.
23. Bogin 1988, 105–106.
24. G. A. Harrison et al. 1988, 300.
25. G. A. Harrison et al. 1988, 198.
26. Huss-Ashmore and Johnston 1985, 482–83.
27. G. A. Harrison et al. 1988, 385–86.
28. Martorell 1980, 81–106.
29. Martorell et al. 1991.
30. Landauer and Whiting 1964; 1981; Gunders and Whiting 1968; Gray and Wolfe 1980.
31. Landauer and Whiting 1964; 1981; Gunders and Whiting 1968.
32. Gray and Wolfe 2009.
33. Landauer and Whiting 1981.
34. Eveleth and Tanner 1990, 205.
35. Landauer 1973.
36. Motulsky 1971, 223.
37. Motulsky 1971, 226.
38. Motulsky 1971, 229.
39. Motulsky 1971, 230.
40. Motulsky 1971, 233.
41. Ibid.
42. Black 1992.
43. An examination of the epidemic diseases spread by Europeans can be found in Chapter 11 of J. Diamond 1997a.
44. Neel et al. 1970; Patrick Tierney in his *Darkness in El Dorado* (New York: Norton, 2000) accused the Neel research team of fueling a measles outbreak among the Yanomamö by administering a harmful measles vaccine. However, the scientific evidence indicates that Tierney is wrong. The vaccine Neel and associates used was widely pretested and there was no way that the vaccine could have caused the epidemic. Measles was already spreading in the Amazon, which was why the vaccination program was initiated. See Gregor and Gross 2004.
45. Relethford 1990, 425–27.
46. Merbs 1992.
47. Durham 1991, 105–07.
48. Ibid.
49. Ibid.
50. G. A. Harrison et al. 1988, 231.
51. For a review of the early research, see Durham 1991, 123–27. The particular form of malaria that is discussed is caused by the species *Plasmodium falciparum*.
52. See Madigral 1989 for a report of her own research and a review of earlier studies.
53. Pennisi 2001a.
54. Durham 1991, 124–45.
55. Motulsky 1971, 238.
56. J. Diamond 1993.
57. Molnar 1998, 158; Pennisi 2001b.
58. Durham 1991, 230.
59. Brodey 1971.

60. Durham 1991, 233–35.
61. Relethford 1990, 127.
62. McCracken 1971; see also references to the work of F. J. Simoons as referred to in Durham 1991, 240–41.
63. McCracken 1971; Huang 2002.
64. Durham 1991, 263–69.
65. Marks 1994; Shanklin 1993, 15–17.
66. Molnar 1998, 19.
67. Brace et al. 1993.
68. Brooks et al. 1993.
69. Brace et al. 1993.
70. Brooks et al. 1993.
71. M. King and Motulsky 2002.
72. Goodrich 1959, 7–15.
73. Coe 1966, 74–76.
74. Thompson 1966, 89.
75. McNeill 1976.
76. Motulsky 1971, 232.
77. Ibid.
78. MacArthur and Wilson 1967.
79. Johanson and Edey 1981.
80. Peregrine et al. 2000; 2003.
81. Lieberman 1999.
82. Klineberg 1935; 1944.
83. Jensen 1969.
84. Herrnstein and Murray 1994.
85. Kamin 1995.
86. Grubb 1987.
87. M. W. Smith 1974.
88. Dobzhansky 1973, 11.
89. Dobzhansky 1973, 14–15.
90. Research by Sandra Scarr and others reported in Boyd and Richerson 1985: 56.
91. Nisbett 2009.
92. Dobzhansky 1962, 243.
93. Haldane 1963.
94. Simpson 1971, 297–308.

Chapter 6

1. The classic description of common primate traits is from Napier and Napier 1967. For primate social organization see Smuts et al. 1987.
2. Bearder 1987, 14.
3. Richard 1985, 22ff.
4. R. Martin 1975, 50. The opossum, which is not a primate but lives in trees and has many babies at one time, is a marsupial and has a pouch in which to keep the babies when they are very young.
5. Harlow et al. 1966.
6. Nicolson 1987, 339.
7. Gray 1985 (144–63) provides an overview of research that attempts to explain the variation among primates in the degree of male parental care.
8. Russon 1990, 379.
9. Dohlinow and Bishop 1972, 321–25.
10. Sade 1965; Hausfater et al. 1982.
11. Visaberghi and Fragaszy 1990, 265; Tomasello 1990, 304–05.
12. van Lawick-Goodall 1971, 242.
13. Visaberghi and Fragaszy 1990, 264–65.
14. R. Martin 1992, 17–19; Conroy 1990, 8–15.
15. This simplified chart of primate classification adapts information provided in R. Martin 1992, 21.
16. Doyle and Martin 1979; Tattersall 1982.
17. Richard 1987, 32.
18. Bearder 1987, 13.
19. Charles-Dominique 1977, 258; also R. Martin and Bearder 1979; Bearder 1987, 18–22.
20. MacKinnon and MacKinnon 1980.
21. Cartmill 1992a, 28; Fleagle 1999, 118–22.
22. Napier and Napier 1967, 32–33.
23. Richard 1985, 164–65.
24. Cartmill 1992a, 29; Goldizen 1987, 34; also Eisenberg 1977; Sussman and Kinzey 1984; Fleagle 1999, 168–74.
25. Eisenberg 1977, 15–17.
26. Robinson, Wright, and Kinzey 1987; Crockett and Eisenberg 1987; Robinson and Janson 1987.
27. Hrdy 1977, 18.
28. Hrdy 1977, 18–19.
29. Napier 1970, 80–82.
30. Fedigan 1982, 11.
31. Fedigan 1982, 123–24.
32. P. Lee 1983, 231.
33. Fleagle 1999, 302.
34. LeGros Clark 1964, 184.
35. Pennisi 2007.
36. Preuschoft 1984.
37. Carpenter 1940; Chivers 1974, 1980.
38. Rijksen 1978, 22.
39. Normile 1998.
40. van Schaik et al. 2003.
41. Galdikas 1979, 220–23.
42. Cheney and Wrangham 1987, 236.
43. Rijksen 1978, 321.
44. Fossey 1983, xvi.
45. Tuttle 1986, 99–114.
46. Schaller 1963; 1964.
47. Fossey 1983, 47.
48. Harcourt 1979, 187–92.
49. Susman 1984; White 1996.
50. Goodall 1963; van Lawick-Goodall 1971.
51. Teleki 1973.
52. Stanford 2009.
53. Stanford 2009.
54. Normile 1998.
55. Tuttle 1986, 266–69.
56. Whiten et al. 1999.
57. M. Goodman 1992.
58. Falk 1987.
59. Female bonobos, or pygmy chimpanzees, engage in sexual intercourse nearly as often as human females—see Thompson-Handler et al. 1984.
60. By male-female bonding, we mean that at least one of the sexes is "faithful," that is, typically has intercourse with just one opposite-sex partner throughout at least one estrus or menstrual cycle or breeding season. Note that the bonding may not be monogamous; an individual may be bonded to more than one individual of the opposite sex. See M. Ember and C. R. Ember 1979.
61. M. Ember and C. R. Ember 1979, 43; also C. R. Ember and M. Ember 1984, 203–04.
62. C. R. Ember and M. Ember 1984, 207.
63. C. R. Ember and M. Ember 1984, 208–09.
64. de Waal and Lanting 1997.
65. Rumbaugh 1970, 52–58.
66. Boesche et al. 1994.
67. Observation by others cited by A. Jolly 1985, 53.
68. Hannah and McGrew 1987.
69. *Newsweek,* "The First Dentist," March 5, 1973, 73.
70. Seyfarth et al. 1980.
71. Gardner and Gardner 1969.
72. Gardner and Gardner 1980.

73. Greenfield and Savage-Rumbaugh 1990.
74. Clutton-Brock and Harvey 1977, 8–9.
75. Aiello 1992; A. Jolly 1985, 53–54.
76. Aiello 1992.
77. A. Jolly 1985, 53–54.
78. Parker 1990, 130.
79. Milton 1981; Clutton-Brock and Harvey 1980.
80. Milton 1988.
81. A. Jolly 1985, 119.
82. Clutton-Brock and Harvey 1977, 9.
83. Terborgh 1983, 224–25.
84. A. Jolly 1985, 120.
85. A. Jolly 1985, 122.
86. Wrangham 1980.

Chapter 7

1. Ciochon and Etler 1994, 33; 37–67.
2. Kay 2000a.
3. B. Wood 1994.
4. Conroy 1990.
5. Gingerich 1986; Szalay 1972; Szalay, Tattersall, and Decker 1975.
6. Fleagle 1994; Ciochon and Etler 1994, 41; Cartmill 2009.
7. Block and Boyer 2002.
8. Conroy 1990, 49–53.
9. Conroy 1990, 53.
10. Habicht 1979.
11. Vrba 1995.
12. Sussman 1991.
13. Richard 1985, 31; Cartmill 1974.
14. Szalay 1968.
15. Cartmill 1974; for more recent statements see Cartmill 1992b; Cartmill 2009.
16. Sussman and Raven 1978.
17. Conroy 1990, 94–95; Bowen et al. 2002.
18. Conroy 1990, 99.
19. Fleagle 1994, 22–23.
20. Conroy 1990, 119.
21. Radinsky 1967.
22. Conroy 1990, 105; Fleagle 1994, 21.
23. Alexander 1992; Conroy 1990, 111.
24. Kay, Ross, and Williams 1997.
25. Martin 1990, 46; Conroy 1990, 46.
26. Kay, Ross, and Williams 1997; Fleagle and Kay 1985, 25.
27. Jaeger et al. 1999.
28. Simons 1995; Simons and Rassmussen 1996.
29. Kay 2000b, 441.
30. Kay 2000b, 441–42; Conroy 1990, 156.
31. Fleagle 1999, 404–09.
32. Rosenberger 1979.
33. Fleagle and Kay 1987.
34. Aiello 1993; Hartwig 1994.
35. Andrews 2000a, 486.
36. Fleagle and Kay 1985, 25, 30; Conroy 1990, 160–61.
37. Fleagle 1999, 413–15; Fleagle and Kay 1983, 205.
38. Conroy 1990, 248–49.
39. Conroy 1990, 56.
40. R. Martin 1990, 56.
41. Begun 2002.
42. Conroy 1990, 206–11.
43. Begun 2002.
44. Andrews 2000b, 485.
45. Begun 2002.
46. Zimmer 1999; Ward et al. 1999.
47. Begun 2002; Kelley 1992, 225.

48. Moyà-Solà et al. 2004.
49. Conroy 1990, 185, 255.
50. T. Harrison 1986; T. Harrison and Rook 1997.
51. Ward 1997.
52. Ciochon, Olsen, and James 1990, 99–102.
53. Begun 2002.
54. Begun 2002.
55. Fleagle 1999, 480–83.
56. Bilsborough 1992, 65.
57. Simons 1992: 207.
58. Sarich and Wilson 1966; Sarich 1968; Lewin 1983a.
59. Jones, Martin, and Pilbeam 1992: 293; R. Martin 1990, 693–709.
60. Cann 1988.
61. Cann 1988.
62. Vigilant et al. 1991.
63. Ruvolo 1997.
64. Pennisi 2007.
65. Takahata and Satta 1997.

Chapter 8

1. Thorpe, Holder, and Crompton 2007.
2. Rose 1984.
3. Bilsborough 1992, 64–65.
4. Oakley 1964.
5. Kingston, Marino, and Hill 1994.
6. Hewes 1961.
7. Shipman 1986; Trinkaus 1987a.
8. Lovejoy 1981.
9. C. Jolly 1970.
10. Washburn 1960.
11. Pilbeam 1972, 153.
12. Wolpoff 1971.
13. Savage-Rumbaugh 1994.
14. Wolpoff 1983.
15. Zimmer 2004.
16. Zihlman 1992.
17. Wheeler 1984; 1991.
18. Falk 1988.
19. Zihlman 1992, 414.
20. Lovejoy 1988.
21. Aiello and Dean 1990, 268–74.
22. Aiello and Dean 1990, 507–08.
23. Gibbons 2002.
24. Brunet et al. 2002; Wong 2003.
25. Aiello and Collard 2001; Pickford et al. 2002; Wong 2003.
26. Richmond and Jungers 2008.
27. White et al. 1995.
28. White et al. 1994.
29. Hailie-Selassie 2001.
30. Susman et al. 1985; Rose 1984.
31. Conroy 1990, 274; Culotta 1995; Wilford 1995.
32. Asfaw et al. 1999.
33. Brunet et al. 1995.
34. Ibid.
35. Leakey et al. 2001.
36. Fleagle 1999, 511–15.
37. Fleagle 1999, 528.
38. White 2003.
39. Culotta 1995.
40. Leakey et al. 1995.
41. Tattersall and Schwartz 2000, 93.
42. Simpson 2009; White et al. 1981; Johanson and White 1979.
43. Johanson and Edey 1981, 17–18.
44. Johanson and White 1979.

45. Lewin 1983b.
46. Conroy 1990, 291–92; Simpson 2009.
47. Fleagle 1999, 515–18.
48. Fleagle 1999, 515, 520.
49. Grine 1988a.
50. Kimbel et al. 1984.
51. Jungers 1988a; Clarke and Tobias 1995.
52. Lovejoy 1988.
53. Tattersall and Schwartz 2000, 88–89; Clarke and Tobias 1995.
54. Dart 1925.
55. Bromage and Dean 1985; Smith 1986.
56. Eldredge and Tattersall 1982, 80–90.
57. Pilbeam 1972, 107.
58. Holloway 1974.
59. Szalay and Delson 1979, 504.
60. Conroy 1990, 280–82.
61. Conroy 1990, 294–303.
62. McHenry 2009.
63. Szalay and Delson 1979, 504; Wood 1992.
64. McHenry 1988; Jungers 1988b.
65. Fleagle 1999, 522.
66. Grine 1993; Walker and Leakey 1988.
67. Broom 1950.
68. Fleagle 1999, 522.
69. McHenry 2009.
70. Ibid.
71. Grine 1988b.
72. Stringer 1985.
73. M. Leakey 1971; 1979.
74. McHenry 2009.
75. Fleagle 1999, 529.
76. Wood 1992.

Chapter 9

1. Susman 1994.
2. Ibid.
3. Holden 1997.
4. Leakey 1960.
5. Clark 1970, 68; Schick and Toth 1993, 97–99.
6. Schick and Toth 1993, 153–70.
7. Ibid., 129.
8. Ibid., 157–59.
9. Isaac 1984.
10. Whittaker 1994, 283–85.
11. Schick and Toth 1993, 175–76.
12. Speth 2009.
13. Shipman 1986. For the idea that scavenging may have been an important food-getting strategy even for protohominids, see Szalay 1975.
14. Speth and Davis 1976; Blumenschine et al. 2003.
15. Isaac 1971.
16. M. Leakey 1971.
17. Potts 1988, 253–58.
18. Potts 1984.
19. Potts 1988, 278–81.
20. Wolf 1984.
21. Boyd and Silk 2000, 249–50.
22. Dobzhansky 1962, 196.
23. Bromage and Dean 1985; B. H. Smith 1986; Gibbons 2008.
24. Chapais 2008.
25. Gowlett 2008.
26. McHenry 2009; 2009; Tobias 1994.
27. McHenry 1982.
28. McHenry 1982.

29. Dunbar and Shultz 2007; Herrmann et al. 2007; Silk 2007.
30. Simpson et al. 2008.
31. Pilbeam and Gould 1974.
32. Leonard 2002.
33. Stedman et al. 2004.
34. McHenry 2009; Tobias 1994.
35. Simpson 2009.
36. Rightmire 2000.
37. Swisher et al. 1994.
38. Balter and Gibbons 2000; Gabunia et al. 2000.
39. Vekua et al. 2002; Gore 2002.
40. Wolpoff and Nkini 1988. See also Rightmire 2000; Balter 2001.
41. Rightmire 1990, 12–14.
42. Swisher et al. 1994.
43. Rightmire 2000.
44. Fleagle 1999, 534–35; Day 1986, 409–12; Kramer 2009.
45. Rightmire 2000; Tobias 1994.
46. Franciscus and Trinkaus 1988.
47. Feibel and Brown 1993.
48. Ruff and Walker 1993.
49. Wolpoff et al. 1993.
50. Morwood et al. 2004; Brown et al. 2004.
51. Falk et al. 2005
52. Diamond 2004.
53. Tocheri et al. 2007.
54. Jungers et al. 2009.
55. Wong 2005; Weston and Lister 2009.
56. Fleagle 1999, 306.
57. M. Ember and C. R. Ember 1979; cf. Lovejoy 1981.
58. Clayman 1989, 857–58.
59. Bordes 1968, 51–97.
60. Rogers et al. 2004.
61. Phillipson 1993, 57.
62. Schick and Toth 1993, 227, 233.
63. Ibid., 231–33; Whittaker 1994, 27.
64. Bordes 1968, 24–25; Whittaker 1994, 27.
65. Schick and Toth 1993, 258–60; Whittaker 1994, 27.
66. Lawrence Keeley's analysis reported in Schick and Toth 1993, 260; see that page for their analysis of tool use.
67. Calvin 1983.
68. Yamei et al. 2000.
69. Ciochon et al. 1990, 178–83; Pope 1989.
70. Howell 1966.
71. Klein 1987; Binford 1987.
72. L. G. Freeman 1994.
73. A good example of this problem is the ongoing debate about fire use at Zhoukoudian cave, as reported by Weiner et al. 1998.
74. Isaac 1984, 35–36. Other evidence for deliberate use of fire comes from the Swartkrans cave in South Africa and is dated 1 million to 1.5 million years ago; see Brain and Sillen 1988.
75. Goren-Inbar et al. 2004.
76. Binford and Ho 1985.
77. Leonard 2002.
78. Clark 1970, 94–95.
79. Ibid., 96–97.
80. de Lumley 1969.
81. Dickson 1990, 42–44.
82. Dickson 1990, 45; Tattersall and Schwartz 2000, 155.

Chapter 10

1. Stringer 1985.
2. Ibid.

3. Rightmire 1997.
4. Carbonell et al. 2008.
5. Rightmire 1997; Fleagle 1999, 535–37.
6. Spencer 1984.
7. Trinkaus 1985.
8. Stringer 2000.
9. Trinkaus and Shipman 1993a; 1993b.
10. F. Smith 1984, 187.
11. Trinkaus 1984, 251–53.
12. Krings et al. 1997.
13. Ibid.
14. Ovchinnikov et al. 2000; Green et al. 2008.
15. Pennisi 2009.
16. Krause et al. 2007.
17. Lalueza-Fox et al. 2007.
18. Pennisi 2009.
19. Serre et al. 2004; Hodgson and Driscoll 2008.
20. Tattersall 1999, 115–16; Gibbons 2001.
21. Mellars 1996: 405–19.
22. Mellars 1998.
23. Strauss 1989.
24. Schick and Toth 1993, 288–92.
25. Klein 1989, 291–96.
26. Schick and Toth 1993, 288–92; Whittaker 1994, 30–31.
27. Klein 1989, 421–22.
28. Binford and Binford 1969.
29. Fish 1981, 377.
30. Butzer 1982, 42.
31. Phillipson 1993, 63.
32. For the controversy about whether the inhabitants of the Dordogne Valley lived in their homesites year-round, see Binford 1973.
33. Schick and Toth 1993, 292.
34. Klein 1977.
35. Klein 1974.
36. Bordes 1961.
37. T. Patterson 1981.
38. Phillipson 1993, 64.
39. Klein 1983, 38–39.
40. Binford 1984, 195–97. To explain the lack of complete skeletons of large animals, Klein (1983) suggests that the hunters may have butchered the large animals elsewhere because they could carry home only small cuts.
41. Wilford 1997.
42. Pfeiffer 1978, 155.
43. Trinkaus 1984.
44. Chase and Dibble 1987.
45. Stringer et al. 1984, 107.
46. Singer and Wymer 1982, 149.
47. Gibbons 2003.
48. Bräuer 1984, 387–89, 394; Rightmire 1984, 320.
49. Valladas et al. 1988.
50. Stringer et al. 1984, 121.
51. For arguments supporting the single-origin theory, see the chapters by Günter Bräuer, F. Clark Howell, and C. B. Stringer et al., in F. Smith and Spencer 1984. For arguments supporting the multiregional theory, see the chapters by C. L. Brace et al., David W. Frayer, Fred H. Smith, and Milford H. Wolpoff et al. in the same volume.
52. Cann et al. 1987.
53. Vigilant et al. 1991.
54. Stoneking 1997.
55. Hammer and Zegura 1996.
56. Hammer and Zegura 2002.
57. Cavalli-Sforza and Feldman 2003.
58. Stringer 2003.
59. Wolpoff 1999, 501–504, 727–31; Frayer et al. 1993.
60. Wolpoff 1999, 735–43; Frayer et al. 1993.
61. D. Lieberman 1995.
62. Templeton 1993.
63. Trinkaus 1986.
64. Eswaran 2002.
65. Templeton 1996. See also Ayala 1995; 1996.
66. Reed et al. 2004.
67. Duarte et al. 1999.
68. Bahn 1998.
69. Tattersall 1999, 198–203.
70. Trinkaus 1986; see also Trinkaus and Howells 1979.
71. Culotta 2005.
72. Klein 2003.

Chapter 11

1. R. White 1982.
2. Strauss 1982.
3. Dawson 1992, 24–71.
4. COHMAP 1988.
5. Martin and Wright 1967.
6. Mellars 1994.
7. T. Patterson 1981.
8. Klima 1962.
9. Whittaker 1994, 33; Schick and Toth 1993, 293–99.
10. Whittaker 1994, 31.
11. Bordaz 1970, 68.
12. Whittaker 1994, 33.
13. Phillipson 1993, 60.
14. Bordaz 1970, 68.
15. We thank Robert L. Kelly (personal communication) for bringing this possibility to our attention. See also J. D. Clark 1977, 136.
16. Ascher 1961.
17. Semenov 1970, 103. For a more recent discussion of research following this strategy, see Keeley 1980.
18. Klein 1994, 508.
19. Soffer 1993, 38–40.
20. Phillipson 1993, 74.
21. Morell 1995.
22. Henshilwood et al. 2002.
23. Ucko and Rosenfeld 1967.
24. Rice and Paterson 1985; 1986.
25. Rice and Paterson 1985, 98.
26. Marshack 1972.
27. McDermott 1996.
28. For a review, see Dobres 1998.
29. Klein and Edgar 2002, 24.
30. Hawkins and Kleindienst 2001.
31. Peregrine 2001a.
32. Jayaswal 2002.
33. Peregrine and Bellwood 2001.
34. McDonald 1998.
35. Hoffecker et al. 1993.
36. Gibbons 1995; Roosevelt et al. 1996.
37. Goebel et al. 2008.
38. Dillehay 2000.
39. Gilbert et al. 2008
40. Greenberg and Ruhlen 1992, 94–99.
41. Turner 1989; also see Kitchen et al. 2008 for a more recent reanalysis of genetic and linguistic evidence for a three-stage colonization of the Americas.
42. McDonald 1998; Turner 2005.
43. Wheat 1967.
44. Fagan 1991, 79.

45. Hoffecker et al. 1993.
46. Jennings 1968, 72–88.
47. Judge and Dawson 1972.
48. Wheat 1967.
49. Fagan 1989, 221.
50. Wheat 1967.
51. Ibid.
52. Fagan 1989, 227.
53. Fagan 1991, 192.
54. Fagan 1989, 227.
55. Collins 1976, 88–125.
56. Chard 1969, 171.
57. G. Clark 1975, 101–61.
58. Petersen 1973, 94–96.
59. Daniel 2001.
60. Sassaman 1996, 58–83.
61. Ibid.
62. J. Brown 1983, 5–10.

Chapter 12

1. N. Miller 1992.
2. Crawford 1992; Phillipson 1993, 118; MacNeish 1991, 256; 268.
3. Flannery 1986, 6–8; Pearsall 1992; B. Smith 1992a.
4. Hole 1992.
5. Binford 1971.
6. Flannery 1973a.
7. Simcha et al. 2000.
8. Harlan 1967.
9. Flannery 1971.
10. Mellaart 1961.
11. Henry 1989, 214–15.
12. Brown and Price 1985.
13. Henry 1989, 38–39, 209–10; 1991. See Olszewski 1991 for some questions about the degree of social complexity in Natufian sites.
14. Martin and Wright 1967.
15. A recent analysis of these changes can be found in Kuehn 1998; see also J. Brown 1985.
16. Marcus and Flannery 1996, 49–50.
17. Ibid., 50–53.
18. Balter 2007; Jones and Liu 2009.
19. Gorman 1970.
20. Chang 1970; Gorman 1970.
21. J. Clark 1970, 171–72.
22. Phillipson 1993, 111–12.
23. Alroy 2001.
24. Martin 1973.
25. Grayson 1977; 1984. See also L. G. Marshall 1984; Guthrie 1984; Barnosky et al. 2004.
26. Holdaway and Jacomb 2000.
27. Cohen 1977b, 12; 85.
28. Cohen 1989, 112–13.
29. Frayer 1981.
30. Cohen 1989, 113–15.
31. Flannery 1973b.
32. Patterson 1971.
33. G. Johnson 1977; D. Harris 1977.
34. Sussman 1972; Lee 1972.
35. For some examples of societies that have practiced infanticide, D. Harris 1977.
36. Howell 1979; Lee 1979.
37. Frisch 1980; Howell 1979.
38. Phillipson 1993, 60–61.
39. Semenov 1970, 63; 203–204; Whittaker 1994, 36–37.
40. Zohary 1969.

41. Flannery 1965.
42. Ibid. For the view that a high proportion of immature animals does not necessarily indicate domestication, see Collier and White 1976.
43. Hole 1992; MacNeish 1991, 127–28.
44. Clutton-Brock 1992; Chessa et al. 2009.
45. Hole et al. 1969.
46. Simmons et al. 1988.
47. Mellaart 1964.
48. Flannery 1986, 3–5; Pringle 1998.
49. Marcus and Flannery 1996, 64–66.
50. Flannery 1986, 6–8.
51. Fedoroff 2003.
52. Flannery 1986, 8–9; Marcus and Flannery 1996, 66–67.
53. Marcus and Flannery 1996, 65–66.
54. Ibid., 66–68.
55. Flannery 1986, 31–42.
56. Ibid., 502.
57. Piperno and Stothert 2003.
58. MacNeish 1991, 37, 47; Hole 1992.
59. B. Smith 1992b, 163, 287.
60. Asch and Asch 1978.
61. B. Smith 1992a; 1992b, 39, 274–75, 292.
62. B. Smith 1992b, 6.
63. Ibid., 180.
64. Savolainen et al. 2002.
65. Clutton-Brock 1992.
66. Crawford 1984.
67. Clutton-Brock 1992.
68. Müller-Haye 1984.
69. Wenke 1984, 350, 397–98.
70. Chang 1981; MacNeish 1991, 159–63.
71. MacNeish 1991, 267–68.
72. Neumann 2003; Denham et al. 2003.
73. Hole 1992.
74. Phillipson 1993, 118.
75. MacNeish 1991, 314.
76. Hanotte et al. 2002; Clutton-Brock 1992.
77. Diamond 1997a; 1997b.
78. Cited in MacNeish 1991, 6.
79. Braidwood 1960.
80. Braidwood and Willey 1962.
81. Binford 1971; Flannery 1973a.
82. Wright 1971.
83. Flannery 1986, 10–11.
84. Cohen 1977a; 1977b, 279.
85. Byrne 1987, referred to in Blumler and Byrne 1991; see also Henry 1989, 30–38; McCorriston and Hole 1991.
86. Henry 1989, 41.
87. McCorriston and Hole 1991.
88. Henry 1989, 54.
89. Speth and Spielmann 1983.
90. B. White 1973; see also Kasarda 1971.
91. C. R. Ember 1983.
92. Konner and Worthman 1980.
93. Roosevelt 1984; see also M. N. Cohen and Armelagos 1984b, 585–602; Cohen 1987; 2009. For evidence suggesting that the transition to food production was not generally associated with declining health, see Wood et al. 1992; Starling and Stock 2007.
94. Roosevelt 1984
95. Goodman and Armelagos 1985; see also A. H. Goodman et al. 1984; Cohen 2009.
96. Clark and Piggott 1965, 240–42.
97. Ibid., 235.
98. Renfrew 1969.

Chapter 13

1. Wenke 1990; Connah 1987; Service 1975.
2. Flannery 1972.
3. Flannery 1972; Redman 1978, 215–16.
4. Wright and Johnson 1975.
5. The discussion in the remainder of this section draws from Wright and Johnson 1975; see also G. Johnson 1987.
6. Wright and Johnson 1975.
7. Flannery 1972.
8. Service 1975, 207.
9. Service 1975; Flannery 1972.
10. This description of Sumerian civilization is based on Kramer 1963.
11. Diamond 1989.
12. Helms 1975, 34–36, 54–55; Sanders et al. 1979.
13. Millon 1967.
14. Millon 1976.
15. Millon 1967.
16. Helms 1975, 61–63; Weaver 1993.
17. Blanton 1981; J. Marcus 1983.
18. Blanton 1976; 1978.
19. B. Turner 1970; Harrison and Turner 1978.
20. Houston 1988.
21. Wenke 1984, 289.
22. Connah 1987, 67.
23. Fagan 1989, 428–30.
24. Connah 1987, 216–17.
25. Vogel 2009.
26. Wenke 1984, 305–20.
27. Chang 1981.
28. Chang 1968, 235–55.
29. Solis et al. 2001; Haas et al. 2004.
30. For an overview, see Lumbreras 1974.
31. M. Fowler 1975.
32. For a more complete review of the available theories, see various chapters in Cohen and Service 1978; see also Chapter 1 in Zeder 1991.
33. Wittfogel 1957.
34. Adams 1960; H. T. Wright 1986.
35. Wheatley 1971, 291.
36. Adams 1960.
37. Adams 1981: 244.
38. Adams 1981, 243; Service 1975, 274–75.
39. Carneiro 1970; Sanders and Price 1968, 230–32.
40. M. Harris 1979, 101–02.
41. T. C. Young 1972.
42. Sanders and Price 1968, 141.
43. Blanton et al. 1981, 224. For the apparent absence of population pressure in the Teotihuacàn Valley, see Brumfiel 1976. For the Oaxaca Valley, see Feinman et al. 1985.
44. Wright and Johnson 1975. Carneiro 1988, however, argued the opposite, that the population grew just before the states emerged in southwestern Iran. Whether or not population declined, Frank Hole (1994) has suggested that climate change around that time may have forced local populations to relocate, some to centers that became cities.
45. Polanyi et al. 1957, 257–62; Sanders 1968.
46. Wright and Johnson 1975.
47. Rathje 1971.
48. Chang 1986, 234–94.
49. For a discussion of how political dynamics may play an important role in state formation, see Brumfiel 1983.
50. Johnson and Earle 1987, 324–26.
51. Childe 1950.
52. Service 1975, 12–15, 89–90.
53. J. Diamond 1997a, 205–07.
54. Dirks 1993.
55. Johnson and Earle 1987, 243–48, 304–06.
56. C. R. Ember and M. Ember 1992.
57. Ferguson and Whitehead 1992.
58. Weiss et al. 1993.
59. Kerr 1998; Grossman 2002.
60. Haug et al. 2003.
61. DeMenocal 2001; Haug et al. 2003; Hodell et al. 2001.
62. Holden 1996.
63. Wilkinson 1995.
64. Tainter 1988, 128–52.
65. Charanis 1953.

Chapter 14

1. Linton 1945, 30.
2. Sapir 1938, cited by Pelto and Pelto 1975, 1.
3. Pelto and Pelto 1975, 14–15.
4. de Waal 2001, 269.
5. de Munck 2000, 22.
6. Ibid. 2000, 22.
7. Ibid. 2000, 8.
8. Durkheim 1938/1895, 3.
9. Asch 1956.
10. Bond and Smith 1996.
11. Berns et al. 2005.
12. M. F. Brown 2008, 372.
13. Hewlett 2004.
14. Miner 1956, 504–05, reproduced by permission of the American Anthropological Association. Although Miner is not a foreign visitor, he wrote this description in a way that shows how these behaviors might be seen from an outside perspective.
15. Lee 1972.
16. M. F. Brown 2008, 364.
17. Hatch 1997.
18. Zechenter 1997.
19. Rosenblatt 2009.
20. Hall 1966, 159–60.
21. Ibid., 120.
22. R. Brown 1965, 549–609.
23. Wagley 1974.
24. Chibnik 1981, 256–68.
25. Linton 1936, 306.
26. Ibid., 310–11.
27. Silver 1981.
28. Greenfield et al. 2000.
29. Rogers 1983, 263–69.
30. Cancian 1980.
31. Hewlett and Cavalli-Sforza 1986; Cavalli-Sforza and Feldman 1981.
32. Valente 1995, 21.
33. W. Cohen 1995.
34. Linton 1936, 326–27.
35. *Britannica Online* 1998; *Academic American Encyclopedia* 1980.
36. Linton 1936, 338–39.
37. G. M. Foster 1962, 26.
38. Bodley 2008.
39. Pelto and Müller-Wille 1987, 207–43.
40. Aporta and Higgs 2005.
41. Bodley 2008.
42. T. Kroeber 1967, 45–47.
43. Schrauf 1999.
44. Roth 2001.
45. Boyd and Richerson 1996/1985, 106.

46. Ibid., p. 135.
47. D. T. Campbell 1965. See also Boyd and Richerson 1996/1985 and Durham 1991.
48. The historical information we refer to comes from a book by Nevins 1927. For how radical the American Revolution was, see G. Wood 1992.
49. Brinton 1938.
50. Paige 1975.
51. Bestor 2001, 76.
52. Trouillot 2001, 128.
53. Durrenberger 2001a; see also Hannerz 1996.
54. McNeill 1967, 283–87; Guest and Jones 2005, 4.
55. Guest and Jones 2005, 4
56. Traphagan and Brown 2002.
57. Trouillot 2001, 128.
58. Bradsher 2002, 3.
59. Guest and Jones 2005.
60. Yergin 2002, A29.
61. G. Thompson 2002, A3.
62. Sengupta 2002, A3.
63. Conklin 2002.
64. J. D. Hill 1996, 1.
65. Bilby 1996, 127–28, referring to Hoogbergen 1990, 23–51.
66. Bilby 1996, 128–37.
67. Sattler 1996, 42.
68. Ibid., 50–51.
69. Ibid., 54.
70. Ibid., 58–59.
71. Kottak 1996, 136; 153.
72. Roosens 1989, 9.
73. Cashdan 2001.
74. C. R. Ember and Levinson 1991.

Chapter 15

1. Keller 1974/1902, 34.
2. Wilden 1987, 124, referred to in Christensen et al. 2001.
3. Lambert 2001.
4. Ekman and Keltner 1997, 32.
5. Poyatos 2002, 103–5, 114–18.
6. von Frisch 1962.
7. King 1999a; Gibson and Jessee 1999, 189–90.
8. Seyfarth and Cheney 1982, 242, 246.
9. Hockett and Ascher 1964.
10. T. S. Eliot 1963.
11. Snowdon 1999, 81.
12. Pepperberg 1999.
13. Mukerjee 1996, 28.
14. Savage-Rumbaugh 1992, 138–41.
15. J. H. Hill 1978, 94; J. H. Hill 2009.
16. Ibid.
17. Senner 1989.
18. Chomsky 1975.
19. Southworth and Daswani 1974, 312. See also Boas 1911/1964, 121–23.
20. Akmajian et al. 2001, 296.
21. Ibid., 298.
22. Bickerton 1983.
23. Ibid., 122.
24. B. Berlin 1992; Hays 1994.
25. G. Miller 2004.
26. Gleitman and Wanner 1982; Blount 1981.
27. R. Brown 1980, 93–4.
28. de Villiers and de Villiers 1979, 48; see also Wanner and Gleitman 1982.
29. Bickerton 1983, 122.
30. E. Bates and Marchman 1988 as referred to by Snowdon 1999, 88–91.
31. Crystal 1971, 168.
32. Ibid., 100–1.
33. Barinaga 1992, 535.
34. Akmajian et al. 1984, 136.
35. R. L. Munroe et al. 1996; M. Ember and C. R. Ember 1999. The theory about the effect of baby-holding on consonant-vowel alternation is an extension of the theory that regular baby-holding encourages a preference for regular rhythm in music; see Ayres 1973.
36. Sapir and Swadesh 1964, 103.
37. Akmajian et al. 2001, 149–54.
38. Chaucer 1926, 8. Our modern English translation is based on the glossary in this book.
39. Katzner 2002, 10.
40. Akmajian et al. 2001, 334.
41. Baldi 1983, 3.
42. Ibid., 12.
43. Friedrich 1970, 168.
44. Ibid., 166.
45. Gimbutas 1974, 293–95. See Skomal and Polomé 1987.
46. Anthony et al. 1991.
47. Renfrew 1987.
48. Greenberg 1972; see also Phillipson 1976, 71.
49. Phillipson 1976, 79.
50. Holmes 2001, 194–95.
51. Trudgill 1983, 34.
52. Gumperz 1961, 976–88.
53. Trudgill 1983, 35.
54. Gumperz 1971, 45.
55. Weinreich 1968: 31.
56. But see Thomason and Kaufman 1988 for a discussion of how grammatical changes due to contact may be more important than was previously assumed.
57. Berlin and Kay 1969.
58. Ibid.
59. Ibid., 5–6.
60. Ibid., 104; Witkowski and Brown 1978.
61. Bornstein 1973, 41–101.
62. M. Ember 1978, 364–67.
63. Ibid.
64. C. H. Brown 1977.
65. C. H. Brown 1979.
66. Witkowski and Burris 1981.
67. Ibid.
68. C. H. Brown and Witkowski 1980, 379.
69. C. H. Brown 1984, 106.
70. Hoijer 1964, 146.
71. Webb 1977, 42–9; see also Rudmin 1988.
72. Sapir 1931, 578; see also J. B. Carroll 1956.
73. Wardhaugh 2002, 222.
74. Denny 1979, 97.
75. Friedrich 1986.
76. Guiora et al. 1982.
77. Lucy 1992, 46.
78. Ibid., 85–148.
79. Hymes 1974, 83–117.
80. Fischer 1958; Wardhaugh 2002, 160–88.
81. Chambers 2002, 352; citing research by Shuy.
82. Trudgill 1983, 41–2.
83. Geertz 1960, 248–60; see also Errington 1985.
84. R. Brown and Ford 1961.
85. Wardhaugh 2002, 315.
86. Shibamoto 1987, 28.
87. Holmes 2001, 153.

88. Chambers 2002, 352, citing research by Shuy.
89. Lakoff 1973; Lakoff 1990.
90. Wardhaugh 2002, 328; Holmes 2001, 158–59; Trudgill 1983, 87–88.
91. M. R. Haas 1944, 142–49.
92. Keenan 1989.
93. Holmes 2001, 289.
94. Tannen 1990, 49–83.
95. Wardhaugh 2002, 100.
96. Heller 1988, 1.
97. Pfaff 1979.
98. Wardhaugh 2002, 108.
99. Gal 1988, 249–55.
100. Collins and Blot 2003, 1–3.

Chapter 16

1. Hitchcock and Beisele 2000, 5.
2. C. R. Ember 1978b.
3. Kent 1996.
4. Schrire 1984a; Myers 1988.
5. Morrison and Junker 2002.
6. The discussion of the Australian aborigines is based on R. A. Gould 1969.
7. Burbank 1994, 23; Burbank 2009b.
8. Burch 2009; 1988.
9. Data from Textor 1967 and Service 1979.
10. Murdock and Provost 1973, 207.
11. R. B. Lee 1968; DeVore and Konner 1974.
12. C. R. Ember 1978b.
13. McCarthy and McArthur 1960.
14. R B. Lee 1979, 256–58, 278–80.
15. Palsson 1988; Roscoe 2002.
16. Keeley 1991; R. L. Kelly 1995, 293–315.
17. Mitchell 2009; Tollefson 2009.
18. C. Ember 1975.
19. Roscoe 2002.
20. D. Werner 1978.
21. Textor 1967.
22. This section is largely based on Hames 2009.
23. Chagnon 1983, 60.
24. This section is based mostly on Melvin Ember's fieldwork on the islands of American Samoa in 1955 to 1956.
25. Oliver 1974, 252–53.
26. S. S. King 1979.
27. Friedl 1962.
28. Hickey 1964, 135–65.
29. C. R. Ember 1983, 289.
30. Textor 1967; Dirks 2009; Messer 1996, 244.
31. Finnis 2006.
32. Barlett 1989, 253–91.
33. U.S. Environmental Protection Agency 2009.
34. Salzman 1996.
35. Lees and Bates 1974; A. L. Johnson 2002.
36. Barth 1965.
37. Whitaker 1955; Itkonen 1951.
38. Paine 1994.
39. Textor 1967.
40. Dirks 2009.
41. Data from Textor 1967.
42. L. R. Binford 1990; see also Low 1990a, 242–43.
43. The few foragers in cold areas relying primarily on hunting have animals (dogs, horses, reindeer) that can carry transportable housing; see L. R. Binford 1990.
44. Bailey et al. 1989.
45. Data from Textor 1967.

46. Janzen 1973. For an argument supporting the "weeding" explanation, see Carneiro 1968.
47. Boserup 1993 [1965].
48. R. C. Hunt 2000.
49. Janzen 1973.
50. Roosevelt 1992.

Chapter 17

1. Hoebel 1968/1954, 46–63.
2. Woodburn 1968.
3. Pryor 2005, 36.
4. Ibid.
5. Leacock and Lee 1982, 8; Pryor 2005, 36.
6. R. Dyson-Hudson and Smith 1978, 121–41; E. Andrews 1994.
7. R. Murphy 1960, 69, 142–43.
8. Salzman 1996.
9. Not all pastoralists have individual ownership. For example, the Tungus of northern Siberia have kin group ownership of reindeer. See Dowling 1975, 422.
10. Barth 1965, 124.
11. Dowling 1975.
12. Salzman 2002.
13. Creed 2009.
14. Fratkin 2008.
15. Ibid., 86–9.
16. Bodley 2008, 77–93; Wilmsen 1989, 1–14.
17. Bodley 2008, 95–98.
18. Ibid., 106–08.
19. Salzman 1996, 904–05.
20. Fratkin 2008.
21. Service 1979, 10.
22. E. M. Thomas 1959, 22.
23. Gröger 1981.
24. Plattner 1989, 379–96.
25. Hage and Powers 1992.
26. Carneiro 1968, cited in Sahlins 1972, 68.
27. M. Harris 1975, 127–28.
28. Sahlins (1972, 87) introduced North American anthropology to Alexander Chayanov and coined the phrase Chayanov's rule. See discussion in Durrenberger and Tannenbaum 2002.
29. Chayanov 1966, 78; for a discussion of Chayanov's analysis, see Durrenberger 1980.
30. Durrenberger and Tannenbaum 2002.
31. Chibnik 1987.
32. Durrenberger and Tannenbaum 2002.
33. Sahlins 1972, 101–48.
34. McClelland 1961.
35. Steward and Faron 1959, 122–25.
36. Bowie 2006, 251.
37. B. B. Whiting and Edwards 1988, 164.
38. Nag et al. 1978, 295–96.
39. B. B. Whiting and Edwards 1988, 97–107.
40. Draper and Cashdan 1988, 348.
41. N. B. Jones et al. 1996, 166–69.
42. Nag et al. 1978, 293; see also Bradley 1984–1985, 160–64.
43. C. R. Ember 1983, 291–97.
44. Udy 1970: 35–37.
45. Sahlins 1962, 50–52.
46. Pospisil 1963, 43.
47. Udy 1970, 35–39.
48. E. A. Smith 1983, 626.
49. K. Hill et al. 1987, 17–18.
50. Sih and Milton 1985.
51. Sosis 2002.

52. Gladwin 1980, 45–85.
53. Chibnik 1980.
54. Polanyi 1957.
55. Sahlins 1972, 188–96.
56. L. Marshall 1961, 239–41.
57. The "//" sign in the name for the G//ana people symbolizes a click sound not unlike the sound we make when we want a horse to move faster.
58. Cashdan 1980, 116–20.
59. H. Kaplan and Hill 1985; H. Kaplan et al. 1990; Gurven et al. 2002, 114.
60. Hames 1990.
61. Gurven et al. 2002, 114.
62. H. Kaplan et al. 1990.
63. Winterhalder 1990.
64. Mooney 1978.
65. Balikci 1970 quoted in Mooney 1978, 392.
66. Mooney 1978, 392.
67. Fehr and Fischbacher 2003; Ensminger 2002; Henrich et al. 2004, as cited by Ensminger 2002.
68. Angier 2002, F1, F8.
69. Marshall 1961, 242.
70. Abler 2009.
71. N. Peacock and Bailey 2004.
72. Gibbs 1965, 223.
73. Humphrey and Hugh-Jones 1992.
74. Blanton 2009; Gregory 1982.
75. Uberoi 1962.
76. Malinowski 1920; Uberoi 1962.
77. J. Leach 1983, 12, 16.
78. Weiner 1976, 77–117.
79. Sahlins 1972, 196–204.
80. Pryor 1977, 204, 276.
81. Vayda et al. 1962.
82. Drucker 1967.
83. M. Harris 1975, 120.
84. Tollefson 2009.
85. Beattie 1960.
86. Thurnwald 1934, 125.
87. Pryor 1977, 284–86.
88. Service 1962, 145–46.
89. M. Harris 1975, 118–21.
90. Plattner 1985, viii.
91. Pryor 1977, 31–33.
92. Thurnwald 1934, 122.
93. Plattner 1985, xii.
94. Pryor 1977, 153–83; Stodder (1995, 205) finds that monetary trade is more likely with capital-intensive agriculture.
95. Pryor 1977, 109–11.
96. B. Foster 1974.
97. Pryor 1977, 125–48.
98. E. Wolf 1955, 452–71; Carrasco 1961.
99. W. R. Smith 1977; M. Harris 1964.
100. Ibid.
101. See, e.g., Gross et al. 1979.
102. Pollier 2000.
103. Vohs et al. 2006.
104. The description of Tikopia is based on Firth 1959, Chapters 5, 6, 7, and 9, passim.
105. Monsutti 2004.
106. Monsutti 2004; Eversole 2005.
107. Eversole 2005.
108. Most of this discussion is based on R. F. Murphy and Steward 1956.
109. Burkhalter and Murphy 1989.
110. E. Wolf 1966, 3–4.
111. Hobsbawm 1970.
112. Gross and Underwood 1971.

Chapter 18

1. In an analysis of many native societies in the New World, Gary Feinman and Jill Neitzel argue that egalitarian and rank societies ("tribes" and "chiefdoms," respectively) are not systematically distinguishable. See Feinman and Neitzel (1984, 57).
2. Fried 1967, 33.
3. Boehm 1993, 230–31; Boehm 1999.
4. M. G. Smith 1966, 152.
5. Salzman 1999.
6. D. Mitchell 2009.
7. Drucker 1965, 56–64.
8. Service 1978, 249.
9. Sahlins 1958, 80–81.
10. Betzig 1988.
11. W. L. Warner and Lunt 1941.
12. Lynd and Lynd 1929; and Lynd and Lynd 1937.
13. Brittain 1978.
14. Higley 1995, 1–47.
15. Argyle 1994.
16. S. R. Barrett 1994, 17–19, 34–35.
17. Ibid., 155.
18. U.S. Census Bureau 2002.
19. Treiman and Ganzeboom 1990, 117; Featherman and Hauser 1978, 4, 481.
20. Solon 2002; Behrman et al. 2001.
21. S. R. Barrett 1994, 17, 41.
22. K. Phillips 1990; U.S. Census Bureau 1993; *New York Times* 1997, A26; Johnston 1999, 16.
23. Leonhardt and Fabrikant 2009.
24. Durrenberger 2001b, who refers to Goldschmidt 1999 and Newman 1988; 1993.
25. Scott and Leonhardt 2005.
26. Klass 2009.
27. Ruskin 1963, 296–314.
28. O. Lewis 1958.
29. Ibid.
30. Kristof 1995, A18.
31. For more information about caste in Japan, see Berreman 1973 and 1972, 403–14.
32. Takezawa 2006.
33. Kristof 1995; Kristof 1997.
34. Tamari 1991; 2005.
35. Taylor 2005.
36. Berreman 1960, 120–27.
37. O. Patterson 1982, vii–xiii, 105.
38. Pryor 1977, 219.
39. Euripides 1937, 52.
40. Nadel 1942.
41. Harper 2003.
42. Lassiter et al. 2004, 49–50.
43. Ibid., 59–67.
44. Pryor 1977, 217–47.
45. Brooks et al. 1993; Tishkoff et al. 2009.
46. M. D. Williams 2004.
47. S. S. Friedman 1980, 206.
48. M. H. Ross 2009a.
49. Marks 1994, 32.
50. Fluehr-Lobban 2006, 12.
51. Marks 1994, 32.

52. Fluehr-Lobban 2006, 12.
53. Armelagos and Goodman 1998, 365.
54. O. Patterson 2000.
55. M. Nash 1989, 2.
56. Ibid., 10.
57. Newbury 1998.
58. C. Taylor 2005.
59. Newbury 1998.
60. *Britannica Online* 1995.
61. See Rwanda in later Books of the Year from Britannica Online http://search.eb.com/search?query=rwanda&x=0&y= 0&ct=.
62. Barth 1994, 27.
63. Yinger 1994, 169.
64. Ibid., 169–71.
65. Ibid., 216–17.
66. Benjamin 1991; see also M. D. Williams 2004.
67. Flannery 1972.
68. Data from Textor 1967.
69. Ibid.
70. Lenski 1984/1966, 308–18.
71. Treiman and Ganzeboom 1990, 117; Cutright 1967, 564.
72. Sahlins 1958.
73. Ibid., 4.
74. Sahlins 1972.
75. Lenski 1984/1966.
76. Gilman 1990.
77. Fried 1967, 201ff; and Harner 1975.
78. Meek 1940, 149–50.

Chapter 19

1. Quoted in Klineberg, "Foreword," in Segall 1979, v.
2. D. E. Brown 1991.
3. C. C. Moore 1997, 8–9; see also C. C. Moore et al. 1999.
4. M. Mead 1961.
5. Malinowski 1927.
6. D. Freeman 1983. For reasons to be skeptical about Freeman's criticism, see M. Ember 1985, 906–909.
7. Spiro 1982.
8. Schlegel and Barry 1991, 44.
9. Piaget 1970, 703–32.
10. Berry et al. 1992, 40.
11. Ibid., 40–41.
12. Dasen and Heron 1981, 305–06.
13. C. R. Ember 1977; and Rogoff 1981.
14. Price-Williams 1961.
15. Segall et al. 1990, 149.
16. Rogoff 1981, 264–67.
17. Kaplan et al. 2000, 156.
18. Lancy 2008, 4–7.
19. A. James 2007.
20. Weisner et al. 1983.
21. J. W. M. Whiting and Child 1953, 69–71.
22. Weisner et al. 1983, 291; Hewlett 2004.
23. For a review of the concept of ethnotheories about parenting, see Super and Harkness 1997.
24. Harkness and Super 1997, in Small 1997, 45.
25. Weisner 2004.
26. J. W. M. Whiting and Child 1953, 310.
27. Edgerton 1992, 206.
28. D. G. Freedman 1979.
29. Ibid., 40–41. For a discussion of possible genetic influences on the social environment, see Scarr and McCartney 1983.
30. See Dasen et al. 1988 for references to research, particularly by Barrett 1984.
31. Dasen et al. 1988, 117–18, 126–28.
32. See R. A. LeVine 2007, for an overview of ethnographic studies of childhood.
33. See the research cited in Hewlett 2004; see also Small 1997.
34. Ibid.
35. Lancy 2008, 113–14.
36. R. H. Munroe and Munroe 1980.
37. R. A. LeVine 1988, 4–6; see also discussion in Hewlett 2004.
38. Lancy 2007.
39. Ibid., 274.
40. Ibid., 275 referring to Howrigan 1988, 41.
41. Lancy 2007, 275, quoting Le 2000, 216, 218.
42. Rohner 1975, 97–105.
43. See research reported in Rohner and Britner 2002, 16–47.
44. Rohner 1975, 112–16.
45. Barry et al. 1959. For a somewhat different analysis of the Barry et al. data, see Hendrix 1985.
46. Hoffman 1988, 101–03.
47. Lancy 2008, 180–81, reporting on Mayer and Mayer 1970, 165, and Kulick 1992, 119.
48. Chagnon 1983, 115.
49. Dentan 1968, 55–56.
50. Ibid., 61.
51. Straus 2001.
52. C. R. Ember and Ember 1994.
53. B. B. Whiting and Whiting 1975, 94; see also R. H. Munroe et al. 1984.
54. B. B. Whiting and Edwards 1988, 265.
55. R. H. Munroe et al. 1984, 374–76; see also C. R. Ember 1973.
56. B. B. Whiting and Whiting 1975, 179.
57. B. B. Whiting and Edwards 1988, 35.
58. Ibid., 152–63; and C. R. Ember 1981, 560.
59. C. R. Ember 1977; Rogoff 1981.
60. Rogoff 1981, 285.
61. For how school experiences may improve particular cognitive skills, rather than higher levels of cognitive development in general, see Rogoff 1990, 46–49.
62. Irwin et al. 1974.
63. Luria 1976, 108; quoted in Rogoff 1981, 254.
64. Scribner and Cole 1981; Berry and Bennett 1989, 429–50, as reported in Berry et al. 1992, 123–24.
65. Godoy et al. 2004; Bowles et al. 2001.
66. Geertz 1984, 123–36.
67. Although Melford Spiro (1993) does not believe that this Western/non-Western pattern exists, readers are referred to his article for the many references to the works of those who do.
68. For a review of the literature on "individualism" versus "collectivism," which is mostly based on studies of educated individuals from industrialized cultures, see Triandis 1995. Using data collected by anthropologists on mostly preindustrial cultures, Carpenter (2000, 38–56), finds support for the idea that the concept of self differs in individualist as compared with collectivist cultures.
69. Bachnik 1992.
70. Stairs 1992.
71. Spiro 1993.
72. Research reported in Hollan 1992, 289–90.
73. Berry 1976.
74. Witkin 1967, 233–50.
75. Dawson 1967, 115–28, 171–85; and Berry 1971, 324–36.
76. C. R. Ember 2009; Halpern 2000, 110–12.
77. Dentan 1968, 55–56.
78. Chagnon 1983.
79. C. R. Ember and M. Ember 1994.
80. Edgerton 1971.

81. Bolton 1973.
82. McClelland 1961.
83. LeVine 1966, 2.
84. Kardiner 1946/1939, 471.
85. J. W. M. Whiting and Child 1953, 32–38.
86. J. M. Roberts and Sutton-Smith 1962, 178.
87. J. M. Roberts et al. (1959, 597–605) first established the relationship between games of strategy and social stratification and political complexity. Chick (1998) has replicated those findings.
88. R. V. Burton and Whiting 1961. See also R. L. Munroe, Munroe, and Whiting 1981. For a review of cross-cultural research on initiation, see Burbank 2009a.
89. Yan 2006.
90. Johnson-Hanks 2006.
91. Perry 2005, 217.

Chapter 20

1. Leibowitz 1978, 43–44.
2. Schlegel 1989, 266; Epstein 1988, 5–6; Chafetz 1990, 28.
3. Jacobs and Roberts 1989.
4. Segal 2004; Segal also cites the work of W. Williams 1992.
5. Lang 1999, 93–94; Blackwood 1984b.
6. Wikan 1982, 168–86.
7. Stini 1971.
8. Frayer and Wolpoff 1985, 431–32.
9. For reviews of theories and research on sexual dimorphism and possible genetic and cultural determinants of variation in degree of dimorphism over time and place, see Frayer and Wolpoff 1985 and Gray 1985, 201–09, 217–25.
10. J. K. Brown 1970b, 1074.
11. Among the Aché hunter-gatherers of Paraguay, women collect the type of honey produced by stingless bees (men collect other honey); this division of labor is consistent with the compatibility theory. See Hurtado et al. 1985, 23.
12. Murdock and Provost 1973, 213; Byrne 1994.
13. R. O'Brian 1999.
14. D. R. White et al. 1977, 1–24.
15. Mukhopadhyay and Higgins 1988, 473.
16. J. K. Brown 1970b, 1073–78; and D. R. White et al. 1977.
17. Nerlove 1974.
18. N. E. Levine 1988.
19. M. J. Goodman et al. 1985.
20. Noss and Hewlett 2001.
21. Brumbach and Jarvenpa 2006a; Jarvenpa and Brumbach 2006.
22. Brumbach and Jarvenpa 2006b.
23. C. R. Ember 1983, 288–89.
24. Mead 1950 [originally published 1935], 180–84.
25. Rivers 1967 [originally published 1906], 567.
26. M. Ember and Ember 1971, 573, Table 1.
27. Schlegel and Barry 1986.
28. Wood and Eagly 2002, 706, drawing on data from H. Kaplan et al. 2000.
29. Boserup 1970, 22–25; see also Schlegel and Barry 1986, 144–45.
30. Boserup 1970, 22–25.
31. Bossen 2000.
32. Ibid., 31–34.
33. C. R. Ember 1983, 286–87; data from Murdock and Provost 1973, 212; Bradley 1995.
34. C. R. Ember 1983.
35. Ibid.
36. Ibid., 287–93.
37. M. Ember and Ember 1971, 579–80.

38. Ibid., 581; see also Sanday 1973, 1684.
39. Nerlove 1974.
40. Schlegel and Barry 1986.
41. Whyte 1978a, 217.
42. Nussbaum 1995, 2, based on data from Human Development Report 1993.
43. Whyte 1978a; D. B. Adams 1983.
44. J. K. Brown 1970a.
45. Sanday 1974; and Divale and Harris 1976.
46. Quinn 1977, 189–90.
47. Graham 1979.
48. D. Werner 1982; and Stogdill 1974, cited in ibid.; see also Handwerker and Crosbie 1982.
49. Draper 1975, 103.
50. D. Werner 1984.
51. M. H. Ross 1986.
52. This description is based on the fieldwork of Elizabeth and Robert Fearnea (1956–1958), as reported in M. K. Martin and Voorhies 1975, 304–31.
53. Begler 1978.
54. Ibid. See also Whyte 1978a, 229–32.
55. Whyte 1978b, 95–120; see also Quinn 1977.
56. Whyte 1978b, 124–29, 145; see also Sanday 1973.
57. Whyte 1978b, 129–30.
58. J. K. Brown 1970a.
59. Whyte 1978b, 135–36.
60. Ibid., 135.
61. Doyle 2005.
62. D. Werner 1984.
63. Quinn 1977, 85; see also Etienne and Leacock 1980, 19–20.
64. Chafetz 1990, 11–19.
65. B. B. Whiting and Edwards 1973.
66. R. L. Munroe et al. 2000, 8–9.
67. Maccoby and Jacklin 1974.
68. For a more extensive discussion of behavior differences and possible explanations of them, see C. R. Ember 1981.
69. B. B. Whiting and Edwards 1973.
70. For references to this research, see C. R. Ember 1981, 559.
71. Rubin et al. 1974.
72. For a discussion of this evidence, see Ellis 1986, 525–27; C. R. Ember 1981.
73. For example, Ellis (1986) considers the evidence for the biological view of aggression "beyond reasonable dispute."
74. For a discussion of other possibilities, see C. R. Ember 1981.
75. Rohner 1976.
76. B. B. Whiting and Whiting 1975; see also B. B. Whiting and Edwards 1988, 273.
77. C. R. Ember 1973, 424–39.
78. B. B. Whiting and Edwards 1973, 175–79; see also Maccoby and Jacklin 1974.
79. Burbank 1994.
80. Heise 1967.
81. C. S. Ford and Beach 1951, 191.
82. O. Lewis 1951, 397.
83. Farley 1996, 60.
84. C. S. Ford and Beach 1951, 23–25, 68–71.
85. Ibid., 40–41, 73.
86. Broude 2009.
87. C. S. Ford and Beach 1951, 82–83.
88. Broude and Greene 1976.
89. Kluckhohn 1948, 101.
90. M. Hunt 1974, 254–57; Lewin 1994.
91. Broude 1980, 184.
92. C. S. Ford and Beach 1951, 114.
93. Jankowiak et al. 2002.
94. Lang 1999, 97, citing Thomas 1993.

95. J. Morris 1938, 191.
96. Underhill 1938, 117, 186.
97. 'Abd Allah 1917, 7, 20.
98. Cardoso and Werner 2004.
99. R. C. Kelly 1974.
100. Cardoso and Werner 2004.
101. Blackwood and Wieringa 1999, 49; Blackwood 1984a.
102. Cardoso and Werner 2004, 207.
103. Data from Textor 1967.
104. W. N. Stephens 1972, 1–28.
105. Broude 1976, 243.
106. D. Werner 1979; D. Werner 1975.
107. D. Werner 1979, 345–62; see also D. Werner 1975, 36.
108. D. Werner 1979, 358.
109. Data from Textor 1967.
110. Schlegel 1991.

Chapter 21

1. W. N. Stephens 1963, 5.
2. Murdock 1949, 8.
3. Stephens 1963, 170–71.
4. Hua 2001.
5. Gough 1959; Unnithan 2009.
6. Hoebel 1960, 77.
7. Evans-Pritchard 1970, 1428–34.
8. D. O'Brien 1977; Oboler 1980.
9. Oboler 2009.
10. Murdock 1949, 7–8.
11. Ibid., 9–10.
12. See, for example, Linton 1936, 135–36.
13. M. Ember and C. R. Ember 1979.
14. Ibid.
15. Marlowe 2003, 221–223.
16. M. Ember and C. R. Ember 1979.
17. Graburn 1969, 188–200.
18. Malinowski 1932, 77.
19. Ibid., 88.
20. J. W. M. Whiting 1941, 125.
21. Doyle 2004.
22. Service 1978.
23. LeVine and LeVine 1963, 65.
24. Ibid.
25. For an extensive discussion of the symbolism of Rotuman weddings, see A. Howard and Rensel 2009.
26. Schlegel and Eloul 1987, 119.
27. Schlegel and Eloul 1988, 295, Table 1. We used the data to calculate the frequency of various types of economic transaction in a worldwide sample of 186 societies.
28. Oboler 2009.
29. Frake 1960.
30. Mead 1931, 206–208.
31. Borgerhoff Mulder et al. 2001.
32. Schlegel and Eloul 1988, 298–99.
33. Pryor 1977, 363–64.
34. Ibid.
35. Spencer 1968, 136.
36. Schlegel and Eloul 1988, 296–97.
37. Ibid.
38. Ibid.
39. Radcliffe-Brown 1922, 73.
40. Murdock 1967; Goody 1973, 17–21.
41. Pryor 1977, 363–65; Schlegel and Eloul 1988, 296–99.
42. Research is reported in Gaulin and Boster 1990, 994–1005. The first theory discussed herein is associated with Boserup 1970. The second is put forward by Gaulin and Boster.

43. Schlegel and Eloul 1988, following Goody 1973, 20.
44. Barth 1965, 18–19; as reported in (and coded as indirect dowry by) Schlegel and Eloul 1987, 131.
45. Middleton 1962, 606.
46. Durham 1991, 293–94, citing research by Hopkins 1980.
47. Westermarck 1894.
48. Talmon 1964, 492.
49. Ibid., 504.
50. A. Wolf 1968, 864.
51. A. Wolf and Chieh-shan Huang 1980, 159, 170, 185.
52. H. Parker and S. Parker 1986.
53. M. Ember 1975; Durham 1991, 341–57.
54. For a discussion of mechanisms that might lead to sexual aversion, see S. Parker 1976; 1984.
55. Freud 1943.
56. Malinowski 1927.
57. Quoted in L. A. White 1949, 313.
58. Kang 1979, 85–99.
59. Rudan and Campbell 2004.
60. Stern 1973, 494–95, as cited in M. Ember 1975, 256. For a review of the theory and evidence, see Durham 1991.
61. Seemanova 1971, 108–28, as cited in Durham 1991, 305–09.
62. Durham 1991, 305–09.
63. Ibid., 346–52.
64. Firth 1957, 287–88, cited (somewhat differently) in Durham 1991, 349–50.
65. A mathematical model of early mating systems suggests that people may have noticed the harmful effects of inbreeding once populations began to expand as a result of agriculture; people therefore may have deliberately adopted the incest taboo to solve the problem of inbreeding. See M. Ember 1975. For a similar subsequent suggestion, see Durham 1991, 331–39.
66. Goode 1982, 61–62.
67. C. S. Ford 1941, 149.
68. A. Howard and Rensel 2004.
69. S. S. Davis 2009.
70. Goode 1970, 210.
71. Lingenfelter 2009.
72. MacDonald and Hewlett 1999, 504–06.
73. M. Ember 1975, 262, Table 3.
74. Busby 2009.
75. M. Ember 1975, 260–69; see also Durham 1991, 341–57.
76. Murdock 1949, 29.
77. Bogoras 1909, cited in W. Stephens 1963, 195.
78. Oliver 1955, 352–53.
79. Ibid., 223–24, quoted in W. Stephens 1963, 58.
80. Mead 1950, 101.
81. Jankowiak et al. 2005.
82. The discussion of these customs is based on W. Stephens 1963, 63–67.
83. Kilbride and Kilbride 1990, 202–06.
84. C. Anderson 2000, 102–03.
85. Linton 1936, 183.
86. J. W. M. Whiting 1964.
87. Ibid., 518.
88. Ibid., 516–17.
89. M. Ember 1974b.
90. M. Ember 1984–1985. The statistical relationship between late age of marriage for men and polygyny was first reported by Witkowski 1975.
91. M. Ember 1974b, 202–205.
92. M. Ember 1984–1985. For other predictors of polygyny, see D. R. White and Burton 1988.
93. Sellen and Hruschka 2004.
94. Low 1990b.

95. M. Ember et al. 2007.
96. Barber 2008.
97. Coult and Habenstein 1965; Murdock 1957.
98. M. C. Goldstein 1987, 39.
99. Stephens 1963, 45.
100. Hiatt 1980.
101. M. Goldstein 1987. Formerly, in feudal Tibet, a class of serfs who owned small parcels of land also practiced polyandry. Goldstein suggests that a shortage of land would explain their polyandry too. See M. C. Goldstein 1971.
102. Haddix 2001.
103. For example, see M. L. Cohen 1976.
104. Pasternak 1976, 96.
105. Silk 1980; Damas 1983.
106. Melvin Ember, pers. comm.
107. K. Gibson 2009.
108. Coult and Habenstein 1965.
109. Mead 1961/1928, quoted in Stephens 1963, 134–35.
110. Ibid., 135.
111. Nimkoff and Middleton 1960.
112. Pasternak et al. 1976, 109–23.
113. Block 1983.

Chapter 22

1. Coult and Habenstein 1965; Murdock 1957.
2. Percentages calculated from Coult and Habenstein 1965.
3. L. Bohannan and P. Bohannan 1953.
4. J. H. Moore and Campbell 2002; Ensor 2003.
5. Lowe 2002.
6. J. D. Freeman 1961.
7. Jarvenpa 2004.
8. Murdock 1949, 49–50.
9. C. R. Ember et al. 1974, 84–89.
10. Pospisil 1963.
11. Schneider 1961a.
12. M. Ember and Ember 1971, 581.
13. Schneider 1961b.
14. Goodenough 1951, 145.
15. Coult and Habenstein 1965.
16. Data from Textor 1967.
17. Fortes 1949.
18. Davenport 1959.
19. The description of the Samoan descent system is based on M. Ember's 1955 to 1956 fieldwork. See also M. Ember 1959, 573–77; and Davenport 1959.
20. M. Ember 1967.
21. M. Ember and C. R. Ember 1971. See also Divale 1974.
22. M. Ember and Ember 1971, 583–85; Divale 1974.
23. M. Ember and Ember 1971. For a different theory—that matrilocal residence precedes, rather than follows, the development of purely external warfare—see Divale 1974.
24. Helms 2009; Herlihy 2007; see also M. Ember and Ember 1971
25. Service 1962, 137.
26. C. R. Ember and M. Ember 1972.
27. C. R. Ember 1975.
28. M. Ember 1974a.
29. Data from Textor 1967.
30. C. R. Ember et al. 1974.
31. The importance of warfare and competition as factors in the formation of unilineal descent groups is also suggested by Service 1962 and Sahlins 1961, 332–45.
32. C. R. Ember and Ember 1972.
33. C. R. Ember and Ember 1997.
34. See, for example, Murdock 1949, 199–222.

35. Reported in Textor 1967.
36. Ibid.
37. Murdock 1949, 125.
38. Textor 1967.
39. L. A. White 1939.
40. Goody 1970.
41. Pasternak 1976, 142.
42. Textor 1967.
43. Ibid.
44. This conjecture is based on unpublished cross-cultural research by the Embers.

Chapter 23

1. This section is based on N. Dyson-Hudson 1966, 155.
2. This section is based on Maybury-Lewis 1967.
3. Leis 1974.
4. Meggitt 1964.
5. Ibid., 207. For why men in some societies may fear sex with women, see C. R. Ember 1978a.
6. Meggitt 1964, 218.
7. Bellman 1984, 8, 25–28, 33.
8. Ibid., 8.
9. Ibid., 8, 80–88.
10. Ibid., 33, 80; also Bledsoe 1980, 67.
11. K. Little 1965/1966; Bledsoe 1980, 68–70.
12. Ericksen 1989.
13. Leis 1974.
14. Hoebel 1960.
15. W. K. Powers and Powers 2004.
16. R. H. Thompson 2009.
17. Mangin 1965, 311–23.
18. Okamura 1983.
19. R. H. Thompson 2009.
20. K. Little 1965; and Meillassoux 1968.
21. K. Little 1957, 582.
22. Ibid., 583.
23. Ardener 1995b/1964, 1.
24. Ardener 1995a/1964, Appendix.
25. See the many chapters in Ardener and Burman 1995/1964 for examples.
26. Fessler 2002.
27. N. Nelson 1995/1964, 58.
28. Bortei-Doku and Aryeetey 1995/1964, 77–94.
29. Fessler 2002.
30. Light and Deng 1995/1964, 217–40.
31. Warry 1986.
32. Ervin 1987.
33. Caulkins 2009.
34. Naroll 1983, 74–75.
35. Eisenstadt 1954, 102.
36. Bernardi 1952.
37. Ritter 1980.
38. Ibid.
39. For an explanation of age-sets among North American Plains Indians, see Hanson 1988.

Chapter 24

1. Service 1962.
2. Schrire 1984b; see also Leacock and Lee 1982, 8.
3. Service 1962, 109.
4. Briggs 1974.
5. Mathiassen 1928, 213.
6. Service 1962, 114–15.
7. Bohannan 1954, 3.
8. Sahlins 1961, 342.

9. R. C. Kelly 1985, 1.
10. Sahlins 1961, 345.
11. N. Dyson-Hudson 1966, Chapters 5 and 6.
12. Ibid.
13. Sahlins 1962, 293–94.
14. Sahlins 1963, 295.
15. Sahlins 1983, 519.
16. Sahlins 1963, 297.
17. Carneiro 1970, 733.
18. Weber 1947, 154.
19. Lightfoot 2005.
20. Ferguson 2004.
21. Wiberg 1983.
22. For an extensive review of the various theories about legitimacy, see R. Cohen 1988, 1–3.
23. Finley 1983.
24. Carcopino 1940, 18–20.
25. Our discussion of Nupe is based on S. F. Nadel 1935, 257–303.
26. Blanton and Fargher 2008.
27. Ibid.
28. M. Ember 1963.
29. Textor 1967.
30. M. Ember 1963.
31. Textor 1967.
32. Naroll 1961. See also Ross 1981.
33. M. Ember 1963, 244–46.
34. Service 1962; see also Braun and Plog 1982; Haas 1990.
35. A. Johnson and Earle 1987, 158; Carneiro 1990.
36. Service 1962, 112, 145.
37. Feinman and Nietzel 1984.
38. For a more detailed description and evaluation of the available theories, see Chapter 12 in C. Ember et al. 2007. See also Cohen and Service 1978. For more details, see chapter on the origin of the state.
39. McNeill 1976.
40. Carneiro 1978, 215.
41. Textor 1967.
42. Carneiro 1978; Hart 1948; Naroll 1967; Marano 1973, 35–40 (cf. Peregrine, Ember, and Ember 2004 and other articles in Graber 2004).
43. For a review of the descriptive literature until the late 1970s, see Vincent 1978.
44. D. Werner 1982.
45. Kracke 1979, 232.
46. D. Werner 1982.
47. Sahlins 1963.
48. Kracke 1979, 41.
49. Lederman 1990.
50. Brandewie 1991.
51. Lepowsky 1990.
52. Todorov et al. 2005.
53. Zebrowitz and Montepare 2005.
54. Ross 1988, 73. The discussion in this section draws mostly from Zebrowitz and Montepare 2005, 73–89, and from Ross 2009b.
55. Bondarenko and Korotayev 2000; Korotayev and Bondarenko 2000.
56. For studies of international relations that support these conclusions, see footnotes 2 and 3 in C. R. Ember, Ember, and Russett 1992; see also Chapter 3 in Russett and Oneal 2001.
57. C. R. Ember, Ember, and Russett 1992.
58. Rummel 2002b.
59. Scaglion 2009b.
60. Hoebel 1968/1954, 4, quoting S. P. Simpson and Field 1946, 858.

61. Fry and Björkqvist 1997.
62. D. Black 1993, 79–83.
63. Ross 1988.
64. Boas 1888, 668.
65. Otterbein 1986, 107.
66. Archer and Gartner 1984, 118–39.
67. Scaglion 2004b; D. Black 1993, 83–86.
68. Ibid.
69. Evans-Pritchard 1940, 291. The discussion of the Nuer follows this source.
70. Hickson 1986.
71. Ibid.; and Koch et al. 1977, 279.
72. J. M. Roberts 1967, 169.
73. Ibid., 192.
74. Hoebel 1968/1954, Chapter 9.
75. Schwartz 1954, 475.
76. Textor 1967.
77. Masumura 1977, 388–99.
78. Scaglion 2009b; Black 1993; Newman 1983, 131.
79. Otterbein and Otterbein 1965 and Fry 2006, 88 do not consider feuding to be warfare.
80. See summaries of the evidence in C. R. Ember and Ember 1994; see also Fry 2006.
81. C. R. Ember and Ember 1994.
82. Chacon and Mendoza 2007.
83. Newman 1983, 131; Ericksen and Horton 1992.
84. Gubser 1965, 151.
85. Otterbein and Otterbein 1965, 1476.
86. D. R. White 1988.
87. Patterson 1982, 345–52.
88. Gat 1999, 373, as referred to in Wadley 2003.
89. Heider 1970, 105–11; Heider 1979, 88–99.
90. M. Ember and Ember 1992, 188–89.
91. C. R. Ember and Ember 1992; M. Ember 1982. For a discussion of how Dani warfare seems to be motivated mainly by economic considerations, see Shankman 1991. B. W. Kang (2000, 878–79) finds a strong correlation between environmental stress and warfare frequency in Korean history.
92. Otterbein 1970.
93. C. R. Ember and Ember 1992; see also Otterbein 1970 and Loftin 1971.
94. C. R. Ember 1974.
95. Otterbein 1968, 283; Ross 1985.
96. Divale and Harris 1976, 521–38; see also Gibbons 1993.
97. C. R. Ember and Ember 1992, 251–52.
98. Singer 1980.
99. Russett and Oneal 2001, 89.
100. Ibid., 145–48.
101. Younger 2008.
102. Russett 1993, 10–11, 14, 138.

Chapter 25

1. Tylor 1979.
2. Marett 1909.
3. Guthrie 1993.
4. Freud 1967/1939; Badcock 1988, 126–27, 133–36.
5. Malinowski 1939, 959; Malinowski 1954, 50–51.
6. W. James 1902.
7. Jung 1938.
8. Fromm 1950.
9. Maslow 1964.
10. Poggie et al. 1976; Poggie and Pollnac 1988.
11. Durkheim 1961/1912.
12. Swanson 1969, 1–31.
13. A. Wallace 1966, 60–61.
14. Malefijt 1968, 153.

15. Ray 1954, 172–89.
16. Rosenblatt et al. 1976, 51.
17. Ibid., 55.
18. Swanson 1969, 97–108; see also Sheils 1975.
19. Middleton 1971, 488.
20. Spiro and D'Andrade 1958.
21. Lambert et al. 1959; Rohner 1975, 108.
22. H. G. Barnett 1960, 79–85.
23. Swanson 1969, 56.
24. Ibid., 55–81; see also W. D. Davis 1971. Peregrine (1996, 84–112) replicated Swanson's finding for North American societies.
25. Textor 1967; R. Underhill 1975.
26. Geertz 1966.
27. Swanson 1969, 153–74.
28. Bunzel 1971.
29. Gossen 1979.
30. Dickson et al. 2005.
31. Stark and Finke 2000, 107–08.
32. A. Wallace 1966, 52–67.
33. Winkelman 1986b, 178–83.
34. Bourguignon 1973.
35. Bourguignon and Evascu 1977; Winkelman 1986b, 196–98.
36. Kehoe and Giletti 1981.
37. Raybeck 1998, referring to Raybeck et al. 1989.
38. Bourguignon 2004, 572.
39. Winkleman and Peck 2004.
40. O. K. Moore 1957.
41. Sheils 1980.
42. Winkelman and Baker 2010, 293–96 and references therein.
43. Evans-Pritchard 1979, 362–66.
44. Swanson 1969, 150; see also H. R. Trevor-Roper 1971, 444–49.
45. Swanson 1969, 150–51.
46. Caporael 1976; Matossian 1982; and Matossian 1989, 70–80. For possible reasons to dismiss the ergot theory, see Spanos 1983.
47. Harner 1972.
48. B. B. Whiting 1950, 36–37; see also Swanson 1969, 137–52, 240–41.
49. Winkelman 1986a.
50. Ibid., 28–29.
51. Knecht 2003, 11.
52. Harner and Doore 1987, 3, 8–9; Noll 1987, 49; Krippner 1987, 128.
53. De Laguna 1972, 701C.
54. See Krippner 1987, 126-27; Noll 1987, 49–50.
55. Winkelman 1986a, 27–28.
56. Ibid., 27.
57. Ibid., 35–37.
58. M. Harris 1966.
59. Buckser and Glazier 2003; Rambo 2003.
60. Discussion is based on Firth 1970.
61. Ibid., 387.
62. Ibid., 418.
63. Mason 1962.
64. Ensminger 1997, 7.
65. Ibid.
66. Reff 2005; see also McNeill 1998 and Stark 1996.
67. C. R. Ember 1982.
68. A. Wallace 1966, 30.
69. A. Wallace 1970, 239.
70. The Quakers, long-time neighbors and trusted advisers of the Seneca, took pains not to interfere with Seneca religion, principles, and attitudes.
71. Worsley 1957, 12.
72. Ibid., 11, 115.
73. Ibid., 122.
74. Aberle 1971.
75. Knauft 1978.
76. Antoun 2001.
77. Nagata 2001.
78. Antoun 2001, 17–18.
79. Ibid., 45.

Chapter 26

1. Maquet 1986, 9.
2. R. L. Anderson 1989, 21.
3. R. P. Armstrong 1981, 11.
4. R. L. Anderson 1990, 278; R. L. Anderson 1992.
5. Malin 1986, 27.
6. R. L. Anderson 1989, 11.
7. Steiner 1990.
8. R. L. Anderson 1990, 225–26.
9. Sweeney 1952, 335.
10. Fischer 1961, 80.
11. Ibid., 81.
12. Peregrine 2007b also finds that the ceramics of complex societies tend toward nonrepetition and complex designs.
13. Ibid., 83.
14. Dressler and Robbins 1975, 427–34.
15. Lomax 1968, 117–28.
16. Words from "Deck the Halls", printed in the *Franklin Square Song Collection,* 1881.
17. Lomax 1968, 166–67.
18. Ibid., 167–69.
19. Ayres 1973.
20. Ayres 1968.
21. E. Erickson 1968.
22. For a study of variation in music within India that does not support some of Lomax's findings, see E. O. Henry 1976.
23. Dundes 1989.
24. Bauman 1992.
25. Brunvand 1993, 14.
26. Ibid., 296.
27. Kluckhohn 1965.
28. As discussed in Robert A. Segal 1987, 1–2.
29. J. Campbell 1949, 30, as quoted in Segal 1987, 4.
30. S. Thompson 1965, 449.
31. Dundes 1965a, reported in F. W. Young 1970.
32. Carroll 1979.
33. G. O. Wright 1954.
34. A. Cohen 1990.
35. S. Price 1989, 82–85.
36. Ibid., 102–103.
37. Ibid., 56–67.
38. Ibid., 112.
39. S. Price 1989, 77–81.
40. J. A. Warner 1986, 172–75.
41. Layton 1992, 93–94.
42. Ibid., 31, 109.
43. J. C. H. King 1986.
44. J. A. Warner 1986, 178–86.
45. Merrill 1987.

Chapter 27

1. Nolan 2003, 2.
2. Kushner 1991.
3. Van Willigen 2002, 10.
4. "Appendix C: Statements on Ethics . . ." 2002; and "Appendix I: Revised Principles . . ." 2002.

5. Appendix A: Report of the Committee on Ethics . . . 2002; and Appendix F: Professional and Ethical Responsibilities . . . 2002.
6. Appendix H: National Association of Practicing Anthropologists' Ethical Guidelines . . . 2002.
7. Scudder 1978.
8. Ibid., 204ff.
9. A good summary of this extraordinary case was put together by Slayman 1997.
10. Public Law 101–601 (25 U.S.C. 3001–3013).
11. Picchi 1991, 26–38; for a more general description of the Bakairí, see Picchi 2009.
12. Murray 1997, 131.
13. Wulff and Fiste 1987; Murray and Bannister 2004.
14. Ibid.
15. Niehoff 1966, 255–67.
16. G. M. Foster 1969, 8–9.
17. Jelliffe and Jelliffe 1975.
18. W. H. Fisher 1994.
19. G. M. Foster 1969, 122–23.
20. Coreil 1989, 149–50.
21. Rogers 1983, 321–31.
22. Bryant and Bailey 1990.
23. Niehoff 1966, 219–24.
24. Coreil 1989, 155.
25. Warren 1989.
26. Warry 1990, 61–62; see also Lassiter 2008.
27. J. Fisher 1996, 57.
28. Ibid., 91; data from Kenya referred to in Oxby 1983.
29. Kedia 2008.
30. Ravesloot 1997, 174.
31. Anyon and Ferguson 1995.
32. Society for American Archaeology 2009.
33. Komar and Buikstra 2008, 11–12.
34. Manhein 1999.
35. Komar and Buikstra 2008, 126–145.
36. Brace 1995.
37. Joans 1997.
38. "Association Business: Clyde Snow . . ." 2000.
39. A. H. Goodman and Leatherman 1998; Kleinman et al. 1997.
40. Baer et al. 1997, viii.
41. Rubel and Haas 1996, 120; Loustaunau and Sobo 1997, 80–81.
42. Loustaunau and Sobo 1997, 82–83, referring to Magner 1992, 93.
43. Loustaunau and Sobo 1997, referring to Gesler 1991, 16.
44. Loustaunau and Sobo 1997, referring to C. Leslie 1976, 4; and G. Foster 1994, 11.
45. Ahern 1975, 92–97, as appearing in eHRAF World Cultures, 2000.
46. Murdock 1980, 20.
47. C. C. Moore 1988.
48. T. Gladwin and Sarason 1953, 64–66.
49. Mahony 1971, 34–38, as seen in eHRAF World Cultures, 2000.
50. Gladwin and Sarason 1953, 65.
51. Hallowell 1976.
52. J. E. Levy 1994, 318.
53. Hahn 1995, 133–39.
54. Loustaunau and Sobo 1997, 115.
55. For an exhaustively documented presentation of the more universalistic approach, see E. A. Berlin and Berlin 1996; see also Browner 1985, 13–32; and Rubel et al. 1984.
56. E. A. Berlin 1996.
57. Browner 1985; Ortiz de Montellano and Browner 1985.
58. Etkin and Ross 1997.
59. Moerman 1997, 240–41.
60. Loustaunau and Sobo 1997, 98–101.
61. Winkelman 1986a.
62. Ibid., 28–29.
63. Levi-Strauss 1963a, 169.
64. Boas 1930, 1–41, reported in Lévi-Strauss 1963b, 169–73.
65. Torrey 1972.
66. Loustaunau and Sobo 1997, 101–102; and Moerman 1997.
67. Loustaunau and Sobo 1997, 102.
68. Dow 1986, 6–9, 125.
69. Hahn 1995, 131–72.
70. Ibid., 165.
71. For a discussion of some of the relevant research, see Hahn 1995, 80–82.
72. Mascie-Taylor 1990, 118–21.
73. See references in Hahn 1995, 82–87.
74. A. Cohen 1999.
75. UNAIDS 2007, 1.
76. Ibid., 4–6.
77. Bolton 1989.
78. Reported in Carey et al. 2004, 462.
79. Bolton 1989.
80. Carrier and Bolton 1991; Schoepf 1988, 625, cited in Carrier and Bolton 1991.
81. Simmons et al. 1996, 64.
82. Ibid., 39–57.
83. L. K. Altman 2008.
84. Schoepf 1988, 637–38.
85. Bolton 1992.
86. Farmer 1997, 414. Married men in Thailand are gradually turning away from commercial sex and having affairs with married women who are believed to be safe; see Lyttleton 2000, 299.
87. Feldman and Johnson 1986, 2.
88. Shen and Siliciano 2000.
89. A. Cohen 2004.
90. Honigmann 1967, 406.
91. Kleinman 1988, 3.
92. Lutz 1985, 63–100.
93. J. Murphy 1981, 813.
94. Edgerton 1966.
95. Edgerton 1992, 16–45.
96. J. S. Allen et al. 1996.
97. Kleinman 1988, 34–52; Berry et al. 1992, 357–64.
98. Honigmann 1967, 401.
99. Kleinman 1988, 19.
100. A. Wallace 1972.
101. Kleinman 1988, 167–85.
102. Rubel et al. 1984, 8–9.
103. Ibid., 15–29, 49–69.
104. Ibid., 71–111.
105. Dressler 1991, 11–16.
106. Ibid., 66–94.
107. Ibid., 165–208.
108. Quandt 1996, 272–89.
109. McElroy and Townsend 2002.
110. See discussion in Leslie Lieberman 2004.
111. Gross and Underwood 1971.
112. McElroy and Townsend 2002, 187, referring to Harvey and Heywood 1983, 27–35.
113. Quandt 1996, 277.
114. McKee 1984, 96.

Braidwood, Robert J. 1960. The agricultural revolution. *Scientific American* (September):130–48.

Braidwood, Robert J., and Gordon R. Willey. 1962. Conclusions and afterthoughts. In *Courses toward urban life*, eds. R. Braidwood and G. Willey. Chicago: Aldine.

Brain, C. K., and A. Sillen. 1988. Evidence from the Swartkrans Cave for the earliest use of fire. *Nature*, 336 (December 1):464–66.

Branda, Richard F., and John W. Eaton. 1978. Skin color and nutrient photolysis: An evolutionary hypothesis. *Science* 201 (August 18): 625–26.

Brandewie, Ernest. 1991. The place of the big man in traditional Hagen society in the central highlands of New Guinea. In *Anthropological approaches to political behavior*, eds. F. McGlynn and A. Tuden. Pittsburgh, PA: University of Pittsburgh Press.

Brandon, Robert N. 1990. *Adaptation and environment*. Princeton, NJ: Princeton University Press.

Bräuer, Günter. 1984. A craniological approach to the origin of anatomically modern *Homo sapiens* in Africa and implications for the appearance of modern Europeans. In *The origins of modern humans*, eds. F. Smith and F Spencer. New York: Alan R. Liss.

Braun, David P., and Stephen Plog. 1982. Evolution of "tribal" social networks: Theory and prehistoric North American evidence. *American Antiquity* 47:504–25.

Brettell, Caroline B. 1996. Migration. In *Encyclopedia of cultural anthropology*, vol. 3, 4 vols., eds. D. Levinson and M. Ember, 793–97. New York: Henry Holt.

Brettell, Caroline, and Robert V. Kemper. 2002. Migration and cities. In *Encyclopedia of urban cultures: Cities and cultures around the world*, vol. 1, 4 vols., eds. M. Ember and C. R. Ember, 30–38. Danbury, CT: Grolier/Scholastic.

Briggs, Jean L. 1974. Eskimo women: Makers of men. In *Many sisters: Women in cross-cultural perspective*, ed. C. J. Matthiasson. New York: Free Press.

Bringa, Tone. 1995. *Being Muslim the Bosnian way: Identity and community in a central Bosnian village*. Princeton, NJ: Princeton University Press, as examined in the eHRAF Collection of Ethnography on the Web.

Brinton, Crane. 1938. *The anatomy of revolution*. Upper Saddle River, NJ: Prentice Hall.

Brittain, John A. 1978. *Inheritance and the inequality of material wealth*. Washington, DC: Brookings Institution.

Britannica Online. 1995. Book of the year (1995): World affairs: Rwanda; and Book of the year (1995): Race and ethnic relations: Rwanda's complex ethnic history. *Britannica Online*, December.

Britannica Online. 1998 (February). Printing, typography, and photoengraving; History of prints: Origins in China: Transmission of paper to Europe (12th century).

Brodey, Jane E. 1971. Effects of milk on blacks noted. *New York Times* October 15, p. 15.

Brodwin, Paul E. 1996. Disease and culture. In *Encyclopedia of cultural anthropology*, vol. 1, eds. D. Levinson and M. Ember, 355–59. New York: Henry Holt.

Bromage, Timothy G., and M. Christopher Dean. 1985. Reevaluation of the age at death of immature fossil hominids. *Nature* 317(October 10):525–27.

Brooks, Alison S., Fatimah Linda Collier Jackson, and R. Richard Grinker. 1993. Race and ethnicity in America. *Anthro Notes* (National Museum of Natural History Bulletin for Teachers), 15, no. 3 (Fall): 1–3, 11–15.

Broom, Robert. 1950. *Finding the missing link*. London: Watts.

Broude, Gwen J. 1976. Cross-cultural patterning of some sexual attitudes and practices. *Behavior Science Research* 11:227–62.

Broude, Gwen J. 1980. Extramarital sex norms in cross-cultural perspective. *Behavior Science Research* 15: 181–218.

Broude, Gwen J. 2004. Sexual attitudes and practices. In *Encyclopedia of sex and gender: Men and women in the world's cultures*, vol. 1, eds. C. Ember and M. Ember, 177–86. New York: Kluwer Academic/Plenum Publishers.

Broude, Gwen J. 2009. Variations in sexual attitudes, norms, and practices. In MyAnthroLibrary, eds. C. R. Ember, M. Ember, and P. N. Peregrine. MyAnthroLibrary.com. Pearson

Broude, Gwen J., and Sarah J. Greene. 1976. Cross-cultural codes on twenty sexual attitudes and practices. *Ethnology* 15:409–29.

Brown, Cecil H. 1977. Folk botanical life-forms: Their universality and growth. *American Anthropologist* 79:317–42.

Brown, Cecil H. 1979. Folk zoological life-forms: Their universality and growth. *American Anthropologist* 81: 791–817.

Brown, Cecil H. 1984. World view and lexical uniformities. *Reviews in Anthropology* 11:99–112.

Brown, Cecil H., and Stanley R. Witkowski. 1980. Language universals. In *Toward explaining human culture*, eds. D. Levinson and M. J. Malone, Appendix B. New Haven, CT: HRAF Press.

Brown, Donald E. 1991. *Human universals*. Philadelphia: Temple University Press.

Brown, Frank H. 1992. Methods of dating. In *The Cambridge encyclopedia of human evolution*, eds. S. Jones, R. Martin, and D. Pilbeam. New York: Cambridge University Press.

Brown, Frank H. 2000. Geochronometry. In *Encyclopedia of human evolution and prehistory*, eds. I. Tattersall, G. Delson, and J. van Couvering. New York: Garland.

Brown, James A. 1983. Summary. In *Archaic hunters and gatherers in the American Midwest*, eds. J. L. Phillips and J. A. Brown, 5–10. New York: Academic Press.

Brown, James A. 1985. Long-term trends to sedentism and the emergence of complexity in the American Midwest. In *Prehistoric hunter-gatherers*, eds. T. Price and J. Brown, 201–31. Orlando, FL: Academic Press.

Brown, James A., and T. Douglas Price. 1985. Complex hunter-gatherers: Retrospect and prospect. In *Prehistoric hunter-gatherers*, eds. T. Price and J. Brown. Orlando, FL: Academic Press.

Brown, Judith K. 1970a. Economic organization and the position of women among the Iroquois. *Ethnohistory* 17:151–67.

Brown, Judith K. 1970b. A note on the division of labor by sex. *American Anthropologist* 72:1073–78.

Brown, Michael F. 2008. Cultural relativism 2.0. *Current Anthropology* 49:363–83.

Brown, Peter J. 1997. Culture and the evolution of obesity. In *Applying cultural anthropology*, eds. A. Podolefsky and P. J. Brown. Mountain View, CA: Mayfield.

Brown, Roger. 1965. *Social psychology*. New York: Free Press.

Brown, Roger. 1980. The first sentence of child and chimpanzee. In *Speaking of apes*, eds. T. A. Sebeok and J. Umiker-Sebeok. New York: Plenum Press.

Brown, Roger, and Marguerite Ford. 1961. Address in American English. *Journal of Abnormal and Social Psychology* 62:375–85.

Browner, C. H. 1985. Criteria for selecting herbal remedies. *Ethnology* 24:13–32.

Brues, Alice. 1992. Forensic diagnosis of race—General race versus specific populations. *Social Science and Medicine* 34:125–28.

Brumbach, Hetty Jo, and Robert Jarvenpa. 2006a. Chipewyan society and gender relations. In *Circumpolar lives and livelihood: A comparative ethnoarchaeology of gender and subsistence*, eds. R. Jarvenpa and H. J. Brumbach, 24–53. Lincoln, Nebraska: University of Nebraska Press.

Brumbach, Hetty Jo, and Robert Jarvenpa. 2006b. Conclusion: Toward a comparative ethnoarchaeology of gender. In *Circumpolar lives and livelihood: A comparative ethnoarchaeology of gender and subsistence*, ed. R. Jarvenpa and H. J. Brumbach, 287–323. Lincoln, Nebraska: University of Nebraska Press.

Brumfiel, Elizabeth M. 1976. Regional growth in the eastern Valley of Mexico: A test of the "population pressure" hypothesis. In *The early Mesoamerican village*, ed. K. Flannery. New York: Academic Press.

Brumfiel, Elizabeth M. 1983. Aztec state making: Ecology, structure, and the origin of the state. *American Anthropologist* 85:261–84.

Brumfiel, Elizabeth M. 1992. Distinguished lecture in archeology: Breaking and entering the ecosystem—gender, class, and faction steal the show. *American Anthropologist* 94: 551–67.

Brumfiel, Elizabeth M. 2009. Origins of social inequality. In MyAnthroLibrary, eds. C. R. Ember, M. Ember, and P. N. Peregrine. MyAnthroLibrary.com. Pearson.

Brunet, Michel, Alain Beauvilain, Yves Coppens, Elile Heintz, Aladji H. E. Moutaye, and David Pilbeam. 1995. The first australopithecine 2,500 kilometers west of the Rift Valley (Chad). *Nature* 378:273–75.

Brunet, Michel, Franck Guy, David Pilbeam, Hassane Taisso Mackaye, Andossa Likius, Djimdoumalbaye Ahounta, Alain Beauvilain, Cécile Blondel, Hervé Bocherens, Jean-Renaud Boisserie, Louis De Bonis, Yves Coppens, Jean Dejax, Christiane Denys, Philippe Duringer, Véra Eisenmann, Gongdibé Fanone, Pierre Fronty, Denis Geraads, Thomas Lehmann, Fabrice Lihoreau, Antoine Louchart, Adoum Mahamat, Gildas Merceron, Guy Mouchelin, Olga Otero, Pablo Pelaez Campomanes, Marcia Ponce De Leon, Jean-Claude Rage, Michel Sapanet, Mathieu Schuster, Jean Sudre, Pascal Tassy, Xavier Valentin, Patrick Vignaud, Laurent Viriot, Antoine Zazzo and Christoph Zollikofer. 2002. A new hominid from the upper Miocene of Chad, Central Africa. *Nature* 418 (July 11):145–51.

Brunvand, Jan Harold. 1993. *The baby train: And other lusty urban legends*. New York: Norton.

Brusco, Elizabeth E. 1996. Religious conversion. In *Encyclopedia of cultural anthropology*, vol. 3, eds. D. Levinson and M. Ember, 1100–04. New York: Henry Holt.

Bryant, Carol A., and Doraine F. C. Bailey. 1990. The use of focus group research in program development. In *Soundings*, eds. J. van Willigen and T. L. Finan. NAPA Bulletin No. 10. Washington, DC: American Anthropological Association.

Buckser, Andrew, and Stephen D. Glazier, eds. 2003. Preface. In *The anthropology of religious conversion*, eds. Andrew Buckser and Stephen D. Glazier. Lanham, MD: Roman & Littlefield.

Budiansky, Stephen. 1992. *The covenant of the wild: Why animals chose domestication*. New York: Morrow.

Buettner-Janusch, John. 1973. *Physical anthropology: A perspective*. New York: Wiley.

Bunzel, Ruth. 1971. The nature of katcinas. In *Reader in comparative religion*, 3rd ed., eds. W. A. Lessa and E. Z. Vogt. New York: Harper & Row.

Burbank, Victoria K. 1994. *Fighting women: Anger and aggression in aboriginal Australia*. Berkeley: University of California Press.

Burbank, Victoria K. 2009a. Adolescent socialization and initiation ceremonies. In MyAnthroLibrary, eds. C. R. Ember, M. Ember, and P. N. Peregrine. MyAnthroLibrary.com. Pearson.

Burbank, Victoria K. 2009b. Australian Aborigines: An adolescent mother and her family. In MyAnthroLibrary, eds. C. R. Ember, M. Ember, and P. N. Peregrine. MyAnthroLibrary.com. Pearson.

Burch, Ernest S., Jr. 2009. North Alaskan Eskimos: A changing way of life. In MyAnthroLibrary, eds. C. R. Ember, M. Ember, and P. N. Peregrine. MyAnthroLibrary.com. Pearson.

Burch, Ernest S., Jr. 1988. *The Eskimos*. Norman: University of Oklahoma Press.

Burkhalter, S. Brian, and Robert F. Murphy. 1989. Tappers and sappers: Rubber, gold and money among the Mundurucú. *American Ethnologist* 16:100–16.

Burns, Alisa, and Cath Scott. 1994. *Mother-headed families and why they have increased*. Hillsdale, NJ: Lawrence Erlbaum Associates.

Burton, Roger V., and John W. M. Whiting. 1961. The absent father and cross-sex identity. *Merrill-Palmer Quarterly Of Behavior And Development* 7(2):85–95.

Busby, Annette. 2009. Kurds: A culture straddling national borders. In MyAnthroLibrary, eds. C. R. Ember, M. Ember, and P. N. Peregrine. MyAnthroLibrary.com. Pearson.

Butzer, Karl W. 1982. Geomorphology and sediment stratigraphy. In *The Middle Stone Age at Klasies River Mouth in South Africa*, eds. R. Singer and J. Wymer. Chicago: University of Chicago Press.

Byrne, Bryan. 1994. Access to subsistence resources and the sexual division of labor among potters. *Cross-Cultural Research* 28:225–50.

Byrne, Roger. 1987. Climatic change and the origins of agriculture. In *Studies in the Neolithic and urban revolutions*, ed. L. Manzanilla. British Archaeological Reports International Series 349. Oxford.

Calvin, William H. 1983. *The throwing Madonna: Essays on the brain*. New York: McGraw-Hill.

Campbell, Donald T. 1965. Variation and selective retention in socio-cultural evolution. In *Social change in developing areas*, eds. H. Barringer, G. Blankstein, and R. Mack. Cambridge, MA: Schenkman.

Campbell, Joseph. 1949. *The hero with a thousand faces*. New York: Pantheon.

Cancian, Frank. 1980. Risk and uncertainty in agricultural decision making. In *Agricultural decision making*, ed. P. F. Barlett. New York: Academic Press.

Cann, Rebecca. 1988. DNA and human origins. *Annual Review of Anthropology* 17:127–43.

Cann, Rebecca, M. Stoneking, and A. C. Wilson. 1987. Mitochondrial DNA and human evolution. *Nature* 325 (January 1):31–36.

Caporael, Linnda R. 1976. Ergotism: The Satan loosed in Salem? *Science* (April 2):21–26.

Carbonell, Eudald, José M. Bermúdez de Castro, Josep M. Parés, Alfredo Pérez-González, Gloria Cuenca-Bescós, Andreu Ollé, Marina Mosquera, Rosa Huguet, Jan van der Made, Antonio Rosas, Robert Sala, Josep Vallverdú, Nuria García, Darryl E. Granger, María Martinón-Torres, Xosé P. Rodríguez, Greg M. Stock, Josep M. Vergès, Ethel Allué, Francesc Burjachs, Isabel Cáceres, Antoni Canals, Alfonso Benito, Carlos Díez, Marina Lozano, Ana Mateos, Marta Navazo, Jesús Rodríguez, Jordi Rosell, Juan L. Arsuaga. 2008. The first hominin of Europe. *Nature* 452 (March 27): 465–69.

Cardoso, Fernando Luis and Dennis Werner. 2004. Homosexuality. In *Encyclopedia of sex and gender: Men and women in the world's cultures*, vol 1., eds. C. Ember and M. Ember, 204–15. New York: Kluwer Academic/Plenum Publishers.

Carey, James W., Erin Picone-DeCaro, Mary Spink Neumann, Devorah Schwartz, Delia Easton, and Daphne Cobb St. John. 2004. HIV/AIDS research and prevention. In *Encyclopedia of medical anthropology: Health and illness in the world's cultures*, vol. 1, eds. C. R. Ember and M. Ember, 462–79. New York: Kluwer Academic/ Plenum.

Carcopino, Jerome. 1940. *Daily life in ancient Rome: The people and the city at the height of the empire*. Edited with bibliography and notes by Henry T. Rowell. Translated from the French by E. O. Lorimer. New Haven, CT: Yale University Press.

Carneiro, Robert L. 1968. Slash-and-burn cultivation among the Kuikuru and its implications for settlement patterns. In *Man in adaptation*, ed. Y. Cohen. Chicago, Aldine.

Carneiro, Robert L. 1970. A theory of the origin of the state. *Science* 169 (August 21):733–38.

Carneiro, Robert L. 1978. Political expansion as an expression of the principle of competitive exclusion. In *Origins of the state*, eds. R. Cohen and E. R. Service. Philadelphia: Institute for the Study of Human Issues.

Carneiro, Robert L. 1988. The circumscription theory: Challenge and response. *American Behavioral Scientist* 31: 497–511.

Carneiro, Robert L. 1990. Chiefdom-level warfare as exemplified in Fiji and the Cauca Valley. In *The anthropology of war*, ed. J. Haas. New York: Cambridge University Press.

Carpenter, C. R. 1940. A field study in Siam of the behavior and social relations of the gibbon (*Hylobates lar*). *Comparative Psychology Monographs* 16(5): 1–212.

Carpenter, Sandra. 2000. Effects of cultural tightness and collectivism on self-concept and causal attributions. *Cross-Cultural Research* 34:38–56.

Carrasco, Pedro. 1961. The civil-religious hierarchy in Mesoamerican communities: Pre-Spanish background and colonial development. *American Anthropologist* 63: 483–97.

Carrier, Joseph, and Ralph Bolton. 1991. Anthropological perspectives on sexuality and HIV prevention. *Annual Review of Sex Research* 2:49–75.

Carroll, John B., ed. 1956. *Language, thought, and reality: Selected writings of Benjamin Lee Whorf*. New York: Wiley.

Carroll, Michael. 1979. A new look at Freud on myth. *Ethos* 7:189–205.

Cartmill, Matt. 1974. Rethinking primate origins. *Science* (April 26):436–37.

Cartmill, Matt. 1992a. New views on primate origins. *Evolutionary Anthropology* 1: 105–11.

Cartmill, Matt. 1992b. Non-human primates. In *The Cambridge encyclopedia of human evolution*, eds. S. Jones, R. Martin, and D. Pilbeam. New York: Cambridge University Press.

Cartmill, Matt. 2009. Explaining primate origins. In MyAnthroLibrary, eds. C. R. Ember, M. Ember, and P. N. Peregrine. MyAnthroLibrary.com. Pearson.

Cashdan, Elizabeth A. 1980. Egalitarianism among hunters and gatherers. *American Anthropologist* 82:116–20.

Cashdan, Elizabeth. 2001. Ethnic diversity and its environmental determinants: Effects of climate, pathogens, and habitat diversity. *American Anthropologist* 103:968–91.

Caulkins, D. Douglas. 1997. Welsh. In *American immigrant cultures: Builders of a nation*, vol. 2, eds. D. Levinson and M. Ember, 935–41. New York: Macmillan Reference.

Caulkins, D. Douglas. 2009. Norwegians: Cooperative individualists. In MyAnthroLibrary, eds. C. R. Ember, M. Ember, and P. N. Peregrine. MyAnthroLibrary.com. Pearson.

Cavalli-Sforza, L. Luca, and Marcus W. Feldman. 1981. *Cultural transmission and evolution: A quantitative approach*. Princeton, NJ: Princeton University Press.

Cavalli-Sforza, L. Luca, and Marcus W. Feldman. 2003. The application of molecular genetic approaches to the study of human evolution. *Nature Genetics Supplement* 33: 266–75.

Caws, Peter. 1969. The structure of discovery. *Science* 166 (December 12): 1375–80.

Ceci, Stephen, and Wendy M. Williams. 2009. YES: The scientific truth must be pursued. *Nature* 457 (February 12): 788–789.

Center for Renewal of Science and Culture. 2001. The wedge strategy, cited in Barbara Forrest, "The wedge at work." In *Intelligent design creationism and its critics*. ed. Robert Pennock, 16. Boston, IT Press.

Cernea, Michael M., ed. 1991. *Putting people first: Sociological variables in development*. 2nd ed. New York: Oxford University Press.

Chacon, Richard J., and Rubén G. Mendoza. 2007. Ethical considerations and conclusions regarding indigenous warfare and ritual violence in Latin America. In *Latin American indigenous warfare and ritual violence*, eds. Richard J. Chacon and Rubén G. Mendoza. Tucson: University of Arizona Press.

Chafetz, Janet Saltzman. 1990. *Gender equity: An integrated theory of stability and change*. Sage Library of Social Research No. 176. Newbury Park, CA: Sage.

Chagnon, Napoleon. 1983. *Yanomamö: The fierce people*. 3rd ed. New York: Holt, Rinehardt, and Winston.

Chambers, J. K. 2002. Patterns of variation including change. In *The handbook of language variation and change*, eds. J. K. Chambers, Peter Trudgill, and Natalie Schilling-Estes. Malden, MA: Blackwell Publishers.

Chang, Kwang-Chih. 1968. *The archaeology of ancient China*. New Haven, CT: Yale University Press.

Chang, Kwang-Chih. 1970. The beginnings of agriculture in the Far East. *Antiquity* 44:175–85.

Chang, Kwang-Chih. 1981. In search of China's beginnings: New light on an old civilization. *American Scientist* 69:148–60.

Chang, Kwang-Chih. 1986. *Archaeology of ancient China*. 4th ed. New Haven, CT: Yale University Press, 234–94.

Chapais, Bernard. 2008. *Primeval kinship: How pair-bonding gave birth to human society*. Cambridge, MA: Harvard University Press.

Chard, Chester S. 1969. *Man in prehistory*. New York: McGraw-Hill.

Charles-Dominique, Pierre. 1977. *Ecology and behaviour of nocturnal primates*, trans. R. D. Martin. New York: Columbia University Press.

Charanis, Peter. 1953. Economic factors in the decline of the Roman Empire. *Journal of Economic History* 13: 412–24.

Chase, Philip, and Harold Dibble. 1987. Middle Paleolithic symbolism: A review of current evidence and interpretations. *Journal of Anthropological Archaeology* 6:263–69.

Chatterjee, Sankar. 1997. *The rise of birds: 225 million years of evolution*. Baltimore: Johns Hopkins.

Chatty, Dawn. 1996. *Mobile pastoralists: Development planning and social change in Oman*. New York: Columbia University Press.

Chaucer, Geoffrey. 1926. *The prologue to the Canterbury Tales, the Knights Tale, the Nonnes Prestes Tale*, ed. Mark H. Liddell. New York: Macmillan.

Chayanov, Alexander V. 1966. *The theory of peasant economy*, eds. Daniel Thorner, Basile Kerblay, and R. E. F. Smith. Homewood, IL: Richard D. Irwin.

Cheney, Dorothy, L., and Richard W. Wrangham. 1987. Predation. In *Primate societies*, eds. B. Smuts et al. Chicago: University of Chicago Press.

Chessa, Bernardo, Filipe Pereira, Frederick Arnaud, Antonio Amorim, Félix Goyache, Ingrid Mainland, Rowland R. Kao, Josephine M. Pemberton, Dario Beraldi, Michael J. Stear, Alberto Alberti, Marco Pittau, Leopoldo Iannuzzi, Mohammad H. Banabazi, Rudovick R. Kazwala, Ya-ping Zhang, Juan J. Arranz, Bahy A. Ali, Zhiliang Wang, Metehan Uzun, Michel M. Dione, Ingrid Olsaker, Lars-Erik Holm, Urmas Saarma, Sohail Ahmad, Nurbiy Marzanov, Emma Eythorsdottir, Martin J. Holland, Paolo Ajmone-Marsan, Michael W. Bruford, Juha Kantanen, Thomas E. Spencer, and Massimo Palmarini. 2009. Revealing the history of sheep domestication using retrovirus integrations. *Science* 324 (April 24):532–36.

Chibnik, Michael. 1980. The statistical behavior approach: The choice between wage labor and cash cropping in rural Belize. In *Agricultural decision making*, ed. P. F. Barlett. New York: Academic Press.

Chibnik, Michael. 1981. The evolution of cultural rules. *Journal of Anthropological Research* 37:256–68.

Chibnik, Michael. 1987. The economic effects of household demography: A cross-cultural assessment of Chayanov's theory. In *Household economies and their transformations*, ed. M. D. MacLachlan. Monographs in Economic Anthropology, No 3. Lanham, MD: University Press of America.

Chick, Garry. 1998. Games in culture revisited: A replication and extension of Roberts, Arth, and Bush [1959]. *Cross-Cultural Research* 32:185–206.

Childe, V. Gordon. 1950. The urban revolution. *Town Planning Review* 21:3–17.

Chimpanzee Sequencing and Analysis Consortium. 2005. Initial sequence of the chimpanzee genome and comparison with the human genome. *Nature* 437 (Sept. 1):69–87.

Chivers, David J. 1974. *The siamang in Malaya*. Basel, Switzerland: Karger.

Chomsky, Noam. 1975. *Reflections on language*. New York: Pantheon.

Christensen, Pia, Jenny Hockey, and Allison James, 2001. Talk, silence and the material world: Patterns of indirect communication among agricultural farmers in northern England. In *An anthropology of indirect communication*, eds. J. Hendry and C. W. Watson, 68–82. London: Routledge.

Ciochon, Russell L., and Dennis A. Etler. 1994. Reinterpreting past primate diversity. In *Integrative paths to the past*, eds. R. Corruccini and R. Ciochon. Upper Saddle River, NJ: Prentice Hall.

Ciochon, Russell L., and John G. Fleagle, eds. 1993. *The human evolution source book*. Upper Saddle River, NJ: Prentice Hall.

Ciochon, Russell, John Olsen, and Jamie James. 1990. *Other origins: The search for the giant ape in human prehistory*. New York: Bantam.

Claassen, Cheryl. 1991. Gender, shellfishing, and the Shell Mound Archaic. In *Engendering Archaeology*, eds. J. Gero and M. Conkey. Oxford: Blackwell.

Claassen, Cheryl. 2009. Gender and archaeology. In MyAnthroLibrary, eds. C. R. Ember, M. Ember, and P. N. Peregrine. MyAnthroLibrary.com. Pearson.

Clark, J. Desmond. 1970. *The prehistory of Africa*. New York: Praeger.

Clark, J. Desmond. 1977. Interpretations of prehistoric technology from ancient Egyptian and other sources. Pt. II: Prehistoric arrow forms in Africa as shown by surviving examples of the traditional arrows of the San Bushmen. *Paleorient* 3:127–50.

Clark, Gracia. 2000. Small-scale traders' key role in stabilizing and diversifying Ghana's rural communities and livelihoods. In *Women farmers and commercial ventures: Increasing food security in developing countries*, ed. Anita Spring, 253–70. Boulder, CO: Lynne Rienner Publishers, Inc.

Clark, Grahame. 1975. *The Earlier Stone Age settlement of Scandinavia*. Cambridge: Cambridge University Press.

Clark, Grahame, and Stuart Piggott. 1965. *Prehistoric societies*. New York: Knopf.

Clark, W. E. Le Gros. 1964. *The fossil evidence for human evolution*, 184. Chicago: University of Chicago Press.

Clarke, Ronald J., and P. V. Tobias. 1995. Sterkfontein member 2 foot bones of the oldest South African hominid. *Science* 269(July 28):521–24.

Clayman, Charles B., ed. 1989. *American Medical Association encyclopedia of medicine*. New York: Random House, 857–58.

Clifford, James. 1986. Introduction: Partial truths." In *Writing culture: The poetics and politics of ethnography*, eds. J. Clifford and G. E. Marcus. Berkeley: University of California Press.

Clottes, Jean. 2008. Rock art: An endangered heritage worldwide. *Journal of Anthropological Research* 64:1–18.

Clutton-Brock, Juliet. 1984. Dog. In *Evolution of domesticated animals*, ed. I. Mason. New York: Longman.

Clutton-Brock, Juliet. 1992. Domestication of animals. In *The Cambridge encyclopedia of human evolution*, eds. S. Jones, R. Martin, and D. Pilbeam. New York: Cambridge University Press.

Clutton-Brock, T. H., and Paul H. Harvey. 1977. Primate ecology and social organization. *Journal of Zoology* 183: 1–39.

Clutton-Brock, T. H., and Paul H. Harvey. 1980. Primates, brains and ecology. *Journal of Zoology* 190: 309–23.

Coale, Ansley J. 1974. The history of the human population. *Scientific American* (September):41–51.

Coe, Michael D. 1966. *The Maya*. New York: Praeger.

Cohen, Alex. 1990. A cross-cultural study of the effects of environmental unpredictability on aggression in folktales. *American Anthropologist* 92:474–79.

Cohen, Alex. 1999. *The mental health of indigenous peoples: An international overview*. Geneva: Department of Mental Health, World Health Organization.

Cohen, Alex. 2004. Mental disorders. In *Encyclopedia of medical anthropology: Health and illness in the world's cultures*, vol. 1, eds. C. R. Ember and M. Ember, 486–93. New York: Kluwer Academic/Plenum.

Cohen, Alex, and Paul Koegel. 2009. Homelessness. In MyAnthroLibrary, eds. C. R. Ember, M. Ember, and P. N. Peregrine. MyAnthroLibrary.com. Pearson.

Cohen, Mark N. 1977a. *The food crisis in prehistory: Overpopulation and the origins of agriculture*. New Haven, CT: Yale University Press.

Cohen, Mark N. 1977b. Population pressure and the origins of agriculture. In *Origins of agriculture*, ed. C. A. Reed. The Hague: Monton.

Cohen, Mark N. 1987. The significance of long-term changes in human diet and food economy. In *Food and evolution*, eds. M. Harris and E Ross. Philadelphia: Temple University Press.

Cohen, Mark. 1989. *Health and the rise of civilization*. New Haven, CT: Yale University Press.

Cohen, Mark N. 2009. Were early agriculturalists less healthy than food collectors? In MyAnthroLibrary, eds. C. R. Ember, M. Ember, and P. N. Peregrine. MyAnthroLibrary.com. Pearson.

Cohen, Mark Nathan, and George J. Armelagos. 1984b. Paleopathology at the origins of agriculture: Editors' summation. In *Paleopathology at the origins of agriculture*, eds. M. N. Cohen and G. J. Armelagos. Orlando, FL: Academic Press.

Cohen, Myron L. 1976. *House united, house divided: The Chinese family in Taiwan*. New York: Columbia University Press.

Cohen, Ronald. 1988. Introduction. In *State formation and political legitimacy*, vol. 6: *Political anthropology*, eds. R. Cohen and J. D. Toland. New Brunswick, NJ: Transaction Books.

Cohen, Ronald, and Elman R. Service, eds. 1978. *Origins of the state: The anthropology of political evolution*. Philadelphia: Institute for the Study of Human Issues.

Cohen, Wesley. 1995. Empirical studies of innovative activity. In *Handbook of the economics of innovation and technological change*, ed. P. Stoneman. Oxford: Blackwell.

COHMAP (Cooperative Holocene Mapping Project) Personnel. 1988. Climatic changes of the last 18,000 years. *Science* 241 (August 26):1043–52.

Colby, Benjamin N. 1996. Cognitive anthropology. In *Encyclopedia of cultural anthropology*, eds. David Levinson and Melvin Ember, vol. 1, 209–15. New York: Henry Holt.

Collier, Stephen, and J. Peter White. 1976. Get them young? Age and sex inferences on animal domestication in archaeology. *American Antiquity* 41:96–102.

Collins, Desmond. 1976. Later hunters in Europe. In *The origins of Europe*, ed. D. Collins. New York: Thomas Y. Crowell.

Collins, James, and Richard Blot. 2003. *Literacy and literacies*. Cambridge: Cambridge University Press.

Conklin, Beth A. 2002. Shamans versus pirates in the Amazonian treasure chest. *American Anthropologist* 104:1050–61.

Connah, Graham. 1987. *African civilizations: Precolonial cities and states in tropical Africa*. Cambridge: Cambridge University Press.

Conroy, Glenn C. 1990. *Primate evolution*. New York: Norton.

Cooper, Richard S., Charles N. Rotimi, and Ryk Ward. 1999. The puzzle of hypertension in African Americans. *Scientific American* (February):56–63.

Coreil, Jeannine. 1989. Lessons from a community study of oral rehydration therapy in Haiti. In *Making our research useful*, eds. J. van Willigen, B. Rylko-Bauer, and A. McElroy. Boulder, CO: Westview.

Coreil, Jeannine. 2004. Malaria and other major insect vector diseases. In *Encyclopedia of medical anthropology: Health and illness in the world's cultures*, vol. 1, eds. C. R. Ember and M. Ember, 479–85. New York: Kluwer Academic/Plenum.

Costin, Cathy Lynne. 2009. Cloth production and gender relations in the Inka Empire. In MyAnthroLibrary, eds. C. R. Ember, M. Ember, and P. N. Peregrine. MyAnthroLibrary.com. Pearson.

Coult, Allan D., and Robert W. Habenstein. 1965. *Cross tabulations of Murdock's "World ethnographic sample."* Columbia: University of Missouri Press.

Crawford, Gary W. 1992. Prehistoric plant domestication in East Asia. In *The origins of agriculture*, eds. C. Cowan and P. Watson. Washington, DC: Smithsonian Institution Press.

Crawford, R. D. 1984. Turkey. In *Evolution of domesticated animals*, ed. I. Mason. New York: Longman.

Creed, Gerald W. 2009. Bulgaria: Anthropological corrections to Cold War stereotypes. In MyAnthroLibrary, eds. C. R. Ember, M. Ember, and P. N. Peregrine. MyAnthroLibrary.com. Pearson.

Crockett, Carolyn, and John F. Eisenberg. 1987. Howlers: Variations in group size and demography. In *Primate societies*. eds. B. Smuts et al. Chicago: University of Chicago Press.

Crystal, David. 1971. *Linguistics*. Middlesex, UK: Penguin.

Crystal, David. 2000. *Language death*. Cambridge: Cambridge University Press.

Culotta, Elizabeth. 1995. New hominid crowds the field. *Science* 269 (August 18):918.

Culotta, Elizabeth. 2005. Calorie count reveals Neandertals out-ate hardiest modern humans. *Science* 307 (February 11):840.

Curtin, Philip D. 1984. *Cross-cultural trade in world history*. Cambridge: Cambridge University Press.

Cutright, Phillips. 1967. Inequality: A cross-national analysis. *American Sociological Review* 32:562–78.

Daiger, Stephen. 2005. Was the human genome project worth the effort? *Science* 308 (April 15):362–64.

Daly, Martin, and Margo Wilson. 1988. *Homicide*. New York: Aldine.

Damas, David. 1983. Demography and kinship as variables of adoption in the Carolines. *American Ethnologist* 10: 328–44.

Daniel, I. Randolph. 2001. Early Eastern Archaic. In *Encyclopedia of prehistory*, vol. 6: North America, eds. P. N. Peregrine and M. Ember. Kluwer: Academic/Plenum.

Dart, Raymond. 1925. *Australopithecus africanus*: The man-ape of South Africa. *Nature* 115:195.

Darwin, Charles. 1970/1859. The origin of species. In *Evolution of man*, ed. L. B. Young. New York: Oxford University Press.

Dasen, Pierre R., John W. Berry, and N. Sartorius, eds. 1988. *Health and cross-cultural psychology: Toward applications.* Newbury Park, CA: Sage.

Dasen, Pierre R., and Alastair Heron. 1981. Cross-cultural tests of Piaget's theory. In *Handbook of cross-cultural psychology*, vol. 4: *Developmental psychology*, eds. H. C. Triandis and A. Heron. Boston: Allyn & Bacon.

Davenport, William. 1959. Nonunilinear descent and descent groups. *American Anthropologist* 61:557–72.

Davis, Deborah, and Stevan Harrell, eds. 1993. *Chinese families in the post-Mao era.* Berkeley: University of California Press.

Davis, Susan Schaefer. 1993. Rebellious teens? A Moroccan instance. Paper presented at MESA, November.

Davis, Susan Schaefer. 2009. Morocco: Adolescents in a small town. In MyAnthroLibrary, eds. C. R. Ember, M. Ember, and P. N. Peregrine. MyAnthroLibrary.com. Pearson

Davis, William D. 1971. Societal complexity and the nature of primitive man's conception of the supernatural. Ph.D. dissertation; University of North Carolina, Chapel Hill.

Dawson, Alistair. 1992. *Ice age earth.* London: Routledge: 24–71.

Dawson, J. L. M. 1967. Cultural and physiological influences upon spatial-perceptual processes in West Africa. *International Journal of Psychology* 2:115–28, 171–85.

Day, Michael. 1986. *Guide to fossil man.* 4th ed. Chicago: University of Chicago Press.

De Laguna, Frederica. 1972. *Under Mount Saint Elias: The history and culture of the Yakutat Tlingit.* Washington, DC: Smithsonian Institution Press, as seen in the eHRAF Collection of Ethnography on the Web, 2000.

De Lumley, Henry. 1969. A Paleolithic camp at Nice. *Scientific American* (May):42–50.

DeMenocal, Peter. 2001. Cultural responses to climate change during the late Holocene. *Science* 292 (April 27):667–73.

de Munck, Victor. 2000. *Culture, self, and meaning.* Prospect Heights, IL: Waveland Press.

De Munck, Victor C., and Andrey Korotayev. 1999. Sexual equality and romantic love: A reanalysis of Rosenblatt's study on the function of romantic love. *Cross-Cultural Research* 33:265–273.

De Villiers, Peter A., and Jill G. De Villiers. 1979. *Early language.* Cambridge, MA: Harvard University Press.

De Waal, Frans. 2001. *The ape and the sushi master: Cultural reflections of a primatologist.* New York: Basic Books.

De Waal, Frans, and Frans Lanting. 1997. *Bonobo: The forgotten ape.* Berkeley: University of California Press.

Deacon, Terrence. 1992. Primate brains and senses. In *The Cambridge encyclopedia of human evolution*, eds. S. Jones, R. Martin, and D. Pilbeam. New York: Cambridge University Press.

Denham, T. P., S. G. Haberle, C. Lentfer, R. Fullagar, J. Field, M. Therin, N. Porch, and B. Winsborough. 2003. Origins of agriculture at Kuk Swamp in the highlands of New Guinea. *Science* 301 (July 11):189–93.

Denny, J. Peter. 1979. The "extendedness" variable in classifier semantics: Universal features and cultural variation. In *Ethnolinguistics*, ed. M. Mathiot. The Hague: Mouton.

Dentan, Robert K. 1968. *The Semai: A nonviolent people of Malaya.* New York: Holt, Rinehart & Winston.

Devillers, Charles, and Jean Chaline. 1993. *Evolution: An evolving theory.* New York: Springer Verlag.

DeVore, Irven, and Melvin J. Konner. 1974. Infancy in hunter-gatherer life: An ethological perspective. In *Ethology and psychiatry*, ed. N. F. White. Toronto: Ontario Mental Health Foundation and University of Toronto Press.

Diament, Michelle. 2005. Diversifying their crops: Agriculture schools, focusing on job prospects, reach out to potential students from cities and suburbs. *The Chronicle of Higher Education* May 6, pp. A32–34.

Diamond, Jared. 1989. The accidental conqueror. *Discover* (December):71–76.

Diamond, Jared. 1991. The saltshaker's curse—Physiological adaptations that helped American Blacks survive slavery may now be predisposing their descendants to hypertension. *Natural History* (October):20–27.

Diamond, Jared. 1993. Who are the Jews? *Natural History* (November): 12–9.

Diamond, Jared. 1997a. *Guns, germs, and steel.* New York: Norton: 205–07.

Diamond, Jared. 1997b. Location, location, location: The first farmers. *Science* 278 (November 14):1243–44.

Diamond, Jared. 2004. The astonishing micropygmies. *Science* 306 (December 17):2047–48.

Diamond, Norma. 1975. Collectivization, kinship, and the status of women in rural China. In R. R. Reiter, *Toward an anthropology of women.* New York: Monthly Review Press.

Diamond, Stanley. 1974. *In search of the primitive: A critique of civilization.* New Brunswick, NJ: Transaction Books.

Dickson, D. Bruce. 1990. *The dawn of belief.* Tucson: University of Arizona Press, 42–44.

Dickson, D. Bruce, Jeffrey Olsen, P. Fred Dahm, and Mitchell S. Wachtel. 2005. Where do you go when you die? A cross-cultural test of the hypothesis that infrastructure predicts individual eschatology. *Journal of Anthropological Research* 1:53–79.

Dillehay, Thomas. 2000. *The settlement of the Americas.* New York: Basic Books.

Dirks, Robert. 1993. Starvation and famine. *Cross-Cultural Research* 27:28–69.

Dirks, Robert. 2009. Hunger and famine. In MyAnthroLibrary, eds. C. R. Ember, M. Ember, and P. N. Peregrine. MyAnthroLibrary.com. Pearson.

Divale, William T. 1974. Migration, external warfare, and matrilocal residence. *Behavior Science Research* 9:75–133.

Divale, William T. 1977. Living floor area and marital residence: A replication. *Behavior Science Research* 2:109–15.

Divale, William T., and Marvin Harris. 1976. Population, warfare, and the male supremacist complex. *American Anthropologist* 78:521–38.

Dobres, Marcia-Anne. 1998. Venus figurines. In *Oxford companion to archaeology*, ed. B. Fagan, 740–41. Oxford: Oxford University Press.

Dobzhansky, Theodosius. 1962. *Mankind evolving: The evolution of the human species.* New Haven, CT: Yale University Press.

Dobzhansky, Theodosius, 1973. *Genetic diversity and human equality.* New York: Basic Books.

Dohlinow, Phyllis Jay, and Naomi Bishop. 1972. The development of motor skills and social relationships among primates through play. In *Primate patterns*, ed. Phyllis Jay Dohlinow. New York: Holt, Rinehart & Winston.

Douglas, Mary. 1975. *Implicit meanings: Essays in anthropology.* London: Routledge and Kegan Paul.

Dow, James. 1986. *The shaman's touch: Otomi Indian symbolic healing*. Salt Lake City: University of Utah Press.

Dowling, John H. 1975. Property relations and productive strategies in pastoral societies. *American Ethnologist* 2: 419–26.

Doyle, Rodger. 2004. Living together: In the U.S. cohabitation is here to stay. *Scientific American* (January):28.

Doyle, Rodger. 2005. Leveling the playing field: Economic development helps women pull even with men. *Scientific American* (June):32.

Doyle, G. A., and R. D. Martin, eds. 1979. *The study of prosimian behavior*. New York: Academic Press.

Draper, Patricia. 1975. !Kung women: Contrasts in sexual egalitarianism in foraging and sedentary contexts. In *Toward an anthropology of women*, ed. R. R. Reiter. New York: Monthly Review Press.

Draper, Patricia, and Elizabeth Cashdan. 1988. Technological change and child behavior among the !Kung. *Ethnology* 27:339–65.

Dressler, William W. 1991. *Stress and adaptation in the context of culture*. Albany: State University of New York Press.

Dressler, William W. 1993. Health in the African American community: Accounting for health inequalities. *Medical Anthropology Quarterly* 7:325–45.

Dressler, William W., and Michael C. Robbins. 1975. Art styles, social stratification, and cognition: An analysis of Greek vase painting. *American Ethnologist* 2:427–34.

Driscoll, Carlos A., Juliet Clutton-Brock, Andrew Kitchener, and Stephen O'Brien. 2009. The taming of the cat. *Scientific American* (June):68–75.

Driscoll, Carlos A., Marilyn Menotti-Raymond, Alfred L. Roca, Karsten Hupe, Warren E. Johnson, Eli Geffen, Eric H. Harley, Miguel Delibes, Dominique Pontier, Andrew C. Kitchener, Nobuyuki Yamaguchi, Stephen J. O'Brien, and David W. Macdonald. 2007. The Near Eastern origin of cat domestication. *Science* (July 27):519–23.

Drucker, Philip. 1965. *Cultures of the north Pacific Coast*. San Francisco: Chandler.

Drucker, Philip. 1967. The potlatch. In *Tribal and peasant economies*, ed. G. Dalton. Garden City, NY: Natural History Press.

Duane, Daniel. 2003. Turning garbage into oil. *New York Times Magazine*, December 14, p. 100.

Du, Shanshan. 2003. Is Buddha a couple: Gender-Unitary perspectives from the Lahu of southwest China. *Ethnology* 42:253–71.

Duarte, Cidalia, J. Mauricio, P. B. Pettitt, P. Souto, E. Trinkaus, H. van der Plicht, and J. Zilhao. 1999. The early Upper Paleolithic human skeleton from the Abrigo do Lagar Velho (Portugal) and modern human emergence in Iberia. *Proceedings of the National Academy of Sciences of the United States* 96:7604–09.

Duhard, Jean-Pierre. 1993. Upper Paleolithic figures as a reflection of human morphology and social organization. *Antiquity* 67:83–91.

Dunbar, Robin, and Susanne Shultz. 2007. Evolution of the social brain. *Science* 317 (September 7):1344–47.

Dundes, Alan. 1965. Structural typology in North American Indian folktales. In *The study of folklore*, ed. A. Dundes. Upper Saddle River, NJ: Prentice Hall.

Dundes, Alan. 1989. *Folklore matters*. Knoxville: University of Tennessee Press.

Durham, William H. 1991. *Coevolution: Genes, culture and human diversity*. Stanford, CA: Stanford University Press.

Durkheim, Émile. 1938/1895. *The rules of sociological method*. 8th ed. Trans. Sarah A. Soloway and John H. Mueller. Ed. George E. Catlin. New York: Free Press.

Durkheim, Émile. 1961/1912. *The elementary forms of the religious life*. Trans. Joseph W. Swain. New York: Collier Books.

Durrenberger, E. Paul. 1980. Chayanov's economic analysis in anthropology. *Journal of Anthropological Research* 36: 133–48.

Durrenberger, E. Paul. 2001a. Anthropology and globalization. *American Anthropologist* 103:531–35.

Durrenberger, E. Paul. 2001b. Explorations of class and consciousness in the U.S. *Journal of Anthropological Research* 57:41–60.

Durrenberger, E. Paul, and Nicola Tannenbaum. 2002. Chayanov and theory in economic anthropology. In *Theory in economic anthropology*, ed. Jean Ensminger, 137–53. Walnut Creek, CA: AltaMira Press.

Dyson-Hudson, Neville. 1966. *Karimojong politics*. Oxford: Clarendon Press.

Dyson-Hudson, Rada, and Eric Alden Smith. 1978. Human territoriality: An ecological reassessment. *American Anthropologist* 80:21–41.

Eckhardt, William. 1975. Primitive militarism. *Journal of Peace Research* 12:55–62.

Eddy, Elizabeth M., and William L. Partridge, eds. 1987. *Applied anthropology in America*. 2nd ed. New York: Columbia University Press.

Edgerton, Robert B. 1966. Conceptions of psychosis in four East African societies. *American Anthropologist* 68:408–25.

Edgerton, Robert B. 1971. *The individual in cultural adaptation: A study of four East African peoples*. Berkeley: University of California Press.

Edgerton, Robert B. 1992. *Sick societies: Challenging the myth of primitive harmony*. New York: Free Press.

Eiseley, Loren C. 1958. The dawn of evolutionary theory. In *Darwin's century: Evolution and the men who discovered it*, ed. L. C. Eiseley, Garden City, NY: Doubleday.

Eisenberg, John F. 1977. Comparative ecology and reproduction of New World monkeys. In *The biology and conservation of the Callitrichidae*. ed. Devra Kleinman. Washington, DC: Smithsonian Institution.

Eisenstadt, S. N. 1954. African age groups. *Africa* 24:100–111.

Ekman, Paul, and Dachner Keltner. 1997. Universal facial expressions of emotion: An old controversy and new findings. In *Nonverbal communication: Where nature meets culture*, eds. U. Segerstrale and P. Molnar. Mahwah, NJ: Lawrence Erlbaum.

Eldredge, Niles, and Ian Tattersall. 1982. *The myths of human evolution*. New York: Columbia University Press.

Eliot, T. S. 1963. The love song of J. Alfred Prufrock. In *Collected poems, 1909–1962*. New York: Harcourt, Brace & World.

Ellis, Lee. 1986. Evidence of neuroandrogenic etiology of sex roles from a combined analysis of human, nonhuman primate and nonprimate mammalian studies. *Personality and Individual Differences* 7:519–52.

Ember, Carol R. 1973. Feminine task assignment and the social behavior of boys. *Ethos* 1:424–39.

Ember, Carol R. 1974. An evaluation of alternative theories of matrilocal versus patrilocal residence. *Behavior Science Research* 9:135–49.

Ember, Carol R. 1975. Residential variation among hunter-gatherers. *Behavior Science Research* 9:135–49.

Ember, Carol R. 1977. Cross-cultural cognitive studies. *Annual Review of Anthropology* 6:33–56.

Ember, Carol R. 1978a. Men's fear of sex with women: A cross-cultural study. *Sex Roles* 4:657–78.

Ember, Carol R. 1978b. Myths about hunter-gatherers. *Ethnology* 17:439–48.

Ember, Carol R. 1981. A cross-cultural perspective on sex differences. In *Handbook of cross-cultural human development*, eds. R. H. Munroe, R. L. Munroe, and B. B. Whiting. New York, Garland.

Ember, Carol R. 1982. The conditions favoring religious conversion. Paper presented at the annual meeting of the Society for Cross-Cultural Research, February. Minneapolis, Minnesota.

Ember, Carol R. 1983. The relative decline in women's contribution to agriculture with intensification. *American Anthropologist* 85:285–304.

Ember, Carol R. 2009. Universal and variable patterns of gender difference. In MyAnthroLibrary, eds. C. R. Ember, M. Ember, and P. N. Peregrine. MyAnthroLibrary.com. Pearson.

Ember, Carol R., and Melvin Ember. 1972. The conditions favoring multilocal residence. *Southwestern Journal of Anthropology* 28:382–400.

Ember, Carol R., and Melvin Ember. 1984. The evolution of human female sexuality: A cross-species perspective. *Journal of Anthropological Research* 40:202–10.

Ember, Carol R., and Melvin Ember. 1992. Resource unpredictability, mistrust, and war: A cross-cultural study. *Journal of Conflict Resolution* 36:242–62.

Ember, Carol R., and Melvin Ember. 1993. Issues in cross-cultural studies of interpersonal violence. *Violence and Victims* 8:217–33.

Ember, Carol R., and Melvin Ember. 1994. War, socialization, and interpersonal violence: A cross-cultural study. *Journal of Conflict Resolution* 38:620–46.

Ember, Carol R., and Melvin Ember. 1997. Violence in the ethnographic record: Results of cross-cultural research on war and aggression. In *Troubled times*, eds. D. Martin and D. Frayer. Langhorn, PA: Gordon and Breach.

Ember, Carol R., and Melvin Ember. 2005. Explaining corporal punishment of children: A cross-cultural study. *American Anthropologist* 107:609–619.

Ember, Carol R., and Melvin Ember. 2009. *Cross-cultural research methods*. 2nd ed. Lanham, CA: AltaMira Press.

Ember, Carol R., Melvin Ember, Andrey Korotayev, Victor de Munck. 2005. Valuing thinness or fatness in women: Reevaluating the effect of resource scarcity. *Evolution and Human Behavior* 26:257–70.

Ember, Carol R., Melvin Ember, and Burton Pasternak. 1974. On the development of unilineal descent. *Journal of Anthropological Research* 30:69–94.

Ember, Carol R., Melvin Ember, and Peter N. Peregrine. 2007. *Anthropology*. 13th ed. Upper Saddle River, NJ: Prentice Hall.

Ember, Carol R., Melvin Ember, and Bruce Russett. 1992. Peace between participatory polities: A cross-cultural test of the "democracies rarely fight each other" hypothesis. *World Politics* 44:573–99.

Ember, Carol R., and David Levinson. 1991. The substantive contributions of worldwide cross-cultural studies using secondary data. *Behavior Science Research* (special issue, Cross-cultural and comparative research: Theory and method), 25:79–140.

Ember, Melvin. 1959. The nonunilinear descent groups of Samoa. *American Anthropologist* 61:573–77.

Ember, Melvin. 1963. The relationship between economic and political development in nonindustrialized societies. *Ethnology* 2:228–48.

Ember, Melvin. 1967. The emergence of neolocal residence. *Transactions of the New York Academy of Sciences* 30: 291–302.

Ember, Melvin. 1970. Taxonomy in comparative studies. In *A handbook of method in cultural anthropology*, eds. R. Naroll and R. Cohen. Garden City, NY: Natural History Press.

Ember, Melvin. 1973. An archaelogical indicator of matrilocal versus patrilocal residence. *American Antiquity* 38: 177–82.

Ember, Melvin. 1974a. The conditions that may favor avunculocal residence. *Behavior Science Research* 9:203–9.

Ember, Melvin. 1974b. Warfare, sex ratio, and polygyny. *Ethnology* 13:197–206.

Ember, Melvin. 1975. On the origin and extension of the incest taboo. *Behavior Science Research* 10:249–81.

Ember, Melvin. 1978. Size of color lexicon: Interaction of cultural and biological factors. *American Anthropologist* 80:364–67.

Ember, Melvin. 1982. Statistical evidence for an ecological explanation of warfare. *American Anthropologist* 84:645–49.

Ember, Melvin 1983. The emergence of neolocal residence. In *Marriage, family, and kinship: Comparative studies of social organization*, eds. Melvin Ember and Carol R. Ember, 333–57. New Haven, CT: HRAF Press.

Ember, Melvin. 1984–1985. Alternative predictors of polygyny. *Behavior Science Research* 19:1–23.

Ember, Melvin. 1985. Evidence and science in ethnography: Reflections on the Freeman-Mead controversy. *American Anthropologist* 87:906–9.

Ember, Melvin, and Carol R. Ember. 1971. The conditions favoring matrilocal versus patrilocal residence. *American Anthropologist* 73:571–94.

Ember, Melvin, and Carol R. Ember. 1979. Male-Female bonding: A cross-species study of mammals and birds. *Behavior Science Research* 14:37–56.

Ember, Melvin, and Carol R. Ember. 1983. *Marriage, family, and kinship: Comparative studies of social organization*. New Haven, CT: HRAF Press.

Ember, Melvin, and Carol R. Ember. 1992. Cross-cultural studies of war and peace: Recent achievements and future possibilities. In *Studying war*, eds. S. P. Reyna and R. E. Downs. New York: Gordon and Breach.

Ember, Melvin, and Carol R. Ember. 1999. Cross-language predictors of consonant-vowel syllables. *American Anthropologist* 101:730–42.

Ember, Melvin, and Carol R. Ember, eds. 2002. *Encyclopedia of urban cultures: Cities and cultures around the world*, 4 vols. Danbury, CT: Grolier/Scholastic.

Ember, Melvin, Carol R. Ember, and Bobbi S. Low. 2007. Comparing explanations of polygyny. *Cross-Cultural Research* 41:428–40.

Ember, Melvin, Carol R. Ember, and Bruce Russett. 1997. Inequality and democracy in the anthropological record. In *Inequality, democracy, and economic development*, ed. M. I. Midlarsky. Cambridge: Cambridge University Press.

Ember, Melvin, Carol R. Ember, and Ian Skoggard, eds. 2005. *Encyclopedia of diasporas: Immigrant and refugee cultures around the world*, 2 vols. New York: Kluwer Academic/Plenum.

Ensminger, Jean. 1997. Transaction costs and Islam: Explaining conversion in Africa. *Journal of Institutional and Theoretical Economics* 153:4–29.

Ensminger, Jean. 2002. Experimental economics: A powerful new method for theory testing in anthropology. In *Theory in economic anthropology*, ed. J. Ensminger, 59–78. Walnut Creek, CA: AltaMira Press.

Ensor, Bradley E. 2003. Kinship and marriage among the Omaha, 1886–1902. *Ethnology* 42:1–14.

Epstein, Cynthia Fuchs. 1988. *Deceptive distinctions: Sex, gender, and the social order*. New York: Russell Sage Foundation.

Erchak, Gerald M. 2009. Family violence. In MyAnthroLibrary, eds. C. R. Ember, M. Ember, and P. N. Peregrine. MyAnthroLibrary.com. Pearson.

Ericksen, Karen Paige. 1989. Male and female age organizations and secret societies in Africa. *Behavior Science Research* 23:234–64.

Ericksen, Karen Paige, and Heather Horton. 1992. "Blood feuds": Cross-cultural variations in kin group vengeance. *Behavior Science Research* 26:57–85.

Erickson, Clark. 1988. Raised field agriculture in the Lake Titicaca basin. *Expedition* 30(1):8–16.

Erickson, Clark. 1989. Raised fields and sustainable agriculture in the Lake Titicaca basin of Peru. In *Fragile lands of Latin America*, ed. John Browder, 230–48. Boulder: Westview.

Erickson, Clark. 1998. Applied archaeology and rural development. In *Crossing currents: Continuity and change in Latin America*, eds. Michael Whiteford and Scott Whiteford, 34–45. Upper Saddle River, NJ: Prentice Hall.

Erickson, Edwin. 1968. Self-assertion, sex role, and vocal rasp. In *Folk song style and culture*, ed. A. Lomax. Washington, DC.

Errington, J. Joseph. 1985. On the nature of the sociolinguistic sign: Describing the Javanese speech levels. In *Semiotic mediation*, eds. E. Mertz and R. J. Parmentier. Orlando, FL: Academic Press.

Ervin, Alexander M. 1987. Styles and strategies of leadership during the Alaskan Native land claims movement: 1959–71. *Anthropologica* 29:21–38.

Eswaran, Vinayak. 2002. A diffusion wave out of Africa. *Current Anthropology* 43:749–74.

Etienne, Mona, and Eleanor Leacock, eds. 1980. *Women and colonization: Anthropological perspectives*. New York: Praeger.

Etienne, Robert. 1992. *Pompeii: The day a city died*. New York: Abrams.

Etkin, Nina L., and Paul J. Ross. 1997. Malaria, medicine, and meals: A biobehavioral perspective. In *The anthropology of medicine*, eds. L. Romanucci-Ross, D. E. Moerman, and L. R. Tancredi, 169–209. Westport, CT: Bergin & Garvey.

Euripides. 1937. The Trojan women. In *Three Greek plays*, trans. E. Hamilton, 52. New York: Norton.

Evans-Pritchard, E. E. 1940. The Nuer of the Southern Sudan. In *African political systems*, eds. M. Fortes and E. E. Evans-Pritchard. New York: Oxford University Press.

Evans-Pritchard, E. E. 1970. Sexual inversion among the Azande. *American Anthropologist* 72:1428–34.

Evans-Pritchard, E. E. 1979. Witchcraft explains unfortunate events. In *Reader in comparative religion*, 3rd ed., eds. W. A. Lessa and E. Z. Vogt. New York: Harper & Row.

Eveleth, Phyllis B., and James M. Tanner. 1990. *Worldwide variation in human growth*. 2nd ed. Cambridge: Cambridge University Press.

Everett, Margaret. 2007. The "I" in gene: Divided property, fragmented personhood, and the making of a genetic privacy law. *American Ethnologist* 34(2): 375–86.

Eversole, Robyn. 2005. "Direct to the poor": Revisited: Migrant remittances and development assistance. In *Migration and economy: Global and local dynamics*, ed. Lillian Trager, 289–322. Walnut Creek, CA: AltaMira Press.

Fagan, Brian M. 1972. *In the beginning*. Boston: Little, Brown.

Fagan, Brian M. 1989. *People of the earth: An introduction to world prehistory*. 6th ed. Glenview, IL: Scott, Foresman.

Fagan, Brian M. 1991. *Ancient North America: The archaeology of a continent*. London: Thames and Hudson.

Falk, Dean. 1987. Hominid paleoneurology. *Annual Review of Anthropology* 16:13–30.

Falk, Dean. 1988. Enlarged occipital/marginal sinuses and emissary foramina: Their significance in hominid evolution. In *Evolutionary history of the "robust" australopithecines*, ed. F. E. Grine. New York: Aldine.

Falk, Dean, C. Hildebolt, K. Smith, M. J. Morwood, T. Sutikna, P. Brown, Jatmiko, E. W. Saptomo, B. Brunsden, F. Prior. 2005. The brain of LBI, *Homo floresiensis*. *Science* 308 (April 8):242–45.

Farley, Reynolds. 1996. *The new American reality: Who we are, how we got here, where we are going*. New York: Russell Sage Foundation.

Farmer, Paul. 1997. Ethnography, social analysis, and the prevention of sexually transmitted HIV infection among poor women in Haiti. In *The anthropology of infectious disease*, eds. M. C. Inhorn and P. J. Brown, 413–38. Amsterdam: Gordon and Breach.

Featherman, David L., and Robert M. Hauser. 1978. *Opportunity and change*. New York: Academic Press.

Feder, Kenneth. 2000. *Past in perspective*. 2d ed. Mountain View, CA: Mayfield Publishing Company.

Fedigan, Linda Marie. 1982. *Primate paradigms: Sex roles and social bonds*. Montreal: Eden Press.

Fedoroff, Nina. 2003. Prehistoric GM corn. *Science* 302 (November 14):1158–59.

Fehr, Ernst and Urs Fischbacher. 2003. The nature of human altruism. *Nature* (October 23):785–91.

Feibel, Craig S., and Francis H. Brown. 1993. Microstratigraphy and paleoenvironments. In *The Nariokotome* Homo erectus *Skeleton*, eds. A. Walker and R. Leakey. Cambridge, MA: Harvard University Press.

Feinman, Gary, and Jill Neitzel. 1984. Too many types: An overview of sedentary prestate societies in the Americas. In *Advances in archaeological methods and theory*, ed. M. B. Schiffer, vol. 7. Orlando, FL: Academic Press.

Feinman, Gary M., Stephen A. Kowalewski, Laura Finsten, Richard E. Blanton, and Linda Nicholas. 1985. Long-term demographic change: A perspective from the Valley of Oaxaca, Mexico. *Journal of Field Archaeology* 12:333–62.

Feldman, Douglas A., and Thomas M. Johnson. 1986. Introduction. In *The social dimensions of AIDS*, eds. D. A. Feldman and T. M. Johnson. New York: Praeger.

Ferguson, R. Brian, and Neil L. Whitehead. 1992. Violent edge of empire. In *War in the tribal zone*, eds. R. B. Ferguson and N. Whitehead, 1–30. Santa Fe, NM: School of American Research Press.

Ferguson, Niall. 2004. *Colossus: The price of America's empire.* New York: Penguin Press.

Fernea, Elizabeth, and Robert Fernea, as reported in M. Kay Martin and Barbara Voorhies, 1975. *Female of the species.* New York: Columbia University Press.

Ferraro, Gary P. 2002. *The cultural dimension of international business.* 4th ed. Upper Saddle River, NJ: Prentice Hall.

Fessler, Daniel M. T. 2002. Windfall and socially distributed willpower: The psychocultural dynamics of rotating savings and credit associations in a Bengkulu village. *Ethos* 30:25–48.

Finley, M. I. 1983. *Politics in the ancient world.* Cambridge: Cambridge University Press.

Finnis, Elizabeth. 2006. Why grow cash crops? Subsistence farming and crop commercialization in the Kolli Hills, South India. *American Anthropologist* 108:363–69.

Firth, Raymond. 1957. *We, the Tikopia.* Boston: Beacon Press.

Firth, Raymond. 1959. *Social change in Tikopia.* New York: Macmillan.

Firth, Raymond. 1970. *Rank and religion in Tikopia.* Boston: Beacon Press.

Fischer, John L. 1958. Social influences on the choice of a linguistic variant. *Word* 14:47–56.

Fischer, John. 1961. Art styles as cultural cognitive maps. *American Anthropologist* 63:80–83.

Fish, Paul R. 1981. Beyond tools: Middle Paleolithic debitage analysis and cultural inference. *Journal of Anthropological Research* 37:374–86.

Fisher, Julie. 1996. Grassroots organizations and grassroots support organizations: Patterns of interaction. In *Transforming societies, transforming anthropology*, ed. E. F. Moran. Ann Arbor: University of Michigan Press.

Fisher, William F. 1997. Doing good? The politics and antipolitics of NGO practices. *Annual Review of Anthropology* 26:439–64.

Fisher, William H. 1994. Megadevelopment, environmentalism, and resistance: The institutional context of Kayapo indigenous politics in central Brazil." *Human Organization* 53:220–32.

Flannery, Kent V. 1965. The ecology of early food production in Mesopotamia. *Science* 147 (March 12):1247–56.

Flannery, Kent V. 1971. The origins and ecological effects of early domestication in Iran and the Near East. In *Prehistoric agriculture*, ed. S. Struever. Garden City, NY: Natural History Press.

Flannery, Kent V. 1972. The cultural evolution of civilizations. *Annual Review of Ecology and Systematics* 3:399–426.

Flannery, Kent V. 1973a. The origins of agriculture. *Annual Review of Anthropology* 2:271–310.

Flannery, Kent V. 1973b. The origins of the village as a settlement type in Mesoamerica and the Near East: A comparative study. In *Territoriality and proxemics*, ed. R. Tringham. Andover, MA: Warner.

Flannery, Kent V., ed. 1986. *Guila Naquitz: Archaic foraging and early agriculture in Oaxaca, Mexico.* Orlando, FL: Academic Press.

Fleagle, John G. 1994. Anthropoid origins. In *Integrative paths to the past*, eds. R. Corruccini and R. Ciochon. Upper Saddle River, NJ: Prentice Hall.

Fleagle, John G. 1999. *Primate adaptation and evolution.* 2nd ed. San Diego: Academic Press.

Fleagle, John G., and Richard F. Kay. 1983. New interpretations of the phyletic position of Oligocene hominoids. In *New interpretations of ape and human ancestry*, eds. R. Ciochon and R. Corruccini. New York: Plenum.

Fleagle, John G., and Richard F. Kay. 1985. The paleobiology of catarrhines. In *Ancestors*, ed. E. Delson. New York: Alan R. Liss.

Fleagle, John G., and Richard F. Kay, 1987. The phyletic position of the *Parapithecidae. Journal of Human Evolution* 16:483–531.

Fluehr-Lobban, Carolyn. 2006. *Race and racism: An introduction.* Lanham,: AltaMira Press.

Ford, Clellan S. 1941. *Smoke from their fires.* New Haven, CT: Yale University Press.

Ford, Clellan S., and Frank A. Beach. 1951. *Patterns of sexual behavior.* New York: Harper.

Forrest, Barbara, 2001. The wedge at work. In *Intelligent design creationism and its critics.* ed. Robert Pennock. Boston: MIT Press.

Fortes, Meyer. 1949. *The web of kinship among the Tallensi.* New York: Oxford University Press.

Fossey, Dian. 1983. *Gorillas in the mist.* Boston: Houghton Mifflin.

Foster, Brian L. 1974. Ethnicity and commerce. *American Ethnologist* 1:437–47.

Foster, George M. 1962. *Traditional cultures and the impact of technological change.* New York: Harper & Row.

Foster, George M. 1969. *Applied anthropology.* Boston: Little, Brown.

Foster, George M. 1994. *Hippocrates' Latin American legacy: Humoral medicine in the New World.* Amsterdam: Gordon and Breach.

Foucault, Michel. 1970. *The order of things: An archaeology of the human sciences.* New York: Random House.

Fowler, Melvin L. 1975. A pre-Columbian urban center on the Mississippi. *Scientific American* (August):92–101.

Frake, Charles O. 1960. The Eastern Subanun of Mindanao. In *Social Structure in Southeast Asia*, ed. G. P. Murdock. Chicago: Quadrangle.

Franciscus, Robert G., and Erik Trinkaus. 1988. Nasal morphology and the emergence of *Homo erectus. American Journal of Physical Anthropology* 75:517–27.

Frank, André Gunder. 1967. *Capitalism and underdevelopment in Latin America: Historical studies of Chile and Brazil.* New York: Monthly Review Press.

Fratkin, Elliot. 2008. Pastures lost: The decline of mobile pastoralism among Maasai and Rendille in Kenya, East Africa. In *Economies and the transformation of landscape*, eds. Lisa Cliggett and Christopher A. Pool, 149–68. Lanham, AltaMira Press.

Frayer, David W. 1981. Body size, weapon use, and natural selection in the European Upper Paleolithic and Mesolithic. *American Anthropologist* 83:57–73.

Frayer, David W., and Milford H. Wolpoff. 1985. Sexual dimorphism. *Annual Review of Anthropology* 14:429–73.

Frayer, David W., M. Wolpoff, A. Thorne, F. Smith, and G. Pope. 1993. Theories of modern human origins: The paleontological test. *American Anthropologist* 95:24–27.

Frayser, Suzanne G. 1985. *Varieties of sexual experience.* New Haven, CT: HRAF Press.

Freedman, Daniel G. 1979. Ethnic differences in babies. *Human Nature* (January):36–43.

Freeman, Derek. 1983. *Margaret Mead and Samoa: The making and unmaking of an anthropological myth.* Cambridge, MA: Harvard University Press.

Freeman, J. D. 1961. On the concept of the kindred. *Journal of the Royal Anthropological Institute* 91:192–220.

Freeman, Leslie G. 1994 Torralba and Ambrona: A review of discoveries. In *Integrative paths to the past*, eds. R. Coruccini and R. Ciochon. Upper Saddle River, NJ: Prentice Hall.

Freud, Sigmund. 1943/1917. *A general introduction to psychoanalysis*. Garden City, NY: Garden City Publishing. (Originally published in German)

Freud, Sigmund. 1967/1939. *Moses and monotheism*. Katherine Jones, trans. New York: Vintage Books.

Freyman, R. 1987. The first technology. *Scientific American* (April): 112.

Fried, Morton H. 1967. *The evolution of political society: An essay in political anthropology*. New York: Random House.

Friedl, Ernestine. 1962. *Vasilika: A village in modern Greece*. New York: Holt, Rinehart & Winston.

Friedman, Jeffrey M. 2003. A war on obesity, not the obese. *Science* 299 (February 7):856–58.

Friedrich, Paul. 1970. *Proto-Indo-European trees: The arboreal system of a prehistoric people*. Chicago: University of Chicago Press.

Friedrich, Paul. 1986. *The language parallax*. Austin: University of Texas Press.

Friedman, Saul S. 1980. Holocaust. In *Academic American* [now Grolier] *Encyclopedia*, vol. 10. Princeton, NJ: Areté.

Frisancho, A. Roberto, and Lawrence P. Greksa. 1989. Development responses in the acquisition of functional adaptation to high altitude. In *Human population biology*, eds. M. Little and J. Haas. New York: Oxford University Press.

Frisch, Rose. E. 1980. Fatness, puberty, and fertility. *Natural History* (October):16–27.

Fromm, Erich. 1950. *Psychoanalysis and religion*. New Haven, CT: Yale University Press.

Fry, Douglas P. 2006. *The human potential for peace: An anthropological challenge to assumptions about war and violence*. New York: Oxford University Press.

Fry, Douglas P., and Kaj Björkqvist, eds. 1997. *Cultural variation in conflict resolution: Alternatives to violence*. Mahwah, NJ: Lawrence Erlbaum Associates.

Futuyma, Douglas. 1982. *Science on trial*. New York: Pantheon.

Gabunia, Leo, A. Vekua, D. Lordkipanidze, et al. 2000. Earliest Pleistocene hominid cranial remains from Dmanisi, Republic of Georgia: Taxonomy, geological setting, and age. *Science* 288 (May 12):1019–25.

Gal, Susan. 1988. The political economy of code choice. In *Codeswitching*, ed. M. Heller. Berlin: Mouton de Gruyter, 245–64.

Galdikas, Biruté M. F. 1979. Orangutan adaptation at Tanjung Puting Reserve: Mating and ecology.” In *The great apes*. eds. D. Hamburg and E. McCown. Menlo Park, CA: Benjamin/Cummings.

Gardner, Beatrice T., and R. Allen Gardner. 1980. Two comparative psychologists look at language acquisition. In *Children's language*, vol. 2, ed. K. Nelson. New York: Halsted Press.

Gardner, R. Allen, and Beatrice T. Gardner. 1969. Teaching sign language to a chimpanzee. *Science* 165 (August 15): 664–72.

Garn, Stanley M. 1971. *Human races*. 3rd ed. Springfield, IL: Charles C Thomas.

Gartner, Rosemary. 2009. Crime variations across cultures and nations. In MyAnthroLibrary, eds. C. R. Ember, M. Ember, and P. N. Peregrine. MyAnthroLibrary.com. Pearson.

Gat, Azar. 1999. The pattern of fighting in simple, small-scale, prestate societies. *Journal of Anthropological Research* 55:563–83.

Gaulin, Steven J. C., and James S. Boster. 1990. Dowry as female competition. *American Anthropologist* 92:994–1005.

Gay, Kathlyn. 1986. *Ergonomics: Making products and places fit people*. Hillside, New Jersey: Enslow.

Geertz, Clifford. 1960. *The religion of Java*. New York: Free Press.

Geertz, Clifford. 1966. Religion as a cultural system. In *Anthropological approaches to the study of religion*, ed. M. Banton. New York: Praeger.

Geertz, Clifford. 1973a. “Deep play: Notes on the Balinese cockfight.” In *The interpretation of cultures*, ed. C. Geertz. New York: Basic Books.

Geertz, Clifford. 1973b. Thick description: Toward an interpretative theory of culture. In *The interpretation of cultures*, ed. C. Geertz. New York: Basic Books.

Geertz, Clifford. 1984. “From the native's point of view”: On the nature of anthropological understanding. In *Culture theory*, eds. R. A. Shweder and R. A. LeVine. New York: Cambridge University Press.

Geiger, H. Jack. 2003. Racial and ethnic disparities in diagnosis and treatment: A review of the evidence and a consideration of causes. In *Unequal treatment: confronting racial and ethnic disparities in health care*, eds. Brian D. Smedley, Adrienne Y. Stith, and Alan R. Nelson, 417–54. Washington, DC: National Academy Press.

Gelles, Richard J., and Murray A. Straus. 1988. *Intimate violence*. New York: Simon & Schuster.

Gentner, W., and H. J. Lippolt. 1963. The potassium-argon dating of upper tertiary and Pleistocene deposits. In *Science in archaeology*, eds. D. Brothwell and E. Higgs. New York: Basic Books.

Gero, Joan M., and Margaret W. Conkey, eds. 1991. *Engendering archaeology: An introduction to women and prehistory*. Oxford: Blackwell.

Gesler, W. 1991. *The cultural geography of health care*. Pittsburgh, PA: University of Pittsburgh Press.

Gibbons, Ann. 1993. Warring over women. *Science* 261 (August 20):987–88.

Gibbons, Ann. 1995. First Americans: Not mammoth hunters, but forest dwellers? *Science* 268 (April 19): 346–47.

Gibbons, Ann. 2001. The riddle of co-existence. *Science* 291(March 2):1725–29.

Gibbons, Ann. 2002. One scientist's quest for the origin of our species. *Science* 298 (November 29):1708–11.

Gibbons, Ann. 2003. Oldest members of *Homo sapiens* discovered in Africa. *Science* 300 (June 13):1641.

Gibbons, Ann. 2008. The birth of childhood. *Science* 322 (November 14): 1040–43.

Gibbs, James L., Jr. 1965. The Kpelle of Liberia. In *Peoples of Africa*, ed. J. L. Gibbs, Jr. New York: Holt, Rinehart & Wintson.

Gibson, Kathleen R., and Stephen Jessee. 1999. Language evolution and expansions of multiple neurological processing areas. In *The origins of language*, ed. B. J. King, 189–227. Santa Fe, NM: School of American Research Press.

Gibson, Kyle. 2009. Differential parental investment in families with both adopted and genetic children. *Evolution and Human Behavior* 30:184–89.

Gilbert, M. Thomas P., Dennis L. Jenkins, Anders Götherstrom, Nuria Naveran, Juan J. Sanchez, Michael Hofreiter, Philip Francis Thomsen, Jonas Binladen, Thomas F. G. Higham, Robert M. Yohe, II, Robert Parr, Linda Scott Cummings, and Eske Willerslev. 2008. DNA from pre-Clovis human coprolites in Oregon, North America. *Science* 320 (May 9):786–89.

Gilligan, Carol. 1982. *In a different voice: Psychological theory and women's development*. Cambridge, MA: Harvard University Press.

Gilligan, Carol, and Jane Attanucci. 1988. Two moral orientations. In *Mapping the moral domain*, eds. C. Gilligan, J. V. Ward, and J. M. Taylor. Cambridge, MA: Harvard University Press.

Gilliland, Mary Kay. 1995. Nationalism and ethnogenesis in the former Yugoslavia. In *Ethnic identity: Creation, conflict, and accommodation*, 3rd ed., eds. L. Romanucci-Ross and G. A. De Vos, 197–221. Walnut Creek, CA: Alta Mira Press.

Gilman, Antonio. 1990. The development of social stratification in Bronze Age Europe. *Current Anthropology* 22:1–23.

Gimbutas, Marija. 1974. An archaeologist's view of PIE* in 1975. *Journal of Indo-European Studies* 2:289–307.

Gingerich, P. D. 1986. *Pleisiadipis* and the delineation of the order primates. In *Major topics in primate evolution*, eds. B. Wood, L. Martin, and P. Andrews, 32–46. Cambridge: Cambridge University Press.

Gladwin, Christina H. 1980. A theory of real-life choice: Applications to agricultural decisions. In *Agricultural decision making*, ed. P. F. Barlett. New York: Academic Press.

Gladwin, Thomas, and Seymour B. Sarason. 1953. *Truk: Man in paradise*. New York: Wenner-Gren Foundation for Anthropological Research.

Gleitman, Lila R., and Eric Wanner. 1982. Language acquisition: The state of the state of the art. In *Language acquisition*, eds. E. Wanner and L. R. Gleitman. Cambridge: Cambridge University Press.

Godoy, Ricardo, Elizabeth Byron, Victoria Reyes-Garcia, William R. Leonard, Karishma Patel, Lilian Apaza, Eddy Pérez, Vincent Vadez, and David Wilke. 2004. Patience in a foraging-horticultural society: A test of competing hypotheses. *Journal of Anthropological Research* 60:179–202.

Goebel, Ted, Michael Waters, and Dennis O'Rourke. 2008. The late Pleistocene dispersal of modern humans in the Americas. *Science* 319 (March 14):1479–1502.

Golden, Frederic, Michael Lemonick, and Dick Thompson. 2000. The race is over. *Time* (July 3): 18–23.

Goldizen, Anne Wilson. 1987. Tamarins and marmosets: Communal care of offspring. In *Primate Societies*, eds. B. Smuts et al. Chicago: University of Chicago Press.

Goldschmidt, Walter. 1999. Dynamics and status in America. *Anthropology Newsletter* 40(5):62, 64.

Goldstein, Donna. 1998. Nothing bad intended: Child discipline, punishment, and survival in a shantytown in Rio de Janeiro. In *Small wars: The cultural politics of childhood*, eds. Nancy Scheper-Hughes and Carolyn Sargeant, 389–415. Berkeley: University of California-Berkeley Press.

Goldstein, Joshua S. 2001. *War and gender: How gender shapes the war system and vice versa*. New York: Cambridge University Press.

Goldstein, Joshua S. 2004. War and gender. In *Encyclopedia of sex and gender: Men and women in the world's cultures*, vol. 1, eds. C. R. Ember and M. Ember, 107–116. New York: Kluwer Academic/Plenum Publishers.

Goldstein, Melvyn C. 1971. Stratification, polyandry, and family structure in central Tibet. *Southwestern Journal of Anthropology* 27:65–74.

Goldstein, Melvyn C. 1987. When brothers share a wife. *Natural History* (March):39–48.

Goodall, Jane. 1963. My life among wild chimpanzees. *National Geographic* (August): 272–308.

Goode, William J. 1970. *World revolution and family patterns*. New York: Free Press.

Goode, William J. 1982. *The family*. 2nd ed. Upper Saddle River, NJ: Prentice Hall.

Goodenough, Ward H. 1951. *Property, kin, and community on Truk*. New Haven, CT: Yale University Press.

Goodman, Alan H., and George J. Armelagos. 1985. Disease and death at Dr. Dickson's Mounds. *Natural History* (September):12–19.

Goodman, Alan H., John Lallo, George J. Armelagos, and Jerome C. Rose. 1984. Health changes at Dickson Mounds, Illinois (A.D. 950–1300). In *Paleopathology at the origins of agriculture*, eds. M. N. Cohen and G. J. Armelagos. Orlando, FL: Academic Press.

Goodman, Alan H., and Thomas L. Leatherman, eds. 1998. *Building a new biocultural synthesis: Political-economic perspectives on human biology*. Ann Arbor: University of Michigan Press.

Goodman, Madeleine J., P. Bion Griffin, Agnes A. Estioko-Griffin, and John S. Grove. 1985. The compatibility of hunting and mothering among the Agta hunter-gatherers of the Philippines. *Sex Roles* 12:1199–209.

Goodman, Morris. 1992. Reconstructing human evolution from proteins. In *The Cambridge encyclopedia of human evolution*. eds. S. Jones, R. Martin, and D. Pilbeam. New York: Cambridge University Press.

Goodrich, L. Carrington. 1959. *A short history of the Chinese people*. 3rd ed. New York: Harper & Row.

Goody, Jack. 1970. Cousin terms. *Southwestern Journal of Anthropology* 26:125–42.

Goody, Jack. 1973. Bridewealth and dowry in Africa and Eurasia. In *Bridewealth and dowry*, eds. J. Goody and S. H. Tambiah. Cambridge: Cambridge University Press.

Gordon, C. G., and K. E. Friedl. 1994. Anthropometry in the U.S. armed forces. In *Anthropometry: The individual and the population*, eds. S. J. Ulijaszek and C. G. N. Mascie-Taylor, 178–210. Cambridge, Cambridge University Press.

Gore, Rick. 2002. The first pioneer? *National Geographic* (August).

Goren-Inbar, Naama, N. Alperson, M. Kislev, O. Simchoni, Y. Melamed, A. Ben-Nun, and E. Werker. 2004. Evidence of hominid control of fire at Gesher Benot Ya'aqov, Israel. *Science* 304 (April 30):725–27.

Gorman, Chester. 1970. The Hoabinhian and after: Subsistence patterns in Southeast Asia during the Late Pleistocene and early recent periods. *World Archaeology* 2:315–19.

Gossen, Gary H. 1979. Temporal and spatial equivalents in Chamula ritual symbolism. In *Reader in comparative religion*, 4th ed., eds. W. A. Lessa and E. Z. Vogt. New York: Harper & Row.

Gough, Kathleen. 1959. The Nayars and the definition of marriage. *Journal of the Royal Anthropological Institute* 89:23–34.

Gould, Richard A. 1969. *Yiwara: Foragers of the Australian desert*. New York: Scribner's.

Gowlett, John A. J. 2008. Deep roots of kin: Developing the evolutionary perspective from prehistory. In *Early human kinship: From sex to social reproduction*, eds. Nicholas Allen, Hilary Callan, Robin Dunbar, and Wendy James, 41–57. Oxford: Blackwell.

Graber, Robert, ed. 2004. Special issue. The future state of the world: An anthropological symposium. *Cross-Cultural Research* 38:95–207.

Graburn, Nelson H. 1969. *Eskimos without igloos*. Boston: Little, Brown.

Graham, Susan Brandt. 1979. Biology and human social behavior: A response to van den Berghe and Barash. *American Anthropologist* 81:357–60.

Grant, Bruce S. 2002. Sour grapes of wrath. *Science* 297 (August 9): 940–41.

Grant, Peter R. 1991. Natural selection and Darwin's finches. *Scientific American* (October): 82–87.

Grant, Peter R., and Rosemary Grant. 2002. Unpredictable evolution in a 30-year study of Darwin's finches. *Science* 296 (April 26):707–11.

Gravlee, Clarence C., H. R. Bernard, and W. R. Leonard. 2003. Heredity, environment, and cranial form: A reanalysis of Boas's immigrant data. *American Anthropologist* 105: 125–38.

Gray, J. Patrick. 1996. Sociobiology. In *Encyclopedia of cultural anthropology*, eds. David Levinson and Melvin Ember, vol. 4, 1212–19. New York: Henry Holt.

Gray, J. Patrick. 1985. *Primate sociobiology*. New Haven, CT: HRAF Press.

Gray, J. Patrick, and Linda D. Wolfe. 1980. Height and sexual dimorphism of stature among human societies. *American Journal of Physical Anthropology* 53: 446–52.

Gray, J. Patrick, and Linda Wolfe. 2009. What accounts for population variation in height? In MyAnthroLibrary, eds. C. R. Ember, M. Ember, and P. N. Peregrine. MyAnthroLibrary.com. Pearson.

Grayson, Donald K. 1977. Pleistocene avifaunas and the overkill hypothesis. *Science* 195 (February 18):691–92.

Grayson, Donald K. 1984. Explaining Pleistocene extinctions: Thoughts on the structure of a debate. In *Quaternary extinctions*, eds. P. S. Martin and R. Klein. Tucson: University of Arizona Press.

Green, Richard E., Anna-Sapfo Malaspinas, Johannes Krause, Adrian W. Briggs, Philip L.F. Johnson, Caroline Uhler, Matthias Meyer, Jeffrey M. Good, Tomislav Maricic, Udo Stenzel, Kay Prüfer, Michael Siebauer, Hernán A. Burbano, Michael Ronan, Jonathan M. Rothberg, Michael Egholm, Pavao Rudan, Dejana Brajković, Željko Kućan, Ivan Gušić, Mårten Wikström, Liisa Laakkonen, Janet Kelso, Montgomery Slatkin, and Svante Pääbo. 2008. A complete Neandertal mitochondrial genome sequence determined by high-throughput sequencing. *Cell* 134: 416–26.

Greenberg, Joseph H. 1972. Linguistic evidence regarding Bantu origins. *Journal of African History* 13:189–216.

Greenberg, Joseph H., and Merritt Ruhlen. 1992. Linguistic origins of Native Americans. *Scientific American* (November):94–99.

Greenfield, Patricia M., Ashley E. Maynard, and Carla P. Childs. 2000. History, culture, learning, and development. *Cross-Cultural Research* 34:351–74.

Greenfield, Patricia Marks, and E. Sue Savage-Rumbaugh. 1990. Grammatical combination in *Pan paniscus*: Processes of learning and invention in the evolution and development of language. In *"Language" and intelligence in monkeys and apes*, eds. S. Parker and K. Gibson. New York: Cambridge University Press.

Gregor, Thomas A., Daniel R. Gross. 2004. Guilt by association: The culture of accusation and the American Anthropological Association's investigation of *Darkness in El Dorado*. *American Anthropologist* 106: 687–98.

Gregory, C. A. 1982. *Gifts and commodities*. New York: Academic Press.

Greksa, Lawrence P., and Cynthia M. Beall. 1989. Development of chest size and lung function at high altitude. In *Human population biology*, eds. M. Little and J. Haas. New York: Oxford University Press.

Grenoble, Lenore A., and Lindsay J. Whaley. 2006. *Saving languages: An introduction to language revitalization*. Cambridge: Cambridge University Press.

Grine, Frederick E. 1988a. Evolutionary history of the 'robust' australopithecines: A summary and historical perspective. In *Evolutionary history of the "robust" australopithecines*, ed. F. E. Grine. New York: Aldine.

Grine, Frederick E., ed. 1988b. *Evolutionary history of the "robust" australopithecines*. New York: Aldine.

Grine, Frederick E. 1993. Australopithecine taxonomy and phylogeny: Historical background and recent interpretation. In *The Human evolution source book*, eds. R. Ciochon and J. Fleagle. Upper Saddle River, NJ: Prentice Hall.

Gröger, B. Lisa. 1981. Of men and machines: Cooperation among French family farmers. *Ethnology* 20:163–75.

Gross, Daniel R., George Eiten, Nancy M. Flowers, Francisca M. Leoi, Madeline Latiman Ritter, and Dennis W. Werner. 1979. Ecology and acculturation among native peoples of central Brazil. *Science* 206 (November 30):1043–50.

Gross, Daniel R., and Barbara A. Underwood. 1971. Technological change and caloric costs: Sisal agriculture in northeastern Brazil. *American Anthropologist* 73:725–40.

Grossman, Daniel. 2002. Parched turf battle. *Scientific American* (December):32–33.

Grubb, Henry J. 1987. Intelligence at the low end of the curve: Where are the racial differences? *Journal of Black Psychology* 14: 25–34.

Gubser, Nicholas J. 1965. *The Nunamiut Eskimos: Hunters of caribou*. New Haven, CT: Yale University Press.

Guest, Greg, and Eric C. Jones. 2005. Globalization, health, and the environment: An introduction. In *Globalization, health, and the environment: An integrated perspective*, ed. Greg Guest, 3–26. Lanham, MD: Roman & Littlefield.

Guiora, Alexander Z., Benjamin Beit-Hallahmi, Risto Fried, and Cecelia Yoder. 1982. Language environment and gender identity attainment. *Language Learning* 32:289–304.

Gumperz, John J. 1961. Speech variation and the study of Indian civilization. *American Anthropologist* 63:976–88.

Gumperz, John J. 1971. Dialect differences and social stratification in a North Indian village. In *Language in social groups: Essays by John J. Gumperz*, selected and introduced by Anwar S. Dil. Stanford, CA: Stanford University Press.

Gunders, S., and J. W. M. Whiting. 1968. Mother-infant separation and physical growth. *Ethnology* 7: 196–206.

Gurr, Ted Robert. 1989a. Historical trends in violent crime: Europe and the United States. In *Violence in America*, vol. 1: *The history of crime*, ed. T. R. Gurr. Newbury Park, CA: Sage.

Gurr, Ted Robert. 1989b. The history of violent crime in America: An overview. In *Violence in America*, vol. 1: *The history of crime*, ed. T. R. Gurr. Newbury Park, CA: Sage.

Gurven, Michael, Kim Hill, and Hillard Kaplan. 2002. From forest to reservation: Transitions in food-sharing behavior among the Ache of Paraguay. *Journal of Anthropological Research* 58:93–120.

Guthrie, Dale R., 1984. Mosaics, allelochemics, and nutrients: An ecological theory of Late Pleistocene megafaunal extinctions. In *Quaternary extinctions*, eds. P. S. Martin and R. Klein. Tucson: University of Arizona Press.

Guthrie, Stewart Elliott. 1993. *Faces in the clouds: A new theory of religion.* New York: Oxford University Press.

Haas, Jonathan. 1990. Warfare and the evolution of tribal polities in the prehistoric Southwest. In *The anthropology of war*, ed. J. Haas. New York: Cambridge University Press.

Haas, Jonathan, Winifred Creamer, and Alvaro Ruiz. 2004. Dating the late Archaic occupation of the Norte Chico region in Peru. *Nature* 432 (December 23):1020–23.

Haas, Mary R. 1944. Men's and women's speech in Koasati. *Language* 20:142–49.

Habicht, J. K. A. 1979. *Paleoclimate, paleomagnetism, and continental drift.* Tulsa, OK: American Association of Petroleum Geologists.

Haddix, Kimber A. 2001. Leaving your wife and your brothers: When polyandrous marriages fall apart. *Evolution and Human Behavior* 22:47–60.

Hage, Jerald, and Charles H. Powers. 1992. *Post-industrial lives: Roles and relationships in the 21st century.* Newbury Park, CA: Sage.

Hahn, Robert A. 1995. *Sickness and healing: An anthropological perspective.* New Haven, CT: Yale University Press.

Hailie-Selassie, Yohannes. 2001. Late Miocene hominids from the Middle Awash, Ethiopia. *Nature* 412 (July 12):178–81.

Haldane, J. B. S. 1963. Human evolution: Past and future. In *Genetics, paleontology, and evolution*, eds. G. Jepsen, E. Mayr, and G. Simpson. New York: Atheneum.

Hall, Edward T. 1966. *The hidden dimension.* Garden City, NY: Doubleday.

Hallowell, A. Irving. 1976. Ojibwa world view and disease. In *Contributions to anthropology: Selected papers of A. Irving Hallowell.* Chicago: University of Chicago Press, 410–13.

Halpern, Diane F. 2000. *Sex differences in cognitive abilities.* 3rd ed. Mahwah, NJ: Lawrence Erlbaum Associates.

Hames, Raymond. 1990. Sharing among the Yanomamö. Part I. The effects of risk. In *Risk and uncertainty in tribal and peasant economies*, ed. E. Cashdan. Boulder, CO: Westview.

Hames, Raymond. 2009. Yanomamö: Varying adaptations of foraging horticulturalists. In *MyAnthroLibrary*, eds. C. R. Ember, M. Ember, and P. N. Peregrine. MyAnthroLibrary.com. Pearson.

Hammer, Michael F., and Stephen L. Zegura. 1996. The role of the Y chromosome in human evolutionary studies. *Evolutionary Anthropology* 5:116–34.

Hammer, Michael F., and Stephen L. Zegura. 2002. The human Y chromosome haplogroup tree. *Annual Review of Anthropology* 31:303–21.

Handwerker, W. Penn, and Paul V. Crosbie. 1982. Sex and dominance. *American Anthropologist* 84:97–104.

Hanna, Joel M., Michael A. Little, and Donald M. Austin. 1989. Climatic physiology. In *Human population biology*, eds. M. Little and J. Haas. New York: Oxford University Press.

Hannah, Alison C., and W. C. McGrew. 1987. Chimpanzees using stones to crack open oil palm nuts in Liberia. *Primates* 28: 31–46.

Hannerz, Ulf. 1996. *Transnational connections: Culture, people, places.* London: Routledge.

Hanotte, Olivier, et al. 2002. African pastoralism: Genetic imprints of origins and migrations. *Science* 296 (April 12): 336–43.

Hanson, Jeffery R. 1988. Age-set theory and Plains Indian age-grading: A critical review and revision. *American Ethnologist* 15:349–64.

Harcourt, A. H. 1979. The social relations and group structure of wild mountain gorillas. In *The great apes.* eds. D. Hamburg and E. McCown. Menlo Park, CA: Benjamin/Cummings.

Hardin, Garrett. 1968. The tragedy of the commons. *Science* 162 (December 13):1243–48.

Hardoy, Jorge, and David Satterthwaite. 1987. The legal and the illegal city. In *Shelter, settlement, and development*, ed. L. Rodwin. Boston: Allen & Unwin.

Hare, Brian, Michelle Brown, Christina Williamson, and Michael Tomasello. 2002. The domestication of social cognition in dogs. *Science*, 298 (November 22): 1634–36.

Harkness, Sara, and Charles M. Super. 1997. An infant's three Rs. A box in M. Small, Our babies, ourselves, *Natural History* (October):45.

Harlan, Jack R. 1967. A wild wheat harvest in Turkey. *Archaeology* 20:197–201.

Harlow, Harry F., et al. 1966. Maternal behavior of rhesus monkeys deprived of mothering and peer association in infancy. *Proceedings of the American Philosophical Society* 110: 58–66.

Harner, Michael. 1972. The role of hallucinogenic plants in European witchcraft. In *Hallucinogens and shamanism*, ed. M. Harner. New York: Oxford University Press.

Harner, Michael J. 1975. Scarcity, the factors of production, and social evolution. In *Population, ecology, and social evolution*, ed. S. Polgar. The Hague: Mouton.

Harner, Michael, and Gary Doore. 1987. The ancient wisdom in shamanic cultures. In *Shamanism*, comp. S. Nicholson. Wheaton, IL: Theosophical Publishing House.

Harper, Douglas. 2003. Slavery in the North. http://www.slavenorth.com/ (accessed June, 2009).

Harrell-Bond, Barbara. 1996. Refugees. In *Encyclopedia of cultural anthropology*, vol. 3, eds. D. Levinson and M. Ember, 1076–81. New York: Henry Holt.

Harris, David R. 1977. Settling down: An evolutionary model for the transformation of mobile bands into sedentary communities. In *The evolution of social systems*, eds. J. Friedman and M. Rowlands. London: Duckworth.

Harris, Marvin. 1964. *Patterns of race in the Americas.* New York: Walker.

Harris, Marvin. 1966. The cultural ecology of India's sacred cattle. *Current Anthropology* 7:51–63.

Harris, Marvin. 1968. *The rise of anthropological theory: A history of theories of culture.* New York: Thomas Y. Crowell.

Harris, Marvin. 1975. *Cows, pigs, wars and witches: The riddles of culture.* New York: Random House, Vintage.

Harris, Marvin. 1979. *Cultural materialism: The struggle for a science of culture.* New York: Random House.

Harrison, G. A., James M. Tanner, David R. Pilbeam, and P. T. Baker. 1988. *Human biology: An introduction to human evolution, variation, growth, and adaptability*. 3rd ed. Oxford: Oxford University Press.

Harrison, Gail G. 1975. Primary adult lactase deficiency: A problem in anthropological genetics. *American Anthropologist* 77: 812–35.

Harrison, Peter D., and B. L. Turner, II, eds. 1978. *Pre-Hispanic Maya agriculture*. Albuquerque: University of New Mexico Press.

Harrison, T. 1986. A reassessment of the phylogenetic relationships of *Oreopithecus bamboli*. *Journal of Human Evolution* 15:541–84.

Harrison, T., and L. Rook. 1997. Enigmatic anthropoid or misunderstood ape? The phylogenetic status of *Oreopithecus bamboli* reconsidered. In *Function, phylogeny and fossils: Miocene hominoid evolution and adaptation*, eds. D. R. Begun, C. V. Ward, and M. D. Rose, 327–62. New York: Plenum.

Hart, Hornell. 1948. The logistic growth of political areas. *Social Forces* 26:396–408.

Hartwig, W. C. 1994. Pattern, puzzles and perspectives on platyrrhine origins. In *Integrative paths to the past*, eds. R. Corruccini and R. Ciochon, 69–93. Upper Saddle River, NJ: Prentice Hall.

Harvey, Philip W., and Peter F. Heywood. 1983. Twenty-five years of dietary change in Simbu Province, Papua New Guinea. *Ecology of Food and Nutrition* 13:27–35.

Hassan, Fekri A. 1981. *Demographic archaeology*. New York: Academic Press.

Hatch, Elvin. 1997. The good side of relativism. *Journal of Anthropological Research* 53:371–81.

Haug, Gerald, et al. 2003. Climate and the collapse of Maya civilization. *Science* 299 (March 14):1731–35.

Hausfater, Glenn, Jeanne Altmann, and Stuart Altmann. 1982. Long-term consistency of dominance relations among female baboons. *Science* 217 (August 20): 752–54.

Hawkins, Alicia, and M. Kleindienst. 2001. Aterian. In *Encyclopedia of prehistory*, vol. 1: *Africa*, eds. P. N. Peregrine and M. Ember. New York: Kluwer Academic/ Plenum, 23–45.

Hayden, Thomas. 2000. A genome milestone. *Newsweek* (July 3):51–52.

Haynes, Vance. 1973. The Calico site: Artifacts or geofacts? *Science* 181 (July 27):305–10.

Hays, Terence E. 1994. Sound symbolism, onomatopoeia, and New Guinea frog names. *Journal of Linguistic Anthropology* 4:153–74.

Hays, Terence E. 2009. From ethnographer to comparativist and back again. In MyAnthroLibrary, eds. C. R. Ember, M. Ember, and P. N. Peregrine. MyAnthroLibrary.com. Pearson.

Heider, Karl. 1970. *The Dugum Dani*. Chicago: Aldine.

Heider, Karl. 1979. *Grand Valley Dani: Peaceful warriors*. New York: Holt, Rinehart & Winston.

Heise, David R. 1967. Cultural patterning of sexual socialization. *American Sociological Review* 32:726–39.

Heller, Monica, ed. 1988. *Codeswitching: Anthropological and sociolinguistic perspectives*. Berlin: Mouton de Gruyter.

Helms, Mary W. 1975. *Middle America*. Upper Saddle River, NJ: Prentice Hall.

Helms, Mary W. 2009. Miskito: Adaptations to colonial empires, past and present. In MyAnthroLibrary, eds. C. R. Ember, M. Ember, and P. N. Peregrine. MyAnthroLibrary. com. Pearson.

Henderson, Harry. 2001. *Global terrorism: The complete reference guide*. New York: Checkmark Books.

Henderson, Stephen. 2002. Weddings: Vows; Rakhi Dhanoa and Ranjeet Purewal. *The New York Times*, August 18, p. 9.2.

Hendrix, Llewellyn. 1985. Economy and child training reexamined. *Ethos* 13:246–61.

Hendrix, Llewellyn. 2009. Varieties of marital relationships. In MyAnthroLibrary, eds. C. R. Ember, M. Ember, and P. N. Peregrine. MyAnthroLibrary.com. Pearson.

Henrich, Joseph, Robert Boyd, Samuel Bowles, Colin Camerer, Ernst Fehr, and Herbert Gintis, eds. 2004. *Foundations of human sociality: Economic experiments and ethnographic evidence from fifteen small-scale societies*. Oxford: Oxford University Press.

Henry, Donald O. 1989. *From foraging to agriculture: The Levant at the end of the ice age*. Philadelphia: University of Pennsylvania Press.

Henry, Donald O. 1991. Foraging, sedentism, and adaptive vigor in the Natufian: Rethinking the linkages. In *Perspectives on the past*, ed. G. A. Clark. Philadelphia: University of Pennsylvania Press.

Henry, Edward O. 1976. The variety of music in a North Indian village: Reassessing cantometrics. *Ethnomusicology* 20:49–66.

Henshilwood, Christopher, et al. 2002. Emergence of modern human behavior: Middle Stone Age engravings from South Africa. *Science*. 295 (February 15):1278–80.

Herlihy, Laura Hobson. 2007. Matrifocality and women's power on the Miskito Coast. *Ethnology* 46:133–49.

Herrmann, Esther, Joseph Call, Maria Victoria Herandez-Lloreda, Brain Hare, and Michael Tomasello. 2007. Humans have evolved specialized skills in social cognition: The cultural intelligence hypothesis. *Science* 317 (September 7): 1360–65.

Herrman, Helen. 1990. A survey of homeless mentally ill people in Melbourne, Australia. *Hospital and Community Psychiatry* 41:1291–92.

Herrnstein, Richard J., and Charles Murray. 1994. *The bell curve: Intelligence and class structure in American life*. New York: Free Press.

Hewes, Gordon W. 1961. Food transport and the origin of hominid bipedalism. *American Anthropologist* 63: 687–710.

Hewlett, Barry. 2004. Diverse contexts of human infancy. In MyAnthroLibrary, eds. C. R. Ember, M. Ember, and P. N. Peregrine. MyAnthroLibrary.com. Pearson.

Hewlett, Barry S., and L. L. Cavalli-Sforza. 1986. Cultural transmission among Aka Pygmies. *American Anthropologist* 88:922–34.

Hiatt, L. R. 1980. Polyandry in Sri Lanka: A test case for parental investment theory. *Man* 15:583–98.

Hickey, Gerald Cannon. 1964. *Village in Vietnam*. New Haven, CT: Yale University Press.

Hickson, Letitia. 1986. The social contexts of apology in dispute settlement: A cross-cultural study. *Ethnology* 25: 283–94.

Higley, Stephen Richard. 1995. *Privilege, power, and place: The geography of the American upper class*, 1–47. Lanham, MD: Rowman & Littlefield.

Hill, Carole. 2000. Strategic issues for rebuilding a theory and practice synthesis, *NAPA Bulletin* 18:1–16.

Hill, Donald R. 2005. Music of the African diaspora in the Americas. In *Encyclopedia of diasporas: Immigrant and refugee cultures around the world*, eds. M. Ember, C. R.

Ember, and I. Skoggard, 363–73. New York: Kluwer Academic/Plenum.

Hill, James N. 1970. *Broken K Pueblo: Prehistoric social organization in the American Southwest. Anthropological Papers of the University of Arizona*, Number 18. Tucson: University of Arizona Press.

Hill, Jane H. 1978. Apes and language. *Annual Review of Anthropology* 7:89–112.

Hill, Jane H. 2009. Do apes have language? In MyAnthroLibrary, eds. C. R. Ember, M. Ember, and P. N. Peregrine. MyAnthroLibrary.com. Pearson.

Hill, Jonathan D. 1996. Introduction: Ethnogenesis in the Americas. 1492–1992. In *Ethnogenesis in the Americas*, ed. J. D. Hill, 1–19. Iowa City: University of Iowa Press.

Hill, Kim, and A. Magdalena Hurtado. 2004. The ethics of anthropological research with remote tribal populations. In *Lost paradises and the ethics of research and publication*, eds. F. M. Salzano and A. M. Hurtado, 193–210. Oxford: Oxford University Press.

Hill, Kim, Hillard Kaplan, Kristen Hawkes, and A. Magdalena Hurtado. 1987. Foraging decisions among Aché hunter-gatherers: New data and implications for optimal foraging models. *Ethology and Sociobiology* 8:1–36.

Hill, Susan T. 2001. *Science and engineering doctorate awards: 2000*, NSF 02-305. National Science Foundation, Division of Science Resources Statistics. VA: Arlington.

Hillel, Daniel. 2000. *Salinity management for sustainable irrigation: Integrating science, environment, and economics.* Washington, DC. The World Bank.

Himmelgreen, David A., and Deborah L. Crooks. 2005. Nutritional anthropology and its application to nutritional issues and problems. In *Applied anthropology: Domains of application*, eds. Satish Kedia and John van Willigen, 149–88. Westport, CT: Praeger. Hinkes, Madeleine. 1993. Race, ethnicity, and forensic anthropology. *National Association for Applied Anthropology Bulletin* 13:48–54.

Hitchcock, Robert K. and Megan Beisele. 2000. Introduction. In *Hunters and gatherers in the modern world: Conflict, resistance, and self-determinations*, eds. P. P. Schweitzer, M. Biesele, and R. K. Hitchcock, 1–27. New York: Berghahn Books.

Hobsbawm, E. J. 1970. *Age of revolution.* New York: Praeger.

Hockett, C. F., and R. Ascher. 1964. The human revolution. *Current Anthropology* 5:135–68.

Hodgson, Jason, and Todd Driscoll. 2008. No evidence of a Neandertal contribution to modern human diversity. *Genome Biology* 9:206.1–206.7.

Hoebel, E. Adamson. 1960. *The Cheyennes: Indians of the Great Plains.* New York: Holt, Rinehart & Winston.

Hoebel, E. Adamson. 1968/1954. *The law of primitive man.* New York: Atheneum.

Hoffecker, John F., W. Roger Powers, and Ted Goebel. 1993. The colonization of Beringia and the peopling of the New World. *Science* 259 (January 1):46–53.

Hoffman, Lois Wladis. 1988. Cross-cultural differences in child-rearing goals. In *Parental behavior in diverse societies*, eds. R. A. LeVine, P. M. Miller, and M. M. West. San Francisco: Jossey-Bass.

Hoijer, Harry. 1964. Cultural implications of some Navaho linguistic categories. In *Language in culture and society*, ed. D. Hymes. New York: Harper & Row.

Holdaway, R. N., and C. Jacomb. 2000. Rapid extinction of the moas (*Aves: Dinornithiformes*): Model, test, and implications. *Science* 287 (March 24):2250–57.

Holden, Constance. 2000. Selective power of UV. *Science* 289 (September 1): 1461.

Hole, Frank. 1992. Origins of agriculture. In *The Cambridge encyclopedia of human evolution*, eds. S. Jones, R. Martin, and D. Pilbeam. New York: Cambridge University Press.

Hole, Frank. 1994. Environmental shock and urban origins. In *Chiefdoms and early states in the Near East*, eds. G. Stein and M. Rothman. Madison, WI: Prehistory Press.

Hole, Frank, Kent V. Flannery, and James A. Neely. 1969. *Prehistory and human ecology of the Deh Luran Plain. Memoirs of the Museum of Anthropology*, No. 1. Ann Arbor: University of Michigan.

Hollan, Douglas. 1992. Cross-cultural differences in the self. *Journal of Anthropological Research* 48:289–90.

Holloway, Marguerite. 1993. Sustaining the Amazon. *Scientific American* (July):91–99.

Holloway, Ralph L. 1974. The casts of fossil hominid brains. *Scientific American* (July):106–15.

Holmes, Janet. 2001. *An introduction to sociolinguistics.* 2nd ed. London: Longman.

Honigmann, John J. 1967. *Personality in culture.* New York: Harper & Row.

Hoogbergen, Wim. 1990. *The Boni Maroon Wars in Suriname.* Leiden: E. J. Brill.

Hooper, Judith. 2002. *Of moths and men: The untold story of science and the peppered moth.* New York: W. W. Norton.

Hopkins, K. 1980. Brother-sister marriage in Roman Egypt. *Comparative Studies in Society and History* 22:303–54.

Houston, Stephen D. 1988. The phonetic decipherment of Mayan glyphs. *Antiquity* 62:126–35.

Howard, Alan, and Jan Rensel. 2009. Rotuma: Interpreting a wedding. In MyAnthroLibrary, eds. C. R. Ember, M. Ember, and P. N. Peregrine. MyAnthroLibrary.com. Pearson.

Howell, F. Clark. 1966. Observations on the earlier phases of the European Lower Paleolithic. In *Recent studies in paleoanthropology. American anthropologist.* Special publication, April, 88–200.

Howell, Nancy. 1979. *Demography of the Dobe !Kung.* New York: Academic Press.

Howrigan, Gail A. 1988. Fertility, infant feeding, and change in Yucatan. *New Directions for Child Development* 40:37–50.

Hrdy, Sarah Blaffer. 1977. *The langurs of Abu: Female and male strategies of reproduction.* Cambridge, MA: Harvard University Press.

Hua, Cai. 2001. *A society without fathers or husbands: the Na of China*, trans. Asti Hustvedt. New York: Zone Books.

Huang, H. T. 2002. Hypolactasia and the Chinese diet. *Current Anthropology* 43: 809–19.

Human Development Report 1993. 1993. Published for the United Nations Development Programme. New York: Oxford University Press, 9–25.

Human Development Report 2001. 2001. Published for the United Nations Development Programme. New York: Oxford University Press, 9–25.

Humphrey, Caroline, and Stephen Hugh-Jones. 1992. Introduction: Barter, exchange and value. In *Barter, exchange and value*, eds. C. Humphrey and S. Hugh-Jones. New York: Cambridge University Press.

Hunt, Morton. 1974. *Sexual behavior in the 1970s.* Chicago: Playboy Press.

Hunt, Robert C. 2000. Labor productivity and agricultural development: Boserup revisited. *Human Ecology* 28: 251–77.

Hurtado, Ana M., Kristen Hawkes, Kim Hill, and Hillard Kaplan. 1985. Female subsistence strategies among the Aché hunter-gatherers of eastern Paraguay. *Human Ecology* 13:1–28.

Huss-Ashmore, Rebecca, and Francis E. Johnston. 1985. Bioanthropological research in developing countries. *Annual Review of Anthropology* 14:475–527.

Huxley, Thomas H. 1970. Man's place in nature. In *Evolution of man*, ed. L. Young. New York: Oxford University Press.

Hymes, Dell. 1974. *Foundations in sociolinguistics: An ethnographic approach.* Philadelphia: University of Pennsylvania Press.

Irons, William. 1979. Natural selection, adaptation, and human social behavior. In *Evolutionary Biology and Human Social Behavior*, eds. N. Chagnon and W. Irons. North Scituate, MA: Duxbury.

Irwin, Marc H., Gary N. Schafer, and Cynthia P. Feiden. 1974. Emic and unfamiliar category sorting of Mano farmers and U.S. undergraduates. *Journal of Cross-Cultural Psychology* 5:407–23.

Isaac, Glynn. 1971. The diet of early man: Aspects of archaeological evidence from Lower and Middle Pleistocene sites in Africa. *World Archaeology* 2:277–99.

Isaac, Glynn. 1984. The archaeology of human origins: Studies of the Lower Pleistocene in East Africa, 1971–1981. In *Advances in world archaeology*, eds. F. Wendorf and A. Close. Orlando, FL: Academic Press.

Isaac, Glynn, ed., assisted by Barbara Isaac. 1997. *Plio-Pleistocene archaeology.* Oxford: Clarendon Press.

Itkonen, T. I. 1951. The Lapps of Finland. *Southwestern Journal of Anthropology* 7:32–68.

Jablonski, Nina G., and George Chaplin. 2000. The evolution of human skin color. *Journal of Human Evolution* 39:57–106.

Jacobs, Sue-Ellen, and Christine Roberts. 1989. Sex, sexuality, gender and gender variance. In *Gender and anthropology*, ed. S. Morgen. Washington, DC: American Anthropological Association.

Jaeger, J., T. Thein, M. Benammi, Y. Chaimanee, A. N. Soe, T. Lwin, T. Tun, S. Wai, and S. Ducrocq. 1999. A new primate from the middle Eocene of Myanmar and the Asian early origins of anthropoids. *Science* 286 (October 15):528–30.

James, Allison. 2007. Giving voice to children's voices: Practices and problems, pitfalls and potentials. *American Anthropologist* 109:261–72.

James, William. 1902. *The varieties of religious experience: A study in human nature.* New York: Modern Library.

Jankowiak, William R. 2009. Urban Mongols: Ethnicity in communist China. In MyAnthroLibrary, eds. C. R. Ember, M. Ember, and P. N. Peregrine. MyAnthroLibrary.com. Pearson.

Jankowiak, William R., and Edward F. Fischer. 1992. A cross-cultural perspective on romantic love. *Ethnology* 31:149–55.

Jankowiak, William, M. Diane Nell, and Ann Buckmaster. 2002. Managing infidelity: A cross-cultural perspective. *Ethnology* 41:85–101.

Jankowiak, William, Monica Sudakov, and Benjamin C. Wilreker. 2005. Co-wife conflict and co-operation. *Ethnology* 44:81–98.

Janzen, Daniel H. 1973. Tropical agroecosystems. *Science* 182 (December 21):1212–19.

Jarvenpa, Robert. 2004. *Silot'ine:* An insurance perspective on Northern Dene kinship networks in recent history. *Journal of Anthropological Research* 60:153–78.

Jarvenpa, Robert, and Hetty Jo Brumbach. 2006. Chipewyan hunters: A task differentiation analysis. In *Circumpolar lives and livelihood: A comparative ethnoarchaeology of gender and subsistence*, eds. Robert Jarvenpa and Hetty Jo Brumbach, 54–78. Lincoln, Nebraska: University of Nebraska Press.

Jayaswal, Vidula. 2002. South Asian Upper Paleolithic. In *Encyclopedia of prehistory*, vol. 8: *South and Southwest Asia*, eds. P. N. Peregrine and M. Ember. New York: Kluwer Academic/Plenum.

Jelliffe, Derrick B., and E. F. Patrice Jelliffe. 1975. Human milk, nutrition, and the world resource crisis. *Science* 188 (May 9):557–61.

Jennings, J. D. 1968. *Prehistory of North America.* New York: McGraw-Hill.

Jensen, Arthur. 1969. How much can we boost IQ and scholastic achievement? *Harvard Educational Review* 29:1–123.

Joans, Barbara. 1997. Problems in Pocatello: A study in linguistic misunderstanding. In *Applying cultural anthropology: An introductory reader*, 3rd ed., eds. A. Podolefsky and P. J. Brown, 51–54. Mountain View: CA: Mayfield.

Johannes, R. E. 1981. *Words of the lagoon: Fishing and marine lore in the Palau District of Micronesia.* Berkeley: University of California Press.

Johanson, Donald C., and Maitland Edey. 1981. *Lucy: The beginnings of humankind.* New York: Simon & Schuster.

Johanson, Donald C., and Tim D. White. 1979. A systematic assessment of early African hominids. *Science* 203 (January 26):321–30.

Johnson, Allen, and Timothy Earle. 1987. *The evolution of human societies: From foraging group to agrarian state.* Stanford, CA: Stanford University Press.

Johnson, Amber Lynn. 2002. Cross-cultural analysis of pastoral adaptations and organizational states: A preliminary study. *Cross-Cultural Research* 36:151–80.

Johnson, Gregory A. 1977. Aspects of regional analysis in archaeology. *Annual Review of Anthropology* 6:479–508.

Johnson, Gregory A. 1987. The changing organization of Uruk administration on the Susiana Plain. In *Archaeology of western Iran*, ed. F. Hole. Washington, DC: Smithsonian Institution Press.

Johnson-Hanks, Jennifer. 2006. *Uncertain honor: Modern motherhood in an African crisis.* Chicago: University of Chicago Press.

Johnson, Jeffrey G., Patricia Cohen, Elizabeth M. Smailies, Stephanie Kasen, and Judith S. Brook. 2002. Television viewing and aggressive behavior during adolescence and adulthood. *Science* 295 (March 29):2468–70.

Johnston, David Cay. 1999. Gap between rich and poor found substantially wider. *New York Times*, National, September 5, p. 16.

Jolly, Alison. 1985. *The evolution of primate behavior.* 2nd ed. New York: Macmillan.

Jolly, Clifford. 1970. The seed-eaters: A new model of hominid differentiation based on a baboon analogy. *Man* 5:5–28.

Jones, Martin, and Xinyi Liu. 2009. Origins of agriculture in East Asia. *Science* 324 (May 8):730–31.

Jones, Nicholas Blurton, Kristen Hawkes, and James F. O'Connell. 1996. The global process and local ecology: How should we explain differences between the Hadza and the !Kung? In *Cultural diversity among twentieth-century foragers*, ed. S. Kent. Cambridge: Cambridge University Press.

Jones, Steve, Robert Martin, and David Pilbeam, eds. 1992. *The Cambridge encyclopedia of human evolution*. New York: Cambridge University Press.

Judge, W. James, and Jerry Dawson. 1972. Paleo-Indian settlement technology in New Mexico. *Science* 176 (June 16): 1210–16.

Jung, Carl G. 1938. *Psychology and religion*. New Haven, CT: Yale University Press.

Jungers, William L. 1988a. Relative joint size and hominoid locomotor adaptations with implications for the evolution of hominid bipedalism. *Journal of Human Evolution* 17:247–65.

Jungers, William L. 1988b. New estimates of body size in australopithecines. In *Evolutionary history of the "robust" australopithecines*, ed. F. Grine. New York: Aldine.

Jungers, William L., W. E. H. Harcourt-Smith, R. E. Wunderlich, M. W. Tocheri, S. G. Larson, T. Sutikna, Rokus Awe Due, and M. J. Morwood. 2009. The foot of *Homo floresiensis*. *Nature* 459 (May 7):81–84.

Kamin, Leon J. 1995. Behind the curve. *Scientific American* (February): 99–103.

Kang, Bong W. 2000. A reconsideration of population pressure and warfare: A protohistoric Korean case. *Current Anthropology* 41:873–81.

Kang, Gay Elizabeth. 1979. Exogamy and peace relations of social units: A cross-cultural test. *Ethnology* 18:85–99.

Kaplan, Hillard, and Kim Hill. 1985. Food sharing among Aché foragers: Tests of explanatory hypotheses. *Current Anthropology* 26:223–46.

Kaplan, Hillard, Kim Hill, and A. Magdalena Hurtado. 1990. Risk, foraging and food sharing among the Aché. In *Risk and uncertainty in tribal and peasant economies*, ed. E. Cashdan. Boulder, CO: Westview.

Kaplan, Hillard, Kim Hill, Jane Lancaster, and A. Magdalena Hurtado. 2000. A theory of human life history evolution, diet, intelligence, and longevity. *Evolutionary Anthropology* 9:156–84.

Kardiner, Abram, with Ralph Linton. 1946/1939. *The individual and his society*. New York: Golden Press. (Originally published 1939 by Columbia University Press.)

Kasarda, John D. 1971. Economic structure and fertility: A comparative analysis. *Demography* 8, no. 3 (August): 307–18.

Katzner, Kenneth. 2002. *Languages of the world*. Routledge.

Kay, Richard F. 2000a. *Parapithecidae*. In *Encyclopedia of human evolution and prehistory*, eds. I. Tattersall, E. Delson, and J. van Couvering. New York: Garland.

Kay, Richard F. 2000b. Teeth. In *Encyclopedia of human evolution and prehistory*, eds. I. Tattersall, E. Delson, and J. van Couvering. New York: Garland.

Kay, Richard F., C. Ross, and B. A. Williams. 1997. Anthropoid origins. *Science* 275 (February 7):797–804.

Kedia, Satish. 2008. Recent changes and trends in the practice of anthropology. *NAPA Bulletin* 29:14–28.

Kedia, Satish, and John van Willigen, eds. 2005. Applied anthropology: Domains of application. Wesport, CT: Praeger.

Keeley, Lawrence H. 1980. *Experimental determination of stone tool uses: A microwear analysis*. Chicago: University of Chicago Press.

Keeley, Lawrence H. 1991. Ethnographic models for late glacial hunter-gatherers. In *The late glacial in north-west Europe: Human adaptation and environmental change at the end of the Pleistocene*, eds. N. Barton, A. J. Roberts, and D. A. Roe. London: Council for British Archaeology. *CBA Research Report* 77:179–90.

Keenan, Elinor. 1989. Norm-makers, norm-breakers: Uses of speech by men and women in a Malagasy community. In *Explorations in the ethnography of speaking*, 2nd ed., eds. R. Bauman and J. Sherzer. New York: Cambridge University Press.

Kehoe, Alice B., and Dody H. Giletti. 1981. Women's preponderance in possession cults: The calcium-deficiency hypothesis extended. *American Anthropologist* 83:549–61.

Keller, Helen. 1974/1902. *The story of my life*. New York: Dell.

Kelley, Jay. 1992. The evolution of apes. In *The Cambridge encyclopedia of human evolution*, eds. S. Jones, R. Martin, and D. Pilbeam. New York: Cambridge University Press.

Kelly, Raymond C. 1974. Witchcraft and sexual relations: An exploration in the social and semantic implications of the structure of belief. Paper presented at the annual meeting of the American Anthropological Association, Mexico City.

Kelly, Raymond C. 1985. *The Nuer conquest: The structure and development of an expansionist system*. Ann Arbor: University of Michigan Press.

Kelly, Robert L. 1995. *The foraging spectrum: Diversity in hunter-gatherer lifeways*. Washington, DC: Smithsonian Institution Press.

Kent, Susan, ed. 1996. *Cultural diversity among twentieth-century foragers: An African perspective*. Cambridge: Cambridge University Press.

Kerr, Richard A. 1998. Sea-floor dust shows drought felled Akkadian empire. *Science* 299 (January 16):325–26.

Khosroshashi, Fatemeh. 1989. Penguins don't care, but women do: A social identity analysis of a Whorfian problem. *Language in Society* 18:505–25.

Kilbride, Philip L., and Janet C. Kilbride. 1990. Polygyny: A modern contradiction? In P. L. Kilbride and J. C. Kilbride, *Changing family life in East Africa: Women and children at risk*. University Park: Pennsylvania State University Press.

Kimbel, William H., T. D. White, and D. C. Johansen. 1984. Cranial morphology of *Australopithecus afarensis*: A comparative study based on composite reconstruction of the adult skull. *American Journal of Physical Anthropology* 64:337–88.

King, Barbara J. 1999a. Introduction. In *The origins of language*, ed. B. J. King, 3–19. Santa Fe, NM: School of American Research Press.

King, Barbara. 1999b. *The origins of language: What nonhuman primates can tell us*. Santa Fe: School of American Research Press.

King, J. C. H. 1986. Tradition in Native American art. In *The arts of the North American Indian*, ed. E. L. Wade. New York: Hudson Hills Press.

King, Marie-Claire, and Arno Motulsky. 2002. Mapping human history. *Science* 298 (December 20): 2,342–43.

King, Seth S. 1979. Some farm machinery seems less than human. *New York Times* April 8, p. E9.

Kingston, John D., Bruno D. Marino, and Andrew Hill. 1994. Isotopic evidence for Neogene hominid paleoenvironments in the Kenya Rift Valley. *Science* 264 (May 13):955–59.

Kitchen, Andrew, Michael Miyamoto, and Connie Mulligan. 2008. A three-stage colonization model for the peopling of the Americas. *PLoS ONE* 3(2):e1596.

Klass, Morton. 2009. Is there "caste" outside of India? In MyAnthroLibrary, eds. C. R. Ember, M. Ember, and P. N. Peregrine. MyAnthroLibrary.com. Pearson.

Klein, Richard G. 1974. Ice-Age hunters of the Ukraine. *Scientific American* (June):96–105.

Klein, Richard G. 1977. The ecology of early man in Southern Africa. *Science* 197 (July 8):115–26.

Klein, Richard G. 1983. The Stone Age prehistory of Southern Africa. *Annual Review of Anthropology* 12:25–48.

Klein, Richard G. 1987. Reconstructing how early people exploited animals: Problems and prospects. In *The evolution of human hunting*, eds. M. Nitecki and D. Nitecki. New York: Plenum.

Klein, Richard G. 1989. *The human career: Human biological and cultural origins*. Chicago: University of Chicago Press.

Klein, Richard G. 1994. Southern Africa before the ice age. In *Integrative paths to the past*, eds. R. Corruccini and R. Ciochon. Upper Saddle River, NJ: Prentice Hall.

Klein, Richard G. 2003. Whither the Neanderthals. *Science* 299 (March 7):1525–28.

Klein, Richard, and Blake Edgar. 2002. *The dawn of human culture*. New York: John Wiley and Sons.

Kleinberg, Jill. 1994. Practical implications of organizational culture where Americans and Japanese work together. In *Practicing anthropology in corporate America*, ed. A. T. Jordan. Arlington, VA: American Anthropological Association.

Kleinman, Arthur. 1988. *Rethinking psychiatry: From cultural category to personal experience*. New York: Macmillan.

Kleinman, Arthur, Veena Das, and Margaret Lock, eds. 1997. *Social suffering*. Berkeley: University of California Press.

Klima, Bohuslav. 1962. The first ground-plan of an Upper Paleolithic loess settlement in Middle Europe and its meaning. In *Courses toward urban life*, eds. R. Braidwood and G. Willey. Chicago: Aldine.

Klineberg, Otto. 1935. *Negro intelligence and selective migration*. New York: Columbia University Press.

Klineberg, Otto, ed. 1944. *Characteristics of the American Negro*. New York: Harper & Brothers.

Klineberg, Otto. 1979. Foreword. In M. H. Segall, *Cross-cultural psychology*. Monterey, CA: Brooks/Cole.

Kluckhohn, Clyde. 1948. As an anthropologist views it. In *Sex habits of American men*, ed. A. Deutsch. Upper Saddle River, NJ: Prentice Hall.

Kluckhohn, Clyde. 1965. Recurrent themes in myths and mythmaking. In *The study of folklore*, ed. A. Dundes. Upper Saddle River, NJ: Prentice Hall.

Knauft, Bruce M. 1978. Cargo cults and relational separation. *Behavior Science Research* 13:185–240.

Knecht, Peter. 2003. Aspects of shamanism: An introduction. In *Shamans in Asia*, eds. C. Chilson and P. Knecht, 1–30. London: RoutledgeCurzon.

Koch, Klaus-Friedrich, Soraya Altorki, Andrew Arno, and Letitia Hickson. 1977. Ritual reconciliation and the obviation of grievances: A comparative study in the ethnography of law. *Ethnology* 16:269–84.

Kolbert, Elizabeth. 2005. Last words. *The New Yorker* (June 6):46–59.

Komar, Debra A., and Jane E. Buikstra. 2008. *Forensic anthropology: Contemporary theory and practice*. New York: Oxford University Press.

Konner, Melvin, and Carol Worthman. 1980. Nursing frequency, gonadal function, and birth spacing among !Kung hunter-gatherers. *Science* 267 (February 15):788–91.

Korbin, Jill E. 1981. Introduction. In *Child abuse and neglect*, ed. J. E. Korbin. Berkeley: University of California Press.

Korotayev, Andrey and Dmitri Bondarenko. 2000. Polygyny and democracy: A cross-cultural comparison. *Cross-Cultural Research* 34:190–208.

Kottak, Conrad Phillip. 1996. The media, development, and social change. In *Transforming societies, transforming anthropology*, ed. E. F. Moran. Ann Arbor: University of Michigan Press.

Kottak, Conrad P. 1999. The new ecological anthropology. *Current Anthropology* 101: 23–35.

Kracke, Waud H. 1979. *Force and persuasion: Leadership in an Amazonian society*. Chicago: University of Chicago Press.

Krahn, H., T. F. Hartnagel, and J. W. Gartrell. 1986. Income inequality and homicide rates: Cross-national data and criminological theories. *Criminology* 24:269–95.

Kramer, Andrew. 2009. The natural history and evolutionary fate of *Homo erectus*. In MyAnthroLibrary, eds. C. R. Ember, M. Ember, and P. N. Peregrine. MyAnthroLibrary.com. Pearson.

Kramer, Samuel Noel. 1963. *The Sumerians: Their history, culture, and character*. Chicago: University of Chicago Press.

Krause, Johannes, Carles Lalueza-Fox, Ludovic Orlando, Wolfgang Enard, Richard E. Green, Hernán A. Burbano, Jean-Jacques Hublin, Catherine Hänni, Javier Fortea, Marco de la Rasilla, Jaume Bertranpetit, Antonio Rosas, and Svante Pääbo. 2007. The derived FOXP2 variant of modern humans was shared with Neandertals. *Current Biology* 17(21):1908–12.

Krebs, J. R., and N. B. Davies, eds. 1984. *Behavioural ecology: An evolutionary approach*. 2nd ed. Sunderland, MA: Sinauer.

Krebs, J. R., and N. B. Davies. 1987. *An introduction to behavioural ecology*. 2nd ed. Sunderland, MA: Sinauer.

Krings, Matthias, A. Stone, R. W. Schmitz, H. Krainitzki, M. Stoneking, and S. Paabo. 1997. Neandertal DNA sequences and the origin of modern humans. *Cell* 90:19–30.

Krippner, Stanley. 1987. Dreams and shamanism. In *Shamanism*, comp. S. Nicholson, 125–32. Wheaton, IL: Theosophical Publishing House.

Kristof, Nicholas D. 1997. Japan's invisible minority: Burakumin. *Britannica Online*, December.

Kristof, Nicholas D. 1995. Japan's invisible minority: Better off than in past, but still outcasts. *New York Times*, International, November 30, A18.

Kroeber, Theodora. 1967. *Ishi in two worlds*. Berkeley: University of California Press.

Kuehn, Steven. 1998. New evidence for Late Paleoindian–early Archaic subsistence behavior in the western Great Lakes. *American Antiquity* 63:457–76.

Kulick, Don. 1992. *Language shift and cultural reproduction*. Cambridge: Cambridge University Press.

Kushner, Gilbert. 1991. Applied anthropology. In *Career explorations in human services*, eds. W. G. Emener and M. Darrow. Springfield, IL: Charles C Thomas.

Lakoff, Robin. 1973. Language and woman's place. *Language in Society* 2:45–80.

Lakoff, Robin. 1990. Why can't a woman be less like a man? In *Talking power*, ed. R. Lakoff. New York: Basic Books.

Lalueza-Fox, Carles, Holger Römpler, David Caramelli, Claudia Stäubert, Giulio Catalano, David Hughes, Nadin Rohland, Elena Pilli, Laura Longo, Silvana Condemi, Marco de la Rasilla, Javier Fortea, Antonio Rosas, Mark Stoneking, Torsten Schöneberg, Jaume Bertranpetit, and Michael

Hofreiter. 2007. A Melanocortin 1 Receptor Allele suggests varying pigmentation among Neanderthals. *Science* 318 (November 30):1453–55.

Lambert, Helen. 2001. Not talking about sex in India: Indirection and the communication of bodily intention. In *An anthropology of indirect communication*, eds. J. Hendry and C. W. Watson, 51–67. London: Routledge.

Lambert, Patricia M., Banks L. Leonard, Brian R. Billman, Richard A. Marlar, Margaret E. Newman, and Karl J. Reinhard. 2000. Response to critique of the claim of cannibalism at Cowboy Wash. *American Antiquity* 65(2):397–406.

Lambert, William W., Leigh Minturn Triandis, and Margery Wolf. 1959. Some correlates of beliefs in the malevolence and benevolence of supernatural beings: A cross-societal study. *Journal of Abnormal and Social Psychology* 58: 162–69.

Lamphere, Louise. 2006. Foreward: Taking stock—The transformation of feminist theorizing in anthropology. In *Feminist anthropology: Past, present, and future*, eds. Pamela L. Geller and Miranda K. Stockett, ix–xvi. Philadelphia: University of Pennsylvania Press.

Lancy, David F. 2007. Accounting for variability in mother-child play. *American Anthropologist* 109:273–84.

Lancy, David F. 2008. *The anthropology of childhood: Cherubs, chattel, changelings*. Cambridge: Cambridge University Press.

Landauer, Thomas K. 1973. Infantile vaccination and the secular trend in stature. *Ethos* 1: 499–503.

Landauer, Thomas K., and John W. M. Whiting. 1964. Infantile stimulation and adult stature of human males. *American Anthropologist* 66:1007–28.

Landauer, Thomas K., and John W. M. Whiting. 1981. Correlates and consequences of stress in infancy. In *Handbook of cross-cultural human development*. eds. R. H. Munroe, R. Munroe, and B. Whiting. New York: Garland.

Landecker, Hannah. 2000. Immortality, in vitro: A history of the HeLa Cell Line. In *Biotechnology and culture: Bodies, anxieties, ethics*, ed. Paul Brodwin, 53–74. Bloomington: Indiana University Press.

Lang, Sabine. 1999. Lesbians, men-women and two-spirits: Homosexuality and gender in Native American cultures. In *Female desires: Same-sex relations and transgender practices across cultures*, eds. Evelyn Blackwood and Saskia E. Weiringa, 91–116. New York: Columbia University Press.

Langness, Lewis L. 1974. *The study of culture*. San Francisco: Chandler and Sharp.

Lareau, Annette. 2003. *Unequal childhoods: Class, race, and family life*. Berkeley, CA: University of California Press.

Larsen, Clark Spenser. 2009. Bare bones anthropology: The bioarchaeology of human remains. In MyAnthroLibrary, eds. C. R. Ember, M. Ember, and P. N. Peregrine. MyAnthroLibrary.com. Pearson.

Larsen, Clark Spenser. 1997. *Bioarchaeology: Interpreting behavior from the human skeleton*. Cambridge, Cambridge University Press.

Larson, C. L., J. Aronoff, I. C. Sarinopoulos, and D. C. Zhu. 2009. Recognizing threat: A simple geometric shape activates neural circuitry for threat detection. *Journal of Cognitive Neuroscience* 21:1523–35.

Larson, C. L., J. Aronoff, and J. Stearns. 2007. The shape of threat: Simple geometric forms evoke rapid and sustained capture of attention. *Emotion* 7:526–34.

Lassiter, Luke. 2008. Moving past public anthropology and doing collaborative research. *NAPA Bulletin* 29:70–86.

Lassiter, Luke Eric, Hurley Goodall, Elizabeth Campbell, and Michelle Natasya Johnson, eds., 2004. *The other side of Middletown: Exploring Muncie's African American community*. Walnut Creek, CA: AltaMira Press.

Lawless, Robert, Vinson H. Sutlive, Jr., and Mario D. Zamora, eds. 1983. *Fieldwork: The human experience*. New York: Gordon and Breach.

Layton, Robert. 1992. *Australian rock art: A new synthesis*. Cambridge: Cambridge University Press.

Le, Huynh-Nhu. 2000. Never leave your little one alone: Raising an Ifaluk child. In *A world of babies: Imagined child care guides for seven societies*, eds. Judy DeLoache and Alma Gottlieb, 199–220. Cambridge: Cambridge University Press.

Leach, Jerry W. 1983. Introduction. In *The kula*, eds. J. W. Leach and E. Leach. Cambridge: Cambridge University Press.

Leacock, Eleanor. 1954. The Montagnais 'hunting territory' and the fur trade. *American Anthropological Association Memoir* 78:1–59.

Leacock, Eleanor, and Richard Lee. 1982. Introduction. In *Politics and history in band societies*, eds. E. Leacock and R. Lee. Cambridge: Cambridge University Press.

Leakey, Louis S. B. 1960. Finding the world's earliest man. *National Geographic* (September): 420–35.

Leakey, Louis S. B. 1965. *Olduvai Gorge, 1951–1961*, vol. I: *A preliminary report on the geology and fauna*. Cambridge: Cambridge University Press.

Leakey, Maeve, C. S. Feibel, I. McDougall, and A. Walker. 1995. New four-million-year-old hominid species from Kanapoi and Allia Bay, Kenya. *Nature* 376 (August 17):565–71.

Leakey, Maeve, Fred Spoor, Frank Brown, Patrick Gathogo, Christopher Kiarie, Louise Leakey, Ian McDougall. 2001. New Hominin genus from Eastern Africa shows diverse middle Pliocene lineages. *Nature* 410 (March 22):433–51.

Leakey, Mary. 1971. *Olduvai Gorge: Excavations in Beds I and II*. Cambridge: Cambridge University Press.

Leakey, Mary. 1979. *Olduvai Gorge: My search for early man*. London: Collins.

Lederman, Rena. 1990. Big men, large and small? Towards a comparative perspective. *Ethnology* 29:3–15.

Lee, Phyllis C. 1983. Home range, territory and intergroup encounters. In *Primate social relationship: An integrated approach*. ed. R. A. Hinde. Sunderland, MA: Sinauer.

Lee, Richard B. 1968. What hunters do for a living, or, how to make out on scarce resources. In *Man the hunter*, eds. R. B. Lee and I. DeVore. Chicago: Aldine.

Lee, Richard B. 1972. Population growth and the beginnings of sedentary life among the !Kung bushmen. In *Population growth*, ed. B. Spooner. Cambridge, MA: MIT Press.

Lee, Richard B. 1979. *The !Kung San: Men, women, and work in a foraging society*. Cambridge: Cambridge University Press.

Lees, Susan H., and Daniel G. Bates. 1974. The origins of specialized nomadic pastoralism: A systemic model. *American Antiquity* 39:187–93.

Leibowitz, Lila. 1978. *Females, males, families: A biosocial approach*. North Scituate, MA: Duxbury.

Leis, Nancy B. 1974. Women in groups: Ijaw women's associations. In *Woman, culture, and society*, eds. M. Z. Rosaldo and L. Lamphere. Stanford, CA: Stanford University Press.

Lenski, Gerhard. 1984/1966. *Power and privilege: A theory of social stratification*. Chapel Hill: University of North Carolina Press.

Moran, Emilio F., ed. 1996. *Transforming societies, transforming anthropology*. Ann Arbor: University of Michigan Press.

Moran, Emilio F. 2000. *Human adaptability: An introduction to ecological anthropology*. 2nd ed. Boulder, CO: Westview.

Morell, Virginia. 1995. The Earliest Art Becomes Older—And More Common." *Science*, 267 (March 31): 1908–09.

Morgan, Lewis H. 1964/1877. *Ancient society*. Cambridge, MA: Harvard University Press.

Morris, John. 1938. *Living with Lepchas: A book about the Sikkim Himalayas*. London: Heinemann.

Morrison, Kathleen D., and Laura L. Junker. 2002. *Forager-traders in South and Southeast Asia: Long-term histories*. Cambridge: Cambridge University Press.

Morwood, M. J., R. Soejono, R. Roberts, T. Sutikna, C. Turney, K. Westaway, W. Rink, J. Zhao, G. van den Bergh, R. Due, D. Hobbs, M. Moore, M. Bird, and L. Fifield. 2004. Archaeology and age of a new hominin from Flores in Eastern Indonesia. *Nature* 431 (October 28): 1087–91.

Moser, Stephanie. 1998. *Ancestral images: The iconography of human origins*. Ithaca, NY: Cornell University Press.

Motulsky, Arno. 1971. Metabolic polymorphisms and the role of infectious diseases in human evolution. In *Human populations, genetic variation, and evolution*, ed. L. N. Morris. San Francisco: Chandler.

Moyá-solá, Salvador, et al. 2004. *Pierolapithecus catalaunicus*. A new middle Miocene great ape from Spain. *Science* 306 (November 19): 1339–44.

Mukerjee, Madhusree. 1996. Field notes: Interview with a parrot. *Scientific American* (April): 28.

Mukhopadhyay, Carol C., and Patricia J. Higgins. 1988. Anthropological studies of women's status revisited: 1977–1987. *Annual Review of Anthropology* 17:461–95.

Muller, Edward N. 1997. Economic determinants of democracy. In *Inequality, democracy, and economic development*, ed. M. Midlarsky, 133–55. Cambridge: Cambridge University Press.

Müller-Haye, B. 1984. Guinea pig or cuy. In *Evolution of domesticated animals*, ed. I. Mason. New York: Longman.

Munroe, Robert L., Robert Hulefeld, James M. Rodgers, Damon L. Tomeo, Steven K. Yamazaki. 2000. Aggression among children in four cultures. *Cross-Cultural Research* 34:3–25.

Munroe, Robert L., and Ruth H. Munroe. 1969. A cross-cultural study of sex, gender, and social structure. *Ethnology* 8:206–11.

Munroe, Robert L., Ruth H. Munroe, and John W. M. Whiting. 1981. Male sex-role resolutions. In *Handbook of cross-cultural human development*, eds. R. H. Munroe, R. L. Munroe, and B. B. Whiting. New York: Garland.

Munroe, Robert L., Ruth H. Munroe, and Stephen Winters. 1996. Cross-cultural correlates of the consonant-vowel (cv) syllable. *Cross-Cultural Research* 30:60–83.

Munroe, Ruth H., and Robert L. Munroe. 1980. Infant experience and childhood affect among the Logoli: A longitudinal study. *Ethos* 8:295–315.

Munroe, Ruth H., Robert L. Munroe, and Harold S. Shimmin. 1984. Children's work in four cultures: Determinants and consequences. *American Anthropologist* 86:369–79.

Murdock, George P. 1949. *Social structure*. New York: Macmillan.

Murdock, George P. 1957. World ethnographic sample. *American Anthropologist* 59:664–87.

Murdock, George P. 1967. Ethnographic atlas: A summary. *Ethnology* 6:109–236.

Murdock, George P. 1980. *Theories of illness: A world survey*. Pittsburgh: University of Pittsburgh Press.

Murdock, George P., and Caterina Provost. 1973. Factors in the division of labor by sex: A cross-cultural analysis. *Ethnology* 12:203–25.

Murdock, George P., and Douglas R. White. 1969. Standard cross-cultural sample. *Ethnology* 8:329–69.

Murphy, Jane. 1981. Abnormal behavior in traditional societies: Labels, explanations, and social reactions. In *Handbook of cross-cultural human development*, eds. R. H. Munroe, R. L. Munroe, and B. B. Whiting. New York: Garland.

Murphy, Robert F. 1960. *Headhunter's heritage: Social and economic change among the Mundurucú*. Berkeley: University of California Press.

Murphy, Robert F., and Julian H. Steward. 1956. Tappers and trappers: Parallel process in acculturation. *Economic Development and Cultural Change* 4 (July): 335–55.

Murray, Gerald F. 1997. The domestication of wood in Haiti: A case study in applied evolution. In *Applying cultural anthropology: An introductory reader*, eds. A. Podolefsky and P. J. Brown. Mountain View CA: Mayfield.

Murray, G. F., and M. E. Bannister. 2004. Peasants, agroforesters, and anthropologists: A 20-year venture in income-generating trees and hedgerows in Haiti. *Agroforestry Systems* 61:383–97.

Musgrave, Jonathan H., R. A. H. Neave, and A. J. N. W. Prag. 1984. The skull from Tomb II at Vergina: King Philip II of Macedon. *Journal of Hellenistic Studies* 104:60–78.

Myers, Fred R. 1988. Critical trends in the study of hunter-gatherers. *Annual Review of Anthropology* 17:261–82.

Nadel, S. F. 1935. Nupe state and community. *Africa* 8:257–303.

Nadel, S. F. 1942. *A black Byzantium: The kingdom of Nupe in Nigeria*. London: Oxford University Press.

Nag, Moni, Benjamin N. F. White, and R. Creighton Peet. 1978. An anthropological approach to the study of the economic value of children in Java and Nepal. *Current Anthropology* 19:293–301.

Nagata, Judith. 2001. Beyond theology: Toward an anthropology of "fundamentalism." *American Anthropologist* 103:481–98.

Nagel, Ernest. 1961. *The structure of science: Problems in the logic of scientific explanation*. New York: Harcourt, Brace & World.

Napier, J. R. 1970. Paleoecology and catarrhine evolution. In *Old World monkeys: Evolution, systematics, and behavior*. eds. J. R. Napier and P. H. Napier. New York: Academic Press.

Napier, J. R., and P. H. Napier. 1967. *A handbook of living primates*. New York: Academic Press.

Naroll, Raoul. 1961. Two solutions for Galton's problem. In *Readings in cross-cultural methodology*, ed. Frank Moore, 221–45. New Haven, CT: HRAF Press.

Naroll, Raoul. 1967. Imperial cycles and world order. *Peace Research Society: Papers* 7:83–101.

Naroll, Raoul. 1983. *The moral order: An introduction to the human situation*. Beverly Hills, CA: Sage.

Nash, Manning. 1989. *The cauldron of ethnicity in the modern world*. Chicago: University of Chicago Press.

National Coalition for the Homeless. 2008 (June). How many people experience homelessness? NCH Fact Sheet #2.

http://www.nationalhomeless.org/factsheets/How_Many.
html (accessed September 3, 2009).

National Science Foundation, Division of Science Resources Statistics. 2008. *Science and engineering doctorate awards: 2006.* Detailed Statistical Tables NSF 09-311. Arlington, VA. Available at http://www.nsf.gov/statistics/nsf09311/ (accessed August 14, 2009).

Neel, James V., Willard R. Centerwall, Napoleon A. Chagnon, and Helen L. Casey. 1970. Notes on the effect of measles and measles vaccine in a virgin-soil population of South American Indians. *American Journal of Epidemiology* 91:418–29.

Nelson, Nici. 1995/1964. The Kiambu group: A successful women's ROSCA in Mathare Valley, Nairobi (1971 to 1990). In *Money-go-rounds: The importance of rotating savings and credit associations for women*, eds. S. Ardener and S. Burman, 49–69. Oxford: Berg.

Nepstead, Daniel C., Claudia M. Stickler, Britaldo Soares-Filho, and Frank Merry. 2008. Interactions among Amazon land use, forests, and climate: Prospects for a near-term forest tipping point. *Philosophical Transactions of the Royal Society* B, 363:1737–46.

Nerlove, Sara B. 1974. Women's workload and infant feeding practices: A relationship with demographic implications. *Ethnology* 13:207–14.

Neumann, Katharina. 2003. New Guinea: A cradle of agriculture. *Science* 301 (July 11):180–81.

Nevins, Allan. 1927. *The American states during and after the revolution.* New York: Macmillan.

Newbury, Catherine. 1988. *The cohesion of oppression: Clientship and ethnicity in Rwanda, 1860–1960.* New York: Columbia University.

Newman, Katherine S. 1983. *Law and economic organization: A Comparative study of preindustrial societies.* Cambridge, MA: Cambridge University Press.

Newman, K. S. 1988. *Falling from grace: The experience of downward mobility in the American middle class.* New York: The Free Press.

Newman, K. S. 1993. *Declining fortunes: The withering of the American dream.* New York: Basic Books.

Newsweek. 1973. The first dentist. *Newsweek*, March 5, 73.

Nicholls, David, ed. 1998. *The Cambridge history of American music.* Cambridge. Cambridge University Press.

Nicolson, Nancy A. 1987. Infants, mothers, and other females. In *Primate Societies*, eds. B. Smuts et al. Chicago: University of Chicago Press.

Niehoff, Arthur H. 1966. *A casebook of social change.* Chicago: Aldine.

Nimkoff, M. F., and Russell Middleton. 1960. Types of family and types of economy. *American Journal of Sociology* 66:215–25.

Nisbett, Richard E. 2009. Education is all in your mind. *New York Times.* Sunday Opinion, February 8, p. 12.

Nishida, Toshisada. 1992. Introduction to the conservation symposium. In Naosuke Itoigawa, Yukimaru Sugiyama, Gene P. Sackett, and Roger K. R. Thompson, *Topics in primatology*, vol. 2. Tokyo: University of Tokyo Press.

Nissen, Henry W. 1958. Axes of behavioral comparison. In *Behavior and evolution*, eds. A. Roe and G. G. Simpson. New Haven, CT: Yale University Press.

Nolan, Riall W. 2003. Anthropology in practice: Building a career outside the academy. Boulder: Lynne Rienner Publishers.

Noll, Richard. 1987. The presence of spirits in magic and madness. In *Shamanism*, comp. S. Nicholson, 47–61. Wheaton, IL: Theosophical Publishing House.

Norenzayan, Ara, and Azim F. Shariff. 2008. The origin and evolution of religious prosociality. *Science* 322 (October 3): 58–62.

Normile, Dennis. 1998. Habitat seen playing larger role in shaping behavior. *Science* 279 (March 6): 1454–55.

Noss, Andrew J., and Barry S. Hewlett. 2001. The contexts of female hunting in central Africa. *American Anthropologist* 103:1024–40.

Nussbaum, Martha C. 1995. Introduction. In M. C. Nussbaum and J. Glover, *Women, culture, and development: A study of human capabilities.* Oxford: Clarendon Press.

Oakley, Kenneth. 1964. On man's use of fire, with comments on tool-making and hunting. In *Social life of early man*, ed. S. L. Washburn. Chicago: Aldine.

Oboler, Regina Smith. 1980. Is the female husband a man? Woman/woman marriage among the Nandi of Kenya. *Ethnology* 19:69–88.

Oboler, Regina Smith. 2009. Nandi: From cattle-keepers to cash-crop farmers. In MyAnthroLibrary, eds. C. R. Ember, M. Ember, and P. N. Peregrine. MyAnthroLibrary.com. Pearson.

O'Brian, Robin. 1999. Who weaves and why? Weaving, loom complexity, and trade. *Cross-Cultural Research* 33:30–42.

O'Brien, Denise. 1977. Female husbands in southern Bantu societies. In *Sexual stratification*, ed. A. Schlegel. New York: Columbia University Press.

Oerlemans, J. 2005. Extracting a climate signal from 169 glacial records. *Science* 38 (April 28):675–77.

Ogburn, William F. 1922. *Social change.* New York: Huebsch.

Okamura, Jonathan Y. 1983. Filipino hometown associations in Hawaii. *Ethnology* 22:341–53.

Oliver, Douglas L. 1955. *A Solomon Island society.* Cambridge, MA: Harvard University Press.

Oliver, Douglas L. 1974. *Ancient Tahitian society*, vol. 1: *Ethnography.* Honolulu: University of Hawaii Press.

Olsen, Steve. 2002. Seeking the signs of selection. *Science* 298 (November 15): 1324–25.

Olszewski, Deborah I. 1991. Social complexity in the Natufian? Assessing the relationship of ideas and data. In *Perspectives on the past*, ed. G. Clark. Philadelphia: University of Pennsylvania Press.

Orlove, Benjamin, and Stephen Brush. 1996. Anthropology and the conservation of biodiversity. *Annual Review of Anthropology* 25:329–52.

Ortiz de Montellano, B. R., and C. H. Browner. 1985. Chemical bases for medicinal plant use in Oaxaca, Mexico. *Journal of Ethnopharmacology* 13:57–88.

Ortner, Sherry B. 1984. Theory in anthropology since the sixties. *Comparative Studies in Society and History* 26:126–66.

Osti, Roberto. 1994. The eloquent bones of Abu Hureyra. *Scientific American* (August):1.

Otterbein, Keith. 1968. Internal war: A cross-cultural study. *American Anthropologist* 70:277–89.

Otterbein, Keith. 1970. *The evolution of war.* New Haven, CT: HRAF Press.

Otterbein, Keith. 1986. *The ultimate coercive sanction: A cross-cultural study of capital punishment.* New Haven, CT: HRAF Press.

Otterbein, Keith, and Charlotte Swanson Otterbein. 1965. An eye for an eye, a tooth for a tooth: A cross-cultural study of feuding. *American Anthropologist* 67:1470–82.

Stockett, Miranda K., and Pamela L. Geller. 2006. Introduction. In *Feminist anthropology: Past, present, and future*, eds. Pamela L. Geller and Miranda K. Stockett, 1–19. Philadelphia: University of Pennsylvania Press.

Stodder, James. 1995. The evolution of complexity in primitive exchange. *Journal of Comparative Economics* 20:205.

Stogdill, Ralph M. 1974. *Handbook of leadership: A survey of theory and research*. New York: Macmillan.

Stokstad, Erik. 2008. Privatization prevents collapse of fish stocks, global analysis shows. *Science* 321:1619.

Stoneking, Mark. 1997. Recent African origin of human mitochondrial DNA. In *Progress in population genetics and human evolution*, eds. P. Donnelly and S. Tavaré, 1–13. New York: Springer.

Straus, Murray A. 1991. Physical violence in American families: Incidence rates, causes, and trends. In *Abused and battered*, eds. D. D. Knudsen and J. L. Miller. New York: Aldine.

Straus, Murray A. 1995. Trends in cultural norms and rates of partner violence: An update to 1992. In *Understanding partner violence: Prevalence, causes, consequences, and solutions*, eds. S. M. Stith and M. A. Straus, 30–33. Minneapolis, MN: National Council on Family Relations. http://pubpages.unh.edu/~mas2/v56.pdf/ (accessed August 2002).

Straus, Murray A. 2001. Physical aggression in the family: Prevalence rates, links to non-family violence, and implications for primary prevention of societal violence. In *Prevention and control of aggression and the impact on its victims*, ed. M. Martinez, 181–200. New York: Kluwer Academic/Plenum.

Straus, Murray A. 2009. Prevalence and social causes of corporal punishment by parents in world perspective. Paper presented at the annual meeting of the Society for Cross-Cultural Research, Las Vegas, Nevada, February 20, 2009.

Straus, Murray A., and Carrie L. Yodanis. 1996. Corporal punishment in adolescence and physical assaults on spouses in later life: What accounts for the link? *Journal of Marriage and the Family* 58:825–41.

Straus, Murray A., and Glenda Kaufman Kantor. 1994 (July). Change in Spouse assault rates from 1975 to 1992: A comparison of three national surveys in the United States. Paper presented at the 13th World Congress of Sociology, Bielefeld, Germany. http://pubpages.unh.edu/~mas2/v55.pdf/ (accessed August 2002).

Straus, Murray A., and Glenda Kaufman Kantor. 1995. Trends in physical abuse by parents from 1975 to 1992: A comparison of three national surveys. Paper presented at the annual meeting of the American Society of Criminology, Boston, November 18. http://pubpages.unh.edu/~mas2/V57.pdf/ (accessed August 2002).

Strauss, Lawrence Guy. 1982. Comment on White. *Current Anthropology* 23:185–86.

Strauss, Lawrence Guy. 1989. On early hominid use of fire. *Current Anthropology* 30:488–91.

Stringer, Christopher B. 1985. Evolution of a species. *Geographical Magazine* 57:601–07.

Stringer, Christopher B. 2000. Neandertals. In *Encyclopedia of human evolution and prehistory*, eds. I. Tattersall, E. Delson, and J. van Couvering. New York: Garland.

Stringer, Christopher. B. 2003. Out of Ethiopia. *Nature* 423 (June 12):692–95.

Stringer, Christopher B, and Clive Gamble. 1993. *In search of the Neandertals*. New York: Thames and Hudson.

Stringer, Christopher B., J. J. Hublin, and B. Vandermeersch. 1984. The origin of anatomically modern humans in western Europe. In *The origins of modern humans*, eds. F. H. Smith and F. Spencer. New York: Alan R. Liss.

Suárez-Orozco, Marcelo. 1992. A grammar of terror: Psycho-cultural responses to state terrorism in dirty war and post-dirty war Argentina. In *The paths to domination, resistance, and terror*, eds. C. Nordstrom and J. Martin, 219–59. Berkeley, CA: University of California Press.

Super, Charles M., and Sara Harkness. 1997. The cultural structuring of child development. In *Handbook of cross-cultural psychology*, vol. 2, 2nd ed., eds. J. W. Berry, P. R. Dasen, and T. S. Saraswathi, 1–39. Boston: Allyn & Bacon.

Susman, Randall L., ed. 1984. *The pygmy chimpanzee: Evolutionary biology and behavior*. New York: Plenum.

Susman, Randall L. 1994. Fossil evidence for early hominid tool use. *Science* 265(September 9):1570–73.

Susman, Randall L., Jack T. Stern, Jr., and William L. Jungers. 1985. Locomotor adaptations in the Hadar hominids. In *Ancestors: The hard evidence*, ed. E. Delson, 184–92. New York: Alan R. Liss.

Sussman, Robert W. 1972. Child transport, family size, and the increase in human population size during the Neolithic. *Current Anthropology* 13:258–67.

Sussman, Robert W. 1991. Primate origins and the evolution of angiosperms. *American Journal of Primatology* 23:209–23.

Sussman, Robert W., and W. G. Kinzey. 1984. The ecological role of the callitrichidae: A review. *American Journal of Physical Anthropology* 64:419–49.

Sussman, Robert W., and Peter H. Raven. 1978. Pollination by lemurs and marsupials: An archaic coevolutionary system. *Science* 200 (May 19):734–35.

Swanson, Guy E. 1969. *The birth of the gods: The origin of primitive beliefs*. Ann Arbor: University of Michigan Press.

Sweeney, James J. 1952. African negro culture. In *African folktales and sculpture*, ed. P. Radin. New York: Pantheon.

Swisher, C. C., III, G. H. Curtis, T. Jacob, A. G. Getty, A. Suprijo, and Widiasmoro. 1994. Age of the earliest known hominids in Java, Indonesia. *Science* 263 (February 25): 1118–21.

Szalay, Frederick S. 1968. The beginnings of primates. *Evolution* 22:32–33.

Szalay, Frederick S. 1972. Paleobiology of the earliest primates. In *The functional and evolutionary biology of the primates*, ed. R. Tuttle, 3–35. Chicago: University of Chicago Press.

Szalay, Frederick S. 1975. Hunting-scavenging proto-hominids: A model for hominid origins. *Man* 10:420–29.

Szalay, Frederick S., and Eric Delson. 1979. *Evolutionary history of the primates*. New York: Academic Press.

Szalay, Frederick S., I. Tattersall, and R. Decker. 1975. Phylogenetic relationships of *Plesiadipis*—Postcranial evidence. *Contributions to Primatology* 5:136–66.

Szklut, Jay, and Reed, Robert Roy. 1991. Community anonymity in anthropological research: A reassessment. In *Ethics and the profession of anthropology: Dialogue for a new era*, ed. Carolyn Fluehr-Lobban, 97–116. Philadelphia: University of Pennsylvania Press.

Tainter, Joseph. 1988. *The collapse of complex societies*. Cambridge: Cambridge University Press, 128–52.

Takahata, Naoyuki, and Yoko Satta. 1997. Evolution of the primate lineage leading to modern humans: Phylogenetic and demographic inferences from DNA sequences. *Publications of the National Academy of Sciences* 94 (April 29):4811–15.

Takezawa, Yasuko. 2006. Race should be discussed and understood across the globe. *Anthropology News* (February/March).

Talmon, Yonina. 1964. Mate selection in collective settlements. *American Sociological Review* 29:491–508.

Tamari, Tal. 1991. The development of caste systems in West Africa. *Journal of African History* 32:221–50.

Tamari, Tal. 2005. Kingship and caste in Africa: History, diffusion and evolution. In *The character of kingship*, ed. Declan Quigley, 141–70. Oxford: Berg Publishers.

Tannenbaum, Nicola. 1984. The misuse of Chayanov: 'Chayanov's Rule' and empiricist bias in anthropology. *American Anthropologist* 86:927–42.

Tannen, Deborah. 1990. *You just don't understand: Women and men in conversation*. New York: William Morrow and Company.

Tattersall, Ian. 1982. *The primates of Madagascar*. New York: Columbia University Press.

Tattersall, Ian. 1997 (April). Out of Africa again . . . and again? *Scientific American* 276:60–68.

Tattersall, Ian. 1999. *The Last Neanderthal*. Boulder, CO: Westview, 115–16.

Tattersall, Ian. 2002. Paleoanthropology and evolutionary theory. In *Physical anthropology: Original readings in method and practice*, eds. P. N. Peregrine, C. R. Ember, and M. Ember. Upper Saddle River, NJ: Prentice Hall.

Tattersall, Ian. 2009. Paleoanthropology and evolutionary theory. In MyAnthroLibrary, eds. C. R. Ember, M. Ember, and P. N. Peregrine. MyAnthroLibrary.com. Pearson.

Tattersall, Ian, and Jeffrey Schwartz. 2000. *Extinct humans*. Boulder, CO: Westview.

Tattersall, Ian, Eric Delson, and John Van Couvering, eds. 2000. *Encyclopedia of Human Evolution and Prehistory*. New York: Garland.

Taylor, Christopher C. 2005. Mutton, mud, and runny noses: A hierarchy of distaste in early Rwanda. *Social Analysis* 49:213–30.

Taylor, R. E., and M. J. Aitken, eds. 1997. *Chronometric Dating in Archaeology*. New York: Plenum.

Teleki, Geza. 1973. The omnivorous chimpanzee. *Scientific American* (January): 32–42.

Templeton, Alan R. 1993. The "Eve" hypotheses: A genetic critique and reanalysis. *American Anthropologist* 95:51–72.

Templeton, Alan R. 1996. Gene lineages and human evolution. *Science* 272 (May 31):1363.

Terborgh, John. 1983. *Five new world primates: A study in comparative ecology*. Princeton, NJ: Princeton University Press.

Textor, Robert B., comp. 1967. *A cross-cultural summary*. New Haven, CT: HRAF Press.

Thomas, David Hurst. 1986. *Refiguring anthropology: First principles of probability and statistics*. Prospect Heights, IL: Waveland.

Thomas, David Hurst. 2000. *Skull wars*. New York: Basic Books.

Thomas, Elizabeth Marshall. 1959. *The harmless people*. New York: Knopf.

Thomas, Wesley. 1993. *A traditional Navajo's perspectives on the cultural construction of gender in the Navajo world*. Paper presented at the University of Frankfurt, Germany. As referred to in Lang 1999.

Thomason, Sarah Grey, and Terrence Kaufman. 1988. *Language contact, creolization, and genetic linguistics*. Berkeley: University of California Press.

Thompson, Elizabeth Bartlett. 1966. *Africa, past and present*. Boston: Houghton Mifflin.

Thompson, Ginger. 2002. Mexico is attracting a better class of factory in its south. *New York Times*, June 29, p. A3.

Thompson, Richard H. 2009. Chinatowns: Immigrant communities in transition. In MyAnthroLibrary, eds. C. R. Ember, M. Ember, and P. N. Peregrine. MyAnthroLibrary. com. Pearson.

Thompson, Richard H. 1996. Assimilation. In *Encyclopedia of cultural anthropology*, vol. 1, 4 vols., eds. D. Levinson and M. Ember, 112–16. New York: Henry Holt.

Thompson, Stith. 1965. Star Husband Tale. In *The study of folklore*, ed. A. Dundes. Upper Saddle River, NJ: Prentice Hall.

Thompson-Handler, Nancy, Richard K. Malenky, and Noel Badrian. 1984. Sexual behavior of *Pan paniscus* under natural conditions in the Lomako Forest, Equateur, Zaire." In *The pygmy chimpanzee*, ed. R. Susman. New York: Plenum.

Thorpe, S. K. S, R. L. Holder, and R. H. Compton. Origin of human bipedalism as an adaptation for locomotion on flexible branches. *Science* 316 (June 2007):1328–31.

Thurnwald, R. C. 1934. Pigs and currency in Buin: Observations about primitive standards of value and economics. *Oceania* 5:119–41.

Tierney, Patrick. 2000. *Darkness in El Dorado*. New York: Norton.

Tishkoff, Sarah A., et al. 2009. The genetic structure and history of Africans and African Americans. *Science Express* 22 (May 2009), 324(5930):1035–44.

Tobias, Philip V. 1994. The craniocerebral interface in early hominids: Cerebral impressions, cranial thickening, paleoneurobiology, and a new hypothesis on encephalization. In *Integrative paths to the past*, eds. R. Corruccini and R. Ciochon. Upper Saddle River, NJ: Prentice Hall.

Tobin, Joseph J., David Y. H. Wu, and Dana H. Davidson. 1989. *Preschool in three cultures: Japan, China, and the United States*. New Haven, CT: Yale University Press.

Tocheri, Matthew, Caley Orr, Susan Larson, Thomas Sutikna, Jatmiko, E. Wahyu Saptomo, Rokus Awe Due, Tony Djubiantono, Michael J. Morwood, William L. Jungers. 2007. The primitive wrist of *Homo floresiensis* and its implications for hominin evolution. *Science* 317 (September 21):1743–45.

Todorov, Alexander, Anesu N. Mandisodza, Amir Goren, and Crystal C. Hall. 2005. Inference of competence from faces predict election outcomes. *Science* 308 (June 10):1623–26.

Tollefson, Kenneth D. 2009. Tlingit: Chiefs past and present. In MyAnthroLibrary, eds. C. R. Ember, M. Ember, and P. N. Peregrine. MyAnthroLibrary.com. Pearson.

Tomasello, Michael. 1990. Cultural transmission in the tool use and communicatory signaling of chimpanzees. In *"Language" and intelligence in monkeys and apes*, eds. S. Parker and K. Gibson. New York: Cambridge University Press.

Torrey, E. Fuller. 1972. *The mind game: Witchdoctors and psychiatrists*. New York: Emerson Hall.

Torry, William I. 1986. Morality and harm: Hindu peasant adjustments to famines. *Social Science Information* 25:125–60.

Traphagan, John W., and L. Keith Brown. 2002. Fast food and intergenerational commensality in Japan: New styles and old patterns. *Ethnology* 41:119–34.

Travis, John. 2000. Human genome work reaches milestone. *Science News* (July 1): 4–5.

Treiman, Donald J., and Harry B. G. Ganzeboom. 1990. Cross-national comparative status-attainment research. *Research in Social Stratification and Mobility* 9:117.

Trevor-Roper, H. R. 1971. The European witch-craze of the sixteenth and seventeenth centuries. In *Reader in comparative religion*, 3rd ed., eds. W. A. Lessa and E. Z. Vogt. New York: Harper & Row.

Triandis, Harry C. 1995. *Individualism and collectivism*. Boulder, CO: Westview.

Trigger, Bruce G. 1989. *A history of archaeological thought*. Cambridge: Cambridge University Press.

Trinkaus, Erik. 1984. Western Asia. In *The origins of modern humans*, eds. F. H. Smith and F. Spencer. New York: Alan R. Liss.

Trinkaus, Erik. 1985. Pathology and the posture of the La Chapelle-aux-Saints Neandertal. *American Journal of Physical Anthropology* 67:19–41.

Trinkaus, Erik. 1986. The Neandertals and modern human origins. *Annual Review of Anthropology* 15:193–218.

Trinkaus, Erik. 1987a. Bodies, brawn, brains and noses: Human ancestors and human predation. In *The evolution of human hunting*, eds. M. Nitecki and D. Nitecki. New York: Plenum.

Trinkaus, Erik. 1987b. "The Neandertal Face: Evolutionary and Functional Perspectives on a Recent Hominid Face." *Journal of Human Evolution*, 16: 429–43.

Trinkaus, Erik, and William W. Howells. 1979. The Neanderthals. *Scientific American* (December):118–33.

Trinkaus, Erik, and Pat Shipman. 1993a. *The Neandertals: Changing the image of mankind*. New York: Knopf.

Trinkaus, Erik, and Pat Shipman. 1993b. Neandertals: Images of ourselves. *Evolutionary Anthropology* 1:194–201.

Trompf, G. W., ed. 1990. *Cargo cults and millenarian movements: Transoceanic comparisons of new religious movements*. Berlin: Mouton de Gruyter.

Trouillot, Michel-Rolph. 2001. The anthropology of the state in the age of globalization: Close encounters of the deceptive kind. *Current Anthropology* 42:125–38.

Trudgill, Peter. 1983. *Sociolinguistics: An introduction to language and society*. Rev. ed. New York: Penguin.

Turner, B. L. 1970. Population density in the classic Maya lowlands: New evidence for old approaches. *Geographical Review* 66 (January):72–82.

Turner, Christy G., II. 1987. Telltale teeth. *Natural History* (January):6–9.

Turner, Christy G., II. 1989. Teeth and prehistory in Asia. *Scientific American* (February):88–95.

Turner, C. G. 2005. A synoptic history of physical anthropological studies on the peopling of Alaska and the Americas. *Alaska Journal of Anthropology* 3:157–70.

Turner, Terence. 1993. The role of indigenous peoples in the environmental crisis: The example of the Kayapo of the Brazilian Amazon. *Perspectives in Biology and Medicine* 36(3):526–45.

Turner, Terence. 1995. An indigenous people's struggle for socially equitable and ecologically sustainable production: The Kayapo revolt against extractivism. *Journal of Latin American Anthropology* 1:98–121.

Tuttle, Russell H. 1986. *Apes of the world: Their social behavior, communication, mentality, and ecology*. Park Ridge, NJ: Noyes.

Tylor, Edward B. 1971/1958. *Primitive culture*. New York: Harper Torchbooks.

Tylor, Edward B. 1979. Animism. In *Reader in comparative religion*, 4th ed., eds. W. A. Lessa and E. Z. Vogt. New York: Harper & Row.

Uberoi, J. P. Singh. 1962. *The politics of the Kula Ring: An analysis of the findings of Bronislaw Malinowski*. Manchester, UK: University of Manchester Press.

Ucko, Peter J., and Andrée Rosenfeld. 1967. *Paleolithic cave art*. New York: McGraw-Hill.

Udy, Stanley H., Jr. 1970. *Work in traditional and modern society*. Upper Saddle River, NJ: Prentice Hall.

UNAIDS. 2007 (December). *AIDS epidemic update*. Retrieved from http://data.unaids.org/pub/EPISlides/2007/2007_epiupdate_en.pdf

UN News Centre. 2005. Norway at top, Niger at bottom of UN's 2005 human development index. http://www.un.org/apps/news/story.asp?NewsID=15707&Cr=human&Cr1=development (accessed June, 20, 2009).

UN Works. n.d. Retrieved from http://www.un.org/works/goingon/mongolia/lessonplan_homelessness.html.

Underhill, Ralph. 1975. Economic and political antecedents of monotheism: A cross-cultural study. *American Journal of Sociology* 80:841–61.

Underhill, Ruth M. 1938. *Social organization of the Papago Indians*. New York: Columbia University Press.

United Nation's Development Programme. 2007. *Human Development Report 2007/2008: Fighting climate change: Human solidarity in a divided world*. http://hdr.undp.org/en/media/HDR_20072008_EN_Complete.pdf (accessed June, 20, 2009).

United Nations Human Settlements Programme. 2003. The challenge of slums: global report on human settlements, 2003. Nairobi, Kenya.

Unnithan, N. Prabha. 2009. Nayars: Tradition and change in marriage and family. In MyAnthroLibrary, eds. C. R. Ember, M. Ember, and P. N. Peregrine. MyAnthroLibrary.com. Pearson.

U.S. Census Bureau. 2002. The big payoff: Educational entertainment and synthetic estimates of work-life earnings. *Statistical abstract of the United States: 1993*. 113th ed. Washington, DC: U.S. Government Printing Office.

U.S. Department of Justice. 1988 (November). Prevalence, incidence, and consequences of violence against women: Findings from the National Violence against Women Survey. Washington, DC.

U.S. Department of Justice. 1994 (April). Violent crime. NCJ-147486. Washington, DC.

U.S. Department of Justice. 2000. Children as victims. *Juvenile Justice Bulletin 1999*. National Report Series. Washington, DC.

U.S. Department of Justice. n.d. Bureau of Justice statistics homicide trends in the U.S: Long-term trends and patterns. http://www.ojp.gov/bjs/homicide/hmrt.htm (accessed Sept. 5, 2009).

U.S. Environmental Protection Agency. 2009. http://epa.gov/oecaagct/ag101/demographics.html (accessed October 15, 2009).

Vadez, Vincent, Victoria Reyes-Garcia, Tomás Huanca, William R. Leonard. 2008. Cash cropping, farm technologies, and deforestation: What are the connections? A model with empirical data from the Bolivian Amazon. *Human Organization* 67:384–96.

Valente, Thomas W. 1995. *Network models of the diffusion of innovations*. Cresskill, NJ: Hampton Press.

Valladas, H., J. L. Joron, G. Valladas, O. Bar-Yosef, and B. Vandermeersch. 1988. Thermoluminescence dating of Mousterian "Proto-Cro-Magnon" remains from Israel and the origin of modern man. *Nature* 337 (February 18):614–16.

Van der Leeuw, Sander. 1999. *The Archaeomedes Project: Understanding the natural and anthropogenic causes of desertification and land degradation*. Luxembourg: European Union.

Van der Leeuw, Sander, François Favory, and Jean Jacques Girardot. 2002. The archaeological study of environmental degradation: An example from southeastern France. In *The archaeology of global change*, eds. C. Redman, S. R. James, P. Fish, and J. D. Rogers, 112–29. Washington, DC: Smithsonian.

Van der Merwe, N. J. 1992. Reconstructing prehistoric diet. In *The Cambridge encyclopedia of human evolution*, eds. S. Jones, R. Martin, and D. Pilbeam. New York: Cambridge University Press.

Van Hear, Nicholas. 2004. Refugee diasporas or refugees in diaspora. In *Encyclopedia of diasporas: Immigrant and refugee cultures around the world*, vol. 1, eds. M. Ember, C. R. Ember, and I. Skoggard, 580–89. New York: Kluwer Academic/Plenum.

Van Lawick-Goodall, Jane. 1971. *In the shadow of man*. Boston: Houghton Mifflin.

Van Schaik, C. P. M. Ancrenaz, G. Borgen, B. Galdikas, C. D. Knott, I. Singleton, A. Suzuki, S. S. Utami, and M. Merrill. 2003. Orangutan cultures and the evolution of material culture. *Science* 299 (January 3):102–05.

Van Willigen, John. 2002. *Applied anthropology: An introduction*. 3rd ed. Westport, CT: Bergin and Garvey.

Vayda, Andrew P., and Roy A. Rappaport. 1968. Ecology: Cultural and noncultural." In *Introduction to cultural anthropology*, ed. J. H. Clifton. Boston: Houghton Mifflin.

Vayda, Andrew P., Anthony Leeds, and David B. Smith. 1962. The place of pigs in Melanesian subsistence. In *Symposium*, ed. V. E. Garfield. Seattle: University of Washington Press.

Vekua, Abesalom, David Lordkipanidze, G. Philip Rightmire, Jordi Agusti, Reid Ferring, Givi Maisuradze, Alexander Mouskhelishvili, Medea Nioradze, Marcia Ponce de Leon, Martha Tappen, Merab Tvalchrelidze, and Christoph Zollikofer. 2002. A new skull of early *Homo* from Dmanisi, Georgia. *Science* 297 (July 5):85–89.

Vigil, James Diego. 1988. Group processes and street identity: Adolescent Chicano gang members. *Ethos* 16:421–45.

Vigil, James Diego. 2009. Mexican Americans: Growing up on the streets of Los Angeles. In MyAnthroLibrary, eds. C. R. Ember, M. Ember, and P. N. Peregrine. MyAnthroLibrary.com. Pearson.

Vigilant, Linda, Mark Stoneking, Henry Harpending, Kristen Hawkes, and Allan C. Wilson. 1991. African populations and the evolution of human mitochrondrial DNA. *Science* 253 (September 27):1503–07.

Vincent, Joan. 1978. Political anthropology: Manipulative strategies. *Annual Review of Anthropology* 7:175–94.

Visaberghi, Elisabetta, and Dorothy Munkenbeck Fragaszy. 1990. Do monkeys ape? In *"Language" and intelligence in monkeys and apes*, eds. S. Parker and K. Gibson. New York: Cambridge University Press.

Vogel, Joseph O. 2009. De-mystifying the past: Great Zimbabwe, King Solomon's mines, and other tales of Old Africa. In MyAnthroLibrary, eds. C. R. Ember, M. Ember, and P. N. Peregrine. MyAnthroLibrary.com. Pearson.

Vohs, Kathleen D., Nicole L. Mead, and Miranda R. Goode. 2006. The psychological consequences of money. *Science* 314 (November 17):1154–56.

von Frisch, Karl. 1962. Dialects in the language of the bees. *Scientific American* (August):78–87.

Vrba, Elizabeth S. 1995. On the connection between paleoclimate and evolution. In *Paleoclimate and evolution*, eds. E. S. Vrba, G. H. Denton, T. C. Partridge, and L. H. Burckle, 24–45. New Haven, CT: Yale University Press.

Wadley, Reed L. 2003. Lethal treachery and the imbalance of power in warfare and feuding. *Journal of Anthropological Research* 59:531–54.

Wagley, Charles. 1974. Cultural influences on population: A comparison of two Tupi tribes. In *Native South Americans*, ed. P. J. Lyon. Boston: Little, Brown.

Wald, Matthew L. 2000. Hybrid cars show up in M.I.T.'s crystal ball. *New York Times* November 3, Fl.

Waldbaum, Jane C. 2005. Helping hand for China. *Archaeology* 58:6.

Waldman, Amy. 2005. Sri Lankan maids' high price for foreign jobs. *The New York Times*, May 8, pp. 1, 20.

Walker, Alan, and R. Leakey. 1988. The evolution of *Australopithecus boisei*. In *Evolutionary history of the "robust" australopithecines*, ed. F. Grine, 247–58. New York: Aldine.

Wallace, Alfred Russell. 1970/1858. On the tendency of varieties to depart indefinitely from the original type. (Originally published in 1858.) In *Evolution of Man*, ed. L. B. Young. New York: Oxford University Press.

Wallace, Anthony. 1966. *Religion: An anthropological view*. New York: Random House.

Wallace, Anthony. 1972. Mental illness, biology and culture. In *Psychological anthropology*, 2nd ed., ed. F. L. K. Hsu. Cambridge, MA: Schenkman.

Wallerstein, Immanuel. 1974. *The modern world-system*. New York: Academic Press.

Wanner, Eric, and Lila R. Gleitman, eds. 1982. *Language acquisition: The state of the art*. Cambridge: Cambridge University Press.

Ward, Peter M. 1982. Introduction and purpose. In *Self-help housing*, ed. P. M. Ward. London: Mansell.

Ward, Steve. 1997. The taxonomy and phylogenetic relationships of *Sivapithecus* revisited. In *Function, phylogeny and fossils: Miocene hominoid evolution and adaptation*, eds. D. R. Begun, C. V. Ward, and M. D. Rose, 269–90. New York: Plenum.

Ward, Steve, B. Brown, A. Hill, J. Kelley, and W. Downs. 1999. *Equatorius*: A new hominoid genus from the middle Miocene of Kenya. *Science* 285 (August 27):1382–86.

Wardhaugh, Ronald. 2002. *An introduction to sociolinguistics*. 4th ed. Oxford: Blackwell.

Warner, John Anson. 1986. The individual in Native American art: A sociological view. In *The arts of the North American Indian*, ed. E. L. Wade. New York: Hudson Hills Press.

Warner, W. Lloyd, and Paul S. Lunt. 1941. *The social life of a modern community*. New Haven, CT: Yale University Press.

Warren, Dennis M. 1989. Utilizing indigenous healers in national health delivery systems: The Ghanaian experiment.

In *Making our research useful*, eds. J. van Willigen, B. Rylko-Bauer, and A. McElroy. Boulder, CO: Westview.

Warry, Wayne. 1986. Kafaina: Female wealth and power in Chuave, Papua New Guinea. *Oceania* 57:4–21.

Warry, Wayne. 1990. Doing unto others: Applied anthropology, collaborative research and native self-determination. *Culture* 10:61–62.

Washburn, Sherwood. 1960. Tools and human evolution. *Scientific American* (September):62–75.

Watson, James L. 2004. Presidential address: Virtual kinship, real estate, and diaspora formation—the Man lineage revisited. *Journal of Asian Studies* 63:893–910.

Weaver, Muriel Porter. 1993. *The Aztecs, Maya, and their predecessors*. 3rd ed. San Diego: Academic Press.

Webb, Karen E. 1977. An evolutionary aspect of social structure and a verb "have." *American Anthropologist* 79:42–49.

Weber, Max. 1947. *The theory of social and economic organization*. Trans. A. M. Henderson and Talcott Parsons. New York: Oxford University Press.

Weiner, Annette B. 1976. *Women of value, men of renown: New perspectives in Trobriand exchange*. Austin: University of Texas Press.

Weiner, Annette B. 1987. *The Trobrianders of Papua New Guinea*. New York: Holt, Rinehart and Winston.

Weiner, J. S. 1954. Nose shape and climate. *Journal of Physical Anthropology* 4:615–18.

Weiner, Jonathan. 1994. *Beak of the finch*. New York: Vintage.

Weiner, Steve, Q. Xi, P. Goldberg, J. Liu, and O. Bar-Yousef. 1998. Evidence for the use of fire at Zhoukoudian, China. *Science*, 281 (July 10):251–53.

Weinreich, Uriel. 1968. *Languages in contact*. The Hague: Mouton.

Weisner, Thomas S. 2004. The American dependency conflict. *Ethos* 29:271–95.

Weisner, Thomas S., and Ronald Gallimore. 1977. My brother's keeper: Child and sibling caretaking. *Current Anthropology* 18:169–90.

Weisner, Thomas S., Mary Bausano, and Madeleine Kornfein. 1983. Putting family ideals into practice: Pronaturalism in conventional and nonconventional California families. *Ethos* 11:278–304.

Weiss, Harvey, and Raymond S. Bradley. 2001. What drives societal collapse? *Science* 291 (January 26):609–10.

Weiss, Harvey, M. A. Courty, W. Wetterstrom, F. Guichard, L. Senior, R. Meadow, and A. Curnow. 1993. The genesis and collapse of third millennium north Mesopotamian civilization. *Science* 261 (August 20):995–1004.

Weller, Susan C. 2009. The research process. In MyAnthroLibrary, eds. C. R. Ember, M. Ember, and P. N. Peregrine. MyAnthroLibrary.com. Pearson.

Wenke, Robert J. 1984. *Patterns in prehistory: Humankind's first three million years*. 2nd ed. New York: Oxford University Press.

Wenke, Robert. 1990. *Patterns in prehistory: Humankind's first three million years*. 3rd ed. New York: Oxford University Press.

Werner, Dennis. 1975. *On the societal acceptance or rejection of male homosexuality*. Master's thesis, Hunter College of the City University of New York.

Werner, Dennis. 1978. Trekking in the Amazon forest. *Natural History* (November):42–54.

Werner, Dennis. 1979. A cross-cultural perspective on theory and research on male homosexuality. *Journal of Homosexuality* 4:345–62.

Werner, Dennis. 1982. Chiefs and presidents: A comparison of leadership traits in the United States and among the Mekranoti-Kayapo of central Brazil. *Ethos* 10:136–48.

Werner, Dennis. 1984. Child care and influence among the Mekranoti of central Brazil. *Sex Roles* 10:395–404.

Westermarck, Edward. 1894. *The history of human marriage*. London: Macmillan.

Weston, Eleanor, and Adrian Lister. 2009. Insular dwarfism in hippos and a model for brain size reduction in *Homo floresiensis*. *Nature* 459 (May 7):85–88.

Wheat, Joe B. 1967. A Paleo-Indian bison kill. *Scientific American* (January):44–52.

Wheatley, Paul. 1971. *The pivot of the four quarters*. Chicago: Aldine.

Wheeler, Peter. 1984. The evolution of bipedality and loss of functional body hair in hominids. *Journal of Human Evolution* 13:91–98.

Wheeler, Peter. 1991. The influence of bipedalism in the energy and water budgets of early hominids. *Journal of Human Evolution* 23:379–88.

Whitaker, Ian. 1955. *Social relations in a nomadic Lappish community*. Oslo: Utgitt av Norsk Folksmuseum.

White, Benjamin. 1973. Demand for labor and population growth in colonial Java. *Human Ecology* 1, no. 3 (March): 217–36.

White, Douglas R. 1988. Rethinking polygyny: Co-wives, codes, and cultural systems. *Current Anthropology* 29:529–88.

White, Douglas R., and Michael L. Burton. 1988. Causes of polygyny: Ecology, economy, kinship, and warfare. *American Anthropologist* 90:871–87.

White, Douglas R., Michael L. Burton, and Lilyan A. Brudner. 1977. Entailment theory and method: A cross-cultural analysis of the sexual division of labor. *Behavior Science Research* 12:1–24.

White, Frances. J. 1996. *Pan paniscus* 1973 to 1996: Twenty-three years of field research. *Evolutionary Anthropology* 5: 11–17.

White, Leslie A. 1939. A problem in kinship terminology. *American Anthropologist* 41:569–70.

White, Leslie A. 1949. *The science of culture: A study of man and civilization*. New York: Farrar, Straus & Cudahy.

White, Leslie A. 1968. The expansion of the scope of science. In *Readings in anthropology*, ed. M. H. Fried, vol. 1, 2nd ed. New York: Thomas Y. Crowell.

White, Randall. 1982. Rethinking the Middle/Upper Paleolithic transition. *Current Anthropology* 23:169–75.

White, Tim D. 2003. Early hominids—Diversity or distortion? *Science* 299 (March 28):1994–97.

White, Tim D., and Pieter Arend Folkens. 2000. *Human osteology*. 2nd ed. San Diego: Academic Press.

White, Tim D., Donald C. Johanson, and William H. Kimbel. 1981. *Australopithecus africanus*: Its phyletic position reconsidered. *South African Journal of Science* 77:445–70.

White, Timothy D., G. Suwa, and B. Asfaw. 1994. *Australopithecus ramidus*, a new species of early hominid from Aramis, Ethiopia. *Nature* 371 (September 22): 306–33.

White, Timothy D., G. Suwa, and B. Asfaw. 1995. Corrigendum: *Australopithecus ramidus*, a new species of early hominid from Aramis, Ethiopia. *Nature* 375 (May 4):88

Whitehead, Barbara Defoe, and David Popenoe. 2005. *The state of our unions: Marriage and family: What does the*

Scandinavian experience tell us? National Marriage Project: Rutgers University.

Whiten, A., J. Goodall, W. McGrew, T. Nishida, V. Reynolds, Y. Yugiyama, Yugiyama, C. Yugiyama, R. Wrangham, and C. Boesch. 1999. Cultures in chimpanzees. *Nature* 399 (June 17): 682–85.

Whiting, Beatrice Blyth. 1950. *Paiute sorcery.* Viking Fund Publications in Anthropology No. 15. New York: Wenner-Gren Foundation.

Whiting, Beatrice B. 1965. Sex identity conflict and physical violence. *American Anthropologist* 67:123–40.

Whiting, Beatrice B., and Carolyn Pope Edwards. 1973. A cross-cultural analysis of sex differences in the behavior of children aged three through eleven. *Journal of Social Psychology* 91:171–88.

Whiting, Beatrice Blyth, and Carolyn Pope Edwards (in collaboration with Carol R. Ember, Gerald M. Erchak, Sara Harkness, Robert L. Munroe, Ruth H. Munroe, Sara B. Nerlove, Susan Seymour, Charles M. Super, Thomas S. Weisner, and Martha Wenger). 1988. *Children of different worlds: The formation of social behavior.* Cambridge, MA: Harvard University Press.

Whiting, Beatrice B., and John W. M. Whiting (in collaboration with Richard Longabaugh). 1975. *Children of six cultures: A psycho-cultural analysis.* Cambridge, MA: Harvard University Press.

Whiting, John W. M. 1941. *Becoming a Kwoma.* New Haven, CT: Yale University Press.

Whiting, John W. M. 1964. Effects of climate on certain cultural practices. In *Explorations in cultural anthropology,* ed. W. Goodenough. New York: McGraw-Hill.

Whiting, John W. M., and Irvin L. Child. 1953. *Child training and personality: A cross-cultural study.* New Haven, CT: Yale University Press.

Whittaker, John C. 1994. *Flintknapping: Making and understanding stone tools.* Austin: University of Texas Press.

Whyte, Martin K. 1978a. Cross-cultural codes dealing with the relative status of women. *Ethnology* 17:211–37.

Whyte, Martin K. 1978b. *The status of women in preindustrial societies.* Princeton, NJ: Princeton University Press.

Wiberg, Hakan. 1983. Self-determination as an international issue. In *Nationalism and self-determination in the Horn of Africa,* ed. I. M. Lewis. London: Ithaca Press.

Wilden, Anthony. 1987. *The rules are no game: The strategy of communication.* London: Routledge and Kegan Paul.

Wikan, Unni. 1982. *Beyond the veil in Arabia.* Baltimore: The Johns Hopkins University Press.

Wilford, John Noble. 1995. The transforming leap, from 4 legs to 2. *New York Times* September 5, p. C1ff.

Wilford, John Noble. 1997. Ancient German spears tell of mighty hunters of Stone Age. *New York Times,* March 4, p. C6.

Wilkinson, Robert L. 1995. Yellow fever: Ecology, epidemiology, and role in the collapse of the classic lowland Maya civilization. *Medical Anthropology* 16:269–94.

Williams, George C. 1992. *Natural selection: Domains, levels, and challenges.* New York: Oxford University Press.

Williams, Melvin D. 2009. Racism: The production, reproduction, and obsolescence of social inferiority. In MyAnthroLibrary, eds. C. R. Ember, M. Ember, and P. N. Peregrine. MyAnthroLibrary.com. Pearson.

Williams, Walter L. 1992. *The spirit and the flesh.* Boston: Beacon Press.

Wilmsen, Edwin N., ed. 1989. *We are here: Politics of Aboriginal land tenure.* Berkeley: University of California Press.

Wilson, Edward O. 1975. *Sociobiology: The new synthesis.* Cambridge, MA: Belknap Press of Harvard University Press.

Wilson, Monica. 1963/1951. *Good company: A study of Nyakyusa age villages.* Boston: Beacon Press.

Winkelman, Michael 1986a. Magico-religious practitioner types and socioeconomic conditions. *Behavior Science Research* 20:17–46.

Winkelman, Michael. 1986b. Trance states: A theoretical model and cross-cultural analysis. *Ethos* 14:174–203.

Winkelman, Michael, and John R. Baker. 2010. *Supernatural as natural: A biocultural approach to religion.* Upper Saddle River, NJ: Pearson Prentice Hall.

Winkleman, Michael, and Philip M. Peck, eds. 2004. *Divination and healing: Potent vision.* Tucson: University of Arizona Press.

Winterbottom, Robert. 1995. The tropical forestry plan: Is it working? In *Global ecosystems: Creating options through anthropological perspectives,* ed. P. J. Puntenney. *NAPA Bulletin* 15.

Winterhalder, Bruce. 1990. Open field, common pot: Harvest variability and risk avoidance in agricultural and foraging societies. In *Risk and uncertainty in tribal and peasant economies,* ed. E. Cashdan. Boulder, CO: Westview.

Witkin, Herman A. 1967. A cognitive style approach to cross-cultural research. *International Journal of Psychology* 2:233–50.

Witkowski, Stanley R. 1975. *Polygyny, age of marriage, and female status.* Paper presented at the annual meeting of the American Anthropological Association, San Francisco.

Witkowski, Stanley R., and Cecil H. Brown. 1978. Lexical universals. *Annual Review of Anthropology* 7:427–51.

Witkowski, Stanley R., and Harold W. Burris. 1981. Societal complexity and lexical growth. *Behavior Science Research* 16:143–59.

Wittfogel, Karl. 1957. *Oriental despotism: A comparative study of total power.* New Haven, CT: Yale University Press.

Wolf, Arthur. 1968. Adopt a daughter-in-law, marry a sister: A Chinese solution to the problem of the incest taboo. *American Anthropologist* 70:864–74.

Wolf, Arthur P., and Chieh-Shan Huang. 1980. *Marriage and adoption in China, 1845–1945.* Stanford, CA: Stanford University Press.

Wolf, Eric. 1955. Types of Latin American peasantry: A preliminary discussion. *American Anthropologist* 57:452–71.

Wolf, Eric R. 1956. San José: Subcultures of a "traditional" coffee municipality. In *The people of Puerto Rico,* J. H. Steward et al. Urbana: University of Illinois Press.

Wolf, Eric. 1966. *Peasants.* Upper Saddle River, NJ: Prentice Hall.

Wolf, Eric. 1984. Culture: Panacea or problem. *American Antiquity* 49:393–400.

Wolf, Naomi. 1991. *The beauty myth: How images of beauty are used against women.* New York: Morrow.

Wolff, Ronald G. 1991. *Functional chordate anatomy.* Lexington, MA: D. C. Heath.

Wolpoff, Milford H. 1971. Competitive exclusion among lower Pleistocene hominids: The single species hypothesis. *Man* 6:601–13.

Wolpoff, Milford H. 1983. *Ramapithecus* and human origins: An anthropologist's perspective of changing interpretations.

In *New interpretations of ape and human ancestry*, eds. R. Ciochon and R. Corruccini. New York: Plenum.

Wolpoff, Milford H. 1999. *Paleoanthropology*. 2nd ed. Boston: McGraw-Hill, 501–04, 727–31.

Wolpoff, Milford H., and Abel Nkini. 1985. Early and Early Middle Pleistocene hominids from Asia and Africa. In *Ancestors*, ed. E. Delson. New York: Alan R. Liss.

Wolpoff, Milford H. A. G. Thorne, J. Jelinek, and Zhang Yinyun. 1993. The case for sinking *Homo erectus:* 100 years of *Pithecanthropus* is enough! In *100 years of* Pithecanthropus: *The* Homo Erectus *problem*, ed. J. L. Franzen. *Courier Forshungsinstitut Senckenberg* 171:341–61.

Women in science '93: Gender and the culture of science. 1993. *Science* 260 (April 16):383–430.

Wong, Kate. 2003. An ancestor to call our own. *Scientific American* (January):54–63.

Wong, Kate, 2005. The littlest human. *Scientific American* (February): 56–65.

Wood, Bernard A. 1992. Evolution of australopithecines. In *The Cambridge encyclopedia of human evolution*, eds. S. Jones, R. Martin, and D. Pilbeam. New York: Cambridge University Press.

Wood, Bernard A. 1994. Hominid paleobiology: Recent achievements and challenges. In *Integrative paths to the past*, eds. R. Corruccini and R. Ciochon. Upper Saddle River, NJ: Prentice Hall.

Wood, Gordon S. 1992. *The radicalism of the American Revolution*. New York: Knopf.

Wood, James W., George R. Milner, Henry C. Harpending, and Kenneth M. Weiss. 1992. The osteological paradox: Problems of inferring prehistoric health from skeletal samples. *Current Anthropology* 33:343–70.

Wood, Wendy, and Alice H. Eagly. 2002. A cross-cultural analysis of the behavior of women and men: Implications for the origins of sex differences. *Psychological Bulletin* 128:699–727.

Woodburn, James. 1968. An introduction to Hadza ecology. In *Man the hunter*, eds. R. B. Lee and I. DeVore. Chicago: Aldine.

World Bank. 2004. *World development indicators 2004*. Washington, DC: World Bank Publications.

Worsley, Peter. 1957. *The trumpet shall sound: A study of "cargo" cults in Melanesia*. London: MacGibbon & Kee,

Wrangham, Richard W. 1980. An ecological model of female-bonded primate groups. *Behaviour* 75:262–300.

Wright, Gary A. 1971. Origins of food production in Southwestern Asia: A survey of ideas. *Current Anthropology* 12:447–78.

Wright, George O. 1954. Projection and displacement: A cross-cultural study of folktale aggression. *Journal of Abnormal and Social Psychology* 49:523–28.

Wright, Henry T. 1986. The evolution of civilizations. In *American archaeology past and future*, ed. D. Meltzer, D. Fowler, and J. Sabloff. Washington, DC: Smithsonian Institution Press.

Wright, Henry T., and Gregory A. Johnson. 1975. Population, exchange, and early state formation in southwestern Iran. *American Anthropologist* 77:267–77.

Wulff, Robert, and Shirley Fiste. 1987. The domestication of wood in Haiti. In R. M. Wulff and S. J. Fiste, *Anthropological praxis*. Boulder, CO: Westview.

Yamei, Hou, R. Potts, Y. Baoyin, et al. 2000. Mid-Pleistocene Acheulean-like stone technology of the Bose Basin, South China. *Science* 287 (March 3):1622–26.

Yan, Yunxiang. 2006. Girl power: Young women and the waning of patriarchy in rural North China. *Ethnology* 45:105–23.

Yergin, Daniel. 2002. Giving aid to world trade. *New York Times*, June 27, p. A29.

Yinger, J. Milton. 1994. *Ethnicity: Source of strength? Source of conflict?* Albany: State University Press.

Young, Frank W. 1970. A fifth analysis of the Star Husband Tale. *Ethnology* 9:389–413.

Young, T. Cuyler, Jr. 1972. Population densities and early Mesopotamian urbanism. In *Man, settlement and urbanism*, eds. P. J. Ucko, R. Tringham, and G. W. Dimbley. Cambridge, MA: Scherkmn.

Younger, Stephen M. 2008. Conditions and mechanisms for peace in precontact Polynesia. *Current Anthropology* 49:927–34.

Zebrowitz, Leslie A., and Joann M. Montepare. 2005. Appearance *does* matter. *Science* 308 (June 10):1565–66.

Zechenter, Elizabeth M. 1997. In the name of culture: Cultural relativism and the abuse of the individual. *Journal of Anthropological Research* 53:319–47.

Zeder, Melinda A. 1991. *Feeding cities: Specialized animal economy in the ancient Near East*. Washington, DC: Smithsonian Institution Press.

Zeder, Melinda A. 1994. After the revolution: Post-Neolithic subsistence in northern Mesopotamia." *American Anthropologist* 96:97–126.

Zihlman, Adrienne L. 1992. The emergence of human locomotion: The evolutionary background and environmental context. In *Topics in primatology*, vol. 1, eds. T. Nishida, et al.

Zimmer, Carl. 1999. Kenyan skeleton shakes ape family tree. *Science* 285 (August 27):1335–37.

Zimmer, Carl. 2004. Faster than a hyena? Running may make humans special. *Science* 306 (November 19):1283.

Zohary, Daniel. 1969. The progenitors of wheat and barley in relation to domestication and agriculture dispersal in the Old World. In *The domestication and exploitation of plants and animals*, eds. P. J. Ucko and G. W. Dimbleby. Chicago: Aldine.

credits

Photos

Chapter 22. Page 389: Dean Conger/CORBIS- NY; Page 390: Porterfield/ Chickering/Photo Researchers, Inc.; Page 392: © Harvey Lloyd/ Taxi/Getty Images, Inc.; Page 399: Reed Kaestner/CORBIS- NY; Page 402: © Ludo Kuipers/CORBIS All Rights Reserved; Page 406: Stock Montage, Inc./ Historical Pictures Collection.

Chapter 23. Page 409: © SW Productions/Photodisc/RF Getty Images, Inc.; Page 412: Leon Oboler/Regina Smith Oboler; Page 413: Photo Courtesy of Anthony Forge, 1962. From George A. Corgin, "Native Arts of North America, Africa and the South Pacific: An Introduction". New York. Harper & Row, Publishers, Inc., 1988.; Page 415: Sylvain Grandadam/Photo Researchers, Inc.; Page 417: Bernard Wong; Page 418: Wayne Warry.

Chapter 24. Page 423: AP Wide World Photos; Page 425: © Arnold Newman/ Peter Arnold Inc.; Page 427: © Anders Ryman/CORBIS All Rights Reserved; Page 430: © Peter Andrews/Reuters/CORBIS All Rights Reserved; Page 431: © Enrico Para/ANSA /epa/CORBIS All Rights Reserved; Page 433: Maria Lepowsky; Page 436: Bill Aron/PhotoEdit Inc.; Page 439: © Yasuyoshi Chiba/AFP/ Getty Images, Inc.; Page 441: ©Paul Assaker/Bettmann/CORBIS All Rights Reserved.

Chapter 25. Page 445: © Dallas and John Heaton/Free Agents Limited/ CORBIS All Rights Reserved; Page 447: Tom Stewart/CORBIS- NY; Page 449: © Jorge Silva/Reuters/CORBIS All Rights Reserved; Page 452: © Peter Arnold, Inc.; Page 453: © Reinhard Dirscherl/WaterFrame.de/Peter Arnold; Page 455: © Catherine Karnow/CORBIS All Rights Reserved; Page 457: © Joerg Boethling/Peter Arnold, Inc.; Page 460: Ogallala Sioux performing the Ghost Dance at the Pine Ridge Indian Agency, South Dakota. Illustration by Frederic Remington, 1890. The Granger Collection.

Chapter 26. Page 465: Art Wolfe/Photo Researchers, Inc.; Page 468: Jack Fields/Photo Researchers, Inc.; Page 468: © Charles & Josette Lenars/CORBIS All Rights Reserved; Page 469: © The Trustees of the British Museum, London, United Kingdom; Page 469: © Araldo de Luca/CORBIS All Rights Reserved; Page 472: Lynton Gardiner © Dorling Kindersley, Courtesy of The American Museum of Natural History; Page 472: © Peter Arnold, Inc.; Page 473: © Lightstone/CORBIS; Page 473: Susan McCartney/Photo Researchers, Inc.; Page 476: © Lake County Museum/Bettmann/CORBIS All Rights Reserved; Page 476: Demetrio Carrasco © Dorling Kindersley, Courtesy of the Cameron Trading Post, Flagstaff, Arizona.

Chapter 27. Page 479: Michael Horowitz; Page 481: © Hallgerd/Shutterstock; Page 482: AFP/Getty Images; Page 483: © Joerg Boethling/Peter Arnold, Inc.; Page 485: © Yannis Kontos/Sygma/CORBIS All Rights Reserved; Page 486: © Horacio Villalobos/Corbis; Page 487: © Tibor Bognar/Alamy; Page 490: © Nigel Dickinson/Peter Arnold, Inc.; Page 491: Martha Cooper/Peter Arnold, Inc.; Page 493: © Jon Hursa/Pool/epa/CORBIS All Rights Reserved; Page 494: © Tony Anderson/CORBIS All Rights Reserved; Page 497: Michael J. Balick/Peter Arnold, Inc.

Chapter 28. Page 501: © David Greedy/News/Getty Images, Inc.; Page 502: © Shamil Zhumatov/Reuters/CORBIS All Rights Reserved; Page 503: © Sucheta Das/Reuters/CORBIS All Rights Reserved; Page 508: Lon C. Diehl/PhotoEdit Inc.; Page 509: © Edourd Berne/Stone/Getty Images, Inc.; Page 510: © Helen Harrison/E&E Image Library/H/age fotostock; Page 512: © epa/CORBIS All Rights Reserved.

Table, Text and Figures

Chapter 2. Page 29: Ember, Melvin R; Ember, Carol R.; Levinson, David, *Portraits Of Culture: Ethnographic Originals,* 1st, © 1994. Electronically reproduced by permission of Pearson Education, Inc., Upper Saddle River, New Jersey.

Chapter 3. Page 37: Based on John W. M. Whiting, "Effects of Climate on Certain Cultural Practices," in Ward H. Goodenough, ed., *Explorations in Cultural Anthropology* (New York: McGraw-Hill, 1964), p. 520; Page 46: Reprinted with the permission of Cambridge University Press; Page 47: Springer/Kluwer Academic/Plenum Publishers,"The Carbon-14 Cycle, "Radiocarbon Dating," by R. E. Taylor, From *Chronmetric Dating in Archaeology* by R. E. Taylor and M. J. Aitken, eds. With kind permission from Springer Science and Business Media.

Chapter 4. Page 60: Boaz, Noel T.; Almquist, Alan J., *Biological Anthropology: A Synthetic Approach To Human Evolution,* 1st, © 1997. Electronically reproduced by permission of Pearson Education, Inc., Upper Saddle River, New Jersey.

Chapter 5. Page 71: From D. F. Roberts, "Body Weight, Race, and Climate," *American Journal of Physical Anthropology,* 11 (1953), Reprinted with permission of John Wiley & Sons, Inc.; Page 73: From *Biological Perspectives on Human Pigmentation* by Ashley H. Robins. Copyright © by Cambridge University Press. Reprinted by permission of Cambridge University Press.

Chapter 6. Page 88: (A) From Ronald G. Wolff, Functional Chordate Anatomy (Lexington, MA: D.C. Heath and Company, 1991), p. 255. Reprinted with permission of Lilia C. Koo, (B and C) From Terrence Deacon, "Primate Brains and Senses," in Stephen Jones, Robert Martin, and David Pilbeam, eds.,*The Cambridge Encyclopedia of Human Evolution* (New York: Cambridge University Press, 1992), p. 110. Reprinted with the permission of Cambridge University Press, (D) From Matt Cartmill, "Non-Human Primates," in Stephen Jones, Robert Martin, and David Pilbeam, eds.,*The Cambridge Encyclopedia of Human Evolution* (New York: Cambridge University Press, 1992), p. 25. Reprinted with the permission of Cambridge University Press, (E and F) From Matt Cartmill, Non-Human Primates," in Stephen Jones, Robert Martin, and David Pilbeam, eds.,*The Cambridge Encyclopedia of Human Evolution* (New York: Cambridge University Press, 1992), p. 24. Reprinted with

the permission of Cambridge University Press; Page 93: From Noel Boaz and Alan J. Almquist, *Biological Anthropology.* © 1997. Reprinted by permission of Pearson Education; Page 97: Difference in Dentition between an Old World Monkey and an Ape. From Noel Boaz and Alan J. Almquist, *Biological Anthropology.* © 1997. Reprinted by permission of Pearson Education; Page 103: From Terrence Deacon, "Primate Brains and Senses," in Stephen Jones, Robert Martin, and David Pilbeam, eds.,*The Cambridge Encyclopedia of Human Evolution* (New York: Cambridge University Press, 1992), p. 111. Reprinted with the permision of Cambridge University Press.

Chapter 7. Page 110: From Noel Boaz and Alan J. Almquist, *Biological Anthropology.* © 1999. Reprinted by permission of Pearson Education; Page 118: What Happened to Gigantopithecus? Source: Russell Ciochon, John Olsen, and Jamie James, Other Origins: The Search for the Giant Ape in Human Prehistory (New York: Bantam, 1990), pp. 99–102.

Chapter 8. Page 126: Skeletal Evidence of Bipedalism, SOURCE: Stephen Jones, Robert Martin, and David Pilbeam, eds.,*The Cambridge Encyclopedia of Human Evolution.* (New York: Cambridge University Press, 1992), p. 78. Reprinted with permission of Cambridge University Press; Page 128: From Russell L. Ciochon and John G. Fleagle, eds., The Human Evolution Source Book. (Englewood Cliffs, NJ: Prentice Hall, 1993);Page 135: Adapted from *The New York Times,* September 5, 1995, p. C9.

Chapter 9. Page 139: From "The First Technology" by R. Freman in *Scientific American.* Reprinted by permission of the artist, Ed. Hanson; Page 143: Estimated cranial capacities from Tattersall, Delson, and van Couvering, eds., 2000. Reproduced by permission of Routledge, Inc., part of the Taylor and Francis Group; Page 146: From Russell L. Ciochon and John G. Fleagle, eds.,*The Human Evolution Source Book.* (Upper Saddle River, NJ: Prentice Hall, 1993); Page 152: Copyright © 1969 by Eric Mose;

Chapter 10. Page 159 (top): From Russell L. Ciochon and John G. Fleagle, eds.,*The Human Evolution Source Book.* (Englewood Cliffs, NJ: Prentice Hall, 1993); Page 159 (bottom): This was published in Differences in mtDNA Sequences Among Humans, the Neandertal, and Chimpanzees, *Cell,* 90 (1997): 25. Elsevier Science; Page 166: From FamilyTreeDNA.com.

Chapter 11. Page 173: From Brian M. Fagan, *In the Beginning* (Boston: Little, Brown, 1972), p. 195. Used with permission of Brian M. Fagan; Page 178: "Pleistocene Peopling of the Americas," *Evolutionary Anthropology,* Vol. 1, 1993. © 1993. John Wiley and Sons. David K. Meltzer, Reprinted with permission of John Wiley & Sons, Inc.; Page 177: From Jean-Pierre Duhard, "Upper Paleolithic Figures as a Reflection of Human Morphology and Social Organization," *Antiquity,* 67 (1993): 86. Antiquity Publications, Ltd.; Page 180: From Christy G. Turner II, "Telltale Teeth," *Natural History,* January 1987, p. 8.

Chapter 12. Page 186 (top): Dates for animal domestication are from Juliet Clutton-Brock, "Domestication of Animals," in Stephen Jones, Robert Martin, and David Pilbeam, eds., The Cambridge Encyclopedia of Human Evolution (New York: Cambridge University Press, 1992), p. 384. Reprinted with the permission of Cambridge University Press; Page 186 (bottom): From Frank Hole, "Origins of Agriculture," in Stephen Jones, Robert Martin, and David Pilbeam, eds., The Cambridge Encyclopedia of Human Evolution (New York: Cambridge University Press, 1992), p. 376. Reprinted with the permission of Cambridge University Press; Page 190: Figure adapted from *Demographic Archaeology* by F. A. Hassan. (New York: Academic Press, 1981); Pages 192 and 196: From *Past in Perspective,* 2nd ed., by K. Feder. (Mountain View, CA: Mayfield, 2000); Page 201: Adapted from Ansley J. Coale, *The History of the Human Population.* Copyright © 1974 by Scientific American Inc.

Chapter 13. Page 210: "Map of the Six Early Civilizations", from The Origins of the State Ad Civilization: The Process of Cultural Evolution by Elman R. Service. Copyright © 1975 by W. W. Norton & Company, Inc. Used by permission of W. W. Norton & Company, Inc; Page 216: From *Archaeology of Ancient China,* 4th ed., by K.-C. Chang (New Haven: Yale, 1986).

Chapter 17. Page 295: From James A. Levine, Robert Weisell, Simon Chevassus, Claudio D. Martinez, and Barbara Burlingame. "The Distribution of Work Tasks for Male and Female Children and Adults Separated by Gender" in "Looking at Child Labor," *Science* 296 (10 May 2002): 1025.

Chapter 18: Page 317: These data are abstracted from Proportion of National Income Earned by the Richest 20 Percent of Households. From World Bank. 2004. World Development Indicators 2004. Washington, DC: World Bank Publications. ISBN/ISSN: 01635085.

Chapter 20: Page 356: Women's Electoral Success on the Northwest Coast SOURCE: B. G. Miller 1992. "Women and Politics: Comparative Evidence from the Northwest Coast," Ethnology 32(4): 367–82. © 1992 by University of Pittsburgh.

Chapter 21. Page 371: Based on data from Alice Schlegel and RohnEloul, "Marriage Transactions: Labor, Property, and Status," *American Anthropologist* 90 (1988): 291–309.

Chapter 22. Page 402: Adapted from Melvin Ember and Carol R. Ember, *Marriage, Family, and Kinship: Comparative Studies of Social Organization* (New Haven, CT: HRAF Press, 1983).

Chapter 24. Page 426: Adapted from Paul Bohannan, "The Migration and Expansion of the Tiv," *Africa,* 24 (1954): 3; Page 429: Based on Ember and Ember 2002.

Chapter 26. Page 467: Clottes 2008—Jean Clottes, "Rock Art" An Endangered Heritage Worldwide." *Journal of Anthropological Research* 64 (2008): 1–18; Page 469: Based on Fischer 1961.

index

The following pages contain maps that have been adapted from the *DK Atlas of World History: Mapping the Human Journey* and *Atlas of Anthropology,* produced by Dorling Kindersley. Each map focuses on a topic that is discussed in more detail within the text itself and is intended to bring the richness of anthropology to life.

maps

Prentice Hall would sincerely like to thank Dorling Kindersley for helping to put this feature together.

TRADING IN HUMAN LIVES

The use of slaves seems to have been endemic in many human societies. Normally taken as prisoners of war, slaves were also acquired as a form of tribute. The establishment of European colonies and overseas empires between the 16th and 19th centuries saw the creation of a slave trade on an industrial scale, a commerce which laid the foundations for pan-global trading networks. Trading concerns such as the English and Dutch East India companies developed trade on a larger scale than ever before; but it was the need to supply labor for the plantations of the Americas which led to the greatest movement of peoples across the face of the earth.

Slaves in the New World

The great plantation systems and mining concerns that arose in the New World from the 16th century onward demanded large reservoirs of labor. Though the Spanish and Portuguese initially used enslaved indigenous people, they soon required a more reliable source of labor. The Portuguese began bringing African slaves to the Caribbean and Brazil in the early 16th century. The cotton plantations of the southern U.S., which boomed in the early 19th century, were a key factor in sustaining the Atlantic trade.

The Atlantic slave trade

From the late 15th to the early 19th century, European merchants—especially the British and Portuguese—carried on a massive trade in African slaves across the Atlantic. As well as utilizing the established sources of slaves from the Central and West African kingdoms, they also raided coastal areas of West Africa for additional supplies of slaves. European manufactured goods, especially guns, were exchanged for slaves destined to work as agricultural laborers on plantations in the Caribbean and the tropical Americas. Slaves transported to the western hemisphere may have numbered 12 million or more.

Slave trades

1502: Introduction of African slaves to the Caribbean

1739: Stono rebellion in South Carolina

1791: Slave revolt in Haiti

1804: Foundation of independent Haitian state

1867: Last known arrival of a slave ship in Cuba

1450   1500   1550   1600   1650   1700   1750   1800   1850   1900

1479: Treaty of Alcaçovas permits Portuguese importation of slaves into Spain

1522: First American slave revolt in Hispaniola

1685: French *Code Noir* restricts slavery in French Caribbean colonies

1807: Slave trade outlawed in Britain

1850: Effective end of slave trade in Brazil

1863: Emancipation proclamation frees slaves in Confederate states

Other slave trades

By the 9th and 10th centuries, a number of complex slave-trading routes were in existence in Europe and the Near East. Viking and Russian merchants traded in slaves from the Balkans who were often sold to harems in southern Spain and North Africa. The Baghdad Caliphate drew slaves from western Europe via the ports of Venice, Prague, and Marseille, and Slavic and Turkic slaves from eastern Europe and Central Asia. In the 13th century, the Mongols sold slaves at Karakorum and in the Volga region. There was long-standing commerce in African slaves—primarily from East Africa before European mariners entered the slave trade. Between the 9th and 19th centuries Muslim merchants may have transported as many as 14 million across the Sahara by camel caravan and through East African ports, principally to destinations in the Indian Ocean basin.

Europe: Labour in the American plantations was also provided by convicts and indentured workers transported to work under contract

Russia: The practice of serfdom, established in 1497, by which peasant farmers were owned, and could be sold, was finally abolished in 1861

China: With the abolition of the trans-Atlantic slave trade, the labour markets of the East Indies and the Americas were supplemented by Chinese indentured labourers

◄ **The world slave trade 1400–1860**

major slave trading nation	
export center for African slaves	
export center for Muslim slaves	
distribution of African slaves	
distribution of Muslim slaves	
African nations with active slave trade	
number of slaves imported	

routes of European slave traders
routes of Ottoman slave traders
routes of Saharan slave traders
routes of Arab slave traders
exports of Muslim slaves from Southeast Asia
goods exported in exchange for slaves
goods exported for slaves
European exports to Africa

• slave factory

Goods produced using slaves
- cocoa beans
- coffee
- cotton
- diamonds
- gold
- silver
- sugar
- tobacco

Other goods traded
- dyestuffs
- furs and hides
- pepper
- silk and textiles
- spices
- tin

Goods imported for slaves
- salt cod

MIGRATION IN THE 19TH CENTURY

The technical innovations of the Industrial Revolution made the 19th-century world a much smaller place. Railroads could quickly transport large human cargoes across continents, the Suez and Panama canals reduced travel times—sometimes by as much as 50%, and ships became larger, faster, and more seaworthy. The mechanization and centralization of industry required the concentration of labor on a scale never seen before. At the same time, the European imperial powers were exploiting their tropical possessions for economic benefit. Cash crops, grown on large plantations, needed a plentiful supply of labor as well. Political upheaval, wars, and economic hardship provided the most dramatic impetus to emigration—especially in the Russian Empire and Central Europe, and in southeastern China.

Batavia

Singapore MALAYA

SIAM BUR

Mekong

AUSTRALIA

DUTCH EAST INDIES

Manila

Hong Kong

Yellow River

Melbourne

Shanghai Beijing

Sydney

Vladivostok

Yokohama

JAPAN

Equator

1 million

PACIFIC OCEAN

NEW
ZEALAND

Migration in the 19th century

More than 80 million people emigrated from their country of origin during the 19th and early 20th centuries. Over half of them moved across the Atlantic to North and South America. The end of the American Civil War in 1865, and the opening up of Native American land to settlers saw the greatest period of immigration to the U.S. and Canada. In the Russian Empire, movement was eastward from European Russia into Siberia and the Caspian region. Europeans moved south and east to take up employment in the colonies, while indentured laborers traveled to the Americas, Africa, and Southeast Asia.

INDIAN OCEAN

Mauritius

MADAGASCAR

CEYLON

Mombasa
Mogadishu
Lake Nyasa

SOUTH AFRICA

Cape Town

Bombay
INDIA
Calcutta
BURMA
Yangtze

CHINA

Tashkent
Baku
Caspian Sea
Novosibirsk
Trans-Siberian Railway 1904
6 million
Siberia
RUSSIAN EMPIRE
Yenisey
Ob

A S I A
4 million

Suez Canal 1869
OTTOMAN EMPIRE
Constantinople
Odessa
Volga
Moscow
European Russia
St. Petersburg
AUSTRIA-HUNGARY
ITALY
Naples
Genoa
Marseille
GERMANY
Hamburg
Antwerp
Amsterdam
Scandinavia
Southampton
BRITAIN: Liverpool
IRELAND
SPAIN
PORTUGAL

EUROPE

A F R I C A
Nile
Euphrates
Tigris
Congo
Lake Victoria
Lake Tanganyika
Niger
Lagos

Dakar

ATLANTIC OCEAN

ARCTIC OCEAN

4.1 million
4.5 million
5.5 million
3.4 million
2.1 million
4.5 million
3 million (2.5 million Britain)
8 million
1 million (returning)
1 million (returning)

CANADA
Vancouver
Canadian Pacific 1885
Québec
Halifax
Northern Pacific 1869
Boston
New York
San Francisco
Central Pacific 1883
UNITED STATES
Los Angeles
NORTH AMERICA
New Orleans
MEXICO
CUBA
JAMAICA
PUERTO RICO
Mexico City
Panama Canal 1914

Belém
BRAZIL
Rio de Janeiro
Amazon

SOUTH AMERICA

PERU
Lima
URUGUAY
Montevideo
Buenos Aires
ARGENTINA
CHILE
Valparaíso

Equator

World migration c.1860–1920

Transatlantic migration
- to North America
- to South America and the Caribbean
- to Europe from the Americas

Other European migration
- to Australia and New Zealand
- to North Africa

Asian migration
- to the Americas and Australia
- Russian migration into Siberia
- Indian intercolonial migration

- - - transcontinental railroad
- major exporters of people
- major importers of people

Migration to the New World

1818: 20,000 Irish emigrate to US as a result of famine

1845–54: Irish Potato Famine leads 1.6 million to emigrate

1849: California Gold Rush draws large numbers of migrants from Europe, Australia, Chile, and China

1882: Beginning of major Jewish emigration from Russian Empire
1882: 80,000 Scandinavians emigrate to US

1900: Start of major Italian emigration to US and Argentina; by 1910, more than two million have arrived

800   1820   1840   1860   1880   1900

1816–17: Emigration from southwest Germany following Napoleonic wars

1831–41: 200,000 people leave Ireland for Canada, many traveling on to the US

1848–49: Revolutions lead to political crackdown and exodus of democrats from Central Europe

1850s: Height of emigration from England and Scotland: more than 50,000 per year

1881–90: Peak years of German emigration to US (1,300,000)

1888: Abolition of slavery in Brazil; next decade sees over a million immigrants

TRADE IN THE 19TH CENTURY

In the first half of the 19th century, world trade and industry was dominated by Britain; by the 1870s, the industrial balance was shifting in favor of other nations, especially Germany, France, Russia, and the U.S., with rapid industrialization occurring throughout most of Europe by the end of the century. A stable currency, a standard (for example, the price of gold) against which the currency's value could be measured, and an effective private banking system were seen as essential to the growth and success of every industrializing nation. The major industrial nations also began to invest heavily overseas. Their aims were the discovery and exploitation of cheaper raw materials, balanced by the development of overseas markets for their products.

The impact of technology on the world trading system 1870–1910 ▶

- most highly industrialized nations
- industrializing nations
- major industrial regions c.1914

Improvements in communications

- major rail networks c.1914
- North Atlantic shipping route
- other shipping route
- underwater telegraph cable route

Location of manufacturing industry

- heavy machinery
- iron and steel
- textile production

Export markets opened up by technology

- beef cattle
- lamb and mutton
- fruit

Major cash crops

- coffee
- cotton
- rubber
- sugarcane
- tea

Refrigerated container ships transport bananas to world markets

Panama Canal Opened in 1914. Journey times reduced by up to 40%

Refrigerated container ships transport South American beef to world markets

PACIFIC OCEAN

MEXICO
Mexico City
UNITED STATES OF AMERICA
New Orleans
Chicago
Montreal
New York
CUBA
PANAMA
San Francisco

ATLANTIC OCEAN

Valparaiso
Santiago
CHILE

ARGENTINA
Buenos Aires
BRAZIL
Montevideo
URUGUAY
Rio de Janeiro

Inventions and the economic revolution

1856: First commercial refrigeration in US; refined technique developed in Australia by 1859

1869: Completion of Transcontinental Railroad in US

1874: Alexander Graham Bell patents telephone

1885: Development of first automobile by Daimler and Benz

| 1835 | 1845 | 1855 | 1865 | 1875 | 1885 | 1895 |

1838: Invention of first electric telegraph in Britain

1856: Bessemer invents process for mass production of steel

1863: Construction of London Underground begins

1880s: Refrigerated ships transport cheese, butter, and meat from New Zealand

1895: Invention of wireless telegraphy (radio) by Marconi

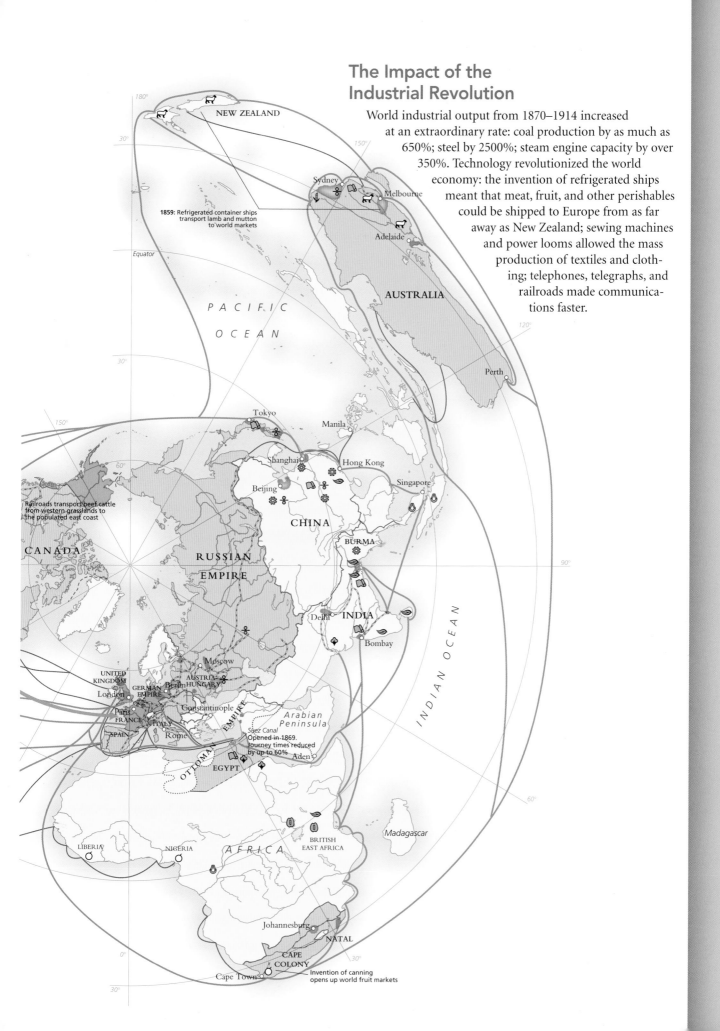

The Impact of the Industrial Revolution

World industrial output from 1870–1914 increased at an extraordinary rate: coal production by as much as 650%; steel by 2500%; steam engine capacity by over 350%. Technology revolutionized the world economy: the invention of refrigerated ships meant that meat, fruit, and other perishables could be shipped to Europe from as far away as New Zealand; sewing machines and power looms allowed the mass production of textiles and clothing; telephones, telegraphs, and railroads made communications faster.

NEW ZEALAND

1859: Refrigerated container ships transport lamb and mutton to world markets

Sydney
Melbourne
Adelaide

AUSTRALIA

Perth

PACIFIC OCEAN

Equator

Tokyo
Manila
Shanghai
Hong Kong
Beijing
Singapore

CHINA

BURMA

Railroads transport beef cattle from western grasslands to the populated east coast

CANADA

RUSSIAN EMPIRE

Delhi   INDIA

Bombay

INDIAN OCEAN

Moscow

UNITED KINGDOM
London
GERMAN
EMPIRE
Paris
FRANCE
AUSTRIA-HUNGARY
Berlin
Constantinople
SPAIN
ITALY
Rome

Arabian Peninsula

Suez Canal
Opened in 1869.
Journey times reduced by up to 60%   Aden

OTTOMAN EMPIRE

EGYPT

LIBERIA
NIGERIA

AFRICA

BRITISH EAST AFRICA

Madagascar

Johannesburg
NATAL
CAPE COLONY
Cape Town

Invention of canning opens up world fruit markets